For the first time in E
rewritten and greatly enlar
ard work for biologists
doctors presents up-to-dat
and full accounts of the life cycles and the
morphology of protozoa, helminths, insects, and other arthropod parasites that
afflict mankind. Although the biology and
ecology of the parasite are emphasized,
diagnosis and treatment are fully developed.

In this book the word parasite applies
to a living organism which has settled in
or on another living being called the host.
As every species of parasite poses its own
particular problems, identity and accurate classification are essential. Each type
and species are clearly and concisely described, including its earliest identification, its geographic distribution and
prevalence, host parasite relationship,
clinical aspects, and the most modern
methods of medical treatment for it. A
list of references, including the most recent current literature, follows each
chapter.

An important section of the book treats
the technical methods and diagnostic procedures used for examination, culture,
fixation, staining and immunoserological
procedures. Laboratory equipment for
parasitological study is covered and many
helpful illustrations carefully supplement
the text. An index of authors and a de-
tailed subject index is included.

1029

ANIMAL PARASITES
IN MAN

by

N. H. SWELLENGREBEL, Ph.D., M.D.

The Royal Tropical Institute, Amsterdam

AND

M. M. STERMAN, M.D.

Public Health Physician, Tropical Disease Diagnostic Service, Bureau of Preventable Diseases, New York City Department of Health; Instructor in Tropical Diseases, College of Physicians and Surgeons, Columbia University; Associate Physician in Tropical Diseases and Parasitology, Knickerbocker and Elmhurst General Hospitals

D. VAN NOSTRAND COMPANY, INC.

PRINCETON, NEW JERSEY

TORONTO　　　　　　　　　　　　　　　LONDON

NEW YORK

D. VAN NOSTRAND COMPANY, INC.

120 Alexander St., Princeton, New Jersey (*Principal Office*)
24 West 40 Street, New York 18, New York

D. VAN NOSTRAND COMPANY, LTD.

358, Kensington High Street, London, W.14, England

D. VAN NOSTRAND COMPANY (Canada), LTD.

25 Hollinger Road, Toronto 16, Canada

Published simultaneously in Canada by
D. VAN NOSTRAND COMPANY (Canada), LTD.

PRINTED IN THE UNITED STATES OF AMERICA
BY LANCASTER PRESS, INC., LANCASTER, PA.

PREFACE

From one point of view, *Animal Parasites in Man* is a first edition in English of a book that was issued in the Netherlands in six revisions over a span of more than sixty years. Readers familiar with that work may perceive in this "seventh edition" the earlier features —e.g., competent accounts of life cycle and morphology, illustrations by gifted craftsmen, and the use of the literature derived from Dutch tropical and marine experience.

On the other hand, the authors must acknowledge that the book is, in large part, new. It is not a translation, but an original English work. Though they have tried to preserve and enhance the features of earlier revisions, the topics have been subjected to a new order, the information on etiological diagnosis and specific drug treatment has been much enlarged, and current literature has been surveyed. Six new chapters deal with diagnostic procedures—laboratory equipment, examination, culture, fixation and staining, and immunoserological procedures.

It is the authors' hope that a combination of biological information and current medical practice will, in the long run, be of usefulness to both physicians and biologists, and that *Animal Parasites in Man* can come to hold something like the place in the English-speaking world that its predecessor held for so long in its more limited field.

Acknowledgments are due to the Chairman and Board of Directors of the Royal Tropical Institute, who for forty-seven years have encouraged the senior author to collect many of the bricks with which this book has been built; likewise to the Society for the Protection of the Interest of Dutch Shipping and Commerce in the Baltic (Oosterse Handel en Rederijen) for their generous grants. Messrs. Scheltema and Holkema, although unable to publish the seventh Dutch edition, have done all in their power to remove the obstacles to publishing a new one in English. Miss Rijpstra and

iii

Mr. Jungen were indefatigable in preparing new microphotographs; Miss Vis and Miss Berlage in converting them into drawings, fit for cheap and effective reproduction. Miss Werner never tired of typing and retyping the succeeding chapters.

N. H. S.

M. M. S.

Amsterdam/New York
October, 1960

CONTENTS

v

CHAPTER I

INTRODUCTION: PARASITES AND THEIR HOSTS

Every animal is associated with an *environment,* i.e. the sum of external influences, animate and inanimate, that affect it. It depends on this environment, and it is in collision with it. The animal depends on its environment for a dwelling place, for food, and for the opportunity to multiply; the collision arises from competition with the living beings that are part of the environment.

The collision always exists. It is especially noticeable if the animal tries to gain a foothold in a new environment. In the struggle to assert itself, the newcomer is likely to upset the long-standing balance between the earlier inhabitants. Eventually, a new equilibrium may be established; in the reconstructed environment the newcomer may find conditions which satisfy its needs and are at the same time consistent with the requirements of the older occupants. However, things may turn out differently; the interference of the newcomer may have a disruptive effect: an irreversible deterioration of the environment, manifested by fertile plains converted into deserts, and forested hillsides into barren slopes. This deterioration may deprive both the newcomer and the earlier settlers of their means of subsistence.

The animals with which this book is dealing, animals parasitizing man, essentially behave in the same way. But they differ from others by the nature of the environment on which they depend, viz., the human body. The collision with this particular environment is a conflict with the living elements of that body, and, indirectly, with parasites belonging to the same species which already inhabit it. The effects of the newcomer's upset to the pre-existing equilibrium are known as parasitic diseases. The irreversible deterioration of the environment is represented here by man's death as a result of the disease.

The object of the study of animals parasitizing man is to learn how they are related to their environment and to find means to influence this relationship to man's advantage, or at least to avoid influencing it in the opposite direction. As every species of parasite poses its own particular problems, it is essential to be quite sure of the identity of the species one is dealing with. Therefore, an accurate classification is fundamental for the completion of this study.

In this book the word *parasite* applies to a living being which has settled in or on another living being which is called the *host*. Its settling in that environment is not merely a matter of chance. The parasite is forced to it by its complete dependence on the living host for everything it needs to continue its survival, as an individual and as a species, viz., dwelling space, nourishment, and multiplication. The emphasis lies on the adjective "living," for a dead host is no host.

The above does not pretend to be a definition. It is no more than an arbitrary statement made for the purpose of limiting the scope of the book. Numerous animals are classified as parasites which do not comply with these criteria; so they are excluded here. There are, for instance, parasites which depend on their host for shelter or food only. Others depend upon their ability to kill their host. They might be considered to be parasites par excellence, but they are not; they are *predators,* as Theobald Smith [1] calls them.

An example of such a predatory pseudoparasite is *Apanteles glomeratus,* an ichneumon fly, the larvas of which prey on the caterpillars of the white butterfly *Pieris brassicae.* The insect deposits its eggs within the body of the young caterpillar, where they become larvas. At first the infested caterpillar behaves and grows like others, but when the time comes for it to pupate it has become too weak to perform this metamorphosis. At this stage the larvas of *Apanteles* escape from their dying victim and pupate within its close vicinity. It may happen that migratory cells of the caterpillar's body kill the inoculated eggs. If this attempt does not succeed, the predator kills the caterpillar. However, this entails no ill effects for the aggressor; it can exist in a free-living state after it has disposed of its host.

The parasites described in this book occasionally behave like predators, killing their host after a period of intense and unlimited multiplication. But they behave differently from the true predators in that they kill themselves in the act; for they cannot exist outside the living host, and they have no means of escaping the total destruction which awaits them within the body of the host they killed. Such is the picture of what Leiper [2] called "pathological parasitism." The state of the parasite *Entamoeba histolytica* in young kittens is an example.

The alternative to this state of things is normal parasitism. It is realized by the host keeping the parasite in check, either by controlling its numbers (*numerical restraint*) or by limiting the space it occupies (*topical restraint*). Once the parasite is reduced to subservience, the host is in a position to *tolerate* its presence. The result of this interaction is a permanent state of *balanced relationship* between host and parasite.

This relationship may present itself in two different forms. The first form is characterized by the parasite taking up its abode in the human body without causing any apparent illness. As far as multiplication is concerned, it is free to continue unchecked. Nevertheless the host controls it by imposing topical restraint. The parasite is allowed to live in well-defined sites only, e.g. on the mucous membrane lining the colon, but not within the tissue of the wall of the gut. There the parasite and its descendants may live for years, never violating the restraint imposed upon it. But it is not to be trusted. It may look harmless and behave harmlessly, but potentially it is aggressive. A temporary weakening of the host's vitality may suffice to allow it to overcome the restraint. Then it becomes a pathogenic organism, the cause of a specific disease. Parasites of this description are called *commensals* by Van Loghem.[3] The change in behavior may be accompanied by morphological changes; they make visible to the eye that the commensal has abandoned its harmless mode of life.

The parasite quoted above as an example of pathological parasitism when settled in young kittens (*Entamoeba histolytica*) offers an example of commensalism when settled in man.

The second form of balanced relationship develops in a way which is the opposite of the first. On entering the human body, the parasite invariably starts its career as the causative agent of an infectious disease, which may end with the death of the host—and of the parasites he harbored. Usually, however, the host (often at an early age) finishes the conflict by cutting down the numbers of the invader, without eradicating it. In this way the host becomes a "healthy," "asymptomatic," or "subclinical" carrier, and the parasite is reduced to a state not unlike that of a commensal. The similarity would be perfect if the parasite, subjugated by numerical restraint, were put to topical restraint by being limited to certain tissues and certain forms of development. This actually seems to happen in some plasmodia (exoerythrocytic forms) and in toxoplasma (true cysts). For the moment, however, it does not appear to be the rule; and so it would seem to be advisable to view this group of *initial aggressors* apart from the *commensals*.

In accordance with Sergent's views [4] it is assumed that the human host, once he has subjugated the invader, is able to ward off subsequent infections with parasites of the same species. He retains this ability as long as he keeps the initial aggressor alive in his body as a *residual parasite population*. If it happens that this population becomes extinct, the host stands defenseless against reinfection with parasites of the same species. This state of defense against renewed infection, dependent upon the continued existence of a residual parasite population, Sergent has termed *premunition*. It differs from the state of *immunity* in that the immunized host can prevent renewed invasion because he has eradicated an earlier invader. In the premunized host, on the contrary, a second invasion is prevented because the life of the first invader has been preserved.

The host-parasite relationship described in the last two paragraphs is often associated with animal parasites in man, but its most striking example is found in the bovine host inhabited by the parasite *Babesia bigemina*.

In the preceding pages it has been tacitly understood that it is the host who is responsible for the balanced relationship with the parasite. That is not the whole truth; the parasite also plays a role by virtue of its *virulence* or *aggressiveness*.

A highly virulent parasite is characterized by its ability to break the barriers the host imposes on it. The host is like wax in its hands; he invariably succumbs to the parasite, with results equally detrimental to both. As a result, a balanced relationship fails to become established. A similar disturbance in equilibrium results if the parasite shows too little aggressiveness. In applying topical or numerical restraint the host, instead of keeping the parasite in check, simply wipes it out. It is only the parasite of medium virulence, yielding to but not overwhelmed by either form of restraint, that is likely to succeed in the establishment of a balanced relationship with its host.

The activities of the host to attain this end manifest themselves in various ways. Some are identical with those the host follows when dealing with invading bacteria; viz., (1) cellular elements of the blood or reticuloendothelial tissues engulf and digest malarial parasites; (2) humoral elements of the blood serum agglutinate and dissolve trypanosomes. Operating against the larvas of helminths or parasitic flies, other methods are applied. The serum of the host causes a dense precipitate to appear in the liquid excretion emanating from the buccal, anal, and sexual orifices of the larvas. The precipitate is supposed to interfere with the ingestion of food and with the motility of the larvas. As a matter of fact, they are seen to fall an easy prey to mobile cells of the host's body, which envelop them tightly and eventually bring about their death.

The activity of the mobile cells (*cellular reaction*) and the blood serum (*humoral reaction*) serve the purpose of topical restraint if directed only against commensals which do not keep within due bounds. They serve the purpose of numerical restraint when dealing with initial aggressors. The same activity will bring about premunition if it is not pushed too far, and immunity if it kills all parasites and afterwards remains available to prevent any further invasion.

Man performs his cellular and humoral activities without being conscious of it. But there are other activities, serving the same purpose, which he carries out at will, although not with the object of establishing a balanced relationship with his parasites. This applies to lice and other *ectoparasites.*[5] Daily catches, together with scrupulous cleanliness of the body, the clothes, and the human habitation, although insufficient to eradicate them, will keep these parasites down to a level which can be tolerated by the human host and accepted by the society he belongs to. Thus the host is not forced to take measures which would be fatal to the parasite population inhabiting the surface of his body. Viewed from this angle, such homely doings keep the host-parasite relationship in balance just as well as the conventional cellular and humoral reactions.

The conscious activities of cleanliness are not specific. They are not directed against lice to the exclusion of fleas or bedbugs. In this they differ from the innate cellular and humoral reactions, which are highly specific. For instance, the serum of a person infected with *Trichinella spiralis* will cause buccal precipitates in the larvas of that worm, but not of other nematodes. This specificity is used in *etiolog-*

ical diagnosis, i.e. the diagnosis of an infectious disease based upon finding the causative organism. If this organism cannot be actually seen (as may well happen in the example cited here) its presence in man is proved by his serum causing buccal precipitates in larvas of *Trichinella* from an entirely different source (e.g. from pigs).

Cellular and humoral reactions, by reducing the number of parasites, allow the host to become tolerant of the residual parasite population.

The process of becoming tolerant may be obscured by a process with the inverse effect of sensitizing the host (i.e. rendering him unduly sensitive) to the products of the parasite. This state of *hypersensitivity* is also specific; it depends on the presence of a certain species of parasite in the human body, e.g. the hydatid of *Echinococcus granulosus.* If this animal cannot be brought to sight, its presence in the human body can be proved by the hypersensitivity of the presumptive carrier to the products of the parasite—in this case to the fluid in the hydatid cyst obtained from man or a domestic animal. The hypersensitivity, in this particular case, is demonstrated by the *skin test,* i.e. the erythematous reactions following an intradermal injection of a small quantity of the cyst fluid.

From the foregoing it will be clear that pathogenic parasites need not always be associated with morbid processes. This holds good for commensals as well as for initial aggressors. It is, therefore, unfortunate that no expression exists simply to say that there are parasites in the human body. The word *infection* is too ambiguous. It had been applied to infectious diseases long before it acquired the additional meaning of parasites settling in man. In our days both meanings continue side by side, without proper distinction. "Malaria infection" may refer to the disease as well as to the plasmodia. The mere presence of a pathogenic parasite is sometimes believed sufficient to explain any concomitant morbid symptom. Thus, the finding of such parasites may be a hindrance rather than a help in arriving at a correct diagnosis.

Of course, the problem does not exist if it is argued that all carriers of plasmodia or cysts of *Entamoeba histolytica* are ill with malaria or amebiasis. That argument is as difficult to answer as the one Heisch [6] was confronted with when asked how he could be sure that an armadillo carrying *Trypanosoma cruzi* did not have a headache.

To avoid all difficulties, the term "infection" will be used here only with reference to parasites, and not diseases.

In the first part of this introductory chapter, dealing with the relationship between host and parasite, the host has taken precedence over the parasite. In the second part the parasite will be given more attention, although the host will continue to claim his share.

To begin with a few words about the multiplication of the parasites: A distinction can be made between *proliferous* parasites and *nonproliferous* parasites.

The *proliferous* parasite enters the human body as one individual, which grows and multiplies and eventually produces a number of daughter individuals. The daughter individuals follow their mother's example: they grow and multiply; so do their daughters, their granddaughters, and further progeny. Thus the host, who begins with one parasite, finishes with harboring many.

The *nonproliferous* parasite also enters the human host as one individual. It likewise grows, but the daughter individuals (the eggs) do not multiply in the host in whom they are born. They must get into another human host before they can multiply. Thus a host infected with one parasite will never have more than one in his body.

The second point to be discussed is how man becomes infected with parasites. There are three ways.

(1) *Infection by contact,* i.e. direct transfer of the parasite from one person to another. This transfer can be seen to happen in *ectoparasites,* i.e. parasites moving on the skin of the host, as lice and fleas. It is not necessary for the person carrying the infection to touch the one to be infected; a flea may bridge the gap by jumping, head lice may crawl from one hat to another one hanging on the same peg. In *endoparasites,* i.e. parasites living inside the human body, the transfer cannot be followed by the naked eye. Indirect evidence, however, proves that it happens, either by touch or through the medium of inanimate objects—food, fluids, etc.

(2) *Soil infection,* i.e. infection with larvas of certain intestinal worms that stay for some days outside the human body in order to reach maturity in loose, moist earth. It is this maturescence in the soil, preparing them for the continuation of their existence in man, that makes it necessary to distinguish soil infection from infection by contact.

(3) *Infection via an intermediate host,* i.e. an animal in which the parasite can live as well as in man. There is, however, this proviso, that the parasite requires for its existence both man and the intermediate host; it cannot do with one *or* the other. It cannot enter the body of the intermediate host except by way of man's body, and *vice versa.*

The intermediate host may serve the parasite in three different ways.

The first applies to parasites which on leaving man's body are well able to live, e.g. in water for a short time; thus another person could easily be infected by drinking the water. But this would be of no use to the parasite, because it simply cannot live in man at that stage of its existence. It has to be prepared for the resumption of its career in the human body, just as the loose earth prepared the larvas of some worms. This preparation is carried out by a class of hosts which, for that reason, are called *preparatory hosts,* e.g. cattle and *Taenia saginata.*

Other parasites on leaving one man are perfectly able to grow and multiply in the next one. But they cannot reach him unless they pass some time in free nature, unprotected by any host. Now that is exactly what they cannot do: an outdoor life means sudden death. Hosts bridging the gap separating one man from another are called *transporting hosts,* e.g. tsetse flies and trypanosomes.

Finally, a parasite may be so immovably encased within its host that it cannot leave him unless he is devoured by a predator. The parasite does not grow inside the predator's body but leaves it immediately in its stools. The predator has done nothing but help the parasite out of a tight hole; it is a *liberating host,* e.g. carnivores and *Capillaria hepatica.*

Up till now it has been assumed that man acquires his parasites from another human being, by contact or through the medium of the soil or of intermediate hosts—in other words, that parasites have only one definitive vertebrate host, that they are what is called *monoxenous.* It makes no difference that some tapeworms pass part of their life in cows or pigs; these vertebrates are merely intermediate hosts.

However, a number of animal parasites are *polyxenous.* They have other definitive vertebrate hosts besides man. These vertebrates are called *alternate hosts.* They are not intermediate hosts, for two reasons: (1) The development of the parasites in the alternate host is the counterpart of that in the human host; in the body of the intermediate host the parasites develop along different lines. (2) The parasites can pass from one alternate host to another, without once settling in man; they do not need him. But the parasites cannot pass from one intermediate host to another. On leaving the one, they have to undergo a cycle of development in man or an alternate host before they can enter into another intermediate host.

Alternate hosts serve as an important source of infection to man. Often they are the only source, e.g. in trichinella, a parasite man always acquires from swine. Groups of vertebrates acting as alternate hosts are collectively called *reservoir*.

Reservoir and human society may exist far apart or in each other's close vicinity. The following categories may be distinguished.

(1) *Sylvatic reservoir*. The parasites live in wild vertebrates, with-out any link with individual man or human society. Man is totally ignorant of the danger lurking in the wilds. It is only by his intruding on wild life that he becomes aware that its parasites may choose his body as a host.

(2) *Domestic reservoir*. This may develop out of the sylvatic res-ervoir when farmers come to settle in a wild area, accompanied by their livestock. Wild life then tends to disappear, but the parasites may remain. If they do, they continue their existence in domestic vertebrates (including cattle, but also rats and mice) and also in man. The course of infection may also go in the opposite direction, spreading from domestic life to wild life.

(3) *Human reservoir*. This stage will be reached if domestic vertebrates cease to be alternate hosts—for whatever reason that may be—leaving man as the only host of the parasite.

The remarks above make no mention of *diseases* caused by sylvatic or domestic parasites. In the sylvatic host they may be wholly absent. There are certain species of wild vertebrates that allow the parasites to live in their body without any apparent harm to themselves or at least without undue mortality of the host interfering with the parasites' existence. It is only man's entry upon the scene, followed by his becoming infected with a foreign parasite, that is likely to bring about a disease. For man, at this stage, is not the natural host of the parasite, and as Wenyon [7] pointed out, the unnatural host is prone to suffer severely from a parasitic invasion which may leave the natural host unscathed. Thus in sylvatic parasitism man and vertebrates share parasites, but not necessarily diseases.

At the domestic stage they share both. This does not imply that the diseases the parasites cause in the animals are similar to those they cause in man. It simply means that the suffering animal infects man with its parasites, and, as a consequence, man falls ill too. Human diseases originating in this way are called *zoonoses*. Although primarily used for infectious diseases that man acquires from his domestic animals and his murine hangers-on, the term is also applied to parasitic infections he acquires from the sylvatic reservoir.

Once man is infected with parasites acquired from wild or domestic animals, there seems to be no reason why he cannot pass them on to his fellow men. This certainly does happen; but if one chooses to call it a rule, it is a rule with many exceptions.

There remains one question to be answered. It is placed at the end of the chapter, because the answer to it serves the purpose of a summary: Is there any fundamental difference between animal and bacterial parasites that justifies their being discussed separately, and not in a textbook of clinical bacteriology?

As regards metazoan parasites, the problems they raise are obviously different from those discussed in such a textbook. Whether or not the differences are fundamental may be left undecided; undoubtedly they are of a nature fully to warrant a separate discussion.

The protozoan parasites are in a different position. If a case is to be made out for their separate treatment, it will have to be on the strength of a difference in shade rather than in terms of black and white; for any general description of the behavior of protozoan parasites can always be matched with the example of some bacterial parasite selected for the purpose. This will have to be borne in mind with regard to the following statement.

The general impression left, after studying the relationship existing between protozoan parasites and their hosts, is that it is a *permanent relationship*. It was not established by going to extremes; the host resorted to keeping the parasite in check rather than to eradication; the parasite resorted to unobtrusive settlement rather than to aggression. This relationship, however, develops in the natural host only; it is easily misunderstood by accepting as normal the behavior of the parasite in a host to which it does not really belong—and that unnatural host may be man himself. The existence of "healthy" carriers is the inevitable consequence of the permanent nature of the relationship; if premunition is what Sergent [4] affirms it to be, the residual parasite population they carry should be preserved, not eradicated.

The relationship existing between pathogenic bacteria and their hosts may be broadly described as transient; the immunity the host develops precludes any permanency. "Healthy" carriers, in these conditions, cannot be anything but rare, and nothing can be urged against the early destruction of their parasites.

This does not apply to bacterial commensals. They behave more like the parasitic protozoa than the pathogenic bacteria. But their existence tends to emphasize the difference between the two rather than to obscure it; for what is a rule among parasitic protozoa is far from being a rule in clinical bacteriology.

Thus, the answer to the question is: fundamental differences there are none. Yet, it is the balanced and permanent relationship with their hosts which sets the protozoan parasites apart and justifies their separate treatment.

The common animal parasites of man belong to the following major divisions.

(1) *Protozoa,* or unicellular animals, with a body which bears some resemblance to a cell of a multicellular animal.

(2) *Metazoa,* or multicellular animals. This major division includes:

(a) *Scolecida,* or lower worms. They are characterized by the absence of leglike appendages, a secondary body cavity, a system of blood vessels and organs specially designed for respiration; moreover, their body is not composed of segments. Their excretory organs are represented by *protonephridia,* a system of branched canals, the narrowest ramifications of which often carry an unicellular *terminal organ* provided with a tuft of cilia.

The *helminths* or *intestinal worms,* belonging to this group, include the parasites which will be discussed here.

(b) The *arthropods,* conspicuous by their legs, composed of segments united to one another by articulations, and by their external skeleton.

REFERENCES FOR CHAPTER I

1. THEOBALD SMITH. *Parasitism and Disease,* 196 pp., Princeton, N. J., 1934, Princeton University Press, pp. 1–19.
2. R. T. LEIPER. *Proc. Roy. Soc. Med.,* 1934, 27: 127–134.
3. J. J. VAN LOGHEM. *Ann. inst. Pasteur Paris,* 1937, 58: 609–624.
4. ED. SERGENT. *Arch. inst. Pasteur Algérie,* 1950, 28: 429–440.
5. K. MELLANBY. *Parasitology,* 1942, 34: 180–184; and 1944, 35: 197–206.
6. R. B. HEISCH. *Brit. Med. J.,* 1956 (2nd half): 669–673.
7. C. M. WENYON. *Protozoölogy,* 2 vol., 1563 pp., London, 1926, Baillière, Tindall & Cox, Vol. 1, p. 135.

PART ONE

Protozoa

CHAPTER II

THE PROTOZOA

Protozoa are microorganisms. Their body is composed of proto-plasm containing one or more nuclei; thus they more or less resemble a single cell of a multicellular organism. They differ from unicell-ular fungi and bacteria by the absence of a cell wall (except in cysts); from unicellular algae by the absence of chlorophyll; from bacteria, bartonellae, and spirochetes by the presence of a well-defined nu-cleus; from the rickettsiae and ultramicroscopic viruses by their comparatively large size.

Protozoa multiply by *binary division* or *fission* (one individual dividing into two) or by *multiple division* or *schizogony* (one indi-vidual dividing into more than two). Besides asexual multiplication, some protozoa show sexual multiplication. This is likewise a binary or multiple division, but with the peculiarity that it follows after a sexual process. The process consists of two individuals merging into one; first their cytoplasms unite and afterwards their nuclei. The individual resulting from this union is called a *zygote;* the united nuclei, a *synkaryon.* This is the simplest form of the sexual process. Many variations and amplifications exist.

Among the protozoa parasitizing man, sexual processes occur in Ciliata and Sporozoa. Cytological research has failed to detect them in amebas and flagellates. This negative result can no longer be regarded as decisive, inasmuch as modern research, based on evidence unknown to conventional cytology, has yielded results which are accepted as proof that such processes exist in bacteria and even in viruses.[1]

The protozoa parasitizing man will be described in five chapters:

(1) *Amoebae,* organisms that crawl, supported by a solid sub-stratum. Their organs of locomotion are protoplasmatic protrusions (*pseudopods*) that are emitted when the amoeba is moving and retracted when it is at rest.

15

(2) *Flagellates,* organisms that swim in a liquid medium with the help of one to eight flagella—long, flexible, threadlike organelles that move in various ways and impart their motion to the body to which they are fixed. Unlike the pseudopods, the flagella are present even when the flagellate is at rest.

(3) *Ciliates,* organisms that likewise move by swimming. Their organs of locomotion are *cilia.* They are short, stiff, bristlelike organelles, present in large numbers, implanted all over the surface of the body. They set it in motion by coordinated upward and downward strokes. Like the flagella, they are permanent.

(4) *Sporozoa,* organisms that live inside certain classes of cells of the human body and multiply by *schizogony.* A sexual phase in their development is initiated by the appearance of male and female individuals. The zygote, resulting from the syngamy of two individuals of opposite sex, multiplies outside the human host or in the body of an intermediate host.

(5) *Protozoa of uncertain systematic position.*

REFERENCES FOR CHAPTER II

1. W. Braun. *Bacterial Genetics,* London and Philadelphia, 1953, W. B. Saunders Co., pp. 46–48, 186–191.

CHAPTER III

AMOEBAE

When at rest, the parasitic amoebae of man are spherical in shape. Their protoplasm is granular and is surrounded by a layer of crystal-clear protoplasm, called *ectoplasm,* the inner granular portion bearing the name of *endoplasm.* However, the ectoplasmatic covering may be so thin as to be hardly visible. When the amoeba is in motion, the ectoplasm becomes conspicuous, because pseudopods are extruded; for pseudopods consist of ectoplasm, either entirely or superficially.

Pseudopods are more than organs of locomotion. They also serve the purpose of ingesting solid particles of food, by enveloping them. Subsequently, the particles are transferred to the endoplasm. Here they are found lying inside vesicles, the so-called *food vacuoles,* where they are digested and assimilated.

Free-living amoebae are characterized by the presence of a *contractile vacuole,* a vesicle which appears, swells, bursts, and reappears, with the regularity of clockwork. It is mentioned here because a contractile vacuole alerts the observer to the fact that the amoeba he is watching is not parasitic, even if it is found in human feces. Free-living amoebae found there are called *coprozoic amoebae.*

Parasitic amoebae of man multiply by binary fission. Under normal conditions they can also multiply in their cystic stage. A *cyst* (as distinct from the motile and food-ingesting phase, which is called *trophozoite*) is a spherical amoeba lying within a wall, the *cyst wall,* which envelopes it in a way so as to leave some space between itself and the amoeba. Inside the cyst wall the amoeba can multiply. The process of becoming a cyst is called *encystation.* The encysted amoeba, protected by the cyst wall, can survive some time in nature, outside the host; unprotected, it dies within a short time; even if it should be swallowed immediately, it could not pass the acid gastric juice alive. Thus the cyst allows the amoeba to pass from one host to another. Upon arrival in the new host, the cyst wall bursts, allowing the amoeba to emerge (*excystation*). The cyst is allowed to pass directly from one host to another; no maturing phase outside the host is required.

The parasitic amoebae are commensals. Man keeps them in check by imposing topical restraint. They live within the lumen of the colon, and not in the tissues of its wall. One of them at least is able to break the barriers. This species is to be dealt with in the next section.

ENTAMOEBA HISTOLYTICA

Entamoeba histolytica Schaudinn, 1903; *E. dysenteriae* (Councilman & Lafleur, 1891) Craig, 1905; *E. tetragena* (Viereck, 1907) Hartmann, 1908; *E. minuta* Elmassian, 1909, has a life cycle in which two stages must be distinguished [1]: the *minuta stage* and the *histolytic stage*.* The minuta stage accepts the topical restraint imposed by its host; thus it is not invasive and consequently not pathogenic. The histolytic stage violates this restraint; therefore it is invasive and consequently pathogenic.

MINUTA STAGE OR NONINVASIVE STAGE

At this stage the commensals inhabit the lumen of the human colon as motile amoebae (minuta-trophozoite) and as cysts (Figs. 3·1, 3·2:*g–i*, 3·10:*B*). Monkeys, rats, dogs, and swine harbor amoebae that cannot be distinguished from it. The first three animals, together with rabbits, can be infected with the human parasite. So can young kittens, but their behavior is that of an unnatural host.

When at rest, the minuta-trophozoite has a diameter of 10–20 μ; the ectoplasm cannot be seen, but it is visible in the pseudopods. When it is moving, small pseudopods are projected in a leisurely fashion, not with the sudden jerk observed in the invasive histolytic trophozoites. The endoplasm is finely granular, with numerous vacuoles. Some of them contain starch granules and bacteria. Glycogen is often seen scattered throughout the protoplasm. The nucleus appears as a vesicle of about 3 μ. Granules of chromatin

---

* Recently Nauck [2] has named this stage "magna-form." This has an advantage over Kuenen and Swellengrebel's "histolytic stage," because the species name *Entamoeba histolytica* applies to the minuta stage as well as to the histolytic stage. But this advantage does not justify discarding a name which has been in use for forty-five years.

mark its margin; one granule, known as the *karyosome* or *endosome,* occupies the center. The trophozoite multiplies by binary fission; stages of nuclear division can be detected in human stools (Fig. 3·1). As a rule, minuta-trophozoites can be readily distinguished from the invasive histolytic trophozoites, but not from those of *E. coli.*

Under suitable laboratory conditions, minuta-trophozoites can be grown on artificial media containing certain species of bacteria as food. Watching them in these conditions, Brug saw them swallow liquid as well as solid food.

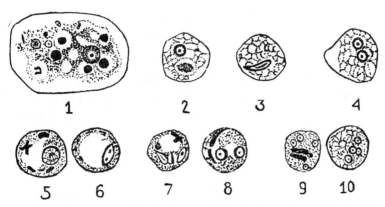

FIG. 3·1 *Entamoeba histolytica,* × 1000 (Heidenhain stain): 1. Histo-lytic trophozoite.—2–4. Minuta-trophozoites.—5–6. Uninucleate cysts.—7–8. Binucleate cysts.—9–10. Quadrinucleate cysts. (After Kuenen and Swellengrebel, 1913. Courtesy, Gustav Fischer, Jena.)

However, these are artificial conditions. In nature, minuta-trophozoites cannot survive outside their host, except in the form of cysts. In evacuated stools the trophozoites die within a short time, whereas the cysts survive for several days. The period of survival can be prolonged if the cysts are removed from the fecal environment and transferred to fresh water,[1] a condition which is reproduced in nature when the rain washes them into small watercourses. In other words, cysts must be kept moist if they are to survive; desiccation destroys them instantly.[1]

The cysts are spherical (Figs. 3·1, 3·2:*g–i*, 3·10:*C*); their diameter usually varies betwen 10 and 15 μ, with an average of 12 μ; their wall is thin. Initially they contain one nucleus, almost twice the size of the nucleus of the noninvasive minuta-trophozoite (5–6 μ). It is situated near the margin of the cyst, pushed aside by a large vacuole.

The vacuole contains glycogen; it stains reddish brown with iodine, contrasting sharply with the protoplasm, which stains yellow. The marginal protoplasm, around the glycogen vacuole, may contain hyaline structures shaped like thick, short bars or rods. In living cysts, if present, they are conspicuous by being more refractive than the protoplasm; in fixed and stained cysts, by staining more darkly. They are known as *chromatoid bodies* or *chromatoidals*.

By nuclear division the uninucleate cyst first becomes binucleate, and finally quadrinucleate. The binucleate stage does not last as long as the uninucleate; therefore cysts with two nuclei are not so common as those with one and four. The quadrinucleate cysts have lost their vacuole; the glycogen, if present, is spread throughout the protoplasm. The chromatoid bars often persist. The nuclei are small, with a maximal size of 3 μ. Occasionally, cysts may be found containing eight nuclei. They are larger than the quadrinucleate cysts: 16 μ on an average.[1] They can be distinguished from the mature cysts of *E. coli* because their protoplasm does not stain darkly and because many of them contain chromatoid bodies.

The noninvasive minuta-trophozoites encyst only in the presence of anaerobic bacteria.[3] A low tension of the surrounding oxygen is also required for *excystation*,[4] which takes place as follows. First, the protoplasm inside the cyst wall becomes motile; then it leaves the cyst, passing through a minute opening in its wall. The protoplasm, liberated in this way, moves about and feeds as a trophozoite. By nuclear division its four nuclei become eight in number. Subsequent division of the individual results in the formation of eight small uninucleate trophozoites, which, from now onward, behave in the usual way.[5] Immature (uni- and binucleate) cysts never show excystation.

Man becomes infected by ingesting mature cysts, often by drinking running water that looks clear and harmless. Schüffner and Kuenen discovered the danger of this kind of water when devising ways and means to control amebic dysentery among the field laborers of eastern Sumatra. Houseflies can also spread the infection. Transfer by contact is of common occurrence, as attested by the intense infection with *E. histolytica* and other intestinal protozoa in inmates of mental hospitals.[6]

Observers in various countries are in agreement that the percentage of carriers of *E. histolytica* is lowest in young children. It rises in the succeeding age groups, until a certain level is reached which is maintained throughout life, or at least until the ages of twenty to thirty. Some investigators assert that this level can only be kept up by continuous reinfection, because the parasite survives in its host for hardly more than one year.[7]

Whatever the truth of this matter may be, it is certain that there are persons who evacuate cysts of *E. histolytica* for years on end. Obviously, examples of this kind must be rare, for it is difficult to

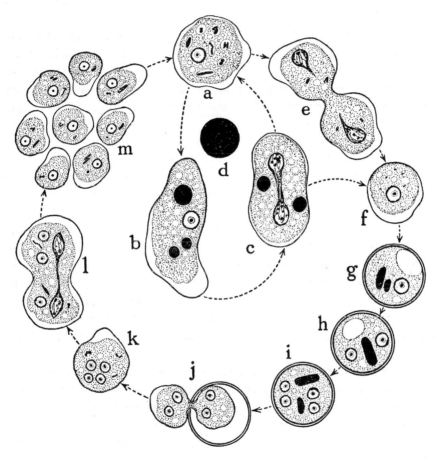

FIG. 3·2 *Entamoeba histolytica.* Schematic representation of its life cycle: *a* and *e–m,* In the lumen of the colon.—*b, c,* In the tissue of the intestinal wall.—*e–f,* Minuta-trophozoites.—*g–i,* Cysts.—*j,* Excystation.— *k–m,* Multiplication following excystation.—*b, c,* Histolytic trophozoites with erythrocytes.—*d,* Normal erythrocyte. (After Hoare, 1949. Courtesy, Baillière, Tindall & Cox, London.)

continue the observations for such a long time, especially if the host
is not affected by his parasite—and that is the rule rather than
the exception.

HISTOLYTIC OR INVASIVE STAGE

Like any other commensal, *E. histolytica* can completely change
its habits by violating topical restraint, i.e. by disturbing the host-
parasite equilibrium. But it is not every commensal that gives a
visible form to this change by taking on a new shape: the *histolytic*
trophozoite.[1]

Histolytic trophozoites live in lesions of the parietal tissue of the
cecum or colon, from which they are discharged together with products of necrosis. In this way they are mixed with the contents of the
lumen of the gut. They are evacuated in the stools, and there they
can be found, mostly in small clumps of mucosanguineous material.
Unlike the minuta-trophozoites, they quickly die when they reach
the lumen, for it is not their normal habitat, as it is of the noninvasive minuta-trophozoites. Thus they will not be recovered alive from
the stools if they were discharged from a lesion situated in the cecum,
which is a considerable distance from the anal orifice.

The histolytic trophozoite (Figs. $3 \cdot 1{:}1$, $3 \cdot 2{:}b{-}c$, $3 \cdot 10{:}A$) differs
from the noninvasive minuta-trophozoite by its larger size, 20–40 μ.
Often its ectoplasmic border is so broad as to be visible at rest. The
pseudopodia it emits are large; moreover, they are "eruptive": one
moment endoplasm is present at the margin of the amoeba; the
next moment a crystal-clear hemisphere appears on top of it, pushing
the surrounding particles aside with a jerk.[9] The nucleus is large,
4–6 μ; it often contains an inner circle of chromatin granules, between the outer circle and the central granule or endosome.

One characteristic remains to be mentioned, the presence of red
blood corpuscles in the endoplasm. They are spherical, not flat, and
they are smaller than normal erythrocytes, but they have the same
color. Brug believes they are not erythrocytes at all, but vacuoles
filled with a solution of hemoglobin. According to some authors
amoebae possessing all the characteristics enumerated here, except
that of carrying erythrocytes, cannot be classified as histolytic
trophozoites; but there are others who do not regard this particular
point as essential.

Most investigators agree that histolytic trophozoites do not encyst, but some deny the existence of minutas as an independent, self-propagating phase in the development of *E. histolytica.* Accordingly, minuta-trophozoites represent a short-lived transitional stage between histolytic trophozoites and cysts, called for that reason *precystic stage.* Others do not admit the existence of such a short-lived stage. Moreover, they affirm that histolytic trophozoites can never change back into minutas. This affirmation is based on the behavior of *E. histolytica* in young kittens. In that unnatural host it assumes

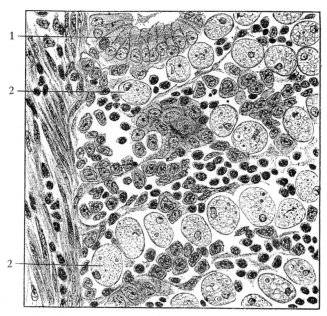

FIG. 3·3   *Entamoeba histolytica* in intestinal tissue of kitten, × 500: 1. Epithelial cells.—2. Amoebae. (After Brumpt, 1922. Courtesy, Masson & Cie, Paris.)

the histolytic shape, and no other, and continues so until both host and invader have been destroyed, without leaving a single cyst to perpetuate the race.

When it takes the histolytic shape, the parasite penetrates the tissues (Fig. 3·3), usually the submucosa of the cecum and the ascending colon, often of the sigmoid colon, the rectum, and the vermiform appendix. Once it has broken the local barriers, it invades the underlying intestinal tissues, the liver, and more rarely, the brain, lungs, spleen, kidneys, uterus, vagina, the wall of the urinary bladder, and the skin. Wherever it penetrates the tissues, it causes severe damage. With its large pseudopods it destroys the cells and blocks the circulation, thus causing extensive necrosis. Conversely, it may stimulate the elements of epitheloid and connective tissues to excessive proliferation. Thus granulomas are produced in the wall of the cecum and the sigmoid colon, and are known as *amebic granulomas* or *amebomas*.

There still exists a good deal of uncertainty as to the factors which induce the noninvasive minuta stage to change into the pathogenic histolytic stage. At first sight, the climate seems to play a preponderant role in this matter. *Entamoeba histolytica* is cosmopolitan; it is found in tropical and subtropical as well as in temperate regions. In hot countries parasite carriers are, on the whole, more numerous than in temperate regions. The difference, however, is insufficient to explain the fact that the classical amebic dysentery is a common disease in hot countries and not so in temperate countries. Investigators who accept the minuta stage as an independent stage in the development of *E. histolytica* [10] are thus called upon to explain why the metamorphosis of the noninvasive minuta stage into the pathogenic histolytic stage is of common occurrence in hot countries and not common in temperate countries.

To avoid misconceptions, it must be pointed out that the expression "hot and temperate countries" means more than mere climatology. It also includes health conditions and socioeconomic conditions, which often are on a lower level of development in hot countries than in temperate ones.[11] On this basis, the following conditions may stimulate *amebic invasion* (i.e. the metamorphosis of the minuta stage into the histolytic stage).

(1) *The state of the host.* In hot countries the tissue of the intestinal wall is particularly exposed to irritation by an intestinal flora composed of numerous species of more or less pathogenic bacteria, which quickly pass from one host to another. This may put the intestinal tissues at a disadvantage when called upon to ward off amebic invasion.[12] The diet of the inhabitants in many of these countries (protein deficiency, excess of carbohydrates) may stimulate amebic invasion by weakening the host or by altering the composition of the intestinal flora.[13]

(2) *The state of the parasite. E. histolytica* may vary in virulence,

i.e. in its readiness to start an amebic invasion. Two possibilities are to be considered.

(*a*) *The virulence is increased by environmental conditions.* Here may be mentioned the nature of the bacteria serving as food to the minuta-trophozoites,[14] the intensity of the infection to which man is exposed,[15] and the speed with which the amoebae pass from one host to another.[9] The increased virulence may be maintained as long as the parasites continue to be passed quickly from one host to another. It is likely to be lost if stagnation sets in, i.e. if the parasites remain in one host for a long time, especially if that host happens to be successful in counteracting the increased invasive tendency and in conditioning the parasite to a more normal behavior.

(*b*) *E. histolytica is a complex species composed of hereditary races, each one endowed with its own particular virulence.* This hypothesis is presented in two different forms: (1) There exist two strains, one harmless, even to young kittens (*E. dispar* Brumpt, 1925), the other pathogenic; or both are pathogenic to young kittens, but only one is pathogenic to rats.[16] (2) There exist at least three strains. All are pathogenic to young kittens; still they can be identified by their degree of virulence.[17] If such races exist, a rapid succession of passages from host to host, or a gross contamination of a water supply,[18] would increase the chances of some particularly virulent race becoming mixed with the parasites ingested by man.

These are the hypotheses to explain the difficulties entailed by the view that the minuta stage is self-propagating and independent of the histolytic stage.

Many investigators avoid these difficulties by denying the existence of an independent minuta stage. They do not worry about the problem of why minutas in one country are more inclined to turn histolytic than in another. In their opinion this metamorphosis is pure fiction. There exists no such a thing as the minuta stage. There exist trophozoites and cysts, and the one turns into the other by way of the precystic stage. That is all there is to it. Persons carrying minutas and cysts only (i.e. healthy carriers) do not exist.[19] They all carry amebic lesions in their intestine, where histolytic trophozoites continue their pernicious activity. The carrier of minuta-trophozoites is considered a sick man; it is wrong to assume that he is healthy.

OTHER AMOEBAE PARASITIZING MAN

The human colon is parasitized by other species of amoebae beside *E. histolytica*. They are commensals, subjected to topical restraint, i.e. to a life in the lumen of the large bowel and not in the tissue of the wall of the gut. Like all commensals, they are potentially pathogenic. They may be expected to violate topical restraint, i.e. to become invasive. There are investigators who believe that *E. coli* and *D. fragilis* actually do so. Although their evidence has not been accepted with regard to these species, it has been in the case of *I. bütschlii*. On the whole, however, it is not believed necessary to eradicate them in the human gut. If this assumption is accepted, if finding amoebae does not *eo ipso* justify therapeutic measures, it obviously becomes necessary to identify the amoebae found in the bowel of a human being.

This consideration explains why a description of the "harmless" intestinal amoebae is added to this chapter.

None of them show stages in their development which could be confused with the histolytic stage of *E. histolytica,* provided one adheres strictly to certain criteria established for their identification. However, confusion with minuta-trophozoites is easy. For this reason identification must be made on the cyst form.[25]

ENTAMOEBA HARTMANNI

Entamoeba hartmanni Von Prowazek, 1912 (*E. tenuis* Kuenen and Swellengrebel, 1917) has often been designated the "small race" of *E. histolytica*. It has, indeed, much in common with the minuta stage of this species, but it is smaller. The trophozoite has a diameter of 6–10 μ, with a nucleus of about 2 μ, the cyst of 6–8 μ. There is no glycogen vacuole in the uninucleate cyst; the chromatoid bodies are often spherical or polyhedric and situated around the nucleus (Fig. 3·4). The mature cyst is quadrinucleate. *E. hartmanni* has never been reported as invading the tissues. Its habitat is in the lumen of the colon.

According to Burrows[20] there exists a true "small race" of *E. histolytica*. It has the size of *E. hartmanni,* but differs from that species by the comparatively large size of the nucleus in the uninucleate cyst (½ to ⅗ of the diameter of the cyst, whereas in *E.*

hartmanni it is ¼ to less than ½). Another point of differentiation is the presence of a glycogen vacuole in the uninucleate cyst.

ENTAMOEBA COLI Grassi, 1879

The trophozoites are somewhat larger than those of the minuta stage (15–30 μ), but an undersized coli may be smaller than a large minuta. They are similar with regard to their ectoplasm, the way they emit their pseudopods, and the food they ingest. The nucleus measures 4–7 μ; it has thick marginal chromatin granules, one central granule, and minute granules in between (Figs. 3·5, 3·10:D–F). Thus the difference between coli- and minuta-trophozoites is not so sharply defined as to differentiate them with any degree of certainty.

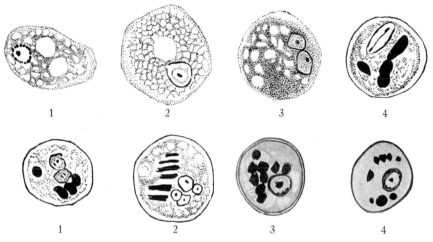

FIG. 3·4 *Entamoeba hartmanni*, × 3000 (Heidenhain stain): *Upper row*, 1–3. Trophozoites.—4. Uninucleate cyst showing nuclear division. *Second row*, 1. Binucleate.—2. Quadrinucleate.—3, 4. Uninucleate cyst. (After Kuenen and Swellengrebel, 1917. Courtesy, *Geneeskundig Tijdschrift voor Nederlands Indië*.)

The cysts are more helpful. Usually they are over 14 μ in diameter, ranging between 15 and 20 μ. Their wall is thicker than in *E. histolytica;* often an inner and an outer margin can be discerned. The most important characteristics are: (1) The uninucleate stage is rare, the binucleate very common; it is this stage which contains a large glycogen vacuole. (2) The mature cyst carries 8 nuclei (occasionally 16–28). In fixed and stained preparations they do not show up as well as in *E. histolytica* because the protoplasm stains so deeply;

in fresh preparations, on the contrary, it is easier to identify them than in mature cysts of *E. histolytica*. (3) Chromatoid bodies, if at all present, are shaped like splinters or thin filaments (Figs. $3 \cdot 5$, $3 \cdot 10 : D-F$).

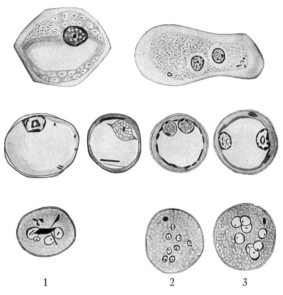

FIG. $3 \cdot 5$ *Entamoeba coli*, $\times$ 1000 (Heidenhain stain): *Upper row.* Trophozoites.—*Second row.* Uni- and binucleate cysts.—*Third row:* 1, Quadrinucleate cyst.—2, Mature cyst with 8 small nuclei.—3, Id. with 8 large nuclei. (After Kuenen and Swellengrebel, 1913. Courtesy, Gustav Fischer, Jena.)

Entamoeba coli is found in the stools of inhabitants of tropical and subtropical as well as of temperate countries, without any conspicuous difference in the rate of infection. As in *E. histolytica,* it is least common in young children. Monkeys, rats, rabbits, and guinea pigs harbor amoebae with cysts quite similar to those of *E. coli*.

ENTAMOEBA POLECKI

Entamoeba polecki Von Prowazek, 1912, is the name assigned to an ill-defined group of intestinal amoebae that have this in common that their cysts are mainly uninucleate, with or without a small glycogen vacuole, and chromatoid bars of various shapes: short rods, spheres, and irregularly formed structures. Their size varies from 10–12 μ to 15–20 μ, with nuclei varying from 4 to 8 μ.

Originally they were recovered from pigs, and subsequently from monkeys, sheep, and cattle. Up to 1958 seven cases of human infection were reported.[21]

ENDOLIMAX NANA

Endolimax nana (Wenyon and O'Connor, 1917) Brug, 1918, an intestinal amoeba of man, is placed into a separate genus (Kuenen and Swellengrebel, 1917) because of the structure of the nucleus: most chromatin is collected into one central sphere, the *karyosome* (Figs. 3·6, 3·10:*J–L*), which fills the greater part of the nucleus.

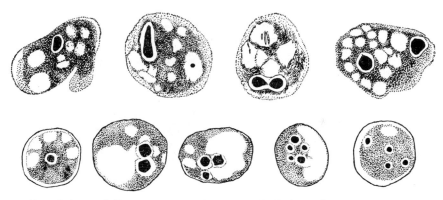

Fig. 3·6   *Endolimax nana,* × 3000 (Heidenhain stain): *Upper row.* Trophozoites.—*Second row.* Cysts. (After Kuenen and Swellengrebel, 1917. Courtesy, *Geneeskundig Tijdschrift voor Nederlands Indië*.)

The trophozoite measures 4–8 μ; its ectoplasm is visible in the pseudopods only, some of which are bilobate. The cysts are slightly elongated; their length is 5–6.5 μ, rarely 8 μ. Initially they contain a glycogen vacuole, which usually disappears by the time the mature (quadrinucleate) stage is reached. The cysts are highly resistant; they may survive for a month in undiluted stools.

The incidence of *E. nana* increases with man's age. Its geographical distribution is similar to that of *E. coli*.

IODAMOEBA BÜTSCHLII

Iodamoeba bütschlii (Von Prowazek, 1911) Dobell, 1919 (*Pseudolimax*, Kuenen and Swellengrebel, 1917, as name of the genus, *Endolimax williamsi*, Brug, 1919), an intestinal amoeba, is found in man; apparently identical amoebae were recovered from swine.

The trophozoite measures 8–15 μ; ectoplasm is visible in the pseudopods only; ingested food is seen to be composed of bacteria, not of starch granules. The nucleus has a diameter of 3–6 μ; it contains a large karyosome, which, however, has not absorbed all the chromatin, for some is left along the margin and in the space between the margin and the karyosome.

The cyst has a diameter of 8–12 μ; its wall is fairly thick. As a rule it contains only one nucleus, which bears a large eccentric karyosome surrounded on one side by a sickle-shaped mass of chromatin. The cyst also contains a glycogen vacuole, essentially identical with that seen in *E. histolytica* and *E. coli,* although it may take on a somewhat darker hue when treated with iodine. Nevertheless, this glycogen vacuole has gained it the name of *iodine cyst* (Figs. 3·7, 3·10:G–I).

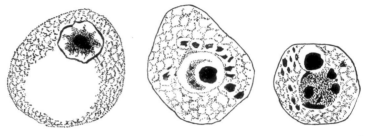

FIG. 3·7   *Iodamoeba bütschlii,* × 3000 (Heidenhain stain): Cysts. (After Kuenen and Swellengrebel, 1917. Courtesy, *Geneeskundig Tijdschrift voor Nederlands Indië.*)

I. bütschlii is of special interest because it is known for certain to have committed excesses as a commensal. In Brisbane, Derrick [22] observed it, on postmortem examination, in sections of intestinal ulcers, lymphatic glands of the abdomen, lungs, and brain of a Japanese soldier who had died in a state of exhaustion and inanition. This is all the more remarkable as *I. bütschlii* is found all over the world and was never known, before or since, to have broken the bounds.

DIENTAMOEBA FRAGILIS

Dientamoeba fragilis Jepps and Dobell, 1918, is probably not an amoeba but an ameboid stage in the development of a flagellate. Usually it is rare. As an exception, Brug [6] found its incidence higher than that of any other intestinal amoeba among the inmates of a mental hospital in Amsterdam, in the following percentages: *E. hart-manni* 3, *Iodamoeba* 2.5, *E. histolytica* 8, *E. coli* 15, *Endolimax* 16, and *Dientamoeba* 36.

D. fragilis is a small amoeba, measuring 8–9 μ. The pseudopods are large, often lobate. The endoplasm contains bacteria and granules of starch. Usually two nuclei are present, each one with a large clump of chromatin granules in its center (Figs. 3·8, 3·10:*M–N*).

As cysts are not produced, it is difficult to explain how the parasite manages to reach another host, especially since it is presumed to die very quickly in the open. However, Brug found it possible to cul-

FIG. 3·8 *Dientamoeba fragilis,* × 3300. (After Rodenhuis, 1921. Courtesy, *Geneeskundig Tijdschrift voor Nederlands Indië.*)

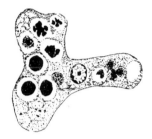

FIG. 3·9 *Entamoeba gingivalis,* × 2000. (After Hartmann. Courtesy, Gustav Fischer, Jena.)

tivate the amoebae from stools which had been passed 13 hours earlier. They thus appear to withstand adverse environmental conditions rather well and may be expected to resist as well the deleterious effect of the gastric juice when they are ingested by the host.

There remains one parasite of the human alimentary tract which has always been classified as an amoeba although it does not form any cysts, but which, nevertheless, needs a separate treatment because it does not inhabit the intestine; namely:

ENTAMOEBA GINGIVALIS

Entamoeba gingivalis (Gros, 1849) Brumpt, 1913 (*Amoeba dentalis* Grassi, 1879; *A. buccalis* Von Prowazek, 1904; *A. maxillaris* Kartulis, 1906) inhabits the buccal cavity of man, where it is found in dental mucus, dental accretions, tonsillar secretions, and alveolar discharge. It has also been recovered from the products of bronchoscopic examination.[23] Dogs, cats, and monkeys have been found to harbor apparently identical amoebae in their mouths.

The amoeba has a diameter of 10–12 μ; at rest the ectoplasm is sometimes visible; the endoplasm is conspicuous by the presence of numerous food vacuoles containing the debris of leucocytes. The nucleus measures 2.5–3 μ; its marginal chromatin consists of granules that may coalesce to form a marginal shell; its central chromatin is represented by one granule or a cluster of granules (Fig. 3·9).

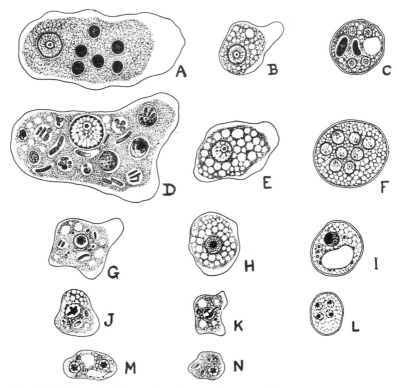

FIG. 3·10   Intestinal amoebae in man drawn to the same scale ($\times$ 1250). Upper row. *E. histolytica.*—Second row. *E. coli.*—Third row. *Iodamoeba bütschlii.*—Fourth row. *Endolimax nana.*—Fifth row. *Dientamoeba fragilis.* (After Wenyon, 1926. Courtesy, Baillière, Tindall & Cox, London.)

E. gingivalis is found in healthy persons, but it may be more than twice as frequent in those suffering from alveolar pyorrhea or tonsillitis.[24] Older reports mentioned the presence of amoebae in maxillary and pulmonary abscesses. Data at present available are insufficient to charge this commensal with becoming invasive, but, if it is not actually responsible for the morbid conditions with which it is found associated, it seems to thrive on them and may well influence them unfavorably.

THE TREATMENT OF AMEBIASIS *

In the treatment of *Entamoeba histolytica* infections, due consideration should be given to cyst passers and to relatively asymptomatic individuals as well as to those having overt clinical symptoms. From a public health point of view the cyst passer is more of a menace to the community than the clinically ill patient who passes trophozoites in the stool; the latter is not generally considered an important hazard in the transmission of the disease. It is difficult to lay down hard and fast rules for the treatment of patients suffering from amebiasis. Many factors are to be taken into consideration, such as the general nutritional status of the patient, the severity of the infection and the associated dysentery, if any, the presence of concomitant bacterial or parasitic infections, and finally, the presence of other constitutional diseases such as hypertension and kidney or liver disease. It is not unusual to find that patients who are suffering from diarrhea may harbor other protozoa such as the flagellate *Giardia lamblia* and/or enteric bacterial pathogens of the shigella or salmonella groups, in addition to the amebic infection. Under these circumstances the physician should use his discretion which one of these infections should be treated first. As a rule, it is advisable to treat the bacterial infection first because by so doing one conditions the patient for more effective benefit from the proposed amebicide. The use of broad spectrum antibiotics is particularly beneficial in this group of patients and should take precedence over the specific amebicides. Incidentally, these antibiotics may simultaneously eradicate the amebic infection.

Even in uncomplicated *E. histolytica* infections it is frequently advisable to precede the administration of a specific amebicide with a short course of a sulfa drug such as sulfasuxidine or sulfaguanidine and/or a few daily intramuscular injections of 600,000 units of penicillin, or 1.0 gm of dihydrostreptomycin for their effect on the

* For literature consulted in preparing this section see numbers 26–33 of the list of references at the end of this chapter.

concomitant bacterial organisms. Very often a marked clinical improvement is noted immediately following the preliminary use of these drugs, even before the specific amebicide is administered. In patients suffering from marked amebic dysentery associated with blood and mucus in the stools, the parenteral use of emetine hydrochloride will very frequently control this severe and distressing symptom. Two or three daily subcutaneous or intramuscular injections of 0.06 gm (gr I) emetine hydrochloride should be adequate.

There are a number of effective amebicides currently used in the treatment of intestinal amebiasis. None of them is 100 percent effective. Most of them, including the broad spectrum antibiotics, yield a cure rate in the order of 80–90 percent. These drugs are grouped into four categories, namely iodo-hydroxyquinolines, arsenicals, broad spectrum antibiotics, and a miscellaneous group which has not as yet been clearly defined or fully evaluated.

IODO—HYDROXYQUINOLINES

These all contain iodine. They are contraindicated in iodine-sensitive individuals and should be used with caution in cases of hyperthyroidism.

(a) DIODOHYDROXYN (Diodoquin), NNR, contains about 60 percent iodine. The recommended adult dose is one tablet (0.65 gm) orally three times a day for twenty days. Children over fifty pounds may be given one tablet twice daily—and under 50 pounds, a half tablet three times a day for twenty days. The drug is nontoxic, causes minimal side effects, is effective in relieving symptoms, and has a high laboratory cure rate.

(b) IODOCHLORHYDROXYQUINOLINE (Vioform, Enterovioform) contains 37–41 percent iodine and 12 percent chlorine. The recommended adult dose is one to two tablets or capsules 0.25 gm orally, three times a day for seven to ten days. Children may be given one tablet three times a day for one week. The drug is used extensively on the European continent and in the Latin American countries.

(c) CHINIOFON, U.S.P., B.P. (Yatren-Bayer, Quinoxyl, Anayodin, Quiniosulphan–May and Baker, Dysentulin–German, 8-hydroxy-5-iodoquinoline-5-sulfonic acid) is one of the oldest hydroxyquinolines. The recommended adult course of treatment is three to four tablets, 0.25 gm three times a day, before meals for seven days. It has a high cure rate but it is apt to cause diarrhea. It is useful in a retension enema. The drug should be freshly dissolved in a pint of water to form a 2.5 percent solution. It should be preceded by a cleansing enema of a 2 percent sodium bicarbonate solution.

EMETINE BISMUTH IODIDE, B.P.

Introduced in 1915, this has since been one of the favorite and most extensively used drugs in Great Britain and in the tropics. It contains about 58 percent iodine, 28 percent emetine and 20 percent bismuth. The recommended adult dose is one tablet or enteric gelatin capsule 0.2 gm (gr III) daily for one week to ten days.

ARSENICALS

(a) CARBARSONE, U.S.P. (p-carbamide-benzene-arsonic acid), a pentavalent organic arsenical. It contains about 29 percent arsenic. The recommended dose is one capsule or tablet (0.25 gm) orally, three times a day for seven to ten days. It is well tolerated, rarely causes any side effects, and has a high percentage of clinical as well as laboratory cure rate. It can also be used in a 2 percent solution as a retention enema. It should not be prescribed in cases with kidney disease or liver damage or in arsenic-sensitive individuals.

(b) BISMUTH GLYCOARSANILITE, NNR (glycobiarsol, Milibis) has recently been introduced in the treatment of intestinal amebiasis. It is well tolerated. The recommended adult course is one tablet three times a day for seven days. It is also available in combination with chloroquine (Aralen) for its alleged prophylactic effects in the prevention of amebic infection of the liver.

(c) ACETARSONE (Stovarsol, Spirocid) contains about 28 percent arsenic. One of the older amebicides, it is now rarely used because of a number of toxic reactions encountered—diarrhea, abdominal cramps, retinal changes, hepatitis, jaundice, and various types of dermatitis. The recommended adult dose is one tablet (0.25 gm) three times a day before meals for one week, followed by one tablet daily for an additional two weeks.

(d) THIOCARBARSONE [33] is a trivalent arsenical introduced as a more effective amebicide. However, it has been shown to cause a number of toxic side effects and has not been widely accepted clinically.

ANTIBIOTICS

The broad spectrum antibiotics [32] such as oxytetracycline (Terramycin), chlortetracycline (Aureomycin), tetracycline, erythromycin, and several others have been found useful in the treatment of intestinal amebiasis, especially in cases that harbor multiple infections. In these cases it is advisable to follow up the treatment with a specific amebicide, either a hydroxyquinoline or an arsenical. The antibiotics are not used extensively because of their prohibitive cost for patients in the low-income group and because they tend to produce a number of undesirable side effects such as nausea, vomiting, diarrhea and rectal itch, oral and perianal inflammations. Besides, when given in larger doses for any length of time they tend to depress the normal bacterial flora of the intestinal tract. The recommended dose for most of these antibiotics is 0.25 gm capsules or pills taken orally every six hours for one week to ten days. Fumagillin [33, 37] (Fumidol), an antibiotic that acts directly on the amoeba, has been found quite effective in intestinal amebiasis. It is available in 10-mg capsules and the recommended dose is one capsule three times a day for five days. The alleged leucopenia following its use has not been confirmed. Paromomycin [34] (Humatin) is another antibiotic with amebicidal activity recently introduced in the treatment of amebiasis. It is available in capsules 0.25 gm and employed in dosage of 3–6 capsules daily for 5 days. The recommended dose for children is 22 mg/kg per day for 5 days. Its effectiveness has not as yet been fully explored.

MISCELLANEOUS GROUP

Other chemotherapeutic agents such as bacitracin and camoform are being used. Their effectiveness and usefulness have not as yet been sufficiently evaluated.

Chemotherapeutic agents used in extraintestinal amebic infections, such as amebic hepatitis, amebic liver abscess, and pulmonary amebiasis, include emetine hydrochloride parenterally and chloroquine phosphate orally.

EMETINE HYDROCHLORIDE, USP, an alkaloid of ipecac, was formerly considered the most effective drug in the treatment of extraintestinal amebiasis, especially amebic hepatitis and localized amebic abscess. It should be borne in mind that emetine is a protoplasmic poison, cumulative in action because it is excreted slowly. It should be used cautiously in cases of myocardial disease and hypertension. A recommended course should, as a rule, not exceed six daily injections at the rate of 1 mg per kg of body weight, with a maximum daily dose of 1 grain (60 mg). The pulse and blood pressure should be taken daily before the drug is injected. A rise in pulse rate or a drop in blood pressure are indications to discontinue its use. Some clinicians advocate that patients be kept in bed during and for one week after the administration of emetine. It should not be repeated within one month, because the drug is excreted slowly. In recent years there has been a tendency to limit its use to cases of severe amebic dysentery for the initial control of a profuse and bloody diarrhea. Two or three daily subcutaneous injections should be adequate for this purpose. A hydroxyquinoline, an arsenical, or an antibiotic could be used concurrently.

Chloroquine phosphate (Aralen diphosphate, Nivaquine, Alvochlor) is a 4-aminoquinoline available in tablets as Aralen diphosphate 0.25 gm (equivalent to 0.15 gm of the base) and in 3-cc ampoules of Aralen hydrochloride. Each cubic centimeter of the ampoules contains 50 mg of the salt (equivalent to 40 mg of the base). Its antiamebic properties in vitro were shown a number of years ago. In view of its great concentration in the liver, Conan [31] introduced it as an amebicide for use in amebic hepatitis and abscess of the liver. It has since been in general use in doses of one tablet two or three times a day for two to three weeks. It has been found just as effective as emetine without any of the toxic side effects of the latter drug. A broad spectrum antibiotic may be used orally at the same time.

REFERENCES FOR CHAPTER III

1. W. A. KUENEN and N. H. SWELLENRGEBEL. *Centr. Bakteriol.* I, Orig., 1913, 71: 378–410.
2. E. G. NAUCK. *Lehrbuch der Tropenkrankheiten,* 432 pp., Stuttgart, 1956, G. Thieme, p. 114.
3. C. DOBELL. *Parasitology,* 1952, 42: 16–39.
4. TH. L. SNYDER and H. E. MELENEY. *Am. J. Trop. Med.,* 1941, 21: 63–69.
5. C. DOBELL. *Parasitology,* 1928, 20: 357–412.
6. S. L. BRUG. *Ann. Trop. Med. Parasitol.,* 1936, 30: 283–284, 441–452.
7. P. C. BEAVER, R. C. JUNG, H. J. SHERMAN, T. R. READ, and T. A. ROBINSON. *Am. J. Trop. Med. Hyg.,* 1956, 5: 1000–1009.
8. E. P. SNIJDERS. *Ned. Tijdschr. Geneesk.,* 1932, 76: 1068 (summary in English).

9. E. P. SNIJDERS. *Ned. Tijdschr. Geneesk.*, 1929, 73 (2): 5835–5847 (summary in English).

10. C. A. HOARE. *Parasitology*, 1952, 42: 43–47.

11. D. H. K. LEE. *Climate and Economic Development in the Tropics*, 182 pp., New York, 1957, Harper & Brothers.

12. A. WESTPHAL. *Arch. Schiffs- u. Tropen-Hyg.*, 1937, 41: 262–279.

13. R. ELSDON DEW. *S. African Med. J.*, 1953, 27: 504–506.

14. T. BALSAM and J. G. SHAFFER. *Am. J. Trop. Med. Hyg.*, 1958, 7: 17–19.

15. L. FREEDMAN. *S. African Med. J.*, 1958, 32: 797–798.

16. R. A. NEAL. *Trans. Roy. Soc. Trop. Med. Hyg.*, 1957, 51: 312–319.

17. H. E. MELENEY and W. W. FRYE. *Am. J. Hyg.*, 1935, 21: 422–437.

18. C. A. LEMAISTRE, R. W. SAPPENFIELD, C. CULBERTSON, F. R. N. CARTER, A. OFFUTT, H. BLACK, and M. M. BROOKE. *Am. J. Hyg.*, 1956, 64: 30–45.

19. E. C. FAUST. *Am. J. Trop. Med.*, 1941, 21: 35–48.

20. R. B. BURROWS. *Am. J. Trop. Med. Hyg.*, 1959, 8: 583–589.

21. R. B. BURROWS and G. E. KLINK. *Am. J. Hyg.*, 1955, 62: 156–157.

22. E. H. DERRICK. *Trans. Roy. Soc. Trop. Med. Hyg.*, 1948, 42: 191–198.

23. W. D. SUTLIFF, F. D. GREEN, and L. S. SUTER. *Am. J. Trop. Med.*, 1951, 31: 718–723.

24. C. E. BENJAMINS. *Arch. ital. otol. rinol.*, 1919, 30 (No. 2).

25. M. M. BROOKE. *Amebiasis: Methods in Laboratory Diagnosis*, 67 pp., Atlanta (Georgia), 1958, Communicable Disease Center, pp. 1–3, 32, 33.

26. T. T. MACKIE, G. W. HUNTER, and C. B. WORTH. *Manual of Tropical Medicine*, 2d ed., 907 pp., Philadelphia and London, 1954, W. B. Saunders Co., pp. 258–265.

27. PH. MANSON BAHR. *Manson's Tropical Medicine*, 14th ed., 2d print., 1144 pp., London, 1957, Cassell & Co., Ltd., pp. 510–511.

28. W. H. HARGREAVES. *Lancet*, 1945 (2): 68–72.

29. P. B. VAN STEENIS. *Amoebiasis*, pp. 375–444 of VAN STEENIS, KOUWENAAR, AND WINCKEL, *Manual of Tropical Medicine* (in Dutch), Amsterdam, 1951, Scheltema & Holkema.

30. E. C. FAUST, P. F. RUSSELL, and D. R. LINCICOME. *Clinical Parasitology*, 1078 pp., Philadelphia, 1957, Lea & Febiger, pp. 223–231.

31. N. J. CONAN. *Bull. N. Y. Acad. Med.*, 1949, 24: 545–546.

32. H. B. SHOOKHOFF and M. M. STERMAN. *Ann. N. Y. Acad. Sci.*, 1952, 55: 1125–1132.

33. H. H. ANDERSON. *Ann. N. Y. Acad. Sci.*, 1952, 55: 1118–1124.

34. O. K. COURTNEY. *Antibiotic Annual*, 1959–60, pp. 304–309.

35. M. C. MCCOWEN, M. E. CALLENDER, and J. F. LAWLIS, JR. *Science*, 1951, 113: 202–203.

36. J. H. KILLOUGH, G. B. MCGILL, and R. C. SMITH. *Science*, 1952, 115: 71.

37. R. C. JUNG, A. GARCIA-LAVERDE, and F. F. KATZ. *Am. J. Trop. Med. Hyg.*, 1955, 4: 989–997.

CHAPTER IV

FLAGELLATES

Flagellates move in a liquid medium by means of their long, flexible flagella. The outer part of their protoplasm, the ectoplasm, is more rigid than the rest, thus allowing the animal to maintain, on the whole, a well-defined shape. Each flagellum begins with a granule, called a *blepharoplast*, situated near the surface or deeper down. Thus the flagellum, starting from the blepharoplast, reaches the surface immediately or it has to pass through the protoplasm for part of its length; the internal part of the flagellum is called the *rhizoplast*.

Flagellates take up food in a dissolved state or as solid particles. The latter are ingested through an aperture in the rigid ectoplasm, called the *cytostome*.

The flagellate parasites of man may be classified according to the site they occupy in his body. Some live in cavities open to the surface through the buccal, anal, or genital orifices; they are called *intestinal flagellates*. Others live in the tissues and the blood; they are called *hemoflagellates*.

INTESTINAL FLAGELLATES

The way of life of the intestinal flagellates is much like that of the intestinal amoebae. They are commensals subjected to topical restraint which is well maintained as a rule. Their incidence in the succeeding age groups is like that of the amoebae: the rate of infection is at its lowest in young children; it rises in older children, till it reaches a certain level which is maintained through adult age. In the gut their principal habitat is the cecum. They are pear-shaped and possess a cytostome and 2–6 flagella.

The one exception to this general description is:

GIARDIA LAMBLIA

Giardia lamblia Stiles, 1915, *Giardia intestinalis* (Lambl, 1859) Alexeieff, 1914, *Lamblia intestinalis (*Lambl, 1859) Blanchard, 1888, inhabits the duodenum and upper jejunum. The rate of infection for this flagellate is higher in children than in adults. On occasions it is pathogenic. It is pear-shaped cut lengthwise and carries eight flagella; a cytostome is lacking.

The trophozoite or motile form measures 10–25 by 6–12 μ. Owing to the absence of a cytostome, the protoplasm is clear of solid particles of food. The ventral side of the animal is flat, its dorsal side

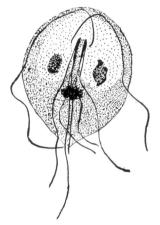

FIG. 4·2 *Giardia lamblia.* Cyst. (After Rodenhuis, 1924.)

FIG. 4·1 *Giardia muris.* Trophozoite, dried and Giemsa-stained, × 2300.

convex; it tapers to a point posteriorly and is round anteriorly. The anterior half of the ventral side shows a kidney-shaped concavity called the *sucking disk.* Its edge is marked by a well-defined line; its anterior half bends smoothly; the curve of its posterior half is interrupted by a notch at the level of the middle line. To the left and right of this notch are situated two slightly elongated nuclei, with a large central karyosome. Below the notch lie a pair of elongated structures, the *parabasal bodies,* and above them a pair of blepharoplasts, a right one and a left one, from which the rhizoplasts of the flagella start. There are eight of them, as follows:

(1) A right and a left *anterolateral rhizoplast.* The left one starts from the right blepharoplast and turns left; the right one does ex-

actly the opposite, and so they cross each other (*chiasma*). Then they skirt the edge of the sucking disk; at the level of the nuclei they reach the surface, from which they emerge as *anterolateral flagella*.

(2) A pair of *posterolateral rhizoplasts*. Each one starts from the blepharoplast on its own side; they reach the surface at a point between the implantation of the anterolateral flagella and the tail end, there to appear as *posterolateral flagella*.

(3) A pair of *ventral rhizoplasts* also arise from the blepharoplasts on their own side. They reach the ventral surface at the level of the notch in the lower margin of the sucking disk, where they appear as *ventral flagella*.

(4) A pair of *caudal rhizoplasts*, running straight from their respective blepharoplasts to the tail end, emerge as *caudal flagella*.

The presence of giardia in the human intestine is established by finding cysts in the stools. The cysts (Fig. 4·2) measure 8–14 μ in length and 6–10 μ in width. They contain two or four nuclei, the blepharoplasts, the rhizoplasts, and straight or curved rodlike structures. Trophozoites are also regularly seen in diarrheic stools.

This flagellate is a cosmopolitan. It does not appear to prefer hot countries to cool ones. However, the rates of infection observed in various regions cannot be compared, because children and adults are not always recorded separately.

Species of the genus *Giardia* are found in wild and domestic animals. Except for *G. simoni* in the rat, they are considered as different from the human species (Figs. 4·1, 4·4).

Apart from reports on *G. lamblia* invading the biliary ducts, it may be described as a commensal keeping well within bounds, i.e. within the lumen of the duodenum and the jejunum, comparable with *Entamoeba coli* rather than with *E. histolytica*. Thus it might be expected (1) that the human host subjects *Giardia* to topical restraint only, i.e. allows it to multiply freely as long as it keeps within the lumen of the gut; (2) that it is nonpathogenic as long as it keeps within bounds.

Both assumptions are incorrect. The host subjects *Giardia* to numerical restraint, as evidenced by the higher prevalence of infection in children [1]; the parasite frequently becomes pathogenic notwithstanding its continuing to keep within bounds, because it multiplies excessively in the lumen of the gut, thereby violating the numerical restraint the host tried to impose.

This apparent contradiction can be explained by taking account of (1) the habitat of *Giardia,* the duodenum and upper jejunum, and (2) the way it is settled there, adhering with its sucking disk to the upper surface of the intestinal mucosa (Fig. 4·3). If *Giardia* is present in large numbers, extensive stretches of the mucosa may be covered in this way, mechanically interfering with the absorptive capacity of the cells. This becomes of particular importance if the *duodenal* mucosa is affected. For then the large numbers of *Giardia* interfere with the physiological activities of the tissues of that organ, which occupies a prominent position in the hormonal regulation of the hepatic and pancreatic secretions, in the absorption of fat and

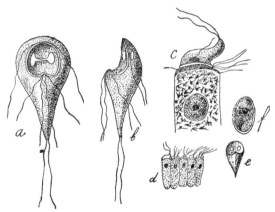

FIG. 4·3   *Giardia lamblia,* trophozoites: *a,* Frontal view.—*b,* Lateral view.—*c* and *d,* Adhering to epithelial cells. (After Grassi and Schewiakoff.)

fat-soluble vitamins, and in the production and resorption of hemopoietic substances. Thus *G. lamblia* in the duodenum is assumed to be responsible for a morbid syndrome known as *giardiasis* or *lambliasis,* if excessive numbers of them occupy this position.[2] This assumption is confirmed by the effectiveness of quinacrine (atabrine) in eradicating the parasite and curing the disease.

The human body does the same, more slowly, but in a more subtle fashion; it imposes numerical restraint, without eradication. This natural cure would have an advantage over the cure by drugs if premunition ruled in giardiasis, i.e. if residual parasites were protecting their host against renewed infection. Up till the present nothing to that effect has transpired.

TREATMENT OF GIARDIASIS. The abdominal complaints ascribed to *G. lamblia* can be relieved by quinacrine (Atabrine,[68] mepacrine). It is administered orally, three tablets of 0.1 gm daily for 3–5 days. Children up to 4 years receive ½ tablet three times daily; from 5–8 years, two tablets daily.

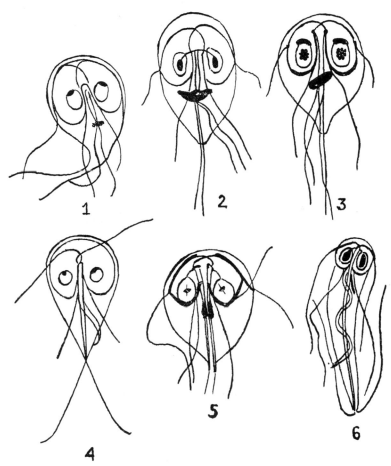

FIG. 4·4   Giardias from various authors, collected by Brug.

The other intestinal flagellates of man conform to the description given in the opening lines of this chapter. They may be classified into two groups according to the presence or absence of an undulating membrane. Those in possession of that organelle are grouped within one genus.

THE TRICHOMONADS

These are ovoid in shape with a pointed posterior end. They carry 3–5 "free" flagella, implanted in front and pointing forward. Another one, the "fixed" flagellum, implanted near the others, runs backwards along the side of the body, to which it is loosely fixed by a thin membrane—the *undulating membrane*. In front, under the blepharoplast from which the flagella arise, a nucleus is situated. On one side it is flanked by (1) the axostyle, a glassy, pointed rod which runs backwards and protrudes at the rear end from the body of the

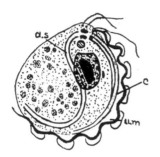

FIG. 4·5 *Trichomonas caviae* (dried and Giemsa-stained): *UM*, Undulating membrane. —*C*, Costa.—*AS*, Axostyle.

FIG. 4·6 *Trichomonas muris.* Cyst showing undulating membrane and costa. (After Brug, 1922.)

flagellate and (2) the cytostome, which may be broad or inconspicuous. On the other side the nucleus is flanked by (1) the elongate *parabasal body* that ends in a thin filament and (2) the *basal filament* or *costa* that marks the line along which the undulating membrane is fixed to the body of the flagellate (Fig. 4·5).

Three species of human parasites belong to this genus: one inhabits the intestine, another the buccal cavity, the third the female and male genitalia.

TRICHOMONAS HOMINIS

Trichomonas hominis (Davaine, 1860) Grassi, 1888, *T. intestinalis* (Leuckart, 1879) inhabits the intestine (Fig. 4·7:*C*). It has a length of 7–8 μ. Its ectoplasm is pliable so as to allow some change of form (amoeboid motion). The number of free flagella may vary from three to five. One of them originates from a blepharoplast situated in front of the nucleus; a second blepharoplast, next to the first, is the starting point of the other free flagella, the fixed flagellum, the conspicuous costa, and the thick axostyle. The fixed flagellum is accompanied by the undulating membrane over the whole length of the flagellate; then it continues for some length as a free flagellum beyond the body of the flagellate. The nucleus is spherical; chromatin granules are lying along its edge, and one in the center. The

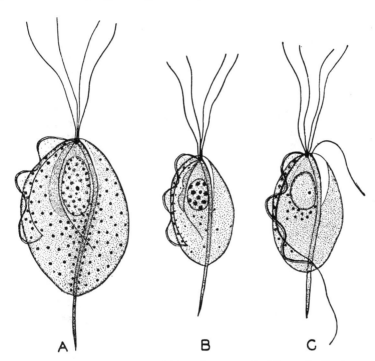

FIG. 4·7 Trichomonads parasitizing in man: A, *T. vaginalis* (a comparatively small specimen).—B, *T. tenax.*—C, *T. hominis.* The organelle to the left of the nucleus in A and B is the parabasal body; the unshaded field to the right of the axostyle (conspicuous in C, less so in B, almost invisible in A) is the cytostome. (After Wenrich, 1944. Courtesy, *Journal of Parasitology.*)

cytostome is conspicuous by its width. No parabasal body is visible. The protoplasm contains vacuoles with solid particles of food (which were ingested through the cytostome), a cluster of granules near the nucleus, and a line of granules skirting the costa.

Trichomonads of various mammals, probably identical with *T. hominis*,[3] inhabit the cecum of their host. It is reasonable to assume that this also holds true for *T. hominis* in man.

Unlike trichomonads of mammals (Fig. 4·6), *T. hominis* is not known to form cysts. It apparently does not need them in order to pass from one man to another, since it survives for days in deposited stools and for one hour in gastric juice.[4]

TRICHOMONAS TENAX

Trichomonas tenax (O. F. Muller, 1773) Dobell, 1939, *T. buccalis* Goodey & Wellings, 1917, *T. elongata* Steinberg, 1862, has its habitat in the buccal cavity of man and monkeys,[5] perhaps also of dogs (Fig. 4·7:*B*). Its length, 6–7.5 μ, is about the same as that of *T. hominis*, from which it differs in the following points: (1) The fixed flagellum does not terminate in a free flagellum; its undulating membrane does not reach the rear of the body of the flagellate. (2) The number of free flagella is always four; they emerge from one blepharoplast. (3) The costa and the axostyle are thin. (4) Chromatin granules are evenly distributed throughout the nucleus. (5) The cytostome is inconspicuous. (6) A parabasal body is present. (7) There is no cluster of protoplasmatic granules near the nucleus.[6] *T. tenax* produces no cysts, but it can survive in water for 3–4 days. It probably is transmitted by droplet infection or some form of intimate contact or through common use of contaminated glassware and dishes. Under these circumstances cysts can apparently be dispensed with.

There are those who affirm that *T. tenax* is found only in diseased buccal cavities; others find the flagellate as readily in healthy mouths. It has been found in certain pulmonary affections, accompanied by other buccal microorganisms.

TRICHOMONAS VAGINALIS Donné, 1837

Unlike the other human trichomonads, one can find *T. vaginalis* pictured in the advertisement columns of medical journals, which recommend the use of various drugs to destroy the flagellate and to cure "trichomonad vaginitis," or "the seventh venereal disease" it is supposed to be the causative agent of.

Formerly there existed some confusion as to its identity; some regarded *T. vaginalis* as a *T. hominis* that had become settled in the vagina. Wenrich,[3] however, has pointed out that they differ in the following respects: (1) *T. vaginalis* is longer, 13 μ on an average; (2) its nucleus is elongate, and the distribution of chromatin resembles that of *T. tenax;* (3) its cytostome is even less conspicuous than in *T. tenax;* (4) it possesses a parabasal body, slightly larger than in *T. tenax;* (5) the undulating membrane is even shorter than in *T. tenax.* Consequently, it is certainly not with *T. hominis* that *T. vaginalis* can be confused. As to *T. tenax,* the difference from *T. vaginalis* is not quite so clear, as it mainly rests on a difference in size (Fig. 4·7A).

The inability to produce cysts is considered to be a more serious defect than in the other trichomonads, because *T. vaginalis* survives for no longer than one day outside the human body.[7] This is taken to be insufficient to secure transmission, except by sexual intercourse (in man) and other forms of intimate contact.

It is generally accepted that *T. vaginalis* is a pathogenic micro-organism. Some assert that it invades the blood of women who harbor the parasite in their vagina. Others were unable to confirm this observation. Even if it is discarded, there still remains the fact that great numbers of women twenty to forty years of age carry the parasite, especially those suffering from leucorrhea, and that *T. vaginalis* is found in men suffering from nongonorrheal urethritis.

There can be no doubt that persons ill with these diseases are often infected with *T. vaginalis,* although healthy carriers of both sexes are just as numerous—and even more numerous. But there remains some doubt whether the parasite is the cause of these morbid conditions in women. It has been suggested [8] that pre-existing diseases of the female genital tract provide a favorable environment that stimulates the parasite to excessive growth.

Contradictory statements on the subject may be reconciled by assuming that *T. vaginalis* is a commensal in healthy women twenty to forty years of age. A variety of morbid conditions may stimulate the parasite to excessive multiplication. This, in turn, may unfavorably influence the conditions, increasing at the same time the virulence of the parasite, and its chance of transmission to other persons. Sexual intercourse with a normal female carrier will result in the male partner becoming a healthy carrier, but he may acquire an urethritis if his partner carries parasites stimulated to excessive multiplication.

TREATMENT OF GENITAL TRICHOMONIASIS. Faust et al.[72] recommend the following treatment of trichomonad vaginitis. (*a*) Destroy the flagellates with suppositories containing an iodohydroquinoline, carbarsone, or oxytetracycline; (*b*) render the vaginal contents less suitable for their growth by a solution of lactic acid; (*c*) destroy the associated bacteria with suppositories containing an appropriate sulfonamide, combined with an oral or parenteral administration of antibiotics. For the treatment of trichomonad urethritis in the male they recommend: (*a*) treatment of the urethra with an ointment containing oxytetracycline, or irrigation with a fluid containing a sulfonamide or an antibiotic; (*b*) oral administration of an iodohydroquinoline, a sulfonamide, or an antibiotic.

CHILOMASTIX MESNILI

Chilomastix mesnili (Wenyon, 1910) Alexeieff, 1912, inhabits the intestine of man, rats, mice, and guinea pigs. In rodents it lives in the cecum; this probably also applies to man.

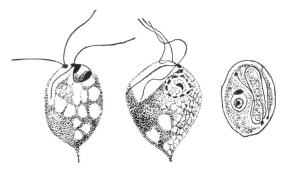

FIG. 4·8   *Chilomastix mesnili* (Heidenhain stain). Trophozoites and (to the right) a cyst. (After Kuenen and Swellengrebel, 1917. Courtesy, *Geneeskundig Tijdschrift voor Nederlandsch Indië.*)

Sometimes its presence is detected only by finding cysts in the stools. They are a little longer (7–9 μ) than broad (6–7 μ); one end is slightly pointed, and the wall of the cyst may be somewhat thickened at that end. The nucleus contains a compact mass of chromatin near its edge and a less conspicuous cluster in its center. The protoplasm contains threadlike inclusions and some granules (Fig. 4·8).

Trophozoites are readily found in diarrheic stools. They usually are 10–14 μ long and half as wide. Living specimens show a crease in the ectoplasm which runs spirally from the front to the rear. Three flagella are implanted anteriorly. Near their base is seen a concavity shaped like a trough, the cytostome; two thin rods run along its longitudinal edges; inside the trough a fourth flagellum may be seen moving. Below the base of the flagella the nucleus is situated, with one or two compact masses of chromatin near its edge. In the protoplasm a varying number of food vacuoles are embedded, containing bacteria.

The presence of this parasite in man has been reported from tropical and temperate countries, the rate of infection depending on sanitary rather than on climatic conditions. It has never been proved to display pathogenic activity.[9]

HEMOFLAGELLATES

The hemoflagellates of man belong to one systematic family, the Trypanosomatidae. They are characterized by possessing one flagellum, arising from a blepharoplast that is always associated with a spherical or rod-shaped structure called the *kinetoplast*.[10] The mem-

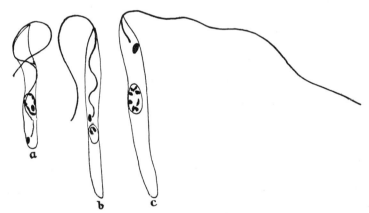

FIG. 4·9 *Herpetomonas muscarum* (dry slide, Giemsa-stained): a. Trypanosoma form.—b. Crithidia form.—c. Leptomonas form.

bers of this family may take a great variety of forms. All these forms are represented in the life cycle of a parasite of the house fly, *Herpetomonas muscarum*. The following description of this parasite serves as an introduction to this section.

Herpetomonas muscarum (Leidy, 1856) inhabits the midgut of the fly in the shape of a long thin flagellate. The nucleus lies halfway between its two extremities, the kinetoplast near the anterior extremity. Next to the kinetoplast the rhizoplast of the flagellum starts from its blepharoplast and runs straight to the anterior extremity of the body, where it emerges as a free flagellum which is twice the length of the body. This stage of development is called the *leptomonas form* (Fig. 4·9:*c*).

In the hindgut the flagellate takes another form. The kinetoplast is situated near, but still in front of, the nucleus. The rhizoplast of the flagellum is short, but the free flagellum, the continuation of the rhizoplast, is not completely free. It runs along the surface and up to the anterior end of the body, to which it is fastened by a thin portion of the ectoplasm called the *undulating membrane*. Beyond the anterior end of the body the flagellum becomes quite free. This state is called the *crithidia form* (Fig. 4·9:*b*).

The crithidia form continues the evolution by the kinetoplast taking a position behind the nucleus; the flagellum now skirts the whole length of the body, to which it remains fastened by the undulating membrane. This stage is called the *trypanosome form* (Fig. 4·9:*a*).

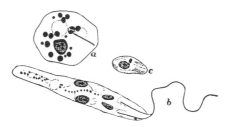

Fig. 4·10 *Herpetomonas muscarum* (dry slide, Giemsa-stained): *a*, Spherical form.—*b*, Leptomonas form.—*c*, Leishmania form.

In the rectum of the fly the flagellates are much reduced in size. Their shape becomes ovoid, their free flagellum disappears, their rhizoplast and blepharoplast often become invisible, and nothing remains but the nucleus and the kinetoplast. This stage is called the *leishmania form* (Fig. 4·10:*c*).

The leishmania forms leave the fly's body in its excreta. Ingested by another fly and arriving in an esophagal diverticulum, they expand and grow spherical (Fig. 4·10:*a*) and finally return to the leptomonas stage (Fig. 4·10:*b*).

This type of flagellate is found in a large number of insects, bloodsucking insects among them. Some bloodsucking insects are inhabited by members of two genera of the Trypanosomatidae, *Trypanosoma* and *Leishmania*. They share their parasites with mammals, man among them, the insect acting as intermediate host that transmits the infection from one mammal to another. In the mammalian host the trypanosomatidae are parasites inhabiting various tissues as well as the blood; in the insect host they behave on the whole like *H. muscarum* in the fly, although there are many differences as to detail. In *Trypanosoma cruzi* the insect host is of major importance; the mammal host may occasionally be dispensed with. In the other trypanosomes the insect host constitutes an indispensable intermediate station. In *Leishmania* this station is not always necessary.

Man often shares his trypanosomal parasites with other mammals that act as alternate hosts. They are of practical and theoretical importance: practical, because they constitute a reservoir, a source of infection to man; theoretical, because it is due to them that the true relationship between host and parasite can be understood. Some of these parasites are as fatal to man as any predator; but other mammals represent natural hosts, with which a balanced relationship can be established.

TRYPANOSOMA CRUZI

Trypanosoma cruzi Chagas, 1909, is the causative agent of American trypanosomiasis. Its trypanosome forms occur in the human and mammalian blood stream, but they do not multiply there. Intracellular parasites of the leishmania type are the ones that multiply in the human and mammalian body. In the intermediate host the development of the parasite takes place in the midgut and hindgut exclusively; it greatly resembles that of *H. muscarum*.

The trypanosome form measures about 20 μ in length and 3–7 μ in width. It has a very short pointed tail, almost hidden behind an uncommonly big kinetoplast (Fig. 4·11:8, 9). The nucleus is elongate, situated halfway between the two extremities of the body of the flagellate. The undulating membrane is narrow; its flagellar border shows few undulations. The free extremity of the flagellum is one-fifth to half as long as the body of the flagellate.

The leishmania forms are round or ovoid, with a diameter of about 4 μ. Their protoplasm contains a nucleus and a rod-shaped kinetoplast (Figs. 4·11:2–4 and 4·12); sometimes a short rhizoplast can be discerned, placed in a direction perpendicular to the kinetoplast. Multiplication of the leishmania form is effected by binary fission.

The leishmania forms are intracellular parasites of striated and smooth muscle fibres; they also occur in neuroglial cells, neurons, cells of the brain, the testes, the thyroid gland, and the skin. In

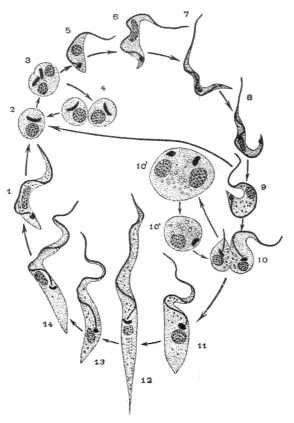

FIG. 4·11 *Trypanosoma cruzi*, life cycle in man (2–9) and triatomid bug (9–14 and 1): 1. Metacyclic trypanosome.—2–4. Leishmania forms. —5–9. Trypanosome forms.—10, 10'. Crithidia and leishmania forms in midgut of bug.—11–14. Transitional stages leading to metacyclic trypanosome (1). (After Brumpt, 1922. Courtesy, Masson & Cie, Paris.)

striated muscles (especially of the heart) they are collected into elongated clusters that may reach a size of 80–100 $\mu \times 10 \mu$, formed by the successive divisions of one specimen and its progeny. These clusters are sometimes called cysts, because they live within a covering, supposed to be a cyst wall, which probably is derived from the greatly extended host cell. In other organs similar clusters are observed, but they never grow to the same size.

The leishmania forms can change into trypanosome forms, a metamorphosis which simultaneously affects all individuals of a cluster. It is assumed that this change is reversible.

Under natural conditions the intermediate hosts of *T. cruzi* are limited to hemipterous bugs of the Triatomidae family. The adults are winged insects, the larvas and nymphs are wingless; at this stage they are as closely associated with man as bedbugs. The most important among them are *Triatoma infestans* in Argentina, Brazil, Chile, Paraguay, and Peru and *Rhodnius prolixus* in Venezuela and Colombia.

These feed on human and mammalian blood. In this way the trypanosome forms of the parasite enter the midgut of the bug.[11] There they change into crithidia forms, subsequently into leptomonas forms, and finally into large-sized leishmania forms (Fig. 4·11:10'). Arriving at that stage of development, they begin to multiply and continue to do so for several months. Eventually, some find their way to the hindgut, where they change back into crithidia forms, but this does not prevent them from continuing their multiplication (Fig. 4·11:11–13).

Three weeks or thereabouts after the bug has ingested the parasites, the crithidia forms change back into trypanosome forms (Fig. 4·11:14, 1) which bear the name of *metacyclic trypanosomes*. This metamorphosis is accomplished in the malpighian tubes.[12] Unlike the crithidia forms, the metacyclic trypanosomes are unable to adhere to the wall of the cavity in which they find themselves. Thus they are carried away to the rectum by the liquid moving in the malpighian tubes. Finally they are evacuated in the insect's excrements.

It is possible to infect suitable animals with *T. cruzi* by depositing excrements of infected bugs on their buccal or anal mucous membrane, their conjunctiva, or their slightly scarified skin; but these excrements do not prove infective unless they contain metacyclic trypanosomes. The appearance of that stage marks the moment at which the bug becomes infective.

Metacyclic trypanosomes are continuously recruited from the crithidia forms in the hindgut—a source which was not yet exhausted after a lapse of two years.[13] The bug that became infective upon the appearance of metacyclic trypanosomes continues in that stage for a long time, perhaps for the rest of its life.

Man becomes infected in a way similar to that described above: by infective triatomid excrements deposited on the skin, the conjunctiva, or the mucous membrane of the lips.[14] This mode of infection is rendered possible by the habits of the bug: (1) it defecates profusely after or even during the blood meal, so that the face and

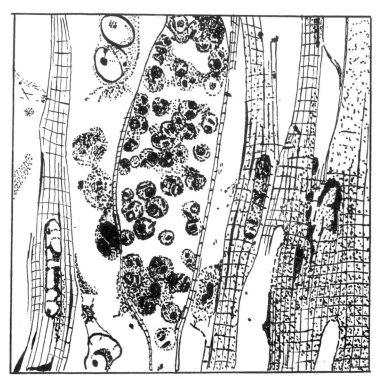

Fig. 4·12 *Trypanosoma cruzi:* Leishmania forms in muscular tissue, × 1300. (Drawn after a microphoto made by the late Dr. P. H. Hartz, San Cristóbal, Táchira, Venezuela.)

the bed sheets of the victim become soiled with the excrements of the bug; (2) it takes its blood meal seated on the skin of the face of man.[15] The bug which infects man has become infected in its turn by feeding on a mammalian alternate host, perhaps on another human being.

T. cruzi may pass directly from one bug to another without the aid of the mammalian host. This mode of infection has been realized in the experiment of making uninfected bugs feed on the liquid excrements of a triatomid that harbored metacyclic trypanosomes [16] or on liquified material derived from the corpses of infected bugs, provided they had not been dead for more than a fortnight.[17]

The alternate hosts of *T. cruzi* are wild-living animals—armadillos, marsupials, rodents, bats, carnivores, and monkeys—and domestic animals—dogs and cats. The former constitute the sylvatic reservoir, the latter the domestic reservoir. The domestic reservoir is likely to be of greater direct importance to man. The sylvatic reservoir, however, may possess the greater stability, if it is true that wild animals, armadillos especially, do not suffer much from the presence of the parasite in their body.

T. cruzi cannot be classified as a commensal. It is an *initial aggressor,* because it starts its career in the human body by making its host ill. This was proved by Galliard's [18] experiment. He injected metacyclic trypanosomes into the skin of 26 cancer patients; after two weeks the patients fell ill with fever, which lasted three weeks and gradually declined in the following two or three weeks.

Observations made on persons infected in nature have shown that this is not the end of the morbid process. Young children, especially, are threatened by an acute disease, *Chagas' disease* or *American trypanosomiasis,* which often begins with a unilateral swelling of the eyelid and conjunctiva (Romaña's sign). The swelling may assume the appearance of a small furuncle, known as a *chagoma,* which is not necessarily limited to the region of the eye, but may be seen anywhere the insect takes its blood meal. The infection which sets in after an incubation period of one to three weeks or longer is characterized by severe headaches, prostration, and a high fever which may be intermittent, remittent, or continuous. The acute stage often terminates fatally or leads to a chronic stage characterized by lymphadenopathy, enlargement of liver and spleen, a chronic anemia and leukopenia, and a variety of nervous disturbances. Cardiac involvement is usually the most frequent and the most pronounced manifestation of this disease. It includes many irregularities in rate and rhythm and evidence of myocardial damage which may cause sudden death or lead to a protracted course with a fatal outcome.

The numerous fatalities caused by the parasite should not, however, obscure the fact that a great number of adults and children harbor the parasite without apparent ill health.[19] It depends upon the virulence of each particular strain of parasites whether or not the host will succeed in subjecting it, even though only temporarily, to numerical restraint.[20] This restraint, if successful, is so effective that it is impossible to detect trypanosome forms in the peripheral circulation by direct microscopical examination. Nevertheless, these forms are still present. This can be proved by allowing selected, trypanosome-free triatomids to feed on the blood of such a healthy carrier. They ingest the blood in such large quantities that it could not be examined under the microscope. However, if the ingested blood contains one trypanosome, it will grow and multiply in the gut of the bug, and after some weeks the hindgut will be full of crithidias. Thus it is proved (1) that there actually were trypanosomes in the blood of the healthy carrier (*xenodiagnosis* [16]), and (2) that the numerical restraint to which the parasite was subjected was not so rigorous as to prevent their reaching the gut of the triatomid and multiplying there.

It may be assumed that the numerical restraint the host imposes on the parasite primarily affects the stages that actually multiply in the human body, viz. the leishmania forms. The scarcity of the trypanosome forms (which do not multiply) in the peripheral circulation is no more than a secondary effect of this restraint.

In South America infected persons are most numerous in Argentina (north of 40° south lat.), Brazil, Chile, Uruguay, and Venezuela; in Bolivia, Ecuador, and Paraguay they are far from rare; in Peru, French Guiana, and Central America they are few in number. In the eastern United States (as far north as Maryland) armadillos, marsupials, rodents, and carnivores (racoons) are the only mammals that were found infected. Pakchanian[21] succeeded in infecting a human being with *T. cruzi* isolated from these animals. Finally, two cases of natural infection in man have been detected in Texas.[20]

TREATMENT OF CHAGAS' DISEASE. None of the drugs specifically effective in other trypanosomiases and in leishmaniases are of any value in American trypanosomiasis.[69] According to Manson-Bahr,[71] Bayer 9736, containing arsenic and sulfur and replacing Bayer 7602, appears to hold great hope for the future. It is administered intravenously, in a 10-percent solution, two to three times weekly. The initial dose is 0.15 gm for adult males, increasing to 0.3–0.4 gm, to a total which is not to surpass 5 gm. Adult females receive 0.8 of these doses, children 0.6.

As a corollary to this section mention must be made of a trypanosome closely associated with, but wholly different from, *T. cruzi:*

TRYPANOSOMA RANGELI

Trypanosoma rangeli Tejera, 1920 (identical, or closely related are *T. escomeli* Yorke, 1921, *T. guatemalense* de Leon, 1946, *T. ariarii* Groot et al., 1951) is closely associated with *T. cruzi* because the two parasites are indigenous to the same countries, among which

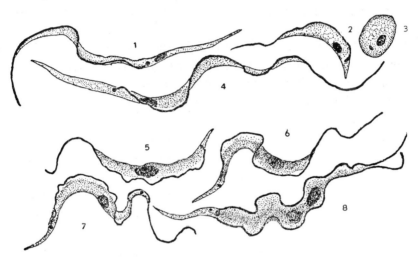

FIG. 4·13   *Trypanosoma rangeli:* 1–4. In intestine of *Rhodnius prolixus.*—5–7. In human blood.—8. Longitudinal fission in blood of mouse; × 2200. (After Groot et al., 1951. Courtesy, *American Journal of Tropical Medicine,* Vol. 31.)

Venezuela merits special attention. They are transmitted by the same intermediate host, viz. *Rhodnius prolixus,* and count the same wild and domestic animals among their alternate hosts, viz. marsupials (opossums) and dogs.

T. rangeli is wholly different from *T. cruzi* because (1) it is found only in mammalian blood, where it occurs as trypanosomes that multiply by binary fission, and (2) it never appears as clusters of multiplying leishmania forms in internal organs.

The most notable difference, however, is seen in the balanced relationship existing between *T. rangeli* and its host as it appears in

Venezuela, where almost two-thirds of the human population and half of the domestic dogs are found infected, and where infection of human volunteers results in a long-lasting but perfectly harmless parasitemia.[22] *T. rangeli* is evidently a commensal successfully subjected to topical restraint by its host.

In human blood *T. rangeli* is long (31 μ) and slender (Fig. 4·13:5–7) with long-drawn pointed extremities and a small kinetoplast situated at some distance from the posterior end. The nucleus lies near the anterior extremity. The undulating membrane is broad and its flagellar margin shows numerous undulations. Divisional forms have been observed in the blood of experimental animals (Fig. 4·13:8).

In *Rhodnius prolixus* the parasite is characterized by its extremely long and slender crithidia (Fig. 4·13:1) and trypanosome (Fig. 4·13:4). Its most important feature, however, is that it penetrates into the salivary glands and the proboscis of the insect; as a consequence the bug is able to transmit the infection by its bite,[23] as well as by its excreta.

OLD–WORLD TRYPANOSOMES

The genus *Trypanosoma* in the Eastern Hemisphere includes two species highly pathogenic to man, besides others no less pathogenic to man's domestic animals. Nevertheless, Wenyon [24] writes that the true vertebrate hosts of these trypanosomes are not those in which disease is produced, but rather the wild animals which harbor them without suffering in any serious manner, just as *Trypanosoma lewisi* occurs in the rat. Accordingly, this section opens with the description of a trypanosome that can hardly be called a parasite of man, although it has once been found in the human body.[25]

TRYPANOSOMA LEWISI

Together with the bovine babesias, *T. lewisi* Kent, 1880, represents the prototype of the initial aggressor; a few weeks of ruthless onslaught, followed by lengthy periods passed in a state resembling commensalism. In this instance the period of aggression is marked not only by the behavior of the parasite, but also by its shape, just as the histolytic stage of *E. histolytica* is marked by its shape as well as by its behavior.

T. lewisi occurs in the blood of rats. They are infected in their infancy by the intermediate host, the rat flea. From six to nine days after the infection, trypanosomes appear in the circulating blood. Some of them look like trypanosomes, 35 μ $\times$ 12 μ in size, but their nuclei and kinetoplasts multiply so profusely, and their protoplasm grows so much, that they are converted into shapeless multinucleate masses (Fig. 4·14:*b*); they finally turn into clusters of short leptomonas forms (Fig. 4·14:*c*) which continue to divide (as proved by their double flagella) without awaiting the moment that they become separated one from another. By this uninhibited multiple fission the number of flagellates rapidly increases in the blood of the young rat.

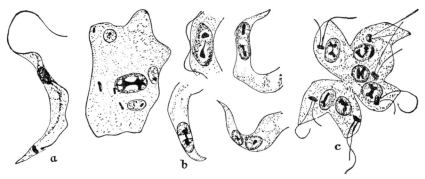

Fig. 4·14   *Trypanosoma lewisi* in rat's blood: *a*, Adult trypanosome.— *b*, Various stages of nuclear division.—*c*, Multiple division; $\times$ 1300. (After Swellengrebel, 1910. Courtesy, *Parasitology*, Cambridge, England.)

This is the stage of initial aggression, to which the host may succumb together with all the parasites in its body. As a rule, however, the final outcome is different.[26] After about three weeks, this period of excessive multiplication suddenly comes to an end. One day the parasites numbered 350,000 per cubic mm; the next day they have dropped to 75,000. The multiformity which characterized the parasite during its aggressive period no longer exists. All parasites now have the uniform appearance of ordinary trypanosomes, called "adult" trypanosomes (Fig. 4·14:*a*), with an average length of 31 μ (including the free portion of the flagellum which is about 8 μ long) and an average width of 1.5 μ. The posterior end is slender and pointed; the kinetoplast lies some distance from the rear; the nucleus is situated near the anterior end; the undulating membrane is narrow and its flagellar margin shows few undulations. The rat harboring the adult trypanosomes has become a healthy carrier.

The adult trypanosomes do not multiply; substances in the serum of the host (*ablastins* [26]) prevent this; nevertheless they keep up their number for a considerable time, even as long as 3½ months, a fact all the more remarkable, considering that the rat cannot be reinfected

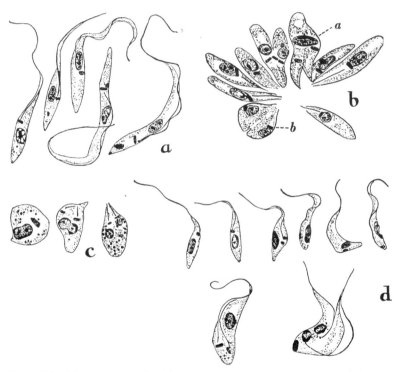

Fig. 4·15 *Trypanosoma lewisi* in the intestine of the rat flea: *a*, Transition from trypanosomes to crithidias.—*b*, Multiplying crithidias.—*c*, Leishmania forms.—*d*, Crithidias changing into metacyclic trypanosomes, 8 days after the infecting meal; × 1300. (After Swellengrebel and Strickland, 1910. Courtesy, *Parasitology*, Cambridge, England.)

during that period.[26] This second stage of the development of *T. lewisi* suddenly comes to an end. One day there still are, say, 50,000 per cubic mm; the next day there are none. Substances in the serum of the host have dissolved them (*trypanolysins* [26]). However, this is not a complete disappearance, it is a latent infection; several months after the last adult trypanosomes have disappeared they can be made to reappear by removing the spleen of the rat.[27] It is difficult to believe that the adult trypanosomes can survive so long without multiplying. It is almost necessary to assume the existence of some internal focus of reproduction which perpetuates them. However, such foci are unknown.

The adult trypanosomes do multiply; not, however, in the blood of the rat but in the gut of the rat flea, its intermediate host; in this respect they resemble the trypanosome forms of *T. cruzi*. In this new environment they change into crithidias, leptomonads, and leishmanias that adhere to the wall of the gut and multiply vigorously (Fig. 4·15: *a, b, c*). After about a week trypanosomes that no longer adhere to the wall make their appearance in the rectum of the flea. They are smaller than the adult trypanosomes in the blood of the rat, their form is stumpy, their posterior end blunt, and the position of their kinetoplast is terminal.[28] They are the metacyclic trypanosomes (Fig. 4·15:*d*). These trypanosomes are carried away by the semifluid contents of the rectum, with which they leave the body of the flea. Other rats are infected by ingesting freshly evacuated feces containing metacyclic trypanosomes, or the whole flea that harbors them.[29]

TRYPANOSOMA GAMBIENSE Dutton, 1902

This parasite is of particular importance as the causative agent mainly of West African human trypanosomiasis (*sleeping sickness*). Although its range of hosts includes some domestic animals, its main host is man. Its classification as an initial aggressor is unsatisfactory, since it never ceases being aggressive until it has destroyed its host. Still, it is able to maintain an unstable equilibrium with its host for quite a long time, so as to afford its progeny ample opportunity for transmission to other people before it is destroyed with the death of its host.

Unlike *T. cruzi* and *T. lewisi*, *T. gambiense* is encountered in the human body as trypanosomes only, which multiply by binary fission. It is found in lymph glands, in reticular tissue of the spleen, in blood and, at a later stage, in the cerebrospinal fluid.

The trypanosomes have a length of 15–32 μ, with a much convoluted undulating membrane and a flagellar margin with many undulations. The nucleus lies slightly nearer to the posterior than to the anterior end. The kinetoplast is round or ovoid. Unlike *T.*

lewisi, the protoplasm contains a row of metachromatic or volutin granules.[30]

Minchin [31] distinguished three types: (1) *slender trypanosomes,* measuring 23–33 $\mu \times$ 1.5–1.8 μ, with a free flagellum, an elongated nucleus, and a kinetoplast some distance from the posterior end (Fig. 4·16:*b*); (2) *stumpy trypanosomes,* measuring 15–20 $\mu \times$ 2–5 μ, without a free flagellum, with a round nucleus, often situated near the broad and blunt posterior end, and a kinetoplast close to the posterior end (Fig. 4·16:*a*); (3) *intermediate trypanosomes* that take

Fig. 4·16   *Trypanosoma gambiense,* × 1500: *a,* Stumpy form.—*b,* Slender form (longitudinal fission). (Original.)

a position between the two extremes. The existence of these types has caused the term *polymorphic trypanosomes* to be applied to this species as well as to its close relatives *T. brucei* and *T. rhodesiense.*

There exists a notable difference of opinion as to the nature of the stumpy forms. Formerly they were considered female individuals, and the slender forms as males. More recently the stumpy forms have been held by some to be the product of a sexual fusion of two slender forms.[32] Others claim that the stumpy forms are the more resistant ones. They survive (1) the attack of the host's defense mechanism, thus assuring the continued existence of the parasite in the human body,[33] and (2) the untoward conditions in the body of the tsetse, thus becoming the initial stage of the developmental cycle in that fly.[34] Still others believe them to be no more than degenerated trypanosomes.

Besides these morphological characteristics, *T. gambiense* shows the following biological peculiarities: (1) it is not destroyed by human serum in vitro; (2) it has a low virulence for rats; (3) it is rare in the human peripheral circulation; (4) it is highly sensitive to certain drugs (suramin, tryparsamide, pentamidine, nitrofurazone).

The intermediate hosts of *T. gambiense* are bloodsucking flies of the genus *Glossina* (tsetse flies), indigenous to Africa south of the Sahara. *Glossina palpalis* and some other related species are the most important transmitters of this form of trypanosomiasis. Unlike the

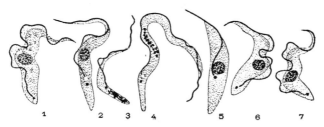

Fig. 4·17 *Trypanosoma gambiense* in *Glossina palpalis,* × 1500: 1. In mammalian blood.—2. In midgut.—3. Rare crithidial form in proventriculus.—4. Proventricular form.—5. Trypanosome form in hindgut.—6, 7. Metacyclic forms in salivary gland. (After Brumpt, 1922. Courtesy, Masson & Cie, Paris.)

triatomid bugs and the fleas, which live and multiply within human and animal habitations, *Glossina palpalis* breeds along the wooded banks of rivers and shores of lakes, where people go to fetch water, meet each other, and come in contact with the tsetse flies, and pass the infection from man to fly and *vice versa*.

Glossina palpalis can infect man in two ways: by direct transmission and by cyclical transmission.

Direct or *mechanical transmission* takes place if (1) a fly bites a man with trypanosomes in his blood, (2) some trypanosomes are caught sticking to the inside of the proboscis of the fly, and (3) are washed into the wound inflicted by the fly when it bites another man, provided the time between the two succeeding bites does not exceed a few hours.[35]

In *cyclical transmission* the flies, which have lost their ability of transmitting the parasite, regain it after about three weeks [36]; at the end of that period the trypanosomes are found occupying the salivary glands of the fly.[37] During the period the trypanosomes pass through a developmental cycle comprising the following stages.[34]

When the fly takes blood containing trypanosomes ("the infecting meal") some of the ingested parasites survive in the midgut of the fly

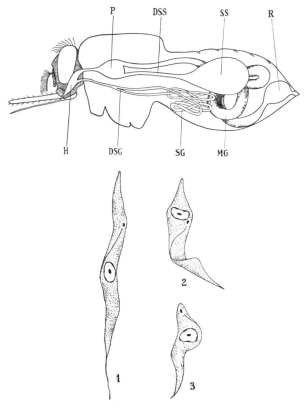

Fig. 4·18   Upper figure: Diagram of a tsetse fly: *H*, Pharynx.—*P*, Proventriculus.—*DSG*, Salivary duct.—*DSS*, Duct of esophagal diverticulum. —*SG*, Salivary gland.—*SS*, Esophagal diverticulum.—*MG*, Midgut.—*R*, Rectum.—Lower figures: 1. Proventricular trypanosome.—2. Crithidia. —3. Metacyclic trypanosome. (After Thomson and Robertson, 1929. Courtesy, Baillière, Tindall & Cox, London.)

(Fig. 4·18:*Mg*) and start multiplying there. In the trypanosome stage (Fig. 4·17:2) they cannot fix themselves to the wall of the gut, and so they are in constant danger of being washed out by the current of the gut. To avoid this risk they retire to the *extraperitrophic space*, a space situated between the wall of the gut and the *peritrophic membrane;*—a thin pellicle which envelops the blood imbibed by the fly. In this space they continue their multiplication.[38] About the tenth day after the infecting meal, numerous trypanosomes collect in the vicinity of the proventriculus (Fig. 4·18:*P*); they pierce the peritrophic membrane and enter the lumen of the proventriculus.

Here they become long (35–40 μ) and slender (1.5–2 μ), with a narrow undulating membrane and a kinetoplast halfway between the nucleus and the posterior extremity. These forms, the *proventricular trypanosomes,* rarely multiply (Figs. 4·17:4 and 4·18:1).

According to Lewis and Langridge's [39] observations on the closely related *T. brucei,* the proventricular trypanosomes change into *post-proventricular trypanosomes* sometime between the tenth and the twentieth day after the infecting meal. They are characterized by the width of their posterior extremity and by the nucleus being situated in that part of the body. By binary fission each individual produces two daughter individuals. Both have the shape of a crithidia, but they are unequal in size: one is long and slender, the other is short. Both leave the proventriculus by way of the esophagus and pass into the buccal cavity of the fly (Fig. 4·18:*H*). Into this cavity the salivary duct opens (Fig. 4·18:*DSG*) through which passes the secretion of the salivary glands (Fig. 4·18:*SG*). Only the short crithidias (Fig. 4·18:2) enter this duct. They reach the salivary glands about the twentieth day after the infecting meal. They fix themselves to the glandular epithelium, and multiply rapidly. About the twenty-fifth day after the infecting meal, some of the crithidias become detached from the epithelium; shortly afterwards they resume the trypanosome form and become *metacyclic trypanosomes* (Figs. 4·17:6, 7 and 4·18:3), the final stage of the cyclical development.

The metacyclic trypanosomes, no longer attached to the glandular epithelium, are caught by the current of saliva that passes through the glandular duct when the fly injects saliva into the wound it has inflicted on biting. In this way the fly transmits the infection to man: it has become *infective.* It can do so only if metacyclic trypanosomes are present in its saliva, where they appear between the third and the fourth week after the fly's initial blood meal. So long as no inter-ruption occurs in the reproduction of the trypanosomes in the extra-peritrophic space, and of the crithidias in the salivary glands, the production of the metacyclic trypanosomes is continued.

Unless the unequal division of the postproventricular trypanosomes (as quoted above) should be interpreted as syngamy, the cyclical development apparently proceeds without sexual development. Thus no nonhereditary characteristic *T. gambiense* may have acquired during its stay in the human host can be eliminated by a sexual process during its stay in the insect host. This theoretical consideration would have a practical issue if there existed a non-hereditary characteristic of that nature. Some believe it actually exists in the form of acquired resistance of the trypanosome against tryparsamide, an arsenical drug administered for the purpose of curing the disease in its more advanced stage. Once acquired in man's body, this resistance is maintained during the passage through the fly's body. Thus, a fly that has ingested *arsenoresistant tryp-anosomes* will pass them on to other human hosts. However, according to Van Hoof,[40] these trypanosomes are not likely to be passed on, because the ability to develop in the fly diminishes in arsenoresistant trypanosomes. Moreover, Van Hoof does not regard arsenoresistance as an acquired characteristic. In his opinion it is a hereditary pecul-iarity of a pre-existing strain of *T. gambiense;* it has been selected from a mixed population by the extinction of all nonresistant strains, consequent upon an intensive campaign of detection and treatment of all available patients in a certain region.

The natural host of *T. gambiense,* i.e. the host that establishes a balanced relationship with the parasite, is expected to meet the following requirements: it is not to interfere with the regular trans-fer of the parasite to the fly, whether by a too rigorous numerical restraint or by a topical restraint so lax as to allow the parasite free entrance to organs of vital importance (central nervous system). According to Van Hoof [40] the domestic pig fulfills these criteria: it harbors *T. gambiense* for over a year without apparently suffering any ill effects; flies taking its blood become infected and pass the parasites on to man.[41]

Nevertheless, Morris [42] adduces epidemiological evidence proving that man himself is the principal source of infection to his fellow men. Although the topical restraint man subjects the parasites to is inadequate, it is not so slight as to prevent him from passing many months and even years in a condition that allows him to attend to his business. He is infected with *T. gambiense,* but it may take the parasites a long time to reach his central nervous system; and in that time his daily occupations take him to places where he is exposed to flies that await a blood meal, which will be an infecting meal if they bite that man. No doubt, scarcity in the peripheral circulation is one of the biological characteristics of *T. gambiense;* yet Van Hoof [40] succeeded in infecting flies by allowing them to take the blood of a man who had been a carrier for ten years.

This does not imply that man always finds ample opportunity to infect *Glossina* before the inevitable progress of the illness puts a stop to his leaving home and meeting the flies in their natural haunts. The relatively well-balanced relationship between host and parasite may be upset at an earlier date. Cattle disease, lost crops, a sharp drop in the profits of export farming, and other adverse economic conditions, may plunge the human host into dire distress and poverty, associated with a notable acceleration of the course of the disease.[43] These conditions tend to turn man into an unnatural host. If this were the rule it would render man unfit to act as a source of infection to his fellow men. Up till now it has not yet seriously endangered the coexistence of this parasite and man.

FIG. 4·19 *Trypanosoma rhodesiense,* × 1600. (After Stephens and Fantham, 1910. Courtesy, Publishers of *Annals of Tropical Medicine and Parasitology.*)

TRYPANOSOMA RHODESIENSE

Trypanosoma rhodesiense Stephens and Fantham, 1910, much resembles *T. gambiense* and even more the cattle trypanosome *T. brucei,* but is in all biological respects the reverse of *T. gambiense.* It is the causative agent of East African sleeping sickness, a disease characterized by the rapidity with which it destroys its victim.

T. rhodesiense differs from *T. gambiense* in the following characteristics. (1) The stumpy forms often show a "posterior nucleus" (Fig. 4·19) situated at the posterior end, beside or even behind the kinetoplast; (2) it is transmitted by *Glossina morsitans* and related species adapted to game; (3) it is sensitive to human serum in vitro; (4) it is highly pathogenic to rats; (5) it is less sensitive to certain drugs (tryparsamide, pentamidine, etc.) than *T. gambiense;* (6) it is numerous in man's peripheral circulations; and (7) it rapidly invades his central nervous system.[44]

All these characteristics it shares with *T. brucei,* a parasite which causes a disease (nagana) of high fatality in domestic animals, but lives as a harmless parasite in antelopes and wild swine.[37] There is this difference, however: attempts to infect man with *T. brucei* have usually failed.

Nevertheless, there are those who believe that *T. rhodesiense* is a modified *T. brucei.* Once exceptional circumstances have allowed it to gain a foothold in man's body, it can maintain itself in that new environment, provided it never returns to its natural host. The frequency of the parasites in the peripheral circulation will render this condition easy of fulfillment, because it will facilitate direct, mechanical transmission from man to man by bloodsucking insects other than tsetse flies. But if the modified *T. brucei* fails to observe this condition, it forfeits its position as a parasite of man.

This ingenious hypothesis has been refuted by the famous Tinde experiment, which proved that *T. rhodesiense,* isolated from man's body, can pass from one sheep to another by cyclical transmission for a period of over 18 years [45] without losing its capacity for multiplying in man. It also retained this capacity after 12 years of passages through Thomson's gazelles (an antelope).

Nothing was known with certainty as to the alternate hosts of *T. rhodesiense.* This was to be expected, since *T. rhodesiense* isolated from antelopes could never be differentiated from *T. brucei* except by successful transmission to man.

Recently, however, Heisch [45a] has isolated from a bush buck in Kenya a strain of trypanosomes of the brucei-rhodesiense type and has successfully infected a volunteer with that strain. Moreover, it has been ascertained (1) that men have become infected in an area of Tanganyika where there were no human settlements and where people were forbidden to come, and (2) that persons collecting beeswax, hunting, or fishing in uninhabited regions of Western Tanganyika often acquire sleeping sickness on their tour.[46]

Accordingly, the hypothesis at present accepted assumes that rhodesiense infection in man is a sylvatic infection, acquired through the bite of *Glossina morsitans*. The fly in turn is infected, not by biting man, but by biting wild animals, notably antelopes. In these animals *T. rhodesiense* probably behaves as a well-adapted commensal, submitting to topical restraint. Perhaps on occasions it may violate this restraint, killing its host by entering the central nervous system; but on the whole the parasites will find ample opportunity of invading the body of tsetse flies. Man, on the other hand, always falls ill, and soon afterward feels too miserable to visit the haunts of the fly. Thus *Glossina* rarely becomes infected by biting man. To the parasite, man is of no value whatever as a host[42]; on the contrary, he is a "dead-end host" which the parasite never leaves alive.

TREATMENT OF AFRICAN TRYPANOSOMIASES. There are three types of drugs effective in the African trypanosomiases. Each has its own particular use. Tryparsamide (Tryponarsyl) and Orsanine (Fourneau 270) are useful and effective during the second stage of the disease, i.e. during the early stages of invasion of the central nervous system, when neither the cell count nor the protein content has increased above 40.[73] If the parasitic invasion is far advanced (cell-count or protein content over 40) this type of drug is no longer effective.[74] Mel B or Arsobal (a BAL derivative of melarsen oxide) is effective in all stages. It is especially useful in far advanced cases, in case of arsenoresistance, and in Rhodesian trypanosomiasis. However, it is highly toxic and should be used very cautiously.

The drugs used in the first stage are suramin (Antrypol) and pentamidine; apart from their curative effect, they are mainly of value in chemoprophylaxis.

SURAMIN (Naphuride, Antrypol, Moranyl, Germanin, Naganol, Bayer 205) is a highly complicated compound, containing urea; it is administered as a 10 percent solution in neutral distilled water, to be prepared shortly before use. The recommended adult dose is 1 gm intravenously.

A smaller initial dose (0.3 gm) is recommended[69] to detect hypersensitivity. The injections are repeated at weekly intervals. Some authors prefer intervals of 1–3 days,[69] especially in recent infections. The dosage in children is 0.20–0.75 gm, according to age; in infants, 0.15–0.20 gm. Often fewer than ten injections will suffice to effect a "cure," i.e. the absence of morbid symptoms, including a normal cerebrospinal fluid for a year.[71] In any case the total dose (i.e. the total quantity injected) is not to surpass 10 gm. If more is needed, a second course should commence after a rest of 6 weeks (13 weeks according to some authors [69]). Suramin is slowly excreted by the kidneys and acts as an irritant, causing albuminuria after the first few injections. Yet serious renal symptoms, such as oliguria, anuria, and incipient uremia necessitating interruption of the course of treatment, are of rare occurrence.[69]

In the early stage of Rhodesian trypanosomiasis, suramin is said to be even more effective than in the Gambian variety.[71] It has also been recommended in chemoprophylaxis. One dose of 1 gm, administered intravenously, sometimes repeated, is reported to afford protection for an average of three months.[69]

Resistance of the parasite to suramin (Antrypol) appears to be exceedingly rare under field conditions.[69]

PENTAMIDINE, 4:4'-diamidino-1:5-diphenoxypentane, either as diisethionate, or as dimethylsulfonate (Lomidine), is proving of particular value in mass chemoprophylaxis. For this purpose it is injected intramuscularly in one dose of 3–4 mg of pentamidine base per kg of body weight. Protection is reported to last for six months.[75]

The drug is also employed to cure the disease in its first stage, in the same dosage as above, with a total of 8–10 injections given intramuscularly on alternate days. The solution, in neutral distilled water, should be freshly prepared. In Rhodesian trypanosomiasis some consider it to be less effective than suramin (Antrypol), but others report a different experience.[76] Hypoglycemia should be guarded against.[70]

TRYPARSAMIDE (Orsanine, Fourneau 270, Tryponarsyl), a pentavalent arsenical, is extensively employed in the second stage of the disease, by intravenous injections (the intramuscular route is less effective) of a 10 or 20 percent solution in neutral distilled water, freshly prepared. According to Nauck [69] the effectiveness of the drug depends on its ability to follow the trypanosomes as they force their way into the central nervous system.

Average courses in adults begin with an injection of 1 gm, followed by injections of 2 gm twice weekly, to a total of 24 gm. In advanced cases Manson-Bahr [71] recommends an initial dose of 20 mg per kg of body weight, increasing to 30 mg per kg of body weight on the fourth day, and 40 mg per kg on the eighth day, and 19 additional doses at four-day intervals. After a three months' rest, a second course of 10 injections may be given at four-day intervals, at the rate of 40 mg per kg of body weight.

The maximum tolerated dose of tryparsamide is no more than twice the average dose required for a cure.[71] Optic neuritis should be guarded against. On the other hand there is the constant menace of the disease becoming incurable when treated with smaller doses, and the additional risk of arsenoresistance developing under the influence of a too cautious regime.

A combination of tryparsamide with suramin (Antrypol), e.g. 3–4 injections of 1.0 gm of suramin at four-day intervals, followed by 4–5 injections of 2.0 gm of tryparsamide at five-day intervals, greatly reduces the total dosage of the latter and is said to be effective.[69]

MELARSEN (melaminyl-substituted phenylarsonate), in combination with BAL (British anti-lewisite: 2'–3'-dimercaptopropanol), known as Mel B, or Arsobal (Friedheim), is administered in cases too far advanced for tryparsamide to be effective, especially in Rhodesian trypanosomiasis, and in the presence of tryparsamide-resistant strains of parasites. An additional advantage is that it attacks the parasites in the blood as well as those in the cerebrospinal fluid. The serious toxic hepatic, renal, and cerebrospinal side effects tend to limit its use.

THE LEISHMANIAS

The members of the genus *Leishmania* occur as leishmania forms in the vertebrate host and as leptomonas forms in the intermediate host. Three of them are parasites in man. They hardly differ one from another in size and shape; therefore the following description applies to all of them.

Leishmanias may occupy various organs. Primarily they are intracellular parasites of the elements of the reticuloendothelial system, such as endothelial cells, large mononuclear leucocytes, and Kupffer cells; later on they may invade ectodermal cells and polynuclear leucocytes.

They are ovoid in shape, measuring $2–5 \mu \times 1.5–2.5 \mu$. The nucleus is slightly elongate; the kinetoplast is rod-shaped, perpendicular to the nucleus, and more deeply staining than the nucleus (Fig. 4·20). A good deal of variation may occur: fusiform parasites, a round kinetoplast, a marginal sickle-shaped nucleus, and a rhizoplast

perpendicular to the kinetoplast; but without a nucleus and a
kinetoplast, no intracellular body is ever accepted as a leishmania.
In appropriate culture media leishmanias can be grown outside
the human body. In these conditions they become leptomonads
(Fig. 4·21).

Multiplication is accomplished by binary fission of the intracellular parasite. By successive divisions the host cell becomes crowded
with parasites. Although this will eventually destroy the cell, it does
not prevent it from dividing into two leishmania-carrying host cells.
This circumstance contributes to the spread of the parasites throughout the body of the host.

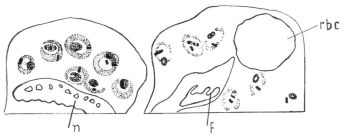

Fɪɢ. 4·20   *Leishmania donovani:* Smear of splenic tissue, Giemsa stain,
× 2100: *rbc,* Erythrocyte.—*f,* Fibrine.—*n,* Nucleus of large monocyte.
(Original.)

Under natural conditions the leishmanias cannot live outside the
body of the vertebrate host, with one exception: the body of the
intermediate host. The intermediate hosts of the human leishmanias
all belong to one genus of insects, the genus *Phlebotomus.* Phlebotomi—*sandflies*—are minute, downy midges with a short proboscis
that bite and suck blood.

The phlebotomi ingest leishmanias with the blood of the vertebrate host (infecting meal). In their midgut the leishmanias expand,
to become spheres with a diameter of 5 μ. After two days a flagellum
emerges, and after 3–4 days the parasites have turned into long and
short leptomonads (Fig. 4·21); they multiply vigorously and soon
reach the proventriculus, a section of the intestine between the midgut and the esophagus. The short leptomonads attach themselves
to the epithelial lining of the proventriculus and continue their
multiplication. On the fourth or fifth day after the infecting meal
the leptomonads form an uninterrupted coating covering the inside

of the wall of the midgut and the proventriculus. Owing to the continuous multiplication, this coating is seen to extend over the inside of the esophagus (fifth to sixth day) and of the pharynx (seventh to eighth day). Multiplication inside the proventriculus eventually causes complete obstruction of this organ. As a consequence the sandfly, trying to ingest blood, fails to fill its midgut.

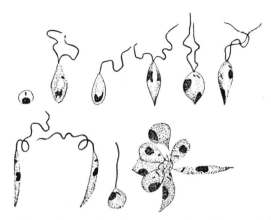

FIG. 4·21 *Leishmania tropica,* forms seen in culture, × 1000. (After Brumpt, 1922. Courtesy, Masson & Cie, Paris.)

The blood gets no farther than the esophagus, which would burst if it did not force the blood back into the proboscis, which is still inserted into the skin of the vertebrate and out of which the sandfly continues to suck blood in a vain attempt to pump it into its midgut. While the blood is thus by turns ingested and expelled, it detaches leptomonads from the wall of the esophagus and pharynx through which it passes. Some of this blood, contaminated with leptomonads, is forced by the pressure exercised by the esophagus into the wound the sandfly has made in the skin of the vertebrate. If this vertebrate (man or one of the alternate hosts) has not already been infected with leishmanias, it will become so by the contaminated blood flowing into the wound in its skin.[47]

The leishmanias living in man are classified according to (1) the organs they inhabit and (2) their geographical distribution. *Visceral leishmanias* inhabit internal organs; *cutaneous leishmanias* inhabit the skin.

Formerly the visceral leishmanias were divided into those of the New World (*L. chagasi*) and of the Old World. The latter were again split up into (1) those mainly attacking children in the Mediterranean Basin, western and central Asia, and China (*L. infantum*), (2) those found in dogs inhabiting the same regions (*L. canis*), and (3) those infesting children and adults alike in southeastern Asia, without a concomitant canine infection (*L. donovani*). Nowadays all visceral leishmanias are collected into one species that bears the last name.

The cutaneous leishmanias of the New World (*L. braziliensis*) are kept separate from those found in the Old World (*L. tropica*).

LEISHMANIA DONOVANI (Laveran and Mesnil, 1903) Ross, 1903

This parasite may be the cause of a febrile disease of long duration and fatal issue known by the name of *kala-azar*. It occurs in eastern India (Assam, Bengal, Madras); in China, from Hangchow to far north of Peking: central Asia and Transcaucasia, the Near East; the Mediterranean Basin (including Portugal); East Africa, from Eritrea and the southern Sudan to Mozambique (excluding Uganda and Tanganyika).

Man is infected by becoming associated with a sylvatic reservoir or a domestic reservoir or by acquiring the parasite from his fellow man.

In the Old World a *sylvatic reservoir* is known in central Asia.[48] In that huge area there lives a population of jackals infected with *L. donovani*. The human population is nomadic and scarce; there is little contact between man and this sylvatic reservoir. Thus human infection is of rare occurrence; but if it appears, children and adults are equally affected. Things become different, however, if numerous laborers come to settle temporarily in the region. Their living in primitive cabins brings about a closer association with wild life, resulting in a greater opportunity of acquiring the sylvatic infection. In a case like this, adults will be the principal sufferers.

A far-reaching and, moreover, permanent change is brought about as the human population increases in size and becomes settled. The jackal, the sylvatic reservoir, disappears. Its function is taken over by the dog, the *domestic reservoir*. The dog's close association with man renders it much more efficient as a source of human infection than the sylvatic reservoir it has replaced. This efficiency is still increased by the fact that *L. donovani* in the dog behaves as an initial aggressor. The infected dogs may fall ill when they first meet the parasite, but they often recover.[49] However, after their recovery the parasites are not eliminated from their body, but subjected to topical restraint which brings about a state of equilibrium. There is no more room for them in the viscera; they are relegated to the tissue of the skin, a localization eminently suitable for a parasite that must be ingested by a bloodsucking intermediate host, viz. *Phlebotomus.*[50]

In the Mediterranean Basin there is no knowledge of the existence of a sylvatic reservoir. But it is well known that the canine population constitutes the domestic reservoir.[51] Man becomes infected at an early age by the bite of a sandfly that acquired its infection by biting an infected dog.[52] Often the disease following infection is so light that it passes unnoticed.[53] The adults born and bred in the area have all passed through this stage of apparent or inapparent illness and have become immune to the disease. But if adult strangers visit the country they may share the fate of the indigenous children, as happened to British and American servicemen in 1943.[48]

Kala-azar limited to indigenous children is called *infantile kala-azar*. It occurs in a wide area reaching from China to Portugal. Its most outstanding epidemiological feature is its dependence on a domestic reservoir, the dog. This reservoir is most always at hand, because the parasite rarely kills the dog, and the dog does not eradicate the parasite but assigns it a place where the sandflies can easily reach it. This ensures a continuous transmission to man from his birth onward. On the other hand, man himself is not a source of infection to his fellow man; he cannot infect sandflies because the parasites he carries are absent in his peripheral circulation.

Kala-azar in eastern India and Pakistan is not always present in the regions it affects; it occurs in epidemics. It has no domestic reservoir; there exists a *human reservoir* only. Man himself infects the sandflies when they ingest his blood, for the parasites he carries do not avoid his peripheral circulation there, as they do in the Mediterranean Basin. The mechanism of transmission does not function faultlessly; it is periodically interrupted, and these interruptions last for 15–20 years.[54] During such a period of quiescence man loses the immunity he acquired in the preceding epidemic, and numerous individuals who never experienced an epidemic are added to the population. Accordingly the succeeding epidemic will cause a heavy mortality to a population wholly unprotected by immunity, with children and adults equally susceptible.

Epidemics of this description last for about ten years.[54] Then they decrease in severity, because numerous survivors have become immune to the disease. This, however, does not imply that they have eradicated the parasites they carried. They have subjected them to topical restraint, expelling them from their viscera but allowing them to settle in the skin, where they may cause a dermatosis known as *dermal leishmanoid*,[55] not unlike the findings in dogs that have recovered from the initial aggression by the leishmania in the Mediterranean Basin. Dermal leishmanoid is regarded as a sign that a state of balanced relationship has been established between host and parasite, which cannot be obtained so long as the parasite is occupying the internal organs. It is of considerable epidemiological importance because sandflies become infected if they take blood from the affected parts of the skin.[56] Thus persons affected by this dermatosis are inconspicuous but abundant sources of infection to their still susceptible fellow men.

In East Africa [56a] entirely different conditions prevail. In a limited area, with a high incidence of the disease, it probably spreads directly from man to man. Elsewhere cases occur sporadically, and here a sylvatic parasitism occurs in gerbils (*Tatera vicina*). Moreover, in ground squirrels a strain of *L. donovani* was detected which differed from the human and gerbil strain.

The human strain, inoculated in man, first causes the appearance of a small subcutaneous nodule, or *leishmaniome;* four months later visceral infection develops. The ground squirrel strain remains in the human skin, without subsequent visceral involvement (*dermatotropic strain*). In the skin it causes the appearance of leishmaniomes, which disappear after 6–10 months. Subinoculation with *L. donovani,* derived from man and from gerbils, proved the existence of a complete immunity against these *viscerotropic strains.* This immunity, however, only developed by the time the ground squirrel parasites had completely disappeared from the skin of the human subject. Thus, immunity against viscerotropic *L. donovani,* provoked by a previous infection with dermatotropic *L. donovani,* is a skin immunity; it also is an absolute immunity, so that it is independent of a residual parasite population.

In Argentina, Paraguay, Bolivia, Colombia, Venezuela, Surinam, and Central America cases of kala-azar occur sporadically; in the state of Ceará (Brazil) they are numerous. The causative agent is considered to be identical with *L. donovani* of the Old World. Here again the intermediate host is a sandfly of the genus *Phlebotomus*, and dogs constitute the domestic reservoir. The epidemiological cycle is completed by the presence of a sylvatic reservoir represented by a certain species of fox (*Lycalopex vetulus*).

Sporadic cases probably are due to man's exposure to sylvatic infection; massed cases in villages acquire their infection from the domestic reservoir. Thus, New World kala-azar resembles the Mediterranean type, a likeness strengthened by the fact that four-fifths of the patients are under 15 years of age. Unlike infantile kala-azar, however, man takes part in the infection of the sandflies by allowing the leishmanias to settle in his skin when he has put an end to the acute infection by subduing the initial aggressor to a state of commensalism.[57]

TREATMENT OF VISCERAL LEISHMANIASIS. A distinction has been made between kala-azar in Asia and kala-azar in the Mediterranean Basin, the Sudan, and East Africa; the dermal leishmanoid will also be dealt with separately.

(1) In *Asian kala-azar* numerous drugs have been recommended. Among them are the following.

NEOSTIBOSAN (Ethylstibamine), the *p*-aminophenylstibinate of diethylamine. This is a comparatively nontoxic pentavalent antimony compound. It is administered intravenously in a solution of 5–10 percent on alternate days. For adults of 50 kg the following dosage is recommended: initial dose 0.1 gm, second dose 0.2 gm, and the subsequent doses 0.3 gm, to a total of 3 gm.

UREA-STIBOSAN (Brahmachari) is neostibosan in which diethylamine is replaced by urea. It is at times effective where other pentavalent antimony compounds fail to effect a cure. According to Faust et al.[72] Brahmachari's standard treatment for adults consists of intravenous injections of a solution of the drug in distilled water twice a week, commencing with an initial dose of 0.05 gm and increasing to 0.15–0.20 gm, to a total dosage of 1.5 gm. In a more intensive course the injections are given daily.

SOLUSTIBOSAN (Pentostam), sodium antimony gluconate, is available in ampoules. It is the least toxic of the pentavalent antimony drugs. The relapse rate is higher than in the other drugs of that class. Nevertheless it is of value in mass treatment and for use in young children. The drug is rapidly excreted; thus individual doses can be higher and can be given at shorter intervals. In adults of 50 kg the dose is 5 ml, administered intravenously or intramuscularly, daily for 10 days. A second course, if indicated, can be initiated shortly after the first.[69]

(2) *Mediterranean, Sudanese* and *East African kala-azar* is rather refractory to the pentavalent antimony drugs. Formerly Stilbamidine was recommended, but this drug may cause neuropathies and epileptiform seizures.[71] At present, pentamidine isethionate and Lomidine have taken its place and are administered as in trypanosomiasis. In East Africa, however, Pentostam has given complete satisfaction.[56a]

(3) *Dermal leishmanoid* is refractory to pentamidine, and often so to the drugs containing antimony. If treatment is desirable, the application of Manson-Bahr's [71] method may be considered. It aims at rendering the parasites in the skin susceptible to urea-stibamine by a preliminary treatment with potassium iodide, which brings about the ulceration of the nodular lesions.

LEISHMANIA TROPICA Wright, 1903

This parasite lives in man's skin, not in his viscera. It causes cutaneous leishmaniasis of the Old World: a tumor tending to ulcerate after a shorter or longer lapse of time, and known by the names of *oriental boil* and *oriental sore* respectively.

There are no reliable morphological characteristics to differentiate it from *L. donovani,* unless perhaps by its size $(5.6 \mu \times 3 \mu)$[58]; but the species may be identified by serological reactions.

The intermediate host belongs to the genus *Phlebotomus.* The time lag between the infecting bite and the appearance of the first lesion may be considerable; cases of five and even of ten years have been recorded.[59]

As in *L. donovani* a distinction must be made between the sylvatic reservoir and the domestic reservoir from which man acquires his infection. In addition, man may act as a human reservoir.

The *sylvatic reservoir* is known in central Asia.[48, 60] It is represented by certain wild-living rodents (*Rhombomys opimus* among them). They are infected with *L. tropica* which is present in little ulcers on the skin of their ears, and they remain infected for a long time.[61] They live in burrows which, even in winter, have a moderate, equable climate, favoring an uninterrupted exchange of parasites between the rodent and the intermediate host, *Phlebotomus caucasicus,* which lives and multiplies in the rodents' burrows. The same burrows are inhabited by still another sandfly, *P. papatasii;* but this one is in the habit of leaving the burrows temporarily, and thus it finds the opportunity of transmitting the infection to man. This happens in summer only; in winter, the climate is too severe outside the rodents' burrows. The boils resulting from this infection are acquired by man in rural settlements on the edge of the desert where the rodents are burrowing. These boils have a tendency to ulcerate at a comparatively early stage of their development; for that reason they are called "wet boils."

A *human reservoir* exists in the central Asiatic cities. Here man is suffering from another kind of boils, also caused by *L. tropica* [61] but different from the wet boils because ulceration is much delayed, and hence known as "dry boils." These are acquired by an infection which is passed on directly from man to man. In other countries man has likewise been proved to be a source of infection to his fellow man, either with the help of the intermediate host or by direct contact. He develops an absolute immunity which kills all parasites and prevents reinfection. As an oriental sore on the face leaves a disfiguring scar, this absolute immunity is used for cosmetic purposes by inoculating infectious material into a part of the skin where the resulting scar will not be conspicuous.[62]

Finally, the dog remains to be mentioned as the *domestic reservoir* in Turkistan, Iran, and Algeria.[63] There can be no doubt that it exists: it has been proved that man becomes infected on being inoculated with infectious material derived from dogs. However, in view of the importance of man-to-man transmission, which may even dispense with the intermediate host, the domestic reservoir can be of no more than secondary interest. It certainly is less important than the sylvatic reservoir, for this, at least, can be credited with keeping the parasite alive in the lasting absence of the human host.

LEISHMANIA BRAZILIENSIS

Leishmania braziliensis Vianna, 1911, is the causative agent of cutaneous and mucocutaneous leishmaniasis of the New World. Its presence may give rise to serious infectious processes in the buccal and nasal cavities and in the pharynx, which always cause considerable disfigurement and sometimes have a fatal issue. This form of the disease is known by the name of *espundia*. Usually, however, morbid conditions are limited to the skin; these bear various names, *uta* being one of them.

Other names, like *bush yaws* in Surinam, remind one that the parasite was first seen in its sylvatic stage. Mucocutaneous leishmaniasis in South and Central America is primarily a disease of the fields and the forests. It attacks the laborers working in this environment, and not the women and children who stay at home.[64] The persons affected may live close together, e.g. a group of laborers employed on the construction of a railway passing through a virgin forest. As a rule, however, the sufferers are isolated individuals whose occupation causes them to wander through the forest in search of various natural products.[65] As the disease is strictly limited to the forest, there must exist a sylvatic reservoir. In Brazil, Argentina, and Paraguay [66] this has actually been found. It consists of a marsupial (opossum) and two rodents (agouti and capybara).

L. braziliensis occasionally leaves the forest to settle among an urban population. In these new surroundings dogs have been found infected and sandflies have been proved to be the intermediate hosts. No longer are male adults the only ones to suffer; women and children are equally affected. In short, conditions become similar to those known in cutaneous leishmaniasis of the Old World. Urbanization of this description has been found to occur in Rio de Janeiro,[67] São Paulo, and Tucumán.

TREATMENT OF DERMAL LEISHMANIASIS: ORIENTAL SORE. Apart from nonspecific treatment with suitable ointments, and an attack on secondary bacterial infection, the treatment for adult males consists of intravenous injections of Neostibosan on alternate days, beginning with 0.1 gm, and increasing to 0.3 or 0.4 gm, to a total dose of 1–2 gms. For women and children the intramuscular route is recommended.[71]

AMERICAN DERMAL LEISHMANIASIS. According to Faust et al.[72] the prognosis is excellent after antimony treatment as long as the mucocutaneous tissues are not yet involved. If they are, three or more courses of Neostibosan are required (intramuscularly in children), supported by an antibiotic to ward off or to suppress bacterial complications.

REFERENCES FOR CHAPTER IV

1. E. C. FAUST. *Am. J. Hyg.*, 1930, 11: 371–384.
2. P. B. VAN STEENIS. *Documenta Med. Geogr. et Trop.*, 1953, 5: 371–378.
3. D. H. WENRICH. *J. Morphol.*, 1944, 74: 189–211.
4. R. W. HEGNER. *Am. J. Hyg.*, 1928, 8: 16–34.
5. R. DESCHIENS and N. KIPCHIDZÉ. *Compt. rend. soc. biol. Paris*, 1929, 102: 518–519.
6. D. H. WENRICH. *Am. J. Trop. Med.*, 1944, 24: 39–51.
7. O. JÍROVEC and R. PETER. *Bull. soc. pathol. exotique*, 1949, 42: 148–151.
8. A. H. VAN LITH DE JEUDE. "Trichomonas vaginalis is non-pathogenic" (in Dutch), Thesis Utrecht, 106 pp., Zeist, 1952, Dijkstra & Co., pp. 91–97.
9. A. WESTPHAL. *Z. Hyg. Infektionskrankh.*, 1939, 122: 146–158.
10. C. A. HOARE. *Trop. Diseases Bull.*, 1955, 52: 617.
11. E. BRUMPT. *Bull. soc. pathol. exotique*, 1912, 5: 360–364.
12. E. DIAS. *Mem. inst. Oswaldo Cruz*, 1934, 28: 1–10.
13. M. MAYER and H. DA ROCHA LIMA. *Beih. Arch. Schiffs- u. Tropen-Hyg.*, 1914, 18: 257–292.
14. C. ROMAÑA. *Bull. soc. pathol. exotique*, 1939, 32: 390–394, 810–813.
15. E. BRUMPT. *Bull. soc. pathol. exotique*, 1913, 6: 172–176.
16. E. BRUMPT. *Bull. soc. pathol. exotique*, 1914, 7: 702–710.
17. S. F. WOOD. *Am. J. Trop. Hyg.*, 1942, 22: 613–621.
18. H. GALLIARD, L. C. BRUMPT, and B. MARTINEZ. *Bull. soc. pathol. exotique*, 1950, 43: 204–216.
19. E. DIAS. *Compt. rend. soc. biol. Paris*, 1938, 129: 430–432.
20. F. C. GOBLE. *Sixth Congr. Trop. Med.*, abstracts, Lisbon, 1958, 71–72.
21. A. PAKCHANIAN. *Am. J. Trop. Med.*, 1943, 23: 309–314.
22. C. F. PIFANO. *Trop. Diseases Bull.*, 1955, 52: 881–882.
23. H. GROOT. *Am. J. Trop. Med. Hyg.*, 1952, 1: 585–592.
24. C. M. WENYON. *Protozoology*, Vol. 1, London, 1926, pp. 507, 508.
25. P. D. JOHNSON. *Trans. Roy. Soc. Trop. Med. Hyg.*, 1933, 26: 467–468.
26. W. H. TALIAFERRO. *Quart. Rev. Biol.*, 1926, 1: 246–269.
27. W. H. TALIAFERRO. *Am. J. Hyg.*, 1932, 16: 32–84.
28. N. H. SWELLENGREBEL and C. STRICKLAND. *Parasitology*, 1910, 3: 360–389.
29. C. STRICKLAND and N. H. SWELLENGREBEL. *Parasitology*, 1910, 3: 436–452.
30. N. H. SWELLENGREBEL. *Compt. rend. soc. biol. Paris*, 1908, 64: 38–40.
31. A. MINCHIN. *Quart. J. Microscop. Sci.*, 1908, 52: 159–260.
32. A. T. and R. E. CULWICK and H. FAIRBAIRN. *Ann. Trop. Med. Parasitol.*, 1951, 45: 11–29.
33. T. A. M. NASH. *Ann. Rep. W. African Inst. Tryp. Res.*, 59 pp., Kaduna, 1958.
34. M. ROBERTSON. *Phil. Trans. Roy. Soc.*, 1913, B 203: 161–184.
35. D. BRUCE. *Brit. Med. J.*, 1903 (2): 1343–1350.
36. F. K. KLEINE. *Deut. med. Wochschr.*, 1909, 35: 469–470, 924–925.
37. D. BRUCE, D. HARVEY, A. E. HAMERTON, J. B. DAVEY, and LADY BRUCE. *Proc. Roy. Soc.*, 1913, B 86: 269–277.
38. R. MURGATROYD and W. YORKE. *Ann. Trop. Med. Parasitol.*, 1937, 31: 173–194.
39. E. A. LEWIS and W. P. LANGRIDGE. *Ann. Trop. Med. Parasitol.*, 1947, 41: 6–13.
40. L. VAN HOOF, D. HENRARD, and E. PEEL. *Ann. soc. belge med. trop.*, 1940, 20: 203–243; *Trans. Roy. Soc. Trop. Med. Hyg.*, 1947, 40: 728–754.

41. P. A. Buxton. *Trypanosomiasis in East Africa,* 44 pp. London, 1948, H. M. Stationary Office.
42. K. R. S. Morris. *Bull. entomol. Research,* 1951, 42: 427–443.
43. M. P. Hutchinson. *Ann. Trop. Med. Parasitol.,* 1954, 48: 75–94.
44. F. Evens. *Ann. soc. belge med. trop.,* 1956, 36: 71–86.
45. K. C. Willett and H. Fairbairn. *Ann. Trop. Med. Parasitol.,* 1955, 49: 278–292.
45a. R. B. Heisch, J. P. McMahon, and P. E. C. Manson-Bahr. *Brit. Med. J.,* 1958 (2): 1203–1204.
46. D. G. Davey. *Am. J. Trop. Med. Hyg.,* 1958, 7: 546–553.
47. C. S. Swaminath, H. E. Shortt, and L. A. P. Anderson. *Indian J. Med. Research,* 1942, 30: 473–477.
48. C. A. Hoare. *Trop. Diseases Bull.,* 1954, 51: 37–40.
49. E. Falchetti and G. Faure-Brac. *Bull. soc. pathol. exotique,* 1932, 25: 1091–1099.
50. S. Adler and O. Theodor. *Proc. Roy. Soc.,* 1932, B 110: 401–412.
51. Ed. Sergent, L. Parrot, A. Donatien, and F. Lestoguard. *Arch. inst. Pasteur Algerie,* 1934, 17: 221–230.
52. S. Adler and O. Theodor. *Proc. Roy. Soc.,* B 108: 447–502.
53. N. L. Corkill. *Ann. Trop. Med. Parasitol.,* 1949, 43: 261–267.
54. H. E. Shortt. *Trans. Roy. Soc. Trop. Med. Hyg.,* 1945, 39: 13–31.
55. H. W. Acton and L. E. Napier. *Indian J. Med. Research,* 1927, 15: 97–106.
56. R. Kirk and D. J. Lewis. *Trans. Roy. Soc. Trop. Med. Hyg.,* 1947, 40: 869–888.
56a. P. E. C. Manson-Bahr. *Trans. Roy. Soc. Trop. Med. Hyg.,* 1959, 53: 123–136.
57. A. Prata and N. Piva. *Hospital, Rio de Janeiro,* 1956, 49: 481–486.
58. R. Kirk. *Parasitology,* 1950, 40: 58–59.
59. R. D. Clay and A. A. Ross. *Brit. Med. J.,* 1956 (1): 1279–1280.
60. C. A. Hoare. *Trop. Diseases Bull.,* 1944, 41: 331–343.
61. N. Ansari and M. Faghim. *Ann. parasitol. humaine et comparée,* 1953, 28: 241–246.
62. J. Katzenellenbogen. *Ann. Trop. Med. Parasitol.,* 1942, 36: 26–31.
63. Et. Sergent, E. Gueidon, A. Bouguet, and A. Catanei. *Bull. soc. pathol. exotique,* 1924, 17: 360 361.
64. E. Beltran and M. E. Bustamente. *Trop. Diseases Bull.,* 1943, 40: 441–442.
65. F. F. Biagi. *Trop. Diseases Bull.,* 1954, 51: 43.
66. C. A. Hoare. *Trop. Diseases Bull.,* 1956, 53: 732–733.
67. H. de Beaurepaire Aragao. *Mem. inst. Oswaldo Cruz,* 1927, 20: 187–195.
68. B. Galli Valerio. *Schweiz. med. Wochschr.,* 1937, 67: 1181–1182.
69. E. G. Nauck. *Lehrbuch der Tropenkrankheiten,* Stuttgart, 1956, pp. 133, 201, 191, 192, 194, 213.
70. L. V. Klinkhamer. *Trop. geogr. Med., Amsterdam,* 1958, 10: 332–336.
71. Ph. H. Manson-Bahr. *Tropical Diseases,* London, 1957, pp. 541, 141, 126, 135, 161, 155, 123, 158, 175.
72. E. C. Faust, P. F. Russell, and D. R. Lincicome. *Clinical Parasitology,* Philadelphia, 1957, pp. 108, 137, 126, 982.
73. J. L. McLetchie. *W. African Med. J.,* 1953, 2(N.S.): 70–76, 138–150.
74. F. I. C. Apted. *Trans. Roy. Soc. Trop. Med. Hyg.,* 1953, 47: 387–398.
75. D. Gall. *Ann. Trop. Med. Parasitol.,* 1954, 48: 242, 258.
76. M. Gelfand and W. D. Alves. *Trans. Roy. Soc. Trop. Med. Hyg.,* 1954, 48: 146–149.
77. R. H. Firth. *Brit. Med. J.,* 1891 (1): 60–62.

CHAPTER V

CILIATES

The main characteristics of this group have already been summarized. The following is a description of the only ciliate that parasitizes man.

BALANTIDIUM COLI

Balantidium coli (Malmsten, 1857) Stein, 1862, is the largest protozoon of the human intestine, inhabiting the cecum and the ascending colon. *B. coli* is egg-shaped (Fig. 5·1); its pointed extremity is at the anterior and its rounded one at the rear. Its length is 68–134 μ, its width 44–89 μ. The surface of the protoplasm, the *pellicle,* is more rigid than the interior. In this solid substratum the organs of locomotion, the *cilia,* are embedded in longitudinal rows. Near the middle of the frontal extremity the pellicle has a funnel-shaped depression, the *peristome;* its bottom has an aperture, called the *cytostome.* The peristomal cilia are longer than those covering the surface of the body. They sweep solid particles of food into the peristome and, through the cytostome, into the protoplasm. There the food particles are seen lying within *food vacuoles,* where they are digested; the undigestible remains are evacuated through an inconspicuous aperture at the rear, called the *cytopyge.* Besides the food vacuoles there exist two *contractile vacuoles.* They are supposed to have an excretory function. Like all ciliates, *B. coli* possesses two nuclei: a kidney-shaped *macronucleus,* and a very small round *micronucleus,* almost hidden within the concavity of the macronucleus.

Asexual multiplication is performed by transverse fission (Fig. 5·1). It is preceded by a division of the nuclei, mitotic in the micronucleus, amitotic in the macronucleus. *Sexual multiplication* is preceded by the process of *conjugation,* which has been observed in chimpanzees and pigs.[1] Its course does not differ essentially from that observed in free-living ciliates.

Like other intestinal parasites *B. coli* is transmitted from one host to another in the form of cysts (Fig. 5·1). They are nearly spherical, about 55×51 μ; their wall is fairly thick. The encysted individual carries cilia and is motile. In pigs, the natural host of *B. coli*, cysts are regularly produced; but in man this is far from being the rule.

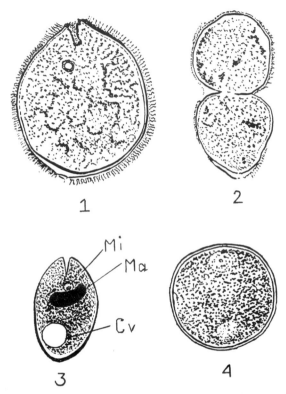

1   2

Mi
Ma

Cv

3   4

Fig. 5·1   *Balantidium coli,* $\times$ 450: 1, 2, 4. Fresh specimens.—3. Stained with Heidenhain's hematoxylin to show the macronucleus.—2. Division. —4. Cyst.

Ciliates that cannot be distinguished from *B. coli* have been observed in various mammals, sewer rats among them, but most of all in pigs. Porcine balantidia have been considered identical with human balantidia because young pigs can be infected with the latter [2]; this, however, was not to be accepted as conclusive since man could not be infected with the porcine parasite. Tsuen Hsiung [3] has explained this by showing that the pig harbors two species of balantidia. One is *B. coli,* which it shares with man; the other is

Balantidium suis, which is not found in man. A pig that carries only *B. suis* cannot infect man; but man can always infect pigs, even though he carries only *B. coli.*

Numerous observations exist to prove that *B. coli* is common in pigs but rare in man. They seem to justify the assumption that the pig is the principal host of the parasite. Man is an incidental host; perhaps he is not even a suitable host, for (1) *B. coli* in his body rarely produces cysts, and (2) *B. coli* can be definitely pathogenic (Fig. 5·2). However, the correctness of this assumption is not yet

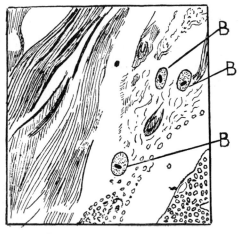

FIG. 5·2   *Balantidium coli,* × 100, in submucosa of colon: B, Balantidia.

beyond doubt, and for two reasons: (1) the high incidence of bal-antidial infections in Abadan, among Moslems who have little con-tact with pigs [4]; (2) the high incidence of cyst-producers among the human carriers of balantidia in central New Guinea.[5]

B. coli is a cosmopolite, in pigs as well as in man. It has been observed as a human parasite in cool countries (Finland, Scandinavia) as well as in hot ones. In man the search for balantidia has usually been limited to patients suffering from some kind of intestinal dis-order. In countries where a systematic search was made in apparently healthy subjects, the number of parasite carriers was usually very low in man and high in pigs. Brug,[7] in Jakarta, found 1 in 2000 inhabitants infected, and 1 in 3 pigs. There are, however, exceptions to this rule, like Van der Hoeven and Rijpstra's findings in central New Guinea,[5] where one-fifth of the human population was infected (half of them with cysts), and all of the porcine population (all with cysts).

The custom of searching for parasites in no one but patients makes it difficult to arrive at a clear conception of the nature of the relationship between the balantidia and their human hosts. Walker's findings,[6] showing that no more than one-fifth of the infected subjects experienced symptoms, appear to indicate that *B. coli* is a commensal.

If that assumption is correct, the commensalism of *B. coli* is not quite as simple as that of *E. histolytica*. *E. histolytica* either lives in the lumen of the gut, feeding on starch and bacteria as a harmless commensal, or it penetrates into the tissues, feeding on red blood corpuscles as a pathogenic microorganism. As far as monkeys are concerned, *B. coli* is known to find its way to the intestinal tissues without causing any apparent pathological effect [6]; and its food is a mixture of the "harmless" and the "harmful," being, by preference, composed of starch and erythrocytes.[7]

TREATMENT OF BALANTIDIASIS. Drugs which can be relied on to destroy the balantidia in the human body are not yet known with certainty; carbarsone and diodoquin, in doses similar to those used in amebiasis, are alleged to possess this ability. At present, antibiotics are the drugs which appear to be most promising and can be administered with safety, e.g. oxytetracycline (Terramycin) 2.0 gm on the first day, 1.5 gm on the following days, for 10 days or a total of 17 gm.[8]

REFERENCES FOR CHAPTER V

1. E. C. NELSON. *Am. J. Hyg.*, 1934, 20: 106–134.
2. T. OHI. *Trop. Diseases Bull.*, 1924, 21: 41.
3. TSUEN HSIUNG. *Z. Parasitenk.*, 1938, 10: 108–131.
4. A. G. McCAREY. *Brit. Med. J.*, 1952 (2): 629–631.
5. J. A. VAN DER HOEVEN and A. C. RIJPSTRA. *Documenta, Amsterdam,* 1957, 9: 225–228.
6. E. L. WALKER. *Philippine J. Sci.*, B, 1913, 8: 333–345.
7. S. L. BRUG. *Geneesk. Tijdsch. Nederl. Indië*, 1919, 59: 894–898.
8. E. C. FAUST, P. F. RUSSELL, and D. R. LINCICOME. *Clinical Parasitology,* Philadelphia, 1957, Lea & Febiger, p. 299.

CHAPTER VI

SPOROZOA

Sporozoa were described as parasitic protozoa that live inside cells. They multiply by asexual schizogony, alternating with sexual multiplication—the sporogonic cycle—which is preceded by a syngamy of male and female individuals. This, however, applies only to sporozoa found in man, and not to all members of the group.

The human sporozoa are divided into (1) *intestinal sporozoa* which develop without an intermediate host (genus *Isospora*) and (2) *visceral sporozoa* transmitted from man to man by intermediate hosts (genus *Plasmodium*).

INTESTINAL SPOROZOA

Three species of intestinal sporozoa have been found in man. One, belonging to the genus *Eimeria* (Fig. 6·4), was last seen in 1890. The other two, belonging to the genus *Isospora,* are better known; they are the only ones to be described here.

ISOSPORA BELLI

The complete life cycle of *Isospora belli* Wenyon, 1923, is not known. It probably does not differ much from that of an *Isospora* found in cats. The life cycle of this feline *Isospora* is therefore described here.

The parasite lives in epithelial cells of the small intestine (Fig. 6·1:1), where it multiplies by schizogony (Fig. 6·1:2–4). The daughter individuals (*merozoites*) are set free by the death of the host cell and invade new cells. There they grow and multiply like their parents. This process is called *asexual multiplication,* or the *schizogonic cycle.* When it has been repeated for some time, certain merozoites start a different course of development. Some grow in their host cell, but they do not multiply (Fig. 6·1:5, 6). Finally they become large parasites, with a large nucleus and protoplasm packed

with highly refractive granules; they are called *macrogametocytes*.
They leave their host cell and mature to *macrogametes* (Fig. 6·1:7).
Others, called *microgametocytes,* grow and multiply (Fig. 6·1:8, 9),

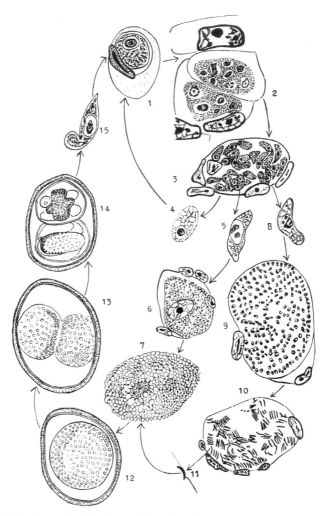

Fig. 6·1 *Isospora rivolta.* Life cycle; for explanation, see the text.
(After Swellengrebel, 1914. Courtesy, Gustav Fischer, Jena.)

but the products of this multiplication are not merozoites but thin
sickle-shaped individuals (Fig. 6·1:10), almost wholly composed of
nuclear matter. These individuals are called *microgametes.* They
are set free and move about with two flagella (Fig. 6·1:11). One

microgamete penetrates the macrogamete, thereby transforming the latter into a fertilized macrogamete or *zygote*. The zygote becomes encysted within a membrane consisting of two layers and is now called an *oocyst* (Fig. 6·1:12). The oocyst is evacuated in the stools.

Within the wall of the oocyst the zygote passes through a process of sexual multiplication, the *sporogonic cycle,* which takes place outside the body of the host. First the zygote divides by binary fission

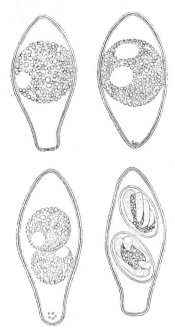

FIG. 6·2 *Isospora belli.* Development of the oocyst, × 1300. UPPER ROW LEFT. Oocyst in freshly evacuated stools.—RIGHT. Two nuclei.— LOWER ROW LEFT. Two sporoblasts.—RIGHT. Two sporocysts, each with four sporozoites and a residual body. (After Dobell & O'Connor, 1921. Courtesy, John Bale Sons & Danielsson, London.)

and produces two daughter individuals called *sporoblasts* (Fig. 6·1:13). Each sporoblast becomes encysted within a thin membrane and is now called a *sporocyst*. Within this membrane the sporoblast divides into (1) four elongate individuals, the *sporozoites,* and (2) one central body, the so-called residual body (Fig. 6·1:14).

If another cat ingests an oocyst containing sporozoites, they are liberated in the cavity of the gut (Fig. 6·1:15) and invade the epithelial cells of the new host.

The presence of *Isospora belli* in the human intestine can be ascertained only by finding the immature (unicellular) oocysts in the feces, where maturation (further development) may be observed (Fig. 6·2). They are elongate, about 29 μ in length and 13 μ in width. Sometimes they are shaped like a bottle with a short neck. The two sporocysts measure, on an average, 13 μ × 9.5 μ. They contain a large spherical residual body, partly covered by four sporozoites. The average size of the sporozoites is 6.5 μ × 2 μ, with one extremity pointed and the other blunt.

Experiments in infecting man by making him ingest mature oocysts [1] have marked *I. belli* as definitely pathogenic. After an incubation of 6–7 days, diarrhea and fever occurred, lasting for 10–30 days. Oocysts appeared on the fourth to the twenty-second day of

FIG. 6·3 *Isospora canis* LEFT. Oocyst with two sporocysts, each with four sporozoites and a residual body.—*Isospora hominis* (RIGHT). Two naked sporocysts. (After Hoare, 1949. Courtesy, Baillière, Tindall & Cox, London.)

the illness and continued to be passed for five days to four months [2] after recovery. Up till one month after the disappearance of the oocysts the subjects of the experiment could not be reinfected. It is evident that the parasite is not an initial aggressor, for it does not succeed in establishing a balanced relationship with its host; accordingly man is not its natural host. But the natural host of *I. belli* is unknown. Isosporas found in cats and dogs are probably different from *I. belli*.

As a human parasite *I. belli* has been found all over the world; from the eastern Mediterranean Basin through western, central, and southeast Asia, to Melanesia and Polynesia; in central and south Africa, and in the Western Hemisphere. As a rule it is extremely rare. The old Gallipoli figures of 2–3 percent have been surpassed only in Natal.[3]

ISOSPORA HOMINIS

Isospora hominis (Rivolta, 1878) Dobbell, 1919, differs from the preceding one by the oocysts reaching maturity while still inside the human body. Accordingly, oocysts in freshly deposited stools show two sporocysts, each one with four sporozoites and a residual body. Often the wall of the oocyst has disappeared and the sporocysts are found in the stools, either solitary or in pairs held together by a flimsy membrane (Fig. 6·3). Their size varies from 10–14 μ $\times$ 7–9 μ.

Isolated sporocysts of isospora are now accepted as belonging to this species. Up till now they have been found in Brazil, Natal,[3] and West New Guinea.

Routh et al.[3a] believe that *I. hominis* is identical with *I. bigemina* found in dogs.

VISCERAL SPOROZOA: PLASMODIA

The human visceral sporozoa belong to the genus *Plasmodium*. They resemble the intestinal sporozoa; they live within cells, their asexual multiplication is a schizogony (here often termed *segmentation*), and their sexual multiplication, or sporogonic cycle, is preceded by an anisogamous sexual process. They differ from the intestinal sporozoa by the place where the sexes meet: not in the human host but in the intermediate host, mosquitoes of the genus *Anopheles* (Fig. 6·5:25–35).*

The plasmodia are the causative agents of a group of febrile diseases collectively called *malaria*. In order to exercise their pathogenic activity they must satisfy two conditions: (1) they must inhabit red blood cells of the host and (2) they must multiply in that site.

These conditions are not always fulfilled. The plasmodia that are able to multiply by asexual reproduction (the so-called *trophozoites*) may, indeed, inhabit red blood cells; they belong to what is called the *erythrocytic cycle* (Fig. 6·5:10–24). But they may also inhabit the parenchymatous cells of the liver; there they are collectively called

* The different species of anopheles regarded as vectors of malaria are mentioned in Chapter XXXII. The magnitude of the subject may be emphasized at this time by quoting Komp,[52] who in a review of the subject in 1948 stated that out of "more than 200 species and subspecies of anophelines known throughout the world more than 50 . . . are important vectors of malaria."

the *hepatic cycle* * (Fig. 6·5:1–9). Only the erythrocytic cycle is the cause of the fever, provided it includes trophozoites, i.e. multiplying individuals. But this cycle also includes individuals that do not multiply, the so-called *gametocytes,* the only ones able to continue life in the mosquito; they are not the cause of malarial fevers (Fig. 6·5:21–24).

If the hepatic cycle were the only one in existence, plasmodia would be commensals strictly observing both topical and numerical restraint and living in a perfectly balanced relationship with a host that otherwise does not interfere with them by humoral or cellular activity.[4] In this way they might continue till the end of the host's life, but they could never leave his body, for the hepatic cycle does not produce gametocytes.

There are plasmodia (*Hepatocystis kochi* [5]), inhabiting the liver of certain monkeys, that multiply only during the hepatic cycle. Nevertheless they produce gametocytes. In their youth these gametocytes enter the red blood corpuscles of the host. This, however, does not mean a violation of the topical restraint to which their host had subjected them. For in this new environment the parasite is as harmless as in the liver, because it does not multiply; it only matures to a full-grown gametocyte, available for transmission to a blood-sucking intermediate host.

The human plasmodia are different. A week after entering the human body, they abandon their hepatic position and violate the topical restraint by multiplying in the red blood corpuscles, thus causing febrile paroxysms.

This new development puts them in the category of "initial aggressors." Starting from this base, a fresh relationship with their host has to be worked out (in which the hepatic cycle is no longer directly concerned). It can, and often does, develop into a balanced relationship.

This relationship is characterized, first, by the host imposing numerical restraint: macrophages destroy large numbers of merozoites; the blood serum stimulates these cells to increased activity, injures the plasmodia, and neutralizes toxic products released during the process of schizogony.[6] These cellular and humoral activities may

* This description applies to human and simian plasmodia only. The exoerythrocytic phase in avian plasmodia is not situated in the hepatic parenchyma. Moreover, it is often far from harmless to its avian host, especially if lodged in the brain.

destroy individual parasites, but they need not jeopardize their existence as a species. In the blood of the host enough gametocytes remain to serve as a source of infection of the intermediate host.[7]

Second, this relationship is characterized by the host acquiring a varying degree of tolerance towards the residual parasite population. This tolerance shows by the disappearance of morbid reactions. In its most perfect state, to be found among the indigenous human

FIG. 6·4:1   Oocyst of *Isospora belli;* 2, 3. Oocysts of eimerias (*E. clupearum* and *E. sardinae* respectively) that are sometimes ingested by man and pass his intestinal tract unchanged. (See p. 91.) (After Dobell, 1919. Courtesy, Cambridge University Press.)

population of some parts of tropical Africa, it includes the disappearance of splenic enlargement, the most permanent stigma of malarial disease.

This state of balanced relationship is not supposed to last forever. If, in some countries and some populations, it seems to continue from early childhood till old age, this is due to the fact that reinfections occur without interruption and that the host continuously responds to the challenge by his cellular and humoral activities. In the absence of reinfections the residual parasite population is expected to die out.

After the parasite population has become extinct, some kind of immunity remains in the form of insusceptibility to *Korteweg's initial fever.*[7] That is a remittent fever, lasting for 3–5 days, not amenable to quinine, and associated with a very low parasitemia. It is the initial stage of vivax- and falciparum-malaria in persons who have had no previous experience of malaria. In a second illness their fever will run a typical course from the very beginning, thus proving that they have become insusceptible to the initial fever. This will happen even if the first illness occurred several years before the second, or if it was caused by a plasmodium different from that which causes the second. In *P. vivax* it is associated with the erythrocytic cycle rather than with the hepatic cycle; for the initial fever, and the insusceptibility to it, also occur in subjects infected with blood parasites.

The lasting insusceptibility to the initial fever does not imply the existence of a lasting *immunity* against the parasites. According to Ed. Sergent [8] there is no such immunity. The humoral and cellular reactions of the host are the exponents of *premunition,* a state of defense which requires the continued existence of the offending agent in the body of the host. This view is not generally accepted. Boyd and Kitchen,[9] for instance, affirm that this state of defense is perpetuated after the disappearance of the parasites, provided previous infections had been numerous and heavy.

Whatever may be the nature of this state, it is certain that it is highly specific. A patient ill with general paralysis may be cured by a long series of febrile paroxysms caused by *P. vivax.* But if, for some reason, he needs a repeated treatment, *P. vivax* has lost its power. The parasite is able to establish itself in the patient's body, but there follows no fever. Nevertheless, there is still hope for a patient in that condition, for an infection with *P. malariae* can cause him to pass through a full complement of paroxysms.

The four (or five) species of human plasmodia can be identified by their erythrocytic cycle and their development in the intermediate host. Therefore these stages will form the subject matter of the description of the species. The hepatic cycle, on the contrary, can be dealt with more conveniently in a separate section relating to the principal species of human plasmodia: the cosmopolitan *P. vivax*, and the plasmodium limited to hot countries, *P. falciparum*.

THE HEPATIC CYCLE OF P. VIVAX AND P. FALCIPARUM

Of all stages in the life cycle of these plasmodia this cycle is the most difficult to recognize, because it can be seen only by liver biopsy or post-mortem examination. Knowledge of the hepatic cycle stems from (1) experimental evidence in man and (2) cytological evidence in man and monkeys.

(1) *Experimental Evidence in Man.* According to N. Hamilton Fairley,[10] this evidence is concerned with (*a*) the form plasmodia enter the human body and (*b*) the origin of the so-called relapses.

(*a*) THE FORM IN WHICH PLASMODIA ENTER THE HUMAN BODY. They do so in the form of sporozoites (Fig. 6·5:1), spindle-shaped parasites, the final stage of the development in the intermediate host (Fig. 6·5:25–35). They are present in the saliva of the mosquito; together with this secretion they are injected into the blood of the human host. There they stay for a period not exceeding one hour, after which they disappear from the circulation. The parasites have gone in hiding in some unknown place, where they have assumed a form which, for the moment, will be designated as X form.

In that place they remain hidden for the next week, or so. Then they reappear in the blood, this time as parasites situated within red blood corpuscles (Fig. 6·5:10–20). During the time the parasites were in hiding the infected person remained in good health; now that they have reappeared in the blood he falls ill with fever. So it is concluded that the X forms are harmless; it is the blood-inhabiting parasites that are pathogenic.

(*b*) THE ORIGIN OF RELAPSES. When malarial fever makes its first appearance, it is called a *primary attack*. It is treated with a variety of drugs, called *antimalarials*. The antimalarial cures the fever and simultaneously destroys the parasites present in the blood. But it cannot kill the parasites as long as they keep in hiding in the shape of X forms. So it is concluded that X forms are resistant to the ordinary drugs.

Once his primary attack has been cured, man might be expected to remain free from malaria—provided he is not *reinfected,* i.e. bitten by a mosquito carrying sporozoites. However, the result may be

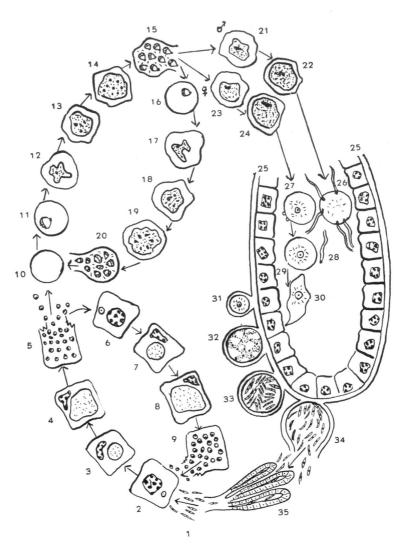

Fig. 6·5 The relation between the three cycles of the malarial parasite. 1–9. *Hepatic cycle:* 1. Sporozoite entering hepatic parenchyma.—
2–5. Growth and segmentation of the pre-erythrocytic generation.—
6–9. The same, of the exoerythrocytic generation.—10–24. *Erythrocytic
cycle:* 10. Erythrocyte soon to be occupied by a merozoite produced by
the pre-erythrocytic generation.—11–15. Growth and segmentation of
erythrocytic parasites of one generation.—16–20. The same of the next
generation.—21, 22. Origin of male gametocyte.—23, 24. Origin of female gametocyte.—25–35. *Cycle in Anopheles:* 25. Wall of midgut.—26.
Microgametocyte produces microgametes.—27. Macrogamete.—28. Microgamete approaching macrogamete.—29. Zygote.—30. Ookinete.—31–
33. Development of oocyst.—34. The oocyst ruptured, the sporozoites
expelled.—35. Salivary gland with sporozoites. (After Shortt, 1948.
Courtesy, Royal Society of Tropical Medicine and Hygiene, London.)

different. Often he suffers from a recurrent malarial fever without being reinfected. Such an attack is called a *relapse*.

Relapses arise because (1) the previous treatment was insufficient to kill all the parasites that were present in the circulation or (2) the X forms intervene.

Relapses caused by insufficient treatment may occur in any form of malaria. But in malaria caused by *P. falciparum* they are the only relapses that are known. Falciparum relapses can always be prevented by a treatment prolonged for 28 days; this is sure to kill all parasites, while a treatment of shorter duration might fail to do so.

But relapses of malaria caused by *P. vivax* cannot always be prevented in this way. No treatment, whatever its length, can safeguard against relapses with vivax malaria.

The difference between the relapses of falciparum malaria and vivax malaria is explained (1) by the known resistance of the X forms to antimalarials and (2) by the assumption that the X forms of *P. falciparum* disappear after the settlement of the parasites in the blood, whereas in *P. vivax* the X forms continue their existence in addition to the presence of parasites in the blood. Thus, in *P. falciparum* nothing remains but blood-inhabiting parasites, and they can be successfully dealt with by any antimalarial. In *P. vivax*, on the contrary, X forms remain that cannot be eradicated by ordinary antimalarials. At any unpredictable time they may enter the blood to cause a relapse.

Vivax malaria induced in man by the injection of blood containing parasites (merozoites) can be definitely cured by ordinary antimalarials; relapses are never seen in these conditions. But if it is induced by mosquito bites (sporozoites) relapses occur as frequently as in nature. This observation seems to warrant the conclusion that blood parasites never change back into X forms.[11]

(2) *Cytological Evidence in Man and Monkeys.* Shortt and Garnham, with their fellow workers,[12] have given a visible form to the hypothetical X forms by their discovery of the hepatic cycle in the development of plasmodia, found in man and monkeys that they had previously infected with sporozoites of human and simian malaria parasites (Fig. 6·5:1–9). They proved that the development of this cycle runs along identical lines in man and monkeys; imperfect knowledge regarding the human parasites may thus be supple-

mented by data derived from the simian parasites, especially from
P. cynomolgi, which greatly resembles the human *P. vivax.*

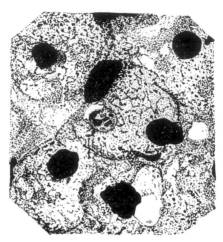

FIG. 6·6 *Plasmodium inui.* Seven-day-old pre-erythrocytic stage of
5.5 μ, with five nuclei, in hepatic parenchyma of monkey. (After Garnham, 1951. Courtesy, Royal Society of Tropical Medicine and Hygiene.)

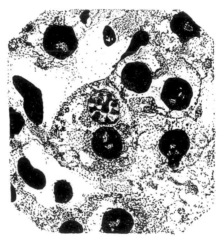

FIG. 6·7 *Plasmodium inui.* Seven-day-old pre-erythrocytic stage of 7 μ,
with 8 nuclei, in hepatic parenchyma of monkey. (After Garnham,
1951. Courtesy, Royal Society of Tropical Medicine and Hygiene.)

The first generation of the parasites of the hepatic cycle, the
so-called *pre-erythrocytic generation* (corresponding to the X forms
of the first week after the infection), is now known to develop inside

the epithelial cells of the liver parenchyma, from sporozoites the mosquito injected into the human or simian body (Fig. 6·5:1–5).

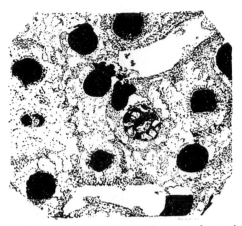

FIG. 6·8   *Plasmodium inui.* Seven-day-old pre-erythrocytic stage of 8 μ, with 10 nuclei, in hepatic parenchyma of monkey. (After Garnham, 1951. Courtesy, Royal Society of Tropical Medicine and Hygiene.)

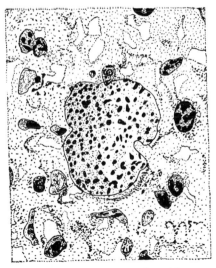

FIG. 6·9   *Plasmodium falciparum.* Four-day-old pre-erythrocytic stage of 31 μ in human hepatic parenchyma. (After Shortt et al., 1951. Courtesy, Royal Society of Tropical Medicine and Hygiene.)

This generation is known from the first day onward.[13] It starts as a unicellular parasite a few microns in diameter. At the end of a week or so, it has grown to a size of 30 μ or over. Unlike the erythrocytic cycle, no pigment is deposited in its protoplasm. The full-grown hepatic parasite now divides by schizogony; it produces thousands of daughter individuals or *merozoites* (Figs. 6·6 to 6·11).

There is no fundamental difference between the pre-erythrocytic generation of *P. vivax* and of *P. falciparum*. But there is a great difference between the destiny of the pre-erythrocytic merozoites produced by these two species. According to cytological evidence it is probable that all merozoites of *P. falciparum* enter the blood stream and that none are left to continue the development in the liver. In *P. vivax,* on the contrary, some of the pre-erythrocytic merozoites must have entered fresh liver cells, because a second generation of parasites of the hepatic cycle has been observed (Fig. 6·5:6–9). It is known as the first of the *exoerythrocytic generations,* which are supposed to continue indefinitely, invading the blood from time to time and thus giving rise to relapses that cannot be prevented by ordinary antimalarials. In *P. cynomolgi* the exoerythrocytic generations have been followed up to 3½ months after the infection of the monkey, and the secondary invasion of the blood has actually been observed.

These investigations [13] have also shown that each succeeding exoerythrocytic generation develops from a very small fraction of the merozoites produced by the preceding one. Thus the host not only subjects the hepatic cycle to topical restraint, so as to prevent its merozoites from settling in the red blood cells, but also to numerical restraint, so as to protect the hepatic parenchyma from an overwhelming number of these merozoites.

Although there still remain many gaps to be filled, it may be confidently asserted that the X forms conform so closely to the hepatic cycle that any fact known about the one can be accepted as applying to the other.

The following description of the erythrocytic cycle, in the development of the plasmodia parasitizing man, is based on the appearance of the parasites in thin blood-films, fixed in alcohol and stained with diluted Giemsa's solution.

PLASMODIUM VIVAX

The erythrocytic trophozoites of *Plasmodium vivax* (Grassi and Feletti, 1890) Labbé, 1899, are the causative agents of *benign tertian malaria,* or *vivax malaria,* an intermittent fever with paroxysms

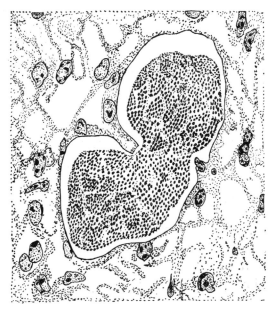

FIG. 6·10 *Plasmodium falciparum.* Six-day-old pre-erythrocytic stage of 60 μ, showing a deep and a shallow indentation, in human hepatic parenchyma. (After Shortt et al., 1951. Courtesy, Royal Society of Tropical Medicine and Hygiene.)

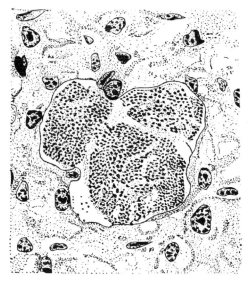

FIG. 6·11 *Plasmodium falciparum.* Six-day-old lobate pre-erythrocytic stage of 60 μ in human hepatic parenchyma. (After Shortt et al., 1951. Courtesy, Royal Society of Tropical Medicine and Hygiene.)

returning every 43 to 44½ hours.[14] The development of the parasite shows a cycle of the same duration (Fig. 6·12). A merozoite, a daughter of a dividing trophozoite (schizont), invades a red blood cell. There it grows and at the end of two days divides into a number of merozoites. So long as the parasite remains within the erythrocyte, the body of the host does not respond to its presence. But the body develops a fever as soon as merozoites are liberated into the blood plasma, together with the residual pigment.

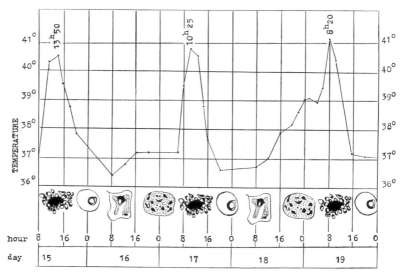

FIG. 6·12   Five days of benign tertian, or *vivax,* malaria, with paroxysms on the 15th, 17th, and 19th of June, coming on at an earlier hour each time. The drawings below the fever curve show the changes in the erythrocytic trophozoites corresponding to the change in the body temperature.

At the height of the paroxysm the young trophozoite has the appearance of a ring. It is, in fact, a flattened mass of protoplasm, with a diameter of 2–2.5 μ, which contains a vacuole (Fig. 6·13:1; Plate I: 1, 2). One half of the ring is often thicker than the other. A deeply staining nucleus of 1 μ is situated in the thinner half. It is assumed [15] that the ring-shaped parasites derive from merozoites circulating in the blood plasma that become fixed to erythrocytes and make their way into these cells. The merozoites appear to prefer young erythrocytes recently released from the bone marrow to older ones.[16]

The young parasites bring about a specific alteration in their host cells, called *Schüffner's effect*. Its earlier stages can be demonstrated only in erythrocytes from which the hemoglobin has been extracted before they are stained. Normal erythrocytes treated in this way are not stained by Giemsa's solution; but if they shelter a young *P. vivax* they take on a rosy hue. The substance in the erythrocyte responsible for this effect is at first spread diffusely throughout the cell. Six hours after the paroxysm reaches its height, it begins to collect into granules that take the same hue; later they stain more deeply. As time goes on, these granules, the *Schüffner dots* or *Schüffner stippling*, become more distinct; they can then also be demonstrated in erythrocytes containing hemoglobin. The ability to cause the host cells to show the Schüffner effect and the Schüffner stippling is a characteristic specific to *P. vivax* and its close relative *P. ovale*. It is absent in *P. malariae* and *P. falciparum*.

At the time the Schüffner dots begin to show in the host cell, outside the body of the parasite, other granules make their appearance inside its protoplasm. They are minute, elongate, yellowish-brown bodies composed of a substance called *pigment* or *hematin*. They are closely associated with the presence of hemoglobin in the host cell, for they are absent in the hepatic cycle.

After 16 hours, when the parasite measures about 5 μ, the host cell begins to grow in size (Fig. 6·13:2; Plate I: 7–10, 12), a feature absent in *P. malariae* and *P. falciparum*. Between 24 and 36 hours after the height of the previous paroxysm the parasite reaches the maximum of its vegetative activity. It becomes increasingly irregular ("ameboid") in form; the original ring has disappeared, or it has been reduced to a small portion of a plasmodium that bears some likeness to a torn rag (Fig. 6·13:3–4; Plate I: 4, 5). These apparent malformations are characteristic of *P. vivax*. In the fixed and stained slides they bear witness to the great motility of the parasite when it was still alive, a motility to which the species owes its name. In the meantime the nucleus grows in size and loses its compact structure (Plate I: 5, 6), the number of pigment granules increases, and the Schüffner dots become more conspicuous.

After 36 hours the host cell has expanded still more. The parasite now enters upon its reproductive activity and is now called *schizont*. It has lost its motility and has become round or elongate, with a diameter of 6–7 μ (Fig. 6·13:5; Plate I: 7). The nucleus, which may

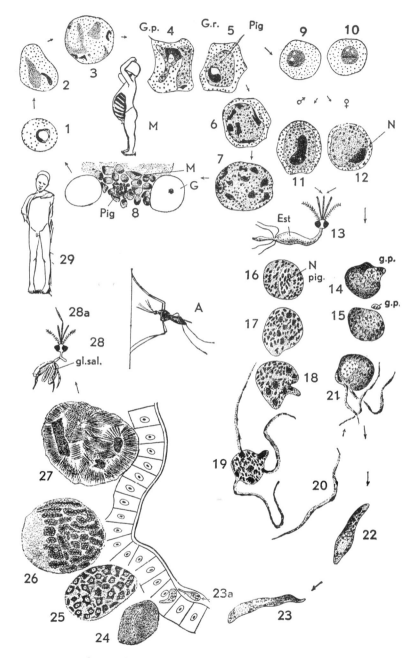

Fig. 6·13 *Plasmodium vivax*, erythrocytic cycle in man and development in mosquito. 1–12. *In malaria patient M* (child with enlarged spleen): 1–8. Schizogonic cycle.—G. Red blood cell.—GP. The same,

have reached a size of 3 μ, begins to divide. During the schizont stage of the erythrocytic trophozoite it may attain a diameter of 10 μ (Fig. 6·13:6, 7; Plate I: 8–10). Successive nuclear divisions eventually produce daughter nuclei, the number of which depends on the strain of *P. vivax* under observation. In individuals belonging to any one strain this number is fairly constant, but it varies from one strain to another; in a Netherlands strain this number was 12–13; in a strain from Madagascar, 17–18.[7]

When the mature schizont is about to divide by schizogony, each nucleus is wrapped in a mass of clear protoplasm containing no granules of pigment (Plate I: 11, 12). Thus daughter individuals are formed, which measure 1–2 μ. They bear the same name as the products of schizogony in the hepatic cycle—*merozoites*—although their number is much smaller. The granules of pigment, which were scattered throughout the protoplasm of the trophozoite, clump together into one or a few clusters during the time the merozoites are taking shape. Finally the host cell disintegrates and by this act the merozoites are set free into the blood plasma, together with the clusters of pigment.

Besides the cycle of erythrocytic trophozoites described above, other parasites occur that obviously do not fit into it (Fig. 6·13:9–12; Plate I: 13–15). They represent the initial stages of the sexual (sporogonic) cycle and are called *gametocytes*. Like the trophozoites they develop from merozoites that penetrated into red blood cells, but they are solid, without a vacuole. In the course of their development they remain immobile; in fixed and stained preparations they are always round, never showing any malformation. They cause the host cell to expand and to produce Schüffner stippling. They grow to a size equal to a schizont; their nucleus, however, remains single, al-

infected.—Gr, Schüffner stippling.—Pig, Pigment.—M, Merozoite.—9–12. Beginning of sporogonic cycle.—9, 10. Young gametocytes.—11. Male gametocyte.—12. Female gametocyte.—13–28a. *In Anopheles A,* continuation of sporogonic cycle.—14, 15. Maturation of female gamete.—16–19. Production of male gametes.—20, 21. Fertilization of female gamete by the male.—22, 23. Ookinetes on their way to the wall of the midgut of anopheles.—23a. Ookinetes penetrate into the intestinal wall.—24–26. Development of the oocyst.—27. Oocyst with sporozoites.—28. Sporozoites entering a salivary gland of anopheles.—28a. Sporozoite leaves proboscis of anopheles to reach another human being, 29. (Combined after Brumpt, 1922. Courtesy, Masson & Cie, Paris.)

though of an unusually large size, and their granules of pigment remain scattered throughout the protoplasm, without collecting into clusters.

There are two forms of full-grown gametocytes: (1) The female or *macrogametocytes* stain as deeply blue as the trophozoites, but they contain more pigment granules; the nucleus is round, measuring 4–5 μ, or elongate, measuring 7–8 $\mu \times$ 1–2 μ,[15] usually situated near the margin. (2) The male or *microgametocytes* are smaller;

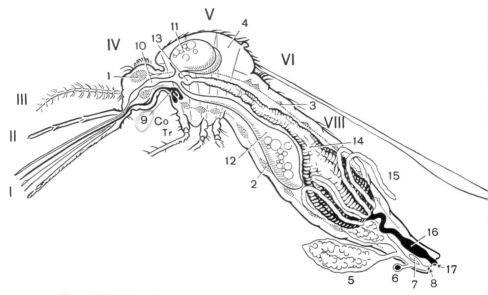

Fig. 6·14 Female anopheles, longitudinal section. Outer parts: I. Proboscis (dissected).—II. Palpus.—III. Antenna.—IV. Head.—V. Thorax. —VI. Wing.—VIII. Abdomen. Inner parts: 1. Cephalic ganglion.—2. Ventral nervous string.—3. Heart.—4. Thoracic muscles.—5. Ovary.—6. Spermatheca.—7. Accessory gland.—8. Genital aperture.—9. Salivary gland.—10. Pharynx.—11, 12. Esophagal diverticula.—13. Proventriculus.—14. Midgut.—15. Malpighian tubes.—16. Rectum.—17. Anus. (After Geigy and Herbig, 1955. Courtesy, Verlag für Recht and Gesellschaft, Basel.)

their protoplasm, on staining, takes a lighter, slightly violet hue, a circumstance which renders the pigment granules unusually distinct; the size of the nucleus may be 10 $\mu \times$ 3–4 μ; usually it is situated centrally. According to Schaudinn [15] the time it takes the gametocytes to become mature is twice as long as in the trophozoites. In man recently infected, gametocytes do not appear until after the

second or third febrile paroxysm.[17] In the human blood the gametocytes have no future; they are harmless to their host because they
do not multiply. Of course they throw a number of erythrocytes
out of function, but they die with the death of their host cell. The
administration of ordinary antimalarials brings about the disappearance of the gametocytes.

As stated before, the sexual multiplication or sporogonic cycle
takes place in the intermediate host, a female mosquito belonging to
the genus *Anopheles*.

When such a female bites a human being infected with *P. vivax*
the ingested blood fills the "stomach" (the midgut; Fig. 6·14:14).
All plasmodia die in this unwonted environment except the gametocytes, which now meet conditions that promise them the future
they lacked in the human host. The gametocytes have lost their host
cells and are lying free in the ingested blood.

The macrogametocyte assumes the form of a sphere; then it ex-
trudes a spherical body, much smaller than itself, and by that act
it becomes a *macrogamete*, ready to accept fertilization by a microgamete (Fig. 6·13:14, 15).

The changes occurring in the microgametocyte are better marked.
Five minutes after ingestion it becomes spherical in shape; then it
grows five or six filamentous appendages that are motile and look
like flagella. That is the reason why this process has been called
exflagellation. However, these appendages are not flagella but male
individuals, the *microgametes*. Soon they are set free and move
about in the stomach's contents (Fig. 6·13:16–19). Ten minutes
after ingestion they are seen moving in the direction of the macrogametes. One microgamete penetrates into one macrogamete, which
becomes fertilized in the act (Fig. 6·13:20, 21).

The fertilized macrogamete, the *zygote*, changes its shape and its
behavior 24 hours after ingestion; from spherical it becomes elongate, and from immobile it becomes motile. In this new state it is
called *ookinete* or *vermicule* (Fig. 6·13:22, 23). The ookinete contains all the pigment granules the macrogametocyte had produced
in the human body. It moves towards the wall of the stomach, forces
its way through the internal epithelial lining of this wall, and comes
to rest between the epithelial and the external, elastic muscular coat
of this wall (the *elastico-muscular tunic*) (Fig. 6·13:23a). The naked
protoplasm of the no longer motile ookinete is covered by this

elastic coat, which envelops it as if it were the wall of a cyst. For that reason the ookinete in this new site is called an *oocyst*. It has become settled there within two days after ingestion.

On the third day the oocyst measures 6.5–7.5 μ. At a temperature of 25° C it reaches maturity on the ninth day.[18] It has then reached a size of 45–50 μ (Fig. 6·13:24–26). In cool countries it may take longer: in the Netherlands, for instance, a fortnight in late summer, and twice as long in early autumn.[7] The oocyst is to be identified as such by the pigment granules it contains (Fig. 6·15). They are most distinct on the fourth or fifth day; then 50–100 greenish brown rodlets may be seen arranged in two or three chains.[19]

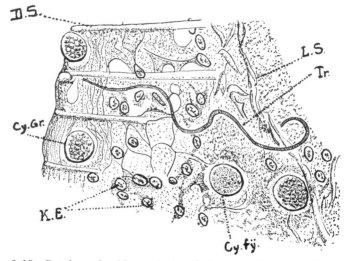

FIG. 6·15   Portion of midgut of *Anopheles maculipennis* with oocysts of *P. vivax:* D.S., Transverse muscle fiber.—L.S., Longitudinal muscle fiber.—K.E., Nuclei of epithelial cells.—*Cy.fij., Cy.gr.,* Oocysts.—*Tr.,* Trachea.

During the final stages, fissures develop in the protoplasm of the oocyst, which separate it into a number of lobes. Along the surface, much enlarged by this process, thousands of nuclei come to be arranged; they are the descendants of the nucleus of the zygote. Portions of the protoplasm of the oocyst collect around each nucleus, and in this way thousands of daughter individuals are formed, called *sporozoites* (Fig. 6·13:27). They are spindle-shaped, slightly curved, and slightly motile. Their length is 6–15 μ, their width one-tenth of that or less. Their nucleus is situated in the middle. Their protoplasm contains no granules of pigment; the latter have been left behind in the undivided part of the protoplasm of the oocyst.

Finally the muscular coat which envelops the oocyst, expanded to the bursting point, gives way, and the whole cluster of sporozoites is thrown into the hemocele of the mosquito. The sporozoites find their way into various organs that stand in open communication with the hemocele. Eventually, however, they all collect in one pair of organs, the salivary glands (Fig. 6·14:9). There the parasites penetrate into the glandular cells, thus becoming once more intracellular, a site they had not occupied since they left the human body. Not for long, however; soon they give up this position to enter into the salivary ducts. They are returned to the human body when the mosquito (like most other bloodsucking insects) injects saliva into the minute wound from which it takes its blood meal.

The multiple division that produced the sporozoites is the one and only act of reproduction of the sporogonic cycle; the sporozoites do not divide in the body of the mosquito. But they may survive for two months in the salivary glands, as evidenced by infected hibernating mosquitoes in cool countries.[ ]

The time elapsing between the infecting bite and the outbreak of the fever is called the *period of incubation*. It is regarded as normal if it does not greatly exceed the period of development of the pre-erythrocytic generation (eight days) and the time required by the erythrocytic parasites to grow in numbers sufficient to cause a fever. An incubation of 12–21 days may be termed normal. In some cool countries, however, the period is prolonged for several months; it is a *protracted incubation*. In the Netherlands, for instance, a man may be infected in late summer or early autumn, but it is not until the next spring or summer that he falls ill with vivax malaria.[7] Russian investigators [20] regard the causative agent of vivax malaria with protracted incubation as a separate subspecies which they call *P. vivax hibernans*.

Protracted incubation can be explained by assuming that the virulence of the *hibernans*-strain is too weak at first to overcome the topical restraint exercised by the host. As a consequence, the merozoites produced by the pre-erythrocytic generation fail to invade the blood. But they are not prevented from continuing their cycle in the hepatic parenchyma. After a succession of exoerythrocytic generations, a new generation evolves which, for some unknown reason, succeeds where its ancestors failed, thereby causing a primary attack and not (as would be quite normal) a relapse. Some notion of the nature of the unknown reason for this success may be gained by remembering that the human *P. vivax,* established in a simian host (the chimpanzee), may be subjected to a continuous topical restraint, but that this restraint can be broken by performing splenectomy on the monkey.[21]

In countries where *P. vivax* is indigenous, it is a common experience to find patients harboring parasites in their circulation after spontaneous recovery, although the plasmodia are much less numerous than during the illness. If recovery has been brought about by antimalarials, a number of the patients treated show a renewed parasitemia, after parasite-free periods of varying duration, without, however, experiencing any symptoms. In the Netherlands, for instance, 30 to 40 percent of the cured patients become asymptomatic carriers.[7]

In regions where malaria patients receive insufficient treatment, they harbor numerous parasites for a long time and infect anopheles as a consequence. But even in those countries, asymptomatic carriers are an important source of infection, especially if the population is exposed to perpetual infection and thus acquires a high degree of tolerance to the parasites in their blood.

If not a single patient goes without treatment, as, for instance, in the Netherlands, asymptomatic carriers are practically the only source of anopheline infection.[7] The degree of infection of the mosquitoes is low because the parasitemia of the asymptomatic carriers is low, but this condition protects the mosquitoes from such heavy infections of their salivary glands as would raise their mortality to three or four times the mortality of lightly infected mosquitoes.[22] Conversely, the human host may benefit by the light anopheline infection, because the illness resulting from the bite of lightly infected mosquitoes has been observed [23] to run a milder course than one induced by heavily infected anopheles.

Under natural conditions, asymptomatic human carriers of *P. vivax* have been observed [7] to lose their ability to infect anopheles, if they had continued in this state for one to a few years, notwithstanding the fact that they still harbor parasites in their peripheral circulation.

Plasmodia greatly resembling *P. vivax* have been discovered in monkeys, among them *P. schwetzi* in tropical Africa. Rodhain [24] succeeded in causing an ephemeral infection with this parasite in man, and Bray [21] could infect chimpanzees with human *P. vivax*. In one instance the exoerythrocytic stage produced no blood parasites till after the ape had been splenectomized, whereas in another it did so without this provocation.

PLASMODIUM OVALE

Plasmodium ovale Stephens, 1922, a near relative of *P. vivax,* is well known in tropical Africa, and also in the Philippine Islands. In Liberia it is more prevalent than *P. vivax,* whereas in East Africa the latter species is the more prevalent.[21] It shares with *P. vivax* its most striking characteristic, namely, that of provoking Schüffner's stippling in the host cell. The fever it causes runs a tertian course.

According to James [25] it differs from *P. vivax* in the following respects: (1) the round form of the half-grown parasites, an expression of their sluggishness (Plate III: 2); (2) the small size of the mature schizont, 6–8 μ only; (3) the small number of merozoites, no more than eight (Plate III: 1); (4) the appearance of Schüffner's stippling in erythrocytes carrying a young ring-shaped plasmodium (Plate III: 1); (5) the frayed margin of many erythrocytes carrying plasmodia; (6) the oval shape of these host cells (Plate III: 3); (7) the host cell enlarging to no more than 1½ times its normal size (Plate III: 3 and *a*); (8) the large, elongate nuclei of the pre-erythrocytic merozoites that begin to separate one from another [21]; (9) two strands of pigment granules lying crosswise in the half-grown oocyst.[19]

Pre-erythrocytic stages do not differ fundamentlaly from those of *P. vivax*. Exoerythrocytic stages have been grown experimentally in chimpanzees. However, parasites did not appear in the blood of the ape unless its spleen had been removed.[21]

PLASMODIUM MALARIAE

Plasmodium malariae (Laveran, 1881) Grassi and Feletti, 1890, causes quartan fever within a period of approximately 72 hours. It is as widespread over hot and cool countries as *P. vivax,* but it is often rare in comparison and variable and unpredictable in its distribution. In the province of Holland (Netherlands), for instance, the town of Alkmaar has had no more than five quartan cases in the last forty years, together with hundreds of cases of vivax malaria; but in the municipality of Alkemade, less than forty miles farther south, there was quartan fever only.[7]

Perhaps its scarcity is due to the fact that *P. malariae* can maintain itself in the human body without overt symptoms.[26] In Rumania one-fourth of the patients with general paralysis subjected to a fever cure could not be treated with *P. malariae* because they were tolerant to it, although overt quartan fever was extremely rare in the area they inhabited.[27]

In hot countries it often constitutes no more than 4 percent of the total plasmodial population, but it may be more prevalent than any other species. It is most numerous at a season of high atmospheric humidity, either because of the comparatively low temperature of the cool season, as in some parts of India,[28] or of the unusually high humidity of the rainy season, as in Surinam.[29]

In the host cells (which are all mature erythrocytes [30]) the young parasites are ring-shaped; it may be difficult to tell them apart from vivax rings. Slightly older rings are easier to identify (Plate II: 1) because of the early appearance of a few coarse, dark granules of pigment and the loose-knit structure of the nucleus. The vacuole disappears 10 hours following the height of the previous paroxysm.

Twelve to eighteen hours after the paroxysm the parasites take a shape which is specific of *P. malariae,* viz. the so-called band form. At first it looks like a filament extending over the whole width of the host cell, containing a nucleus and dark granules of pigment (Plate II: 2). After 18 hours the band is as broad as $\frac{1}{3}$ to $\frac{1}{2}$ the diameter of the host-cell; some strands of pigment granules are arranged lengthwise; the nucleus is drawn out in the same direction (Plate II: 3, 4, 6). According to Brug,[31] band forms show only in the portions of a blood slide that have dried very quickly. That is the reason they are never seen in thick films, which take much longer to dry.

After 48 hours the parasite almost fills the host cell. The nucleus may begin to divide (Plate II: 7) fully 24 hours before the schizogony (in *P. vivax* nuclear division begins 4 to 6 hours before schizogony). Twelve hours later the segmentation of the nucleus is pushed on vigorously. During the last 12 hours preceding schizogony the dark and coarse pigment granules collect into one or a few clusters, and the six to eight merozoites begin to show as separate individuals (Plate II: 10–12).

The macrogametocytes (Plate II: 14) can hardly be differentiated from trophozoites which show a retarded nuclear division and no longer have the form of a band. The microgametocytes can be identified because they look like a clump of pigment with a large nucleus in the center (Plate II: 13). Quartan gametocytes, like those of *P. vivax*, disappear after the administration of ordinary antimalarials.

The changes *P. vivax* brings about in its host cell are not seen in erythrocytes that carry *P. malariae;* they do not increase in size, and they do not show Schüffner's dots. The absence of stippling is a help in differentiating (1) *P. malariae* from *P. ovale,* and (2) *P. malariae* producing an unusually large number of merozoites (viz. 10 to 12) from a strain of *P. vivax* with an unusually small number of the same (viz. 12 to 13).

Apart from morphological characteristics, *P. malariae* differs from *P. vivax* by the comparative scarcity of trophozoites in the peripheral circulation; the maximal number of infected erythrocytes rarely exceeds 8000 per cubic mm, whereas it may rise to 60,000 in *P. vivax.*[32]

According to Bray [12] it can be confidently assumed that the hepatic cycle of *P. malariae* follows the same course of development as in *P. vivax.*[48]

The difficulties encountered by investigators who endeavored to infect anopheles with *P. malariae* induced E. Marchoux in 1930 to speak of the "Quartan Mystery" and to assert that the parasite is transmitted by an intermediate host that is not an anopheles. But Hylkema,[33] in Sumatra, succeeded in infecting *Anopheles sundaicus* with *P. malariae* up to the final stage; he infected himself by the bite of the sporozoite-carrying mosquito. Later on de Buck,[34] in Amsterdam, infected *A. atroparvus,* which transmitted *P. malariae* to four human subjects.

The sexual or sporogonic cycle of *P. malariae* is not fundamentally different from that of *P. vivax.* It is completed in 10 (Sumatra), 15 (Amsterdam), or 31 days (Australia [18]). There are rarely more than 30 pigment granules in the oocysts; they are larger than in *P. vivax* but smaller than in *P. falciparum,* and they are dark in color. In 3–8-day-old oocysts they are evenly distributed; later they lie in clumps.[19]

The period of incubation, after experimental infection of man by the bite of mosquitoes, varied from 12 days (Sumatra) or 16 days

(England) to 24–31 days (Netherlands) or 28–35 days (North America [35]).

P. malariae, in its wild state, inhabits the forests of Central Africa, where it is found in the blood of apes, under the name of *P. rodhaini.* There can be no doubt of the latter's identity with *P. malariae.* Not only has it the same form, but it develops freely in man, causing a typical quartan fever; and human *P. malariae* behaves the same in chimpanzees.[36]

PLASMODIUM FALCIPARUM

The malarial fever of which *Plasmodium falciparum* Welch, 1897, is the causative agent, *falciparum malaria,* is known by various names, such as *subtertian, malignant tertian,* and *aestivoautumnal fever.* Another name, *tropical malaria,* is particularly inappropriate because the disease, and its etiologic agent, are by no means confined to the tropics. Nevertheless, *P. falciparum* does not show the world-wide distribution of *P. vivax* and *P. malariae.* As a rule it is limited to countries with hot and long summers, for its sporogonic cycle is very sensitive to cold. Anopheles carrying sporozoites of *P. vivax* can be safely kept at low temperatures for the sake of prolonging the mosquitoes' span of life. To apply this method of *P. falciparum* means the survival of the mosquitoes, but the extinction of the sporozoites they harbored.

It is an experience of long standing that persons who have suffered from an attack of falciparum malaria in the tropics come down with a vivax relapse after their return to a cool country. It was used as an argument by those who asserted that all human plasmodia belong to one single species; in the tropics it reveals itself as *P. falciparum,* in a cool country as *P. vivax.* The correct explanation is based on the following data.

(1) Infections with both parasites are much more common than it is generally recognized. They are missed because (*a*) the large numbers of falciparum rings detract the attention of the observer from the few, but perfectly visible, vivax plasmodia; (*b*) vivax plasmodia are too scarce to be detected, even by the careful observer; but their presence becomes apparent in the form of oocysts on the stomach wall of an anopheles that ingested blood containing both species but allowed the development of *P. vivax* only.[37]

(2) As has been stated before, *P. falciparum* can be eradicated

from the human body by a four-week treatment with ordinary anti-malarials, whereas *P. vivax* cannot be removed in this way.

(3) *P. falciparum* is able to suppress *P. vivax* present in the same host, as has been proved by N. Hamilton Fairley,[10] whose human subjects were infected simultaneously with *P. falciparum* and *P. vivax*. Both infections were successful, but the second did not become apparent until several months had elapsed after the eradication of the first.

To prevent misunderstanding it should be added that falciparum infections may persist for a long time in the human body, even up to three-quarters of a year [38] if the blood-inhabiting parasites are not eradicated by a course of antimalarial therapy.

In *P. falciparum* the correspondence between the periodicity of the fever and that of the erythrocytic cycle is not manifest, because only a portion of the latter can be observed in the peripheral circulation. Schizonts occur in the capillaries of the viscera; in young indigenous children of the Belgian Congo they are also found in the skin.[39]

It is asserted that only in very serious cases of falciparum malaria may schizonts be seen developing in the peripheral circulation. If that is the rule, it is not without exceptions, for several cases of nonfatal falciparum malaria have been described with fully developed schizonts in the peripheral blood.[40] The same observation was made in some parts of West New Guinea, where more than one-fifth of the persons infected with *P. falciparum* had schizonts in the peripheral circulation, without marked symptoms.

When the fever has reached its highest level, *P. falciparum* is seen as rings of 1–2 μ, "small falciparum rings," occupying immature as well as mature erythrocytes [30] (Plate III: 1). Often the parasites are located at the margin of the host cell, the ring protruding from the cell, with two excrescences stretching along the margin of the erythrocyte (Plate III: 3). Other parasites are reduced to a marginal nucleus flanked by the same excrescences (Plate III: 2). Two nuclei to a ring are of common occurrence, situated opposite each other or at both ends of an incomplete ring. A considerable portion of the host cells harbor two rings or more (Plate III: 4). Multiple infections, double nuclei, and a marginal location are characteristics helpful in identifying young falciparum rings. Occasionally the protoplasm shows tenuous, ramified shoots spreading through the whole erythrocyte. Formerly plasmodia of that kind were regarded as a separate species, *Plasmodium tenue.*

Twelve to eighteen hours after the febrile paroxysm, the rings have grown to a size of 2.5–3.8 μ ("large falciparum rings"; Plate III: 5). One side of the ring is broader than the other and may contain granules of dark pigment. The nucleus may assume the shape of a ring, a dumbbell, or a horseshoe. The host cell stains more deeply than normal, especially the margin; provided the staining is perfect, the so-called *Maurer dots* are always present in the form of a limited number of deeply staining rings, patches, rods, or loops (Plate III: 1–6).

Twenty-four to thirty hours after the starting point the rings disappear from the peripheral circulation, as has been stated before. In their new environment they become round and solid, half the size of the somewhat shrunken host cell. Although the nucleus is still single, the pigment granules are always clumped together into a solid black mass occupying the center of the parasite. The full-grown parasite (schizont) measures hardly more than three-quarters of the host cell. Successive divisions produce 16–18 nuclei; then schizogony separates an equal number of merozoites (Plate III: 8, 9). According to Peel and Van Hoof [39] the number of merozoites is about 30 when they are produced in the placenta and other internal organs.

These morphological characteristics are insufficient to identify the various strains of *P. falciparum* which have been discovered in the course of time. They have to be differentiated by their biological characteristics, such as a marked tendency to provoke blackwater fever,[41] insusceptibility to certain antimalarials, length of the period of incubation,[42] the fact that tolerance to one strain does not imply tolerance to others and that some strains can develop in a particular species of anopheles in which others fail to grow.[43]

The gametocytes of *P. falciparum* are found in the peripheral circulation. They are called *crescents* because they are banana- or kidney-shaped. They measure 9–14 μ in length and 2–3 μ in width; thus they have to stretch their host cell lengthwise and cannot completely fill it crosswise. As a consequence, part of the host cell is left empty; that part often shows as a semicircle on the concave side of the crescent (Plate III: 10).

The macrogametocytes have a compactly built nucleus, closely surrounded by pigment granules. The microgametocytes are some-times bean-shaped, their nuclei are loosely knit, the pigment granules are distributed over a wider area, and the protoplasm often stains a faint violet.

According to Garnham,[44] crescents make their appearance in the peripheral circulation on or about the eleventh day of the fever. In one and the same subject their numbers rise and decline in periods varying from 14 to 66 days.

Unlike the gametocytes of *P. vivax* and *P. malariae,* crescents cannot be made to disappear from the peripheral circulation by ordinary antimalarials. They stop an acute attack, but the patient remains a crescent carrier and a source of anopheline infection, even if the administration of the drug is continued. However, the deriva-tives of 8-aminoquinoline (e.g. primaquine) cause their disappear-ance (incidentally, they also destroy the exoerythrocytic generation of *P. vivax*); proguanil and pyrimethamine render them unfit for development in anopheles.

The sporogonic cycle develops in the ordinary way. The pigment in the oocysts consists of 10–12 almost black, fairly big, coarse granules. From the third until the seventh day they are arranged in two semicircles situated near the surface, or in a smaller complete circle near the center, or, finally, in a double straight chain. At a temperature of 25° C, the oocyst matures in ten days; its size is then 54–56 μ. The sporozoites have a length of 11–12 μ.[19]

It is assumed that a human carrier of *P. falciparum* cannot infect anopheles if his blood contains less than 1 crescent to 300 leucocytes. In highly endemic areas crescent carriers are mainly found in chil-dren. In adults they are entirely absent, or if present, they are so few in number that they do not reach that level; accordingly they are supposed not to contribute to anopheline infection. Muirhead Thomson,[45] however, believes that the importance of the adult crescent carrier has been underrated. He found numerous adult carriers who did not come up to the minimum level, as quoted above; nevertheless, they were able to induce a slight, but perfectly efficient, infection in anopheles that took their blood.

The fever induced by *P. falciparum* runs a tertian course, but every paroxysm is of such a long duration that the intervening afebrile periods are very short and sometimes absent. The disease fully merits the names of "malignant tertian" and "pernicious fever," for it is not rare for it to terminate fatally in patients who have had no previous malarial experience. In infants particularly the risk is of a high order.

As far as the parasite is concerned, Schüffner [32] gives the following reasons for this malignancy.

(1) In *P. vivax* and *P. malariae* the multiplication of the blood-inhabiting parasites is soon inhibited by the humoral and cellular activity of the host. During the fever the number of parasites, after an initial increase, is kept at a level not endangering the life of the

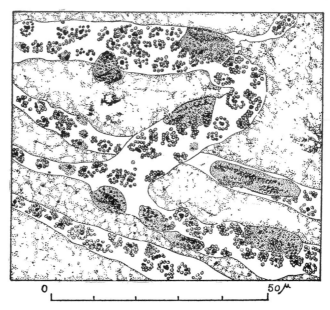

FIG. 6·16   Capillaries in brain tissue filled with large numbers of segmenting *P. falciparum*. (After Brumpt, 1936. Courtesy, Masson & Cie, Paris.)

patient. Finally it decreases to a point which can be tolerated by the host. In *P. falciparum*, on the other hand, this inhibition may come too late. The parasites continue to increase in numbers, apparently without restriction. When the patient dies, no less than 35 percent of the erythrocytes have been found infected on occasions. The critical limit seems to lie somewhere near 15 percent. According to Covell et al.,[46] 10 percent is the danger sign urging parenteral application of appropriate drugs.

(2) Host cells of "large falciparum rings" show a marked tendency

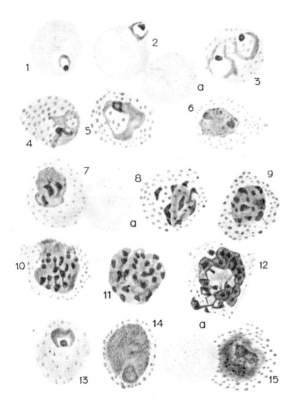

Plate I *Plasmodium vivax,* thin film, Giemsa stain: 1. Young ring. 2. Marginal ring (rare!). 3. Double infection in red cell with basophil granules. 4, 5. Ameboid parasites, Schüffner stippling. 6. Segmentation begins. 7-10. Segmentation progresses. 11. Merozoites separate. 12. Merozoites with ectoplasm staining red, residual body blue. 13. Young gametocyte. 14. Female gametocyte. 15. Male gametocyte. *a,* Normal red cell.

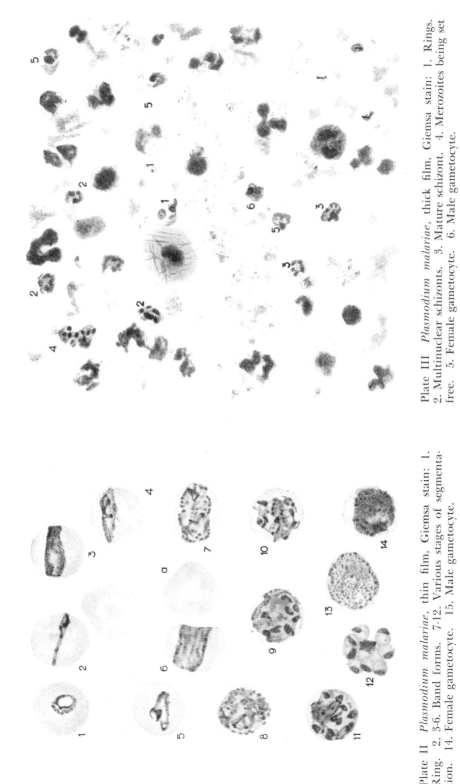

Plate II *Plasmodium malariae*, thin film, Giemsa stain: 1. Ring. 2. 3-6. Band forms. 7-12. Various stages of segmentation. 14. Female gametocyte. 15. Male gametocyte.

Plate III *Plasmodium malariae*, thick film, Giemsa stain: 1. Rings. 2. Multinuclear schizonts. 3. Mature schizont. 4. Merozoites being set free. 5. Female gametocyte. 6. Male gametocyte.

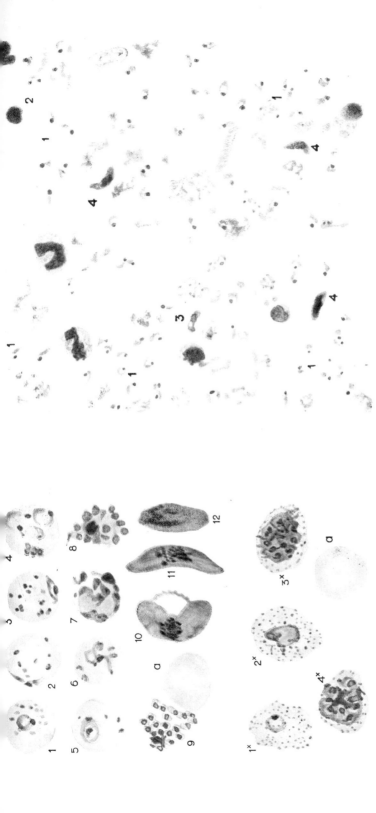

Plate IV *Plasmodium falciparum* (three upper rows) thin film, Giemsa stain: 1. Small ring. 2, 3. Marginal position. 4. Double infection, one ring with two chromatin granules. 5. Large ring. 6. Ring with excrescence. 1-5. Maurer flecks. 7, 8. Segmentation. 9. Cluster of merozoites. 10-12. Gametocytes. *a*, Normal red cell. — *Plasmodium ovale* (two lower rows) thin film, Giemsa stain: 1×. Young form. 2×. Older form. 3×, 4×. Segmentation. *a*, Normal red cell.

Plate V *Plasmodium falciparum*, thick film, Giemsa stain: 1. Rings. 2. Ring with two chromatin granules. 3. Female gametocyte (crescent). 4. Male gametocyte (crescent).

to adhere to the wall of the capillaries of internal organs. In this way they may impede the circulation, constituting a serious hazard if the brain is involved.

(3) Host cells of parasites in an advanced state of development show a tendency to adhere to one another, forming large clusters that may act as emboli (Fig. 6·16).

In central Africa a plasmodium is found in apes which is closely related to *P. falciparum,* because its gametocytes are crescent-shaped. It is called *P. reichenowi* and is considered to be different from its relative. It could not be transmitted to man [47] by the inoculation of the blood of an infected ape.

Chimpanzees, on the other hand, could be infected with *P. falciparum* by the inoculation of sporozoites. Only a pre-erythrocytic stage of infection was induced in this way. After splenectomy, however, parasites appeared in the blood.[48]

PLASMODIUM KNOWLESI

Plasmodium knowlesi Sinton and Mulligan, 1932, is not a human plasmodium, but a parasite of monkeys in southeastern Asia. Its young stages resemble *P. falciparum,* its advanced stages *P. malariae,* but its cycle of development in the blood has a duration of 24 hours only.

The reason why the species is mentioned here is that it readily infects man under experimental conditions and has been used in the treatment of general paresis. Garnham [49] foresees the possibility of man becoming naturally infected in certain areas of the Malay Peninsula that are difficult of access. Up till now this event has not materialized.

TREATMENT OF MALARIA

Antimalarials, i.e. drugs that can be relied upon to destroy certain stages in the life cycle of the malaria parasites in the human body, fall into three groups: (1) drugs administered in order to effect a clinical cure in overt malaria; (2) those which are to prevent relapses; (3) those administered to healthy persons in order to keep them in good health.

In accordance with Covell et al.,[46] the doses mentioned in the following pages apply to adults of 70 kg body weight.

(a) *Drugs Effecting a Clinical Cure.* These drugs are chloroquine, amodiaquine, quinacrine, and quinine.[46] None of them are effective against the stages of the hepatic cycle in the development of the plasmodia, nor against the gametocytes of *P. falciparum*.

Chloroquine is regarded as the most important because (1) given in normal doses there exists no contraindication to its use, (2) its efficiency is not hampered by drug resistance of plasmodia, (3) it is successful in single-dose treatment, (4) it offers safety in the presence of blackwater fever. Although knowledge has not yet advanced to the point where chloroquine can take the place of quinine in intravenous administration, that stage may well be reached in the near future.

The dose prescribed is adapted to the patient's previous malaria experience. If he is born and bred in a highly malarious area, he is termed "semi-immune." He can do with smaller doses, administered for a shorter period, than the person who rarely or never has had malaria: the "nonimmune."

CHLOROQUINE, a 4-aminoquinoline, is used as diphosphate (Aralen or Resochin) or as monosulfate (Nivaquine).

The diphosphate is administered as tablets of 250 mg containing 150 mg of chloroquine base. Nonimmunes receive a loading dose of 4 tablets, six hours later 2 tablets, and the next two days 2 tablets daily. Semi-immunes receive a single dose of 4 tablets.

In severe cases a single intramuscular injection of chloroquine hydrochloride is recommended, containing 200–300 mg of base, to be repeated six hours later if necessary. The intramuscular route is considered safer than the intravenous route, which is only recommended in the form of an intravenous infusion.[46]

AMODIAQUINE (Camoquine, Miaquine, Flavoquine), another 4-aminoquinoline, is used as dihydrochloride dihydrate, administered in tablets containing 200 mg of base. Nonimmunes receive 3 tablets on the first day, and 2 tablets daily on the next two days. Semi-immunes receive a single dose of 3 tablets.

QUINACRINE (Mepacrine, Atebrin, Atabrine), a 9-amino-acridine, is used as a dihydrochloride dihydrate, administered in tablets of 100 mg, containing 79 mg of base. Nonimmunes receive 2 tablets 5 times on the first day as a loading dose, and 1 tablet 3 times daily on the next six days. Semi-immunes receive 6 tablets on the first day, and 3 tablets daily on the next three days. Single-dose treatment is not recommended.

Intramuscularly, quinacrine is administered as methanesulfonate, in a single dose not exceeding 300 mg; the total maximal dose in 24 hours is not to exceed 600 mg. Intravenous injection is not recommended.

QUININE is used as sulfate or hydrochloride, for children (no bitter taste) as ethylcarbonate (Euchinin); both contain 82 percent of base. The first is administered in sugar-coated tablets of 200 mg of the salt. It is unnecessary to prescribe the drug in the form of a solution so long as the tablets disintegrate in water within 10 minutes. This precaution also renders superfluous the additional administration of a julep containing a modicum of hydrochloric acid.

In vivax and quartan malaria the daily dose is 1000 mg; in falciparum malaria, 1500 mg, continued for one week, to non- and semi-immunes alike.[51]

For intravenous injection a sterilized solution of quinine-urethan is recommended, containing 500 mg of quinine hydrochloride and 250 mg of urethan per 10 ml. To this solution sterile saline is added to make up a total of 20 ml (pH: 6.1). This dilution is thoroughly mixed. While the patient's pulse is constantly watched by an assistant, and with a clock marking the time, the solution is injected at the rate of 2 ml every 2 minutes; thus the whole quantity is injected in 20 minutes' time. If necessary, the injection may be repeated after a lapse of 5 hours.[51]

Intramuscular injection, with the necessary precautions as to sterility and the exact place of injection, is administered in a single dose of 1000 mg, to be repeated, if necessary, after a lapse of 12 hours.[51]

(b) *Drugs for the Prevention of Relapses.* Renewed attacks of malaria are often termed relapses, whereas they are really due to reinfections. Measures to prevent reinfection have often been known to reduce the so-called relapse rate. Here only true relapses are considered. Their prevention is particularly useful if the patient is no longer exposed to reinfection.

In *falciparum malaria,* in which the pre-erythrocytic generation of the hepatic cycle is not followed by exoerythrocytic generations, relapses can be prevented by continuing for one month the administration of the drug that had effected a clinical cure. However, smaller quantities suffice for this purpose. Recommended are chloroquine and amodiaquine 2 tablets weekly; quinacrine 1 tablet, and quinine 3 tablets daily. If it is deemed desirable, falciparum game-

tocytes can be destroyed by adding a fortnightly course of primaquine or pamaquine (*vide infra*). Quinacrine, however, is not to be
given concurrently with these drugs.[46]

Two drugs, not yet mentioned above, are likewise recommended
for this purpose, viz. chlorguanide (Proguanil, Paludrine), 100 mg
daily, and pyrimethamine (Daraprim, Malocide), 25 mg weekly.
They offer the additional advantage of rendering falciparum gametocytes unfit for development in mosquitoes.

In *vivax and quartan malaria* the above procedure is insufficient,
because relapses are partly due to exoerythrocytic generations following the pre-erythrocytic generation. The four drugs, which were
able to master any overt attack of malaria, cannot cope with the
exoerythrocytic generations; consequently, they cannot prevent the
relapses due to these stages.

Drugs of the group of 8-aminoquinolines (pamaquine, penta- and
isopentaquine, and primaquine) although not quite appropriate to
cure an overt attack, possess the specific ability to destroy the exoerythrocytic (but not the pre-erythrocytic) generations. Accordingly,
they are to be administered separately, after the completion of the
clinical cure or, during that cure, in combination with quinine or
one of the 4-aminoquinolines. Quinacrine is to be excluded from
this combination.

PRIMAQUINE is used as tablets containing 13.2 mg of the diphosphate (7.5 mg of base). Two tablets are administered daily for a
fortnight, if the drug is given separately. A combination with
quinine sulfate is marketed in the form of tablets containing 4.5
mg of the diphosphate and 150 mg of the sulfate, of which 6 are
taken daily for a fortnight.

PAMAQUINE (plasmochin) is used as tablets containing 10 mg of
the dihydrochloride (8 mg of base); 3 tablets are administered daily
for a fortnight. It is considerably more toxic than primaquine and
preference should be given to the latter.

(c) *Prophylactic and Suppressive Drugs.* Both types of drugs are
administered to healthy persons with the object of preventing them
from falling ill with malaria. If the treatment keeps the parasites
away from the red blood cells, this effect is called *prophylaxis*. If it
fails to do so, but succeeds in keeping the parasites at a level too
low for clinical symptoms to appear, this is called *suppression*.

There are two drugs that achieve prophylaxis, because they are effective against the pre-erythrocytic (not the exoerythrocytic) generation. Thus they attack the infection very near its root, although not *at* its root; for they are powerless against the sporozoites. Unfortunately, their use is limited by the tendency inherent in some strains of malarial parasites to grow resistant to their destructive effect. As a consequence their use is not recommended in areas where the prevailing malaria is known to be resistant to either of them.[46] These drugs are the following.

CHLORGUANIDE (Proguanil, Paludrine), a biguanide, administered daily as one tablet containing 100 mg of the monochloride (87 mg of base), to be raised to 200 mg if the chances of infection are unusually great.[46]

PYRIMETHAMINE (Daraprim, Malocide), a diamino-pyrimidine, administered once weekly in the form of 25 mg of base.

Drugs that achieve suppression only are the following.

CHLOROQUINE (ARALEN) DIPHOSPHATE: 2 tablets of 250 mg (150 mg of base) weekly. Following Pinotti's [51] prescriptions, it is being used for mass suppression mixed with the table salt bought and consumed by the public.

AMODIAQUINE (CAMOQUINE, FLAVOQUINE) DIHYDROCHLORIDE DIHYDRATE: 2 tablets of 261 mg (200 mg of base) weekly.

QUINACRINE DIHYDROCHLORIDE DIHYDRATE: 1 tablet of 100 mg (78.5 mg of base) daily; the administration is to begin 10 days before exposure to infection.

QUININE HYDROCHLORIDE: 2–3 tablets of 200 mg daily, according to the intensity of infection or exposure. Even those who know the great value of "quinine prophylaxis" by personal experience in the past, agree that it is only to be recommended if no other suppressive is available.

REFERENCES FOR CHAPTER VI

1. M. HISIKATI and N. TAKASHI. *Am. J. Trop. Med.,* 1948, 41: 633–637.
2. M. LIMINE. *Bull. soc. pathol. exotique,* 1935, 28: 914–915; G. M. JEFFERY. *Am. J. Hyg.,* 1958, 67: 251–255.
3. R. ELSDON-DEW and L. FREEDMAN. *Trans. Roy. Soc. Trop. Med. Hyg.,* 1953, 47: 209–214.
3a. C. F. ROUTH, J. E. McCROAN, and C. G. HAMES. *Am. J. Trop. Med. Hyg.,* 1955, 4: 1–8.
4. P. C. C. GARNHAM and R. S. BRAY. *Rev. brasil. de malariol.,* 1956, 8: 151–160.
5. P. C. C. GARNHAM. *Trans. Roy. Soc. Trop. Med. Hyg.,* 1948, 41: 601–616.
6. J. A. SINTON. *Proc. Roy. Soc. Med.,* 1938, 31: 1298–1302.

7. N. H. SWELLENGREBEL and A. DE BUCK. *Malaria in the Netherlands*, 267 pp., Amsterdam, 1938, Scheltema & Holkema Ltd., pp. 174, 51, 52, 227, 135, 130, 131, 96, 166, 171, 179, 180, 49, 188, 189.
8. ED. SERGENT. *Presse méd.*, 1931: 1765–1766.
9. M. F. BOYD and S. F. KITCHEN. *Am. J. Trop. Med.*, 1943, 23: 209–225.
10. N. HAMILTON FAIRLEY. *Trans. Roy. Soc. Trop. Med. Hyg.*, 1945, 38: 311–355; 1947, 40: 621–676.
11. D. G. DAVEY. *Trans. Roy. Soc. Trop. Med. Hyg.*, 1946, 40: 171–182.
12. R. S. BRAY. *Studies on the Exo-erythrocytic Cycle in Plasmodium*, 192 pp., London, 1957, H. K. Lewis.
13. R. S. BRAY. *Trans. Roy. Soc. Trop. Med. Hyg.*, 1957, 51: 248–252.
14. A. WILCOX, G. M. JEFFERY, and M. D. YOUNG. *Am. J. Trop. Med. Hyg.*, 1954, 3: 638–645.
15. F. SCHAUDINN. *Arb. kaiserl. Gesundh.*, 1903, 19: 169–250.
16. W. A. P. SCHÜFFNER and W. DE GRAAF. *Festschr. Bernhard Nocht*, Hamburg, 1937, pp. 559–564.
17. P. C. KORTEWEG. *Ned. Tijdschr. Geneesk.*, 1922, 66 (I): 846–848, English summary, 848.
18. M. J. MACKERRAS and Q. N. ERCOLE. *Australian J. Exptl. Biol. Med. Sci.*, 1948, 26: 439–447.
19. P. G. SHUTE and M. MARYON. *Trans. Roy. Soc. Trop. Med. Hyg.*, 1952, 46: 275–292.
20. M. JANICKI, Z. DYMOWSKA, and J. LUKASIAK. *Tropic. geogr. Med. Amsterdam*, 1958, 10: 371–378.
21. R. S. BRAY. *Am. J. Trop. Med. Hyg.*, 1957, 6: 514–520, 638–645, 961–970.
22. A. DE BUCK and N. H. SWELLENGREBEL. *Proc. Roy. Acad. Sci. Amsterdam*, 1935, 38: 342–343.
23. M. F. BOYD and W. K. STRATTMAN-THOMAS. *Am. J. Hyg.*, 1933, 17: 666–685.
24. J. RODHAIN. *Bull. acad. méd. Belge*, 1941, 6: 21–60.
25. S. P. JAMES. *Parasitology*, 1933, 25: 87–95.
26. P. G. SHUTE and M. MARYON. *Ann. Trop. Med. Parasitol.*, 1955, 49: 451–454.
27. M. CIUCA, G. BADENSCHI, P. CONSTANTINESCU, and E. TERITEANU. *Trop. Diseases Bull.*, 1944, 41: 645.
28. L. B. SIDDONS. *J. Malaria Inst. India*, 1944, 5: 361–373.
29. E. VAN DER KUYP. *Contribution to the Study of the Malarial Epidemiology in Surinam*, 146 pp., Utrecht, 1950, Vijlbrief & Co.
30. L. J. CHWATT. *Ann. Trop. Med. Parasitol.*, 1948, 42: 101–112.
31. S. L. BRUG. *Riv. malariol.*, 1934, 13: 121–142.
32. W. A. P. SCHÜFFNER. *Deut. med. Wochschr.*, 1941, 67: 1251–1256.
33. B. HYLKEMA. *Mededeel. Dienst Volksgezondheid Ned. Indië* (English ed.), 1920, 9: 50–99.
34. A. DE BUCK. *Ann. Trop. Med. Parasitol.*, 1935, 29: 171–175.
35. M. F. BOYD. *Am. J. Trop. Med.*, 1940, 20: 749–798.
36. J. RODHAIN. *Ann. soc. belge méd. trop.*, 1943, 23: 19–46; 1948, 28: 39–49.
37. N. H. SWELLENGREBEL. *Bull. Soc. pathol. exotique*, 1920, 13: 20–22.
38. G. M. JEFFERY and D. E. EYLES. *Am. J. Trop. Med. Hyg.*, 1954, 3: 219–224.
39. E. PEEL and L. VAN HOOF. *Ann. soc. belge méd. trop.*, 1948, 28: 273–277, 413–420.
40. B. C. BASU and A. P. RAY. *Indian J. Malariol.*, 1956, 10: 269–271.
41. S. P. JAMES, W. D. NICOL, and P. G. SHUTE. *Proc. Roy. Soc. Med.*, 1932, 25: 1153–1186.

42. M. F. Boyd and S. F. Kitchen. *Am. J. Trop. Med.*, 1937, 17: 845–848.
43. P. G. Shute and M. Maryon. *Riv. malariol.*, 1954, 33: 1–21.
44. P. C. C. Garnham. *Kenya & E. African Med. J.*, 1931, 3: 2–21.
45. R. C. Muirhead-Thomson. *Trans. Roy. Soc. Trop. Med. Hyg.*, 1954, 48: 208–225.
46. G. Covell, G. R. Coatney, J. W. Field, and Jasivant Singh. *Chemotherapy of Malaria*, 123 pp., Genève, 1955, World Health Organization, pp. 77, 97, 78, 80, 84, 85, 87, 91, 92, 98.
47. J. Rodhain. *Act. Conv. tert. trop. & malar. Morb. Amsterdam*, 1938, 2: 539–543.
48. R. S. Bray. *Am. J. Trop. Med. Hyg.*, 1958, 7: 20–24.
49. P. C. C. Garnham, R. Lainson, and W. Cooper. *Trans. Roy. Soc. Trop. Med. Hyg.*, 1957, 51: 384–396.
50. E. C. Faust, P. F. Russell, and D. R. Lincicome. *Clinical Parasitology*, Philadelphia, 1957, Lea & Febiger, pp. 241, 283, 981.
51. M. Pinotti. *Sixth Intern. Congr. Trop. Med.*, Lisbon, 1958; abstracts, pp. 322–323.
52. W. H. W. Komp. *Fourth Internat. Congr. Trop. Med.*, Washington, D. C., 1948, pp. 644–655.

CHAPTER VII

PROTOZOA OF UNCERTAIN SYSTEMATIC POSITION

The parasites of this group, belonging to the genera *Babesia* (*Piroplasma*), *Toxoplasma, Sarcocystis,* and *Pneumocystis,* are usually assigned a place among the sporozoa because they are or are supposed to be intracellular parasites multiplying by schizogony. It is by no means sure that they all meet these requirements. So it is more convenient to deal with them separately.

BABESIA (PIROPLASMA)

Members of this genus live and multiply in red blood cells of mammals, like the plasmodia. Unlike these true sporozoa, they multiply by binary fission, both in the erythrocytes of the mammal and in the organs of the intermediate host, various species of hard ticks. When in the erythrocytes, they produce no pigment, and in the ticks they do not pass through a sexual cycle. Therefore, notwithstanding their erythrocytic habitat, they bear no relationship to the plasmodia.[1]

From an ecological point of view the babesias are the most interesting of all protozoan parasites, as has been proved by Theobald Smith and Kilborne's[2] classical investigations in the southeastern United States. They showed how, in certain circumstances, the host and the parasite succeed in establishing a state of balanced relationship, the prototype of what since has become known as *premunition;* and how, in adverse circumstances, they fail to do so, to the detriment of both.

The parasites which formed the object of these investigations are *Babesia bigemina;* the mammal hosts are cattle and the intermediate hosts are ticks, *Boophilus annulatus.* The tick takes the blood of an infected bovine, thus becoming an infected tick. It passes the infection on to its offspring, and these young ticks reintroduce the parasites into a fresh bovine host.

In a herd of cattle permanently infested with ticks and babesias, the calves are the only hosts to suffer. They are all infected shortly after birth, and they all contract a fever; *B. bigemina* is an *initial aggressor*. In the region in which Smith and Kilborne were working, the calves usually recovered from the fever because they succeeded in bringing the parasites under control before conditions got past mending. From that stage onward the young bovine, attaining adult life, was safe from any renewed attack of the fever. Parasites, however, continued to live in its blood; the bovine had become a healthy carrier, subjugating the babesias by numerical restraint without eradicating them. The host's defense mechanism was kept constantly on the alert by the residual parasite population; without this stimulant it would have lost its activity sooner or later.

Thus the young calf succeeds in gaining the mastery at its first encounter with the parasites, perhaps with the help of antibodies acquired from its mother. The adult fails to do so if it is exposed to infection for the first time in its life, e.g. by leaving an uninfected area where it had grown to adult age and entering a region full of babesias and ticks. Under these conditions the adult bovine, not protected by premunition, contracts a serious disease known as *redwater fever* or *piroplasmosis*, which, if left untreated, ends with the death of the host and of all the parasites it had failed to keep in subjection.

BABESIA BOVIS

Whatever the scientific value of the babesias may have been, there was nothing to justify their being included in a book dealing with animal parasites in man. At present this justification exists because a close relative of *B. bigemina, B. bovis* Starcovici, 1893 (or one greatly resembling it) has been found in man.

In 1956 Škrabalo and Deanović [3] observed large numbers of this parasite in the erythrocytes of an adult male inhabitant of a Croatian village. In the grazing grounds of the vicinity, bovine babesial infection was of common occurrence, and so was the tick *Ixodes ricinus,* one of the well-known intermediate hosts of *B. bovis.* The human host was suffering from a fever which ended fatally after ten days; it was accompanied by morbid symptoms (grave anemia and hemoglobinuria) which are of common occurrence in bovine piroplasmosis.

The parasites found in the human host cannot be distinguished from *B. bovis*. In slides stained after Giemsa, they are round (Fig. 7·1) or elongate, with a sharp and a blunt extremity. The elongate or piriform parasites measure 1.9 μ × 1.3 μ. They are solitary or lie

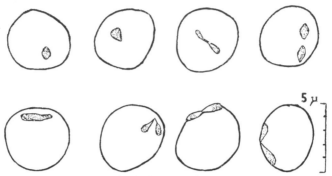

Fig. 7·1a   *Babesia bovis*. After Ed. Sergent.

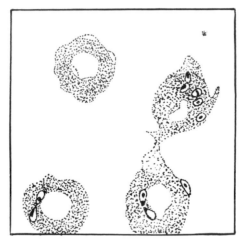

Fig. 7·1b   *Babesia bovis*-like organism in human red blood cells. Top row. Uninfected cell.—Right. Round forms.—Bottom row left. A pair of elongate organisms lying in a straight line. Right, forming an angle; a third one in a marginal position. (After Škrabalo and Deanović, 1957. Courtesy, *Documenta,* Amsterdam.)

in pairs with the sharp extremities touching each other. The pairs are placed in such a way as to trace a straight line or a blunt angle. About one-tenth of the parasites are situated on the margin of the erythrocyte. In the protoplasm, staining blue, dark red chromatin is present in the shape of a minute round or elongate mass. The piriform babesias derive from the round ones by a process of binary fission. The details of this fission are seen in Fig. 7·2, picturing them as they occur in *B. canis,* a parasite of dogs, which by its slightly larger size brings them out more clearly.

In order to complete the picture of the life cycle of this human parasite, several unproved assumptions must be made: (1) that the parasite was *B. bovis,* and not a closely related species peculiar to man; (2) that the life cycle of the parasite was completed in the tick

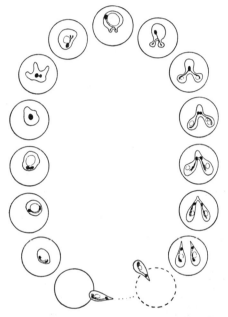

Fig. 7·2   *Babesia canis* in canine red blood cells: Left side. Round forms.—Right side. Production of two daughter individuals by budding. (After Nuttall and Graham Smith. Courtesy, *Journal of Hygiene,* Cambridge, England.)

Ixodes ricinus and that it resembled other babesias; (3) that there existed some particular reason why this one man should fall a victim, and none of the hundreds of people that must have been bitten, in the course of years, by infected ticks in the fields around this and other villages, spread over large parts of Europe, North Africa, and other continents. As to this last point the particular reason, assumed to exist, may have been the fact that the victim's spleen had been removed twelve years before his death. It is well known [4] that calves that have recovered from piroplasmosis fall ill again if their defense mechanism has become impaired by the removal of their spleen. Still it remains unexplained why it took the parasites twelve years to be lured into entering the victim's defenseless body.

Taking these assumptions for granted, the description of the parasite may be continued as follows.

The eggs of the aforementioned tick are laid in the fields where babesia-infected cattle are grazing. The tick emerging from the egg is called a *larva*. It attaches itself to an animal and takes its blood. It sticks to this first animal as long as it remains a larva, i.e. as long as it does not metamorphose. When it is ready to do so, it drops to the ground and there sheds its skin. From this *first ecdysis* it emerges as a *nymph*, which attaches itself to a second animal. On the second animal it remains and feeds till it is ready for the *second ecdysis*, which takes place on the ground, like the first one. This introduces the third, and last, stage of development: the adult male or female tick, called the *imago*, which attaches itself to and feeds on a third animal. In that site the female tick is fertilized by the male and develops its eggs. It remains attached to the same (third) animal until ready for oviposition. Then it drops to the ground, deposits eggs, and dies.

If animal No. 1 was a healthy carrier of *B. bovis*, the larva becomes infected with the parasite. The nymph, emerging from the larva, after metamorphosis and ecdysis, is now able to transmit the babesias to animal No. 2. This applies also to the nymph and the adult, as well as to animals No. 2 and No. 3. As to the infected female imago, even she can infect No. 4—not directly, for she dies after leaving animal No. 3, but by *transovarian infection*, i.e. by passing on the parasites to her ova and to the larvas of the next generation emerging from them. It may be added that the tick *Boophilus annulatus*, which formed part of Smith and Kilborne's [2] experiments, passes its whole life on one animal. Thus transovarian infection is in this case an indispensable part of the transmission cycle.

Judging by what is known in other babesias, *B. bovis* multiplies vigorously in the body of the tick. In the course of its development, vermiform, motile individuals arise that invade the muscles of the larva and of the nymph. In this way they insure the transmission of the parasites from the larva to the nymph and from the nymph to the imago, because it is the muscular tissue that remains intact during each process of metamorphosis. The same vermiform parasites, lodged within the female adult, make their way to the ova, thus bringing about transovarian infection. As to the infection of the bovine (or human) host, this is rendered possible by small spherical parasites invading the salivary glands of the tick. When the tick injects saliva into the skin of the future host, these parasites, suspended in the saliva, are carried into the bovine or human body.

TREATMENT OF BABESIOSIS

Experience in the treatment of human babesiosis is nonexistent; the one known case gives no clue on this matter. Nevertheless, specific treatment of bovine babesiosis offers a point of general biological interest which is worth recording. Unlike the specific treatment of malaria, that of babesiosis closely follows the natural course of events: its object is to cure the sick animal by destroying numerous babesias, but it deliberately avoids eradicating the parasites. On the contrary, it aims at conserving a residual parasite population in the body of the recovered animal so as to promote the establishment of premunition.[1]

This principle is demonstrated most clearly in the treatment and the prevention of the disease caused in bovines by *B. bigemina,* as described by Ed. Sergent et al.[4] The specific drug against this parasite is a benzidine dye, *trypanoblue,* administered in an aqueous solution by intravenous injection. Originally it was employed in a single dose of 1 gm per 100 kg of body weight, with the object of destroying the whole parasite population in the bovine body. This "therapia sterilisans magna," to quote Ed. Sergent, "is not desirable: the complete destruction of the parasites would deprive the subject of the premunition that can only persist in the presence of *B. bigemina.*" Accordingly, a much smaller dose is administered, viz. one injection of 0.1–0.2 gm of trypanoblue to bovines of 200–300 kg, which brings the temperature down to normal and greatly reduces the number of parasites after a lapse of 24 hours.

In order to protect nonresistant bovines from the disease, they are injected with a live vaccine in the form of blood from bovines that had become symptomless carriers no less than three months and no longer than one year before the date of vaccination. The state of premunition, thus artificially conferred upon the vaccinated bovines, is not expected to last for more than two years in the absence of natural reinfection. Consequently, vaccination is re-peated annually.[4]

With reference to *human babesial infection,* such as the Croatian case quoted above, it should be remembered that trypanoblue is inactive against *Babesia bovis.* Against bovine infections with *B. berbera* (closely related to *B. bovis*) Sergent et al.[4] recommend two intravenous injections of 1 gm of Ichthargan (as a 1 percent aqueous solution) followed, if necessary, after an interval of 24 hours, by one subcutaneous injection of 4–12 ml of a 5 percent aqueous solution of *zothelone (acaprine).*

TOXOPLASMA GONDII

The members of *Toxoplasma gondii* Nicolle & Manceaux, 1908 [*Toxoplasma hominis* Wolf & Cowen, 1937] are initial aggressors. If they are pathogenic, they are so only during the first or acute phase of infection. They cease to be so during the second or chronic phase.

In the acute phase, termed by Lainson[5] the *pseudocystic phase,* they are ovoid or sickle-shaped microorganisms lying within or outside lymphoid cells or macrophages[5] in several organs of the host's body. Their size and shape depend on the method of prepara-

FIG. 7·3   *Toxoplasma gondii,* × 2000. FROM LEFT TO RIGHT. 1–4. Forms seen in peripheral circulation, showing longitudinal fission.—5–6. Forms in deeper organs, interpreted as multiple division. (After Chatton and Blanc, 1917. Courtesy, *Archives de l'institut Pasteur de Tunis.*)

tion. In histological sections, only ovoid parasites are seen, measuring on an average 2–3 μ × 1.5–2 μ, with 0.9 μ × 0.7 μ and 3.5 μ × 2 μ as extremes. In cerebrospinal or intraperitoneal fluid, sickle-shaped parasites are common. When alive they measure 4–6 μ × 2–3 μ; in fixed and stained slides they vary more in size (2–6.4 μ × 1.3–4 μ). The parasite possesses a single nucleus, situated in the middle or near one extremity. In the latter case Chatton and Blanc[6] noticed a deeply staining mass at the other extremity, which they called the *paranuclear body* (Fig. 7·3).

Multiplication takes place by longitudinal binary fission within the host cell. Thus the host cell becomes gradually filled with parasites. A host cell containing a few parasites only still has all the characteristics of a cell; but when it becomes replete with toxoplasma, nothing remains but a thin membrane that holds together a mass of multiplying parasites. The membrane is part of the host cell; it is not the wall of a cyst. For this reason such a bladder full of toxoplasma (occasionally proving its origin by the

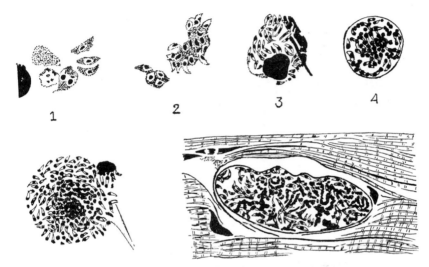

FIG. 7·4   *Toxoplasma gondii*. 1. To the left, four toxoplasms, one in longitudinal fission.—2. A clump of toxoplasms, × 1500 (drawing after microphoto by Brug).—3. Pseudocyst in host cell the nucleus of which is still visible.—4. 14-day-old cyst.—5. A similar cyst, highly flattened, showing individual nature of contained toxoplasmas.—6. Six-month-old cyst apparently within a muscle fiber. 3–6 × 1000. (After Lainson, 1958. Courtesy, Royal Society of Tropical Medicine and Hygiene.)

persistence of the nucleus of the host cell: Fig. 7·4:3) is called a *pseudocyst*. It necessarily contains numerous parasites. Pseudocysts are easily broken, setting free the toxoplasmas, which then appear as extracellular parasites, lying separate (Fig. 7·4:1) or still in clusters (Fig. 7·4:2).

This phase of acute infection, characterized by intracellular multiplication resulting in the formation of pseudocysts, is termed the *pseudocystic phase*.[5] The parasites involved in it may be compared with *Trypanosoma lewisi* infecting young rats. In both cases, little inconvenience is caused to the host during the stage of acute infection. However, both parasites may occasionally proliferate so extensively as to cause the death of the host before the onset of the chronic infection.

In the life cycle of toxoplasma this is of particular importance because it is only during the chronic infection that the parasite produces the true cysts (*v. infra*) which enable it to pass from one host to another. Consequently, the early death of the host is fatal to *Toxoplasma,* collectively as well as individually, because it prevents the perpetuation of the species by cutting off its retreat, just as *Entamoeba histolytica's* retreat from young kittens is cut off by its inability to produce cysts.

The extensive proliferation during the stage of acute or pseudocystic infection is a peculiarity of certain strains of the species *Toxoplasma gondii* and marks them as particularly virulent. It can be counted on to reappear through each succeeding passage. Thus these strains appear to be races breeding true to type. Nevertheless, a strain of low virulence, never known to abuse its initial freedom, can be rendered highly virulent by passages through certain rodents to which it is not accustomed.[5] Thus, low virulence is apparently not an unalterable characteristic, and the same perhaps applies to its alternative, high virulence.

Under normal conditions, i.e. in strains of low virulence, the pseudocystic phase, with toxoplasma constantly liberated by rupturing pseudocysts, soon dies down. After 8–11 days it is replaced by a much more prolonged period of binary fission in the viscera (brain, lungs, skeletal muscles, and others). This phase is called by Lainson [5] the *cystic phase.* It is characterized by the host subjecting the parasites to topical restraint, not unlike that acting on the hepatic cycle of the plasmodia. The toxoplasmas are free to live and even to multiply vigorously within certain cells of the viscera just mentioned, which are destroyed beyond recognition. But they are only allowed to do so in the form of *true cysts* (Fig. 7·4:4–6), i.e. imprisoned within a highly elastic, tough membrane produced by the parasites themselves and distinctly separate from that of any enclosing host cell. Unlike the pseudocysts, they are ruptured only with difficulty after heavy pressure between glass slides.

The youngest known cyst contains no more than three toxoplasmas.[5] In the course of four months it grows to reach a size of

30–60 μ, with some 3000 parasites contained within its membrane. Further growth has not been observed. Cysts recovered five years after infection are still viable (i.e. able to cause infection after ingestion by a suitable host), but they are no larger than the four-month-old cysts. It is not known whether the older cysts are the same as those found after four months. It is assumed that they are the remote descendants of the earlier cysts. Furthermore, it is assumed that they owe their origin to the spontaneous rupture of a cyst, the destruction of the majority of the toxoplasmas therein contained, and the formation of fresh cysts by the few survivors,[5] in a way analogous to the production of a succeeding exoerythrocytic generation by a few surviving merozoites of the preceding one.

No *cellular reaction* has been observed around the cysts located in the tissues of the host, not even around ruptured cysts.[5] This offers another analogy with the hepatic cycle of the plasmodia, neither of which provokes a cellular reaction. It is unknown, however, whether the *humoral reactions* of the host's body, made apparent by complement fixation, hemagglutination, intradermal and dye tests, are provoked by free toxoplasms or by those enclosed within cysts.

Toxoplasmas are delicate microorganisms. As individuals they do not survive for any length of time outside the host's body. If they appear in the peripheral blood, as occasionally occurs in the acute initial infection, bloodsucking arthropods may act as vectors, as has actually been observed.[7] Infants are known to have become infected by intrauterine transmission of *Toxoplasma* from mother to child. It is not known, however, whether the apparently healthy mother infects her child with toxoplasma in her blood, derived from ruptured cysts, or by small cysts *in toto*.

The cysts characteristic of the chronic stage of infection are the elements most likely to be successfully transmitted from one host to another. Sabrailhé's [8] old observation that *Toxoplasma*, kept at 25° C, can survive for 17 days outside the host's body and for 2 days in a putrefying carcass, may now be accepted as referring to cysts. Oral infection is known to succeed best if the material ingested contains cysts.[9]

The hypothesis which relies mainly on the cysts as means of transmission has to face the difficulty that they are located in the deeper tissues. Thus their future host cannot reach them unless it is a carnivorous animal, including man consuming underdone pork [11] or mutton.[10] Now *T. gondii* is a polyxenous parasite with an astonishingly wide range of mammal hosts, and many of them are herbivorous animals. However, as has been pointed out by Lainson,[5] the cysts can be relied upon even in this case, because one of the viscera they inhabit is the lungs. There they are found not only within the pulmonary tissue but also in the lumen of the alveoli and bronchioles; from this location they can readily spread by droplet infection.

In man *T. gondii* was discovered in newborn children as the causative agent of a particular form of encephalomyelitis (*toxoplasmosis*) affecting mainly the brain and eyes (chorioretinitis). Clinically it is characterized by hydrocephalus, microcephaly, mental retardation, convulsive episodes, and other nervous disturbances in addition to the eye lesions. Roentgenologically, intracerebral calcification is frequently encountered. Older children and even adults have been detected ill with a disease more or less different from the former, but caused by the identical microorganism. The human parasite can be successfully transmitted to various rodents, to chickens, and to monkeys.

In infants toxoplasmas are found in the brain, the spinal cord, the eye (retina and choroid), the myocardium, and the subcutaneous adipose tissue. In adults ill with toxoplasmosis the parasites were also detected in the lungs, liver, kidneys, suprarenal glands, lymph glands, and bone marrow.

In the myocardium the cysts may grow to an unusual size, which sometimes may cause confusion with *Sarcocystis* (*v. infra*).[12] Conversely *Sarcocystis* may masquerade as *Toxoplasma* [13] when the latter is to be detected by serological tests. Finally, toxoplasmas have been confused with a unicellular fungus of the genus *Encephalitozoon,* a parasite of rodents, which, however, possesses a cellular membrane absent in *Toxoplasma.*

The prevalence of *Toxoplasma* in man is probably much higher than might be gathered from the comparatively small number of cases of overt toxoplasmosis. The majority of infected persons are asymptomatic carriers; their infection is in the cystic phase. As a rule they cannot be identified by the detection of the parasites; but they can be identified by serological alterations brought about as a response of the human body to the presence of toxoplasma. Among these serological alterations, the *dye-test of Sabin and Feldman* [26] takes a prominent place. As an example Polman,[14] in Holland, found 27 Sabin positive (a titer of 1:64 or higher) among a total of 1260 persons. In children 1 in 116 were positive, in adults 1 in 27, showing that a person can become positive when he has already passed the years of childhood.

There are those who do not accept a positive Sabin test as a definitive diagnostic tool. Even they can be convinced of the existence of asymptomatic carriers by the evidence of intrauterine infection in children born of women who were not and never had been ill with toxoplasmosis. The value of this evidence is not decreased by the fact that it is not known (1) whether these mothers had in the past been infected with a particularly virulent strain of toxoplasma, (2) whether the strain had gained in virulence by the passage through her body, (3) whether the infant had been particularly suspectible, i.e. unable to cope successfully with the pseudocystic phase of a strain of toxoplasma in no way remarkable for its virulence.

Intrauterine infection is the only example known at present of toxoplasma transmitted directly from man to man. In all other instances man is supposed to acquire his infection from animal sources, such as household pets, notably from dogs, as they are known to show pulmonary infection with parasites of the cystic phase.[5]

Although the relation of toxoplasma to its hosts cannot yet be regarded as clarified, Sabin's [15] tentative description may be accepted as correct:

> In toxoplasmosis we have found an example of that almost perfect host-parasite relationship in which the parasite only rarely causes serious damage to its hosts, and the hosts are not too intent on destroying the parasite.

TREATMENT OF TOXOPLASMOSIS

No drugs are known which are sure to destroy toxoplasma in the human body. In mice pyrimidine-sulfonamides (sulfadiazine, sulfamerazine, sulfamethazine) are reported to be effective, if administration is initiated before the third day after infection and continued for 14 days.[23] Occasionally favorable results have been obtained in human infections with the administration of pyrimethamine (1 mg/kg), in combination with sulfadiazine (35 mg/kg), and hydrocortisone 80 mg, daily for four weeks.[24]

SARCOCYSTIS

Parasites belonging to this genus are lodged in the striated muscles of a number of herbivorous and omnivorous mammals, numerous birds and some reptiles. If they are found in man they bear the name of *Sarcocystis lindemanni*.

SARCOCYSTIS LINDEMANNI

Sarcocystis lindemanni Rivolta, 1878, is known only in the form of elongated cysts (Fig. 7·5) containing a large number of crescent-shaped bodies, with a blunt and a pointed end, a nucleus near the former, and a vacuole near the latter: the so-called *spores* or *Rainey bodies* (Fig. 7·6).

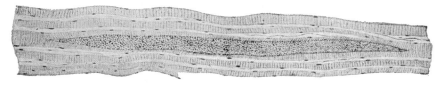

Fig. 7·5   *Sarcocystis lindemanni*. (After Baraban and St. Rémy.)

Two types of cysts may be distinguished.[16] (1) The large type (up to 5 cm long) has large spores (12–15 × 4–9 μ). The wall of the cyst is thick and transversely striated (Fig. 7·8). From the interior surface of the cyst wall, septa arise which divide the lumen of the cyst into a number of cubicles. The outer cubicles are densely packed with spores; those farther inward are not so well provided (Fig. 7·7). The central ones may be almost empty. These cysts represent true sarcocystis. (2) The small type (84 μ × 27 μ), with small spores 4 μ × 2 μ. The cyst wall is thin, without striation; its lumen is not partitioned off into cubicles. These cysts are not *sarcocystis* but *Toxoplasma gondii*.

Apart from a number of doubtful cases, *S. lindemanni* was found in muscles of the tongue, the face, the larynx, the chest, the upper arm, the thigh, and the foot. It was found more often in the myocardium than anywhere else. Cases were reported in France (2), England (2), India (3), China (1), Indonesia (1), the Caribbean region (1), Central America (1), North America (2), Africa (2); in total, 4 women, 10 men, and 1 child.

It is not known how man becomes infected with the parasite, but something may be learnt about possible modes of transmission from what is known in related parasites of sheep (*S. tenella*, Fig. 7·6), rats (*S. muris*) and pigs (*S. miescheriana*, Fig. 7·8).[17]

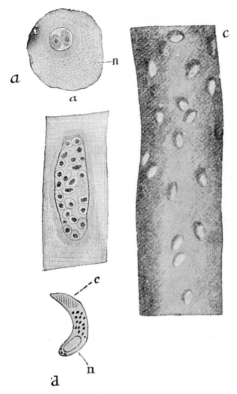

FIG. 7·6 *Sarcocystis tenella: a,* Very young parasite, cross section.—*b,* The same, longitudinal section.—*c,* Esophagus of sheep with sarcocystis. —*d,* Spore. (After Doeflein. Courtesy, Gustav Fischer, Jena.)

Various experimental animals which were made to swallow infected meat were found to harbor young cysts after a lapse of six to seven weeks. Moreover the stools of animals infected in this way became infectious from three to seven weeks after the infecting meal; i.e., other animals eating food mixed with these stools became infected. It is not known in which form the parasite was present in these stools; it must have been a highly resistant form, for the stools remained infective after they had been dried for as long as a month, or after they had been exposed for half an hour to a temperature of

60° C. The unseen parasite in such stools has been given the name of "Nègre's resistant form."

Four hours after the experimental animal has ingested infected meat, the spores contained in it are found lodged under the epithelial cells of the gut wall. Two hours later they occur in the circulating blood. At that point, however, all traces are lost for the next 35–40 days. After that lapse of time the parasites are rediscovered in mus-

Fig. 7·7 *Sarcocystis* sp. Section through portion of cyst; LEFT, periphery with cubicles closely packed with spores; RIGHT, central portion, with half-empty cubicles; FARTHER RIGHT, isolated spore at high magnification. (After Blacklock and Southwell, 1944. Courtesy, H. K. Lewis, London.)

cular tissue, in the shape of young cysts, measuring $25 \times 5 \mu$ (Fig. 7·6:*a, b*), with a tenuous cyst wall. They contain a number of spherical parasites, of $4–5 \mu$, that show stages of nuclear division. It takes them another 35–50 days to evolve to the stage of mature cysts, in which the parasites situated in the center have already taken the shape of crescents. Still later, 110–120 days after the infecting meal, they have all turned into spores.

The life span of the cysts is limited to four months or less.[18] They are supposed to disintegrate, and to set free their spores, which thereupon find their way to the blood stream, where they have been actually detected. It is supposed that the spores are unable to develop into new cysts in the host in whose body they grew up. For that, they must leave the first host and enter a second one, either by muscles of the first host being consumed by the second, or by the second host's food being contaminated by stools containing Nègre's resistant bodies.

S. lindemanni is either a specific human parasite, or identical with one or all of the several "species" of *Sarcocystis* which inhabit the body of domestic animals and rats. In these animals the parasite is a common occurrence. In man it is presumably rare. But even that is not certain, because an adequate systematic search has never been made.

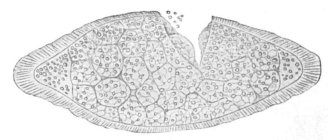

Fig. 7·8 *Sarcocystis miescheriana,* full-grown cyst, isolated from muscle, partly ruptured. (After Manz.)

Nothing definite is known about the pathogenic activity of *S. lindemanni*. Finding thousands of cysts in the heart muscle, and a myocardial focus around a dead cyst, is apt to create an unfavorable impression,[19] but does not prove that the patient dying of diabetic coma was in any way incommoded by the parasite.

Domestic animals offer a wider field of experience. As a rule the presence of *Sarcocystis* cannot be associated with any definite morbid condition, but there are exceptions, and there always are the toxic products (sarcocystin, sarcosporidiotoxin) ready for all who want to make out a case against the parasite.

PNEUMOCYSTIS

Pneumocystis carinii Delanoë, 1912, is a spherical or oval parasite, with a diameter of 4–6.5 μ, enclosed by a cell wall. Within that wall it multiplies by schizogony, producing eight daughter individuals, without a residual body. These daughter individuals are first spherical; later they become sickle-shaped; they measure 1.5–2.5 $\times$ 0.5 μ (Fig. 7·9). They were found in the lungs of rats, mice, guinea pigs, dogs, goats, and sheep. There they usually live extracellularly, rarely inside mononuclear leucocytes.[20]

Pneumocystis at first evoked some interest because it was described as a stage in the life cycle of *Trypanosoma cruzi*, *T. lewisi*, and *T. gambiense* in the lungs of laboratory animals experimentally infected with these parasites. This developmental stage was supposed to confirm the view, current at that time, that trypanosomes can multiply by schizogony, testifying thereby their close relationship with the *Plasmodia*. Later it became evident that pneumocystis has nothing to do with trypanosomes and interest in the parasite waned

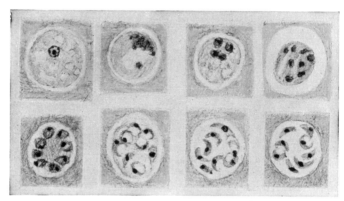

Fig. 7·9   *Pneumocystis carinii*, in human lung, × 1500. (Drawing by Professor Brug.)

G. van der Meer and S. L. Brug,[21] in Amsterdam, imparted renewed interest to the subject by describing pneumocystis as a (usually extracellular) parasite in the human body. They found it in the lungs of a 3-month-old infant that had died of congenital heart disease, complicated by malaria, and also in the lungs of a 4-month-old infant and of a 21-year-old adult, as well as in the lungs of guinea pigs and white and wild rats and mice. Since that time numerous cases have been described of a usually fatal form of interstitial pneumonia in undernourished or prematurely born infants. Often part of the alveoli and bronchioles is filled with a frothy semiliquid substance which, on microscopic examination, is seen to be composed mainly of huge masses of pneumocystis.[22] Possibly it is an ubiquitous commensal, inhabiting the lungs in discreet numbers, which on comparatively rare occasions is stimulated to excessive multiplication that may aggravate a pre-existing morbid condition.

If, as has been suggested, pneumocystis is not a protozoon but a fungus, its spores might easily be transported by air, a supposition which would offer a ready explanation for the location of the parasite in the lungs of all animal and human carriers.

TREATMENT OF PNEUMOCYSTIC INFECTION. Faust et al.[25] record considerable improvement in some cases of *Pneumocystis* infection following the administraton of antimalarial drugs (quinine, 8-aminoquinolines) and amebicides (emetine, Stovarsol).

REFERENCES FOR CHAPTER VII

1. E. REICHENOW. *Lehrbuch der Protozoenkunde,* 6th ed., 1213 pp., Jena, 1953, Gustav Fischer, pp. 941–960, 965.
2. THEOBALD SMITH and F. L. KILBORNE. *Texas or Southern Cattle Fever,* U. S. Dept. Agricult., Bur. Anim. Industr., Bull. No. 1, 301 pp., Washington, D. C., 1893.
3. Z. ŠKRABALO and Z. DEANOVIĆ. *Documenta Med. Geograph. et Trop. Amsterdam,* 1957, 9: 11–16.
4. ED. SERGENT, A. DONATIEN, L. PARROT, and F. LESTOQUARD. *Etudes sur les piroplasmoses bovines,* 816 pp., Algiers, 1946, pp. 138, 183, 184, 142–144, 720–722, 192–195, 83, 169, 109, 110.
5. R. LAINSON. *Trans. Roy. Soc. Trop. Med. Hyg.,* 1958, 52: 396–407.
6. E. CHATTON and G. BLANC. *Arch. inst. Pasteur Tunis,* 1917, 10: 1–40.
7. J. J. LAARMAN. *Documenta Med. Geograph. et Trop. Amsterdam,* 1956, 8: 293–298.
8. A. SABRAILHÉ. *Bull. soc. pathol. exotique,* 1914, 7: 232–240.
9. P. H. VAN THIEL and D. VAN DER WAAY. *Documenta Med. Geograph. et Trop. Amsterdam,* 1956, 8: 392–396.
10. H. DE ROEVER-BONNET. *Documenta Med. Geograph. et Trop. Amsterdam,* 1957, 9: 336–338.
11. D. WEINMAN and A. H. CHANDLER. *J. Am. Med. Assoc.,* 1956, 161: 229–232.
12. C. LEVADITI and R. SCHOEN. *Bull. soc. pathol. exotique,* 1933, 26: 402–405.
13. I. A. B. CATHIE and G. W. CECIL. *Lancet,* 1957 (1): 816–818.
14. A. POLMAN. *Documenta Trop. Geogr. Med. Amsterdam,* 1959, 11: 13–23.
15. A. B. SABIN. *Am. J. Trop. Med. Hyg.,* 1953, 2: 360–364.
16. B. H. KEAN and R. G. GROCOTT. *Am. J. Pathol.,* 1954, 21: 467–483.
17. J. W. SCOTT. *Wyoming Agr. Expt. Sta., Bull.* Nos. 259 and 262.
18. S. T. DARLING. *Arch. Internal Med.,* 1909, 3: 183–192.
19. F. KOBERLE. *Z. tropenmed. Parasitol.,* 1958, 9: 1–6.
20. A. PORTER. *Parasitology,* 1916, 8: 255–259.
21. G. VAN DER MEER and S. L. BRUG. *Ann. soc. belge méd. trop.,* 1942, 22: 301–307.
22. H. HAMPERL. *Am. J. Pathol.,* 1956, 32: 1–13.
23. P. H. VAN THIEL. *Documenta Med. Geograph. et Trop. Amsterdam,* 1950, 2: 51–58.
24. H. J. J. FESEVUR. *Ned. Tijdschr. Geneesk.,* 1956, 100: 342–346 (English summary, 346).
25. E. C. FAUST, P. F. RUSSELL, and D. R. LINCICOME. *Clinical Parasitology,* Philadelphia, 1957, Lea & Febiger, p. 309.
26. A. B. SABIN and H. A. FELDMAN. *Science,* 1948, 108: 660–663.

PART TWO

Helminths: Trematodes

CHAPTER VIII

HELMINTHS (GENERAL CONSIDERATIONS) —TREMATODES

A large number of metazoan animal parasites living in various parts of the human body (not necessarily the intestine) are brought together under the name of *helminths* or *intestinal worms.*

From a taxonomic point of view the helminths belong to the phylum of the *Scolecida,* characterized by the absence of segmentation and a true celom, and the presence of *protonephridia,* i.e. branched excretory canals carrying unicellular *terminal organs* (*flame cells*) provided with a bundle of long cilia.

The name "intestinal worms" suggests that they look like worms, i.e. that they are long and thin and round like an eel, as indeed some of them are. These are the *roundworms* or *nematodes.* Others are long and thin, but flat, like a piece of tape rather than a worm; these are the *tapeworms* or *cestodes.* A third group has lost all likeness to a worm; they are not long and thin and round but flat and broad for their length, like a flatfish or the leaf of a tree; they are the *flukes* or *trematodes.*

There are fundamental differences between the host-parasite relationship of protozoa and that of helminths. Protozoa multiply in the human body; helminths do not, as a rule. The number of helminths in a single host is not determined by the rate of proliferation of the parasite within that particular host, since there is no proliferation. In protozoal infections numerical restraint directly reduces the number of parasites. In helminth infections it can only bring about a decrease in the number of eggs produced (e.g. in hookworms). If all hosts forming part of a human community collaborate in this fashion, the final outcome will be a diminished chance of infection for every single human member of that community, i.e. an indirect reduction in the number of parasites per head of population. But a direct reduction of the number of helminths in the individual host can only result from the host successfully attacking the parasite in its larval stage, when it enters the human body or migrates through the body to reach its definitive habitat.

Another difference relates to intermediate hosts. In protozoa all intermediate hosts are *transporting hosts* (*v.* Introduction, above). *Trypanosoma, Leishmania, Plasmodium,* and *Babesia* can all do without it in experimental conditions, although this rarely happens under perfectly natural conditions. Helminths transmitted by intermediate hosts simply *have* to pass through that host and undergo certain changes before they can resume their normal development in the human host: the intermediate hosts of the helminths are *preparatory hosts.*

TREMATODES OR FLUKES

Apart from their form, the trematodes with which this book is concerned are characterized by the possession of two suckers: (1) the *oral sucker* has a terminal position; its bottom is pierced by the oral aperture; (2) the *ventral sucker,* or *acetabulum,* is usually situated

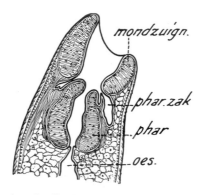

FIG. 8·1   Median longitudinal section through the anterior extremity of *Fasciola hepatica: mondzuign,* Oral sucker.—*phar.zak,* Pharyngeal pouch.—*phar,* Pharynx.—*oes,* Esophagus. (After Ihle and Nierstrasz, 1928. Courtesy, Oosthoek, Publishers, Utrecht.)

in the midline of the ventral side (i.e. the side on which the genital apertures are located), some distance behind the oral sucker; its bottom is closed. The suckers are provided with a strong musculature.

The body is covered with a thick elastic *cuticle* that sometimes carries scales or tubercles on its outer surface. Under the cuticle lies the *dermal muscular pouch,* composed of smooth muscle fibers. Jointly with dorsoventral muscles, they enable the animal to move about and to change its shape considerably.

The mouth, situated in a terminal or subterminal position, gives access to the *esophagus.* The anterior part of the esophagus, the *pharynx,* is well provided with muscles (Fig. 8·1); its posterior portion has a thin wall. This part leads to the two branches (or *ceca*) of the *bifid intestine,* which end blindly. The suckers and the bifid intestine are the distinguishing characteristics of the trematodes.

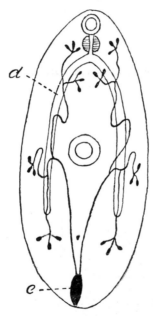

FIG. 8·2 Schematic representation of the excretory system of a trematode: *d,* Intestine.—*e,* Excretory bladder into which open the two excretory ducts.—The ramifications of these ducts terminate in 8 groups of 3 flame cells (terminal organs) each. (After Fuhrmann, 1928–1933.)

The trematode possesses two organs of excretion, the *protonephridia.* They are two longitudinal canals, one placed to the right, the other to the left of the midline (Fig. 8·2). The two canals open into the *excretory bladder,* usually situated in the median line of the posterior end with a terminal excretory atrium. Each canal has multiple ramifications terminating in capillaries, each one ending in a *terminal organ,* known as a *flame cell* (Fig. 8·3:*E*). The terminal organ is a single cell prolonged into a capillary which is a part of the cell. It carries a bundle of long cilia, moving within the lumen of the capillary.

Except for the schistosomes, the trematodes are hermaphrodites. The male and female ducts lead to a common aperture, the *genital atrium*, situated between the two suckers.

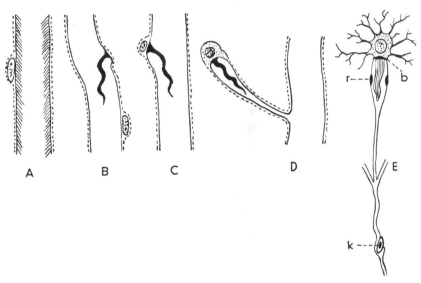

Fig. 8·3 Schematic representation of the supposed origin of the excretory canals: A, Canal with evenly disposed vibratile cilia.—B and C, Reduction of the cilia to one bundle, in B independent of the position of the nucleus; in C the bundle is situated in a corner close to a nucleus.—D, Typical flame cell.—E, One flame cell (terminal organ) at higher magnification: *b*, Basal plate on which the vibratile cilia are inserted.—*r*, Annular thickening of the capillary wall.—*k*, Nucleus of the capillary common to the three flame cells, of which one only is represented.—E, Place where the capillaries of the three flame cells meet. (After Reisinger, 1928.)

There are two male genital organs, the *testes*, each with an efferent duct, the *vas efferens*. The two vasa efferentia join into one common duct, the *vas deferens*. The distal extremity of the latter may be a *cirrus*, located within a pouch possessing a muscular wall, the *cirrus pouch*. The muscular contractions of the cirrus pouch expel the cirrus in an inverted position (inside out), and thus it functions as a copulatory organ (Fig. 8·4).

There are three female organs: one *ovary*, producing the eggs, and two *vitelline glands,* producing the *vitelline cells* that serve as food for the embryo developing within the eggshell. The ovary is situated near the midline; the vitelline glands to its left and right. Each vitelline gland transports its products along a canal that first runs

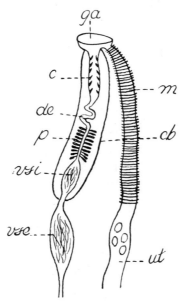

FIG. 8·4 Schematic representation of the distal ending of the vas deferens and the uterus of a trematode: *c*, Cirrus.—*cb*, Cirrus pouch.— *de*, Ejaculatory duct.—*ga*, Genital atrium into which open cirrus and metraterm (*m*).—*p*, Pars prostatica.—*ut*, Uterus.—*vse, vsi*, External and internal seminal vesicle, outside and inside cirrus pouch. (After Fuhrmann, 1928–1933.)

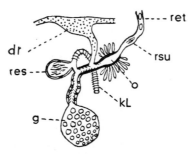

FIG. 8·5 Schematic representation of the female genital ducts within a trematode: *dr*, Vitelline reservoir at the meeting of the transverse vitelline ducts.—*g*, Ovary.—*KL*, Laurer's canal.—*o*, Ootype.—*res*, Seminal receptacle to Laurer's canal.—*rsu*, Seminal receptacle to the origin of the uterus.—*ret*, Uterus. (After Fuhrmann, 1928–1931.)

in a longitudinal direction, and finally in a transverse direction. The transverse canals of the two ducts meet in the midline to form the *vitelline reservoir*. From the ovary emerges the *oviduct*. Shortly after leaving the ovary the oviduct is joined by two canals, (1) the common duct of the vitelline glands emerging from the vitelline reservoir and (2) *Laurer's canal* (absent in schistosomes). Then the oviduct widens into a vesicle, the ootype, characterized by numerous densely packed unicellular glands that open into its lumen, and form together *Mehlis' organ* or the *shell gland* (Fig. 8·5). Beyond the ootype the oviduct becomes a convoluted, wide tube: the *uterus*. It takes its course towards the female genital aperture in the genital atrium. Its terminal portion is called the *metraterm*. It is the place

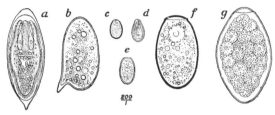

FIG. 8·6   Eggs of various trematodes, × 800: *a*, *Schistosoma haematobium* (embryonated).—*b*, *S. mansoni* (immature).—*c*, *Heterophyes heterophyes*.—*d*, *Clonorchis sinensis*.—*e*, *Opistorchis noverca*.—*f*, *Paragonimus westermani*.—*g*, *Fasciolopsis buski*. (After Manson, from Brumpt, 1922. Courtesy, Masson & Cie, Paris.)

where the spermatozoids enter the body and where the fertilized eggs leave it (Fig. 8·4).

Initially the contents of the egg consist of the fertilized ovum, surrounded by numerous vitelline cells. The shell of the egg shows an opening at one pole, closed by a lid, the *operculum* (*operculate eggs*). When the egg leaves the human body in the feces, the urine, or the sputa, it may be in the form described here (*immature eggs*) or in an advanced stage of development, containing a miracidium (*embryonated egg*) (Fig. 8·6).

Within the eggshell the fertilized ovum develops into a first-stage larva, the *miracidium* (Figs. 8·7; 8·8). It is covered with cilia, by the motion of which it swims in water. The miracidium leaves the eggshell by pushing open the lid, or through a rent in the shell (schistosomes). In this way it finds itself in water, an actively motile miracidium, unless a snail has already ingested the embryonated egg

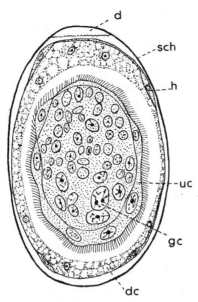

Fig. 8·7 Miracidium of *Fasciola hepatica* within eggshell (*sch*), with operculum (*d*), cellular envelope (*h*) and degenerating vitelline cells (*dc*). Within miracidium: *gc*, germ-cells; *uc*, external layer of cells carrying cilia. (After Korschelt and Heider, 1936.)

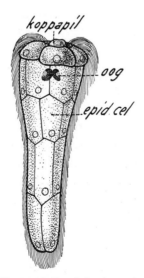

Fig. 8·8 Free miracidium of *Fasciola hepatica: koppapil*, Cephalic papilla.—*oog*, Eye.—*epid.cel*, Epidermal cells. (After A. P. Thomas, 1883. Courtesy, Publishers of *Quarterly Journal of Microscopical Science,* London.)

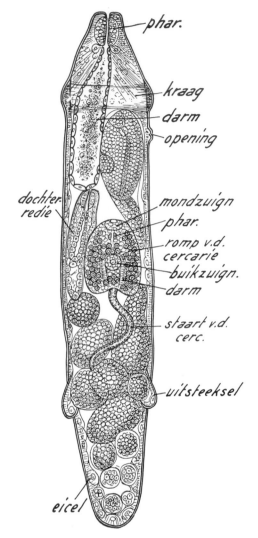

FIG. 8·9 Redia of *Fasciola hepatica: Phar,* Pharynx.—*Kraag,* Annular swelling.—*darm,* Intestine.—*opening,* Birth pore.—*uitsteeksel,* Blunt process.—*dochter redie,* Daughter redia.—*eicel,* Germ cell. Referring to the cercarias contained within the redia: *mondzuign,* Oral sucker. —*phar,* Pharynx.—*romp v.d. cercarie,* Body of cercaria.—*buikzuign,* Acetabulum.—*staart v.d. cercarie,* Tail of cercaria. (After A. P. Thomas, 1883. Courtesy, Publishers of *Quarterly Journal of Microscopical Science,* London.)

before the miracidium emerged. The miracidium then seeks out its appropriate snail, adapted to serve as the first intermediate host to the species of trematode concerned.

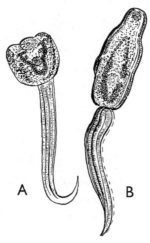

FIG. 8·10   Living cercarias of a trematode, × 53: A, In a state of contraction.—B, In a state of relaxation.

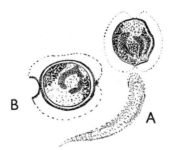

FIG. 8·11   The cercarias of Fig. 8·10 fixed to the coverslip of the microscopic preparation, × 53: A, The tail has been shed and the metacercaria enveloped within a jellylike mass which makes it stick to the coverslip.—B, Within this mass the metacercaria has produced a cyst wall. The process depicted here was accomplished in less than one minute.

Lodged within the body of that snail, the miracidium sheds its cilia and becomes metamorphosed into a saclike body, the *sporocyst.* This second-stage larva contains within its body certain groups of cells, the *germ balls,* which develop into third-stage larvas within the body of the sporocyst. In some trematodes these third-stage larvas do not differ materially from the second stage. In that case they are called *sporocysts of the second generation* or *sporocysts* ii. In others the third-stage larva is a cylindrical *redia,* characterized by a mouth, a pharynx, a short, blind-ended intestine, an annular swelling towards the anterior end, and a pair of blunt processes near the posterior end (Fig. 8·9). The third-stage larvas contain certain cells which develop into fourth-stage larvas, or *cercarias* (Fig. 8·10). The cercaria resembles an adult trematode by the possession of two suckers, a pharynx, a bifid intestine, and an excretory bladder. Nevertheless it is a larva and not an immature trematode, because it possesses an organ which is absent in the full-grown trematode, viz. a *tail*.

The cercarias leave the body of the first intermediate host, the snail, and move in water with their tail and their contractile body (Fig. 8·10). In the genus *Schistosoma* they penetrate the human body through the skin. In all other trematodes parasitizing man they seek out a second intermediate host, fish, crab, mollusc, a water plant, or parts of a plant accidentally immersed in water. Fixed within or on that substratum, the cercaria sheds its tail, thereby changing into an immature trematode or *metacercaria,* and becomes encased within a double cyst-wall (Fig. 8·11). Man becomes infected by ingesting the animal or vegetable substance containing metacercarias that have not been destroyed by heating or other culinary processes.

The general remarks on host-parasite relationship in helminths apply to the trematodes. In schistosomes, data are available that seem to warrant the conclusion that children are more heavily infected than adults, at least in intensely infected regions. From what is known about some nematodes and cestodes, this might justify the further conclusion that repeated infections stimulate the host's defense mechanism, enabling him in the course of time to prevent or suppress renewed infections with which he was unable to cope in childhood.

There can be no doubt that there are numerous asymptomatic carriers of small numbers of parasitic trematodes, even of highly pathogenic species. But a satisfactory answer cannot yet be given to the question whether it is by mere chance that they have avoided heavy infections, or whether their defense mechanism was actively engaged in bringing about this result. However, experiments with monkeys, exposed to repeated monthly infections with moderate quantities of cercarias of *Schistosoma mansoni* and *S. japonicum* which hardly affected their state of health,[1] finally brought about a state of tolerance which allowed the monkeys to sustain, without any apparent harm, an infection with cercarias in numbers sufficient to bring about the death of nonimmunized monkeys. The heavy infection did not even increase the number of parasites present in the body of the immunized monkeys. Accordingly, their state of immunity greatly resembled that of premunition as encountered in babesiosis (Chapter VII).

TREMATODES THAT OFTEN PARASITIZE MAN

(1) Sexes separate; eggs nonoperculate; cercarias, on leaving the snail, are ready to enter the human body ....*Schistosoma*

Hermaphrodites; eggs operculate; cercarias, on leaving the snail, encyst as metacercarias in or on various animals or plants ......(2)

(2) Eggs long, 80 μ or over; they leave the human body in a nonembryonated state ....(3)

Eggs short, 30–45 μ; they leave the human body in an embryonated state ....(6)

(3) Acetabulum situated at the posterior extremity ....*Gastrodiscoides*

Acetabulum situated some distance from the posterior extremity .(4)

(4) The lung is the principal habitat of the adult ....*Paragonimus*

The intestine or bile ducts are their principal habitat ....(5)

(5) The adults possess a circumoral disk surmounted with a number of spines; metacercarias encyst in fishes or molluscs

Echinostoma and *Euparyphium*

Circumoral disk absent; metacercarias encyst on plants

Fasciolopsis and *Fasciola*

(6) Genital sucker present in adults; testes and uterus situated posteriorly ....*Heterophyes* and *Metagonimus*

Genital sucker absent; either testes or uterus situated anteriorly .(7)

(7) Testes situated near acetabulum, the uterus in a posterior position

Dicrocoelium

Testes situated posteriorly, the uterus anteriorly

Opistorchis and *Clonorchis*

REFERENCES FOR CHAPTER VIII

1. H. VOGEL and W. MINNING. *Zentr. Bakteriol.*, Abt. I, On., 1949, 154: 118*–126*; *Z. Tropenmed. u. Parasitol.*, 1953, 4: 418–505.

CHAPTER IX

THE SCHISTOSOMES

The schistosomes have two characteristics which separate them from all other trematodes.

(1) The first characteristic is the place where the schistosomes lay their eggs. Other trematodes oviposit in places from which the eggs can leave the human body without encountering any impediment (intestine, biliary ducts, bronchioles). The female schistosome lays its eggs in the venules in the tissue of the wall of the bowel and the urinary bladder, and there are no natural channels for the eggs to leave the host. The pressure exercised by the blood and by

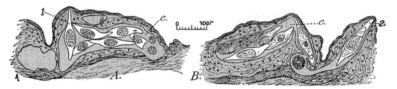

FIG. 9·1 Schistosome eggs in capillaries of mucosa (*c*). In (1) the egg is leaving the capillary; in (2) it has almost reached the lumen of the gut. (After Brumpt, 1922. Courtesy, Masson & Cie, Paris.)

the voluminous male,[1] the increased contractions of the musculature of the tissue irritated by the presence of the parasites, the propelling force of each freshly deposited egg, and the histolytic secretion produced by the females and the miracidia within the eggshell [2]—all these are said to combine in causing the eggs to be forced through the superficial capillaries (Fig. 9·1). In this way a number of eggs are discharged into the lumen of the bowel or the bladder, together with extravasated blood, but many more never reach their destination, since their span of life does not exceed three weeks.[3] Alive or dead, so long as they are passively wandering through the tissues, these eggs damage the tissue by provoking the appearance of the so-called miliary pseudoabscesses. This curiously inefficient way of disposing of their eggs undoubtedly is one of the main underlying causes of

the pathogenicity of the schistosomes. However, judging by Torrealba's [27] experiments (*v. infra*), it need not be an inefficient way,
provided the host does not interfere with the elimination of the
eggs by cellular reactions.

(2) The second characteristic separating the schistosomes from
other trematodes does not concern the pathogenic activity of the
parasite. It is related to the difficulty man finds in protecting himself
from the parasitic invasion. Infection with other trematodes can be
avoided by abstaining from raw fish, crabs, clams, water nuts, or
water cress. Against schistosomes nothing suffices short of giving up
swimimng, bathing, or wading in open water; for it is in this way
that man acquires his infection. The fact is that the cercarias of the
schistosomes, on leaving the snail, do not seek a second intermediate

Fig. 9·2   Coupled schistosomes; the slender female partly hidden within
the gynecophoral groove of the male. (After Brumpt, 1936. Courtesy,
Masson & Cie, Paris.)

host, like the other trematodes, but immediately enter the human
body by piercing its skin. In countries with a long, hot summer it is
obviously far more difficult to abstain from bathing or swimming in
the open than from certain flavorings of the diet. Field laborers
and washerwomen may find it altogether impossible to meet this
requirement.

As stated above, the schistosomes are of separate sex. Males and
females, each in their own way, have adapted themselves to a life
within very narrow blood vessels. A flat trematode does not fit into
a tube. Accordingly, the females are not flat but as round as roundworms, for which they might easily be taken if it were not for their
bifid intestine and their two suckers. The ceca (the branches of the
intestine) lie close together, and they even reunite posteriorly. All
organs are crowded together, or lying one behind the other. The

uterus is not convoluted as in other trematodes, but runs in a straight
course from its origin to its aperture. In other trematodes the uterus
contains innumerable eggs at any given moment; in schistosomes
no more than fifty or so.

The male has not lost the flatness characteristic of the trematodes,
but hides it by rolling itself into a cylindrical shape. In this way the
male takes the form of a tube with a not completely closed lumen,
the *gynecophoral canal* or *groove,* in which the young female finds
room (Figs. 9·2, 9·3). This canal serves the purpose of saving room,

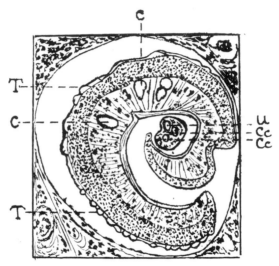

FIG. 9·3 Cross section through couple of *Schistosoma haematobium*
in tissue of portio vaginalis, × 100: *C, C,* Ceca of male worm.—*T,* Tubercles on integument of male worm.—*U,* Uterus of female worm.—
Ce, Ce, Ceca of female worm.

but it is of more importance than that. The young female cannot
grow to sexual maturity unless in close embrace with the male.
Conversely, the female occupying this position stimulates its partner
to undertake an expedition through various blood vessels, which
takes the couple to the organs where the female is to deposit its eggs.[4]

The sexual dimorphism here described is apparent in adults only.
Nevertheless, the sex of the future adult is already determined in the
miracidium. A snail infected with one single miracidium produces
numerous cercarias, which can infect many mice. But the schistosomes attaining maturity in these rodents are all males or all females.[5]

A number of schistosomes parasitize cattle, birds, or other verte-brates. But their cercarias are able to penetrate the skin of persons bathing in water in which the parasite is moving. The cercarias, on penetrating the human skin, find themselves in uncongenial sur-roundings and soon die, but they may occasionally get as far as the lungs.[6] This cercarial invasion does not cause much discomfort to a person experiencing it for the first time. Repeated exposure, how-ever, causes severe dermatitis and itching, known all over the world as *cercarial dermatitis* or *swimmer's itch*. It usually is associated with fresh water, but it has been observed at the seashore.[7]

Schistosomes habitually parasitizing man are the following.

SCHISTOSOMA HAEMATOBIUM

Schistosoma haematobium (Bilharz, 1852) Weinland, 1858, is the causative agent of *genitourinary bilharziasis (schistosomiasis)*, pro-duced by infection of the pelvic veins, particularly those of the bladder, occasionally those of the rectum.[8] Adult worms have been collected from *ectopic sites*,[9] i.e. beyond the portal and pulmonary circulation, viz. in the skin and the conjunctiva. In these habitats they may persist for many years.

S. haematobium is indigenous in many parts of the African con-tinent (that of South Africa is sometimes given a separate name, *S. capense*). The Sudan, Ethiopia, Liberia, and the Congo are im-portant foci, as well as the Upper Nile Valley. It is also prevalent in the islands off the coast of East Africa (Madagascar, Mauritius), in the Mediterranean Basin (including southern Portugal), the Near East, and Bombay Province (western India).

The male (Fig. 9·2, 9·3, 9·4) measures 10–15 × 0.8–1 mm. Its anterior extremity is cylindrical; beyond the acetabulum the body is flat, with the edges folded inwards in such a way as to form a deep groove, as described before. The oral sucker is small, the nearby acetabulum more than twice its size. Dorsal to the latter lies the excretory pore, and posterior to it the four or five testes and the genital aperture. At this level the intestinal tract splits into two ceca which reunite in the posterior third of the worm. The cuticle is finely tuberculated all over the body posterior to the acetabulum.

The female (Figs. 9·2, 9·4) is longer but much more slender than the male, measuring 15–20 mm in length and 0.2–0.3 mm in width. The fused ceca of the intestinal tract form a single serpentine, blindly

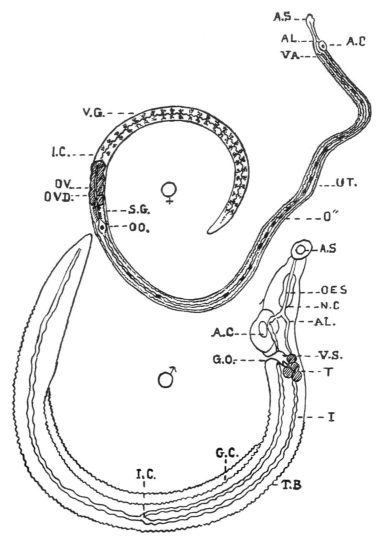

Fig. 9·4 *Schistosoma haematobium,* female (*above*), male (*below*) × 30: *A.S,* Oral sucker.—*AL,* Bifurcation of intestine.—*A.C,* Acetabulum.—*VA,* Vagina.—*UT,* Uterus.—*O'* and *O",* Eggs.—*OO,* Ootype.—*OVD,* Oviduct.—*OV,* Ovary.—*I.C,* Union of intestinal ceca.—*V.G,* Vitelline glands.—*S.G,* Shell gland.—*OES,* Esophagus.—*N.C,* Nerve center.—*V.S,* Seminal vesicle.—*T,* Testes.—*I,* Intestinal cecum.—*G.C,* Folded edge of male body.—*G.O,* Male genital opening. (After Manson-Bahr and Fairley, 1920. Courtesy, Publishers of *Parasitology,* Vol. 12, Cambridge, England.)

ending trunk in the posterior fourth of the body; the vitelline glands accompany this part of the intestine. The ovary is situated anteriorly to the place where the ceca fuse, in the posterior half of the body. The oviduct emerges at the rear of the ovary, then it turns cephalad, takes up the vitelline ducts, passes the ootype, and is continued in the form of the straight uterus, containing hardly more than 50 ova at a time. The cuticle of the anterior and posterior extremity is finely tuberculated.

The embryonated eggs (containing a miracidium) are usually found in the urine, occasionally in the feces. They are nonoperculate, and measure 120–160 × 40–60 μ. They have a brownish yellow shell, drawn out at one pole in the form of the so-called *terminal spine* (Fig. 9·5).

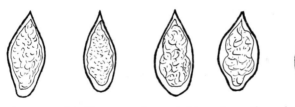

F𝐼G. 9·5   Eggs of *Schistosoma haematobium* from the urine of an inhabitant of Uganda. (After Schwetz, 1951. Courtesy, Publishers of *Annals of Tropical Medicine and Parasitology,* Liverpool.)

When the eggs are lying in water, the miracidium escapes through a rent in the shell and is propelled through the water by the cilia which cover its body (Fig. 9·10). In this state it survives for no longer than 36 hours. There is one milieu only wherein it can develop, namely, in the body of an appropriate fresh-water snail.

Here the miracidia develop into sporocysts of the first generation. They produce no redias, but a second generation of sporocysts, which invade the hepatopancreas and ovotestis and develop into greatly ramified bodies. Four to eight weeks after the infection of the snail the sporocysts II produce cercarias (Fig. 9·6). Their body measures 140–200 × 57–100 μ; their tail has a length of 175–250 μ and carries two terminal branches of 35–50 μ (*furcocercous cercaria*). The body possesses an oral sucker and an acetabulum, a bifid intestine, and initial stages of the excretory, nervous, and genital systems. Conspicuous are the *penetration glands* (Fig. 9·11), excreting a substance that dissolves tissues and functions at the time the cercarias penetrate into the human skin. They leave the snail's body, and move in water in search of the definitive host. If they cannot find one they die after one to three days.

In the whole region of the geographical distribution of *S. haematobium* there exist numerous species of snails that act as intermediate hosts, but in every single area there exists only one species, or at most a few closely related ones. In Africa, north of 11° N. lat. *S. haematobium* develops only in *Bulinus truncatus (contortus)*. South of that latitude *Bulinus africanus* is the intermediate host; in Mauritius it is *Bulinus forskalii*.[10]

When the cercarias penetrate into the human skin they shed their tail. Then they enter the venous circulation, and along this route they first reach the lung. Here they stay for several days and then

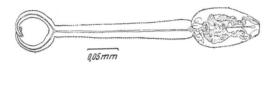

FIG. 9·6 Cercarias of *Schistosoma haematobium* (ABOVE) and *S. mansoni* (BELOW). (After Faust.)

proceed to the portal system in the liver, by way of the left heart and the general circulation through the mesenteric artery and the capillaries. In the liver they reach maturity. Two months or so after entering the definitive host's body they make their way to the permanent habitat mentioned above. Here oviposition takes place, and from that moment onward eggs may be expected to appear in the urine, where they are commonly found by examination of specimens mixed with blood and pus taken at the end of micturition.

Under natural conditions *S. haematobium* possesses one definitive host only: man; a monkey, *Cercocebus fuliginosus,* and some rodents are rare exceptions. Monkeys, hamsters, and hedgehogs have been experimentally infected. The worms grown in their body reach maturity and produce viable eggs as readily as in the human body.

In communities in Tanganyika, in which infection is heavy in the early years of life, Maclean et al.[11] found the highest rate of infection in the age group of 11–15 years. Where opportunities for infection were scarce, the highest rate of infection was found in the over-40 age group. However, it is not known whether this partial protection of advanced age groups, following numerous infections in youth, is due to an insufficient immunity or to a residual parasite population guarding against reinfection (premunition).

Apart from this protection, the response of the human organism to the parasites settled in the body becomes apparent by hypersensitivity and by serological reactions. The former is demonstrated by the reaction of the skin of a parasite carrier to intradermal injection of an extract of cercarias [12] or adult schistosomes. Serological reactions are the response of living cercarias to contact with the serum of a parasite carrier. This response consists in either the production of a voluminous precipitate around the cercarias, accompanied by the immobilization of these organisms, or the formation of a fine, close-fitting membrane around the cercarias, which does not impede their locomotion.[13]

Morphologically related to *S. haematobium* are the following species occasionally found parasitizing man.

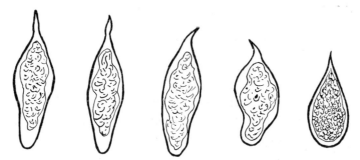

Fig. 9·7   Eggs of *Schistosoma intercalatum* from feces of an inhabitant of the environment of Stanleyville in the Congo. (After Schwetz, 1951. Courtesy, Publishers of *Annals of Tropical Medicine and Parasitology*, Liverpool.)

SCHISTOSOMA INTERCALATUM Fisher, 1934

This parasite differs from *S. haematobium* by the shape of its embryonated eggs (Fig. 9·7). They are of a larger size (140–240 × 50–80 μ) and more elongate; their terminal spines are often longer. Schwetz [14] found them often in human stools in the neighborhood of Stanleyville (Congo). They have also been recorded in southern Nigeria and the adjacent parts of Gabon.

Unlike *S. haematobium, S. intercalatum* is found only in the tissue of the rectum. It is regarded as a causative agent of rectal bilharziasis (schistosomiasis).

This parasite merits special attention because of man's immunological response to its presence. What has been said of *S. haematobium* applies to *S. intercalatum,* but much more markedly: in heavily infected areas of the Congo the rate of infection of inhabitants over 30 years of age was no more than 4 percent, against 80 percent in younger people.

Conversely, in less heavily infected areas the rate of infection of both age groups was about 30 percent.[15]

SCHISTOSOMA BOVIS (Sonsino, 1876) Blanchard, 1895

The eggs of this species fall almost outside the range of variation of *S. haematobium,* for they are 230–380 μ long and 70–90 μ wide. They show an equatorial bulge; one pole is pointed, the other rounded, but a true terminal spine is absent.

S. bovis inhabits the mesenteric-portal system of cattle, sheep, and goats in southern Europe, Africa, and Iraq. It is mentioned here because Raper [16] was infected with the parasite while bathing in Lake Victoria. From the 35th until the 43rd day after the infection he passed eggs in his stools that were accepted as belonging to this species. Another case of human infection was reported from the Transvaal, in an area where bovine infection was rife. In this case the infection was urinary, and recovery was not spontaneous; it had to be effected with the aid of drugs, which, however, cleared the case in an unusually short time—six days.[17]

SCHISTOSOMA MANSONI

Schistosoma mansoni Sambon, 1907, is the etiological agent of a chronic endemic disease characterized by symptoms referable to the intestinal tract (*intestinal bilharziasis*) and/or to other viscera (*hepatolienal fibrosis* or *Egyptian splenomegaly, Ayerza's disease*).[9] The principal habitat of the coupled sexes is the mesenteric venules draining the large bowel and the terminal segment of the ileum.

The geographical distribution corresponds in broad lines with that of *S. haematobium* as far as Africa is concerned. But *S. mansoni* is absent in Asia, except for Yemen and Israel. On the other hand it has an extensive area of distribution in many of the tropical regions of the Western Hemisphere, especially in northern Brazil and a few foci in Venezuela and in Surinam. In the West Indies it is endemic in a number of islands and in many regions in Puerto Rico. Out

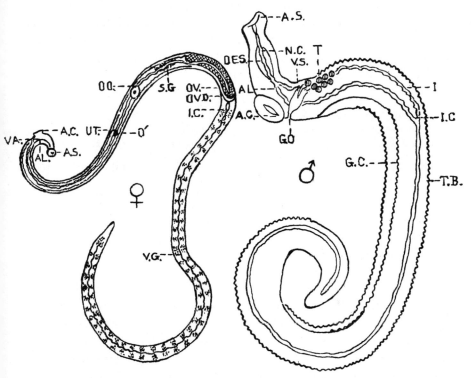

FIG. 9·8 *Schistosoma mansoni,* female *(left),* male *(right)* × 30. The lettering is the same as in Fig. 8·9. (After Manson-Bahr and Fairley, 1920. Courtesy, Publishers of *Parasitology,* Vol. 12, Cambridge, England.)

of an estimated incidence of 29.2 million of *S. mansoni* infections throughout the world, Stoll [45] reported 6.2 million in tropical America. The figures of the World Health Organization are similar.[46]

The male has a length of 6–10 mm, a little shorter than *S. haematobium*. It possesses more testes than the latter species: eight or nine; the intestinal ceca reunite in the anterior half of the body (Fig. 9·8); the cuticular tubercles are more conspicuous.

The female is also shorter, 7–14 mm; the vitelline glands are relatively longer than in *S. haematobium,* for they occupy the whole of the posterior half of the body; the ovary and ootype are situated in the anterior half; the uterus contains no more than two eggs at a time (Fig. 9·8).

The eggs of *S. mansoni* found in the feces are conspicuously different from those of *S. haematobium* found in the urine, although they are of almost the same size (152 × 64 μ on an average [18]), with the same color of shell. The terminal spine is replaced by a large *lateral spine* (Fig. 9·9). In Egypt 15 percent of the samples of schistosome eggs found in the urine are of the mansoni type.[19]

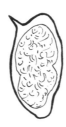

FIG. 9·9   Eggs of *Schistosoma mansoni* from feces of inhabitant of Elisabethville in the Congo. (After Schwetz, 1951. Courtesy, Publishers of *Annals of Tropical Medicine and Parasitology,* Liverpool.)

The development of *S. mansoni* in its intermediate host does not differ greatly from that of *S. haematobium:* the life of the miracidium in water lasts 40 hours or less [20]; sporocysts I are found in the vicinity of the intestine 3–4 days after the infection of the snail; sporocysts II settle in the hepatopancreas or the ovotestis during the second or third week; thirty days after the infection cercarias make their appearance; on the 33rd–34th day they commence to leave the snail's body (in the daytime only) and continue to do so for the next 65 days, to an approximate total of 172,000.[20] According to Faust and Hoffmann [18] the average length of the cercaria (body 214 μ, tail 225 μ, branches of the tail 104 μ) does not differ much from *S. haematobium* (Fig. 9·6). They survive in water for 24 hours.

There are other differences between the intermediate molluscan hosts of the two schistosomes: they belong to different genera. In Egypt the intermediate host of *S. mansoni* is *Biomphalaria alexandrina (Planorbis boissyi),* in West Africa *B. pfeifferi.* In South America as well as in Puerto Rico and other islands of the West

Indies *Australorbis glabratus* is the predominant molluscan host, with spotty distribution of *Tropicorbis centimetralis* and *A. nigricans* in Brazil and *A. antiguensis* in the West Indies. It is claimed [21] that the American snail is identical with the West African. If that is correct it would explain why the West African snail can be readily infected with *S. mansoni* of American origin, whereas the Egyptian snail cannot [22]; and why the American snail is highly susceptible to infection with *S. mansoni* of West African origin [23] but not to that of Egyptian origin.[24]

The cercarias, after penetrating into the skin of the definitive host, reach the lungs by way of the venous blood vessels 20 hours later. After four days they find themselves in the liver, where they arrived through the general circulation. Usually they do not stay there, but return to the lungs, from where they make one or more excursions through the whole circulation before settling definitively in the portal system about the 13th day. Between the 35th and the 40th day the parasites attain sexual maturity, and between the 37th and the 44th day pregnant females are found in the subterminal venules of the ileocolic and colic ramifications of the superior and the colic branches of the inferior mesenteric veins. Later (sometimes as late as the 70th day after the infection) eggs are passed in the feces of the host.[18] According to Lampe [20] the young worms may migrate directly from the lungs to the liver, through the diaphragm; in that case they reach the portal system some time after the eighth day.

In experimental infection of a human subject the first eggs were encountered in the stools on the 71st day after the cercarias had been deposited on the subject's skin.[29]

The paragraphs above describe the normal or usual course of events: the migration of the young parasites from the skin of the host to the lungs and from the lungs through the left heart and systemic circulation to the liver; then the migration from the liver to the subterminal venules of the tissue of the colon; finally the migration of the eggs from the venules in which they were deposited to the lumen of the colon.

Various circumstances can disturb this course. Two of them are brought about by natural events, the third by human interference. The natural events are (1) a prolonged stay of the parasite in the host and (2) the presence of an unusually large number of parasites. Human interference implies the administration of specific drugs.

(1) *S. mansoni* can survive in the human body for a considerable time; periods as long as 30 years are on record.[25] The longer their stay, the smaller the number of eggs that reach their normal destination (i.e. the lumen of the colon) and the larger the number prevented from reaching the lumen of the bowel by the thickening of the wall and the formation of scar tissue as a response to the parasitic invasion. As a result they are transported to the liver, and, rarely, to other organs such as the spinal cord and the brain. Wherever these aberrant eggs are deposited they may become centers of inflammation, necrosis, and fibrosis, particularly in the liver and the spleen. In mansoni infections, disturbances of this nature are much more common than in haematobium infections.

(2) In heavy mansoni infections, sexually mature worms may migrate to other organs, e.g. the urinary bladder, lungs, spleen, brain, uterus, oviduct, ovary, and testes. In these organs they continue the egg-laying process, and provoke characteristic pathological changes. Prolonged infiltration of the liver may eventually lead to hepatic cirrhosis.

Both events (1) and (2) may offer examples of schistosomes in *ectopic* situations [9] if organs beyond the portal and pulmonary circulation are involved.

(3) By the administration of a course of specific treatment (miracil D or tartar emetic) to mice infected with *S. mansoni,* Standen [26] brought about the following disturbances. First, egg production was diminished. Then the worms were damaged, especially the females. Coupled males and females were separated, because of depression of muscular tonus, and swept back to the liver by the venous blood stream. In this way they arrived in the liver in a stunned state. Eventually the cellular activity of the liver tissue would have destroyed them. But this activity needed time to be set into motion. Thus the worms were allowed a period of grace to recover from their lethargy, to couple again, and to return to the venules of the colon. This could, however, be prevented by a second course of treatment, following within 18 days of the first. This renewed attack on worms that had not yet recovered from the effect of the first course made them an easy prey to the cellular activity, now ready to cope with them effectively.

Like *S. haematobium, S. mansoni* can develop in certain laboratory animals—monkeys, dogs, cats, and several rodents. However, some of them are ill-adapted hosts. The guinea pig, for instance, allows the parasite to attain maturity in its body; but the fact that a number of male worms have grown an ovary shows that it is not a normal maturity.[27]

Whether *S. mansoni* must be regarded as a species with a wide range of hosts depends on the interpretation of reports on monkeys, rodents, and marsupials found infected with schistosomes that cannot be distinguished from *S. mansoni* by their morphological characteristics. If these reports are to be accepted at their face value *S. mansoni* is certainly polyxenous. On the island of St. Kitts in the Lesser Antilles the monkey *Cercopithecus sabaeus* has been repeatedly found infected with a worm undistinguishable from *S. mansoni*. The same applies to the Egyptian desert mouse *Gerbillus pyramidium* and the rice rat *Oryzomys*, rabbits, house rats, wild rats, and opossums in South America, wild rats in South Africa, baboons in East Africa, and wild rodents in the Congo. The fact that similar animals in the Congo were found infected with a schistosome which differed but slightly from the human parasite and still was given the rank of a separate species ("*S. rodentorum*" Schwetz, 1954) justifies some caution in accepting the others as true specimens of *S. mansoni*. For the present, the evidence available proves only that *S. mansoni* is one of a group of closely related species. Each species may be adapted to one host only, but together they inhabit a wide variety of hosts.

Torrealba and his colleagues,[27] trying to solve the problem of alternate hosts, shed fresh light on the relation of *S. mansoni* to its host. They exposed to infection a great variety of wild animals. Most of them proved inappropriate hosts, either because they did not become infected or because no eggs were passed in their feces. Of the latter class, some showed a limited infection, but the eggs remained in the liver and the pancreas and caused the formation of large fibrous granulomas. Others became heavily infected, but the eggs were retained in the intestinal submucosa, surrounded by pseudotubercles and pseudoabscesses, or carried to the liver, where they provoked intense inflammatory lesions, similar to those observed in man.

One species, the peccary (*Pecari tajacu torvus*), behaved in an entirely different manner. Its intestinal tissue did not put any serious obstacle to the eggs reaching the lumen of the gut. The eggs were not damaged in the submucosa by the numerous small cellular infiltrations that surrounded them, and they in their turn provoked no lesions on their passage through the mucosa. Thus, large numbers of eggs were evacuated in the feces. The almost normal aspect of the liver, the lungs, the pancreas, and the spleen, was evidence that only a few eggs were left to be carried to these organs. In short, the peccary proved to be a better host than many a human being, although this comparison is probably biased in favor of the peccary by disregarding the numerous asymptomatic human carriers.

The difference between the rate of infection in the younger and older age groups observed in haematobium infection and interpreted as evidence of immunity, or rather premunition developing with advancing years, is not apparent in mansoni infections. In Egypt [20] 69 percent of the children and 55 percent of the adults were harboring *S. haematobium,* but the rate of mansoni infection was practically the same in the two groups, 46 and 43 percent respectively.

Nevertheless, there are experiments by Vogel and by Vogel and Minning,[1] cited above in the Introduction to the trematodes, which prove that a state of immunity, perhaps of premunition, may develop in monkeys exposed to moderate infections with *S. mansoni* repeated at intervals of one month.

According to J. Schwetz,[28] a balanced relationship between the parasite and the human host may be brought about by conditions similar to those in the experiments cited above, viz. by a long series of light infections occurring at lengthy intervals. Heavy infections at short intervals have the reverse effect of causing the severe forms of mansonian bilharziasis which have given the parasite its sinister fame. Schwetz's assumption does not justify the application of Vogel's findings in monkeys to human conditions. Nevertheless, it raises a problem, the practical implications of which have been clearly stated by Sir Neil Hamilton Fairley as follows.[12]

> If an immunity to superinfection can develop in man, a drug which produces clinical rather than radical cure may be desirable in heavily infected areas. The ideal drug would reduce the schistosome load to a subclinical level in all three human species, leaving a reduced number of worms to maintain a state of immunity to superinfection.

Certain serological tests are used in the diagnosis of the infection. As such may be mentioned (1) the antigens prepared from cercarias, or adult worms, with which (a) an allergic reaction may be elicited by intradermal injection into the skin of the parasite carrier,[12] or (b) a complement fixation may be performed with the serum of the presumptive parasite carrier [12]; (2) the ability of the serum of the parasite carrier (a) to immobilize the miracidia,[30] (b) to cause a precipitate around the eggs,[31] (c) to cause the formation of a closely fitting membrane around the cercarias (see above, S. haematobium). However, the indications for treatment should be based on more definitive evidence, such as finding viable eggs in the feces or in a rectal snip.

SCHISTOSOMA JAPONICUM

Schistosoma japonicum Katsurada, 1904, is the causative agent of *Oriental bilharziasis* (in Japan called *katayama*), characterized in the advanced stages of the disease by great enlargement of the spleen and the liver and by ascites. It is considered the most pathogenic of the three schistosomes and the most resistant to specific treatment. However, the majority of the japonicum carriers apparently are not seriously inconvenienced by the presence of the parasite.[32] In this respect S. *japonicum* resembles the other two; for the same remark applies to S. *haematobium* and S. *mansoni*.[8]

Its usual habitat comprises the venules of the intestinal wall and the liver, with secondary invasion of the lungs and ectopic localization in organs beyond the portal and pulmonary circulation, including the brain and the skin.[9]

S. *japonicum* resembles S. *mansoni* in its biological aspects. At first this appeared to be confirmed by their genetic relationship, for they did interbreed. Cross-breeding experiments with S. *japonicum* as male partner proved entirely fertile, although the reciprocal cross did not. This, however, could not be accepted as evidence of a close genetic relationship; the "hybrid" generations were identical in type with the mother parent and bore as little likeness to the father as the copulating partners bore to each other. So it was asssumed that the japonicum spermatozoids did not fertilize the mansoni ova, but only stimulated them to parthenogenetic development.[33]

The geographical distribution embraces the whole of the Far East,

China, Japan, Formosa, the Philippine Islands, as far south as the island of Celebes in Indonesia.[34]

The male is slightly longer than *S. haematobium,* but less in width, viz. 12–20 × 0.50–0.55 mm; in number of testes, 6–7, it is intermediate between the other schistosomes; the absence of cuticular tubercles distinguishes it from both. The female is longer than *S. haematobium* and slightly wider, measuring on an average 26 × 3 mm. The position of the ovary and the vitelline glands and the number of eggs present in the uterus at any given moment (50 or so)

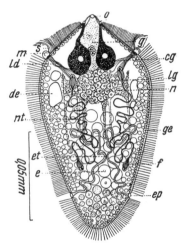

FIG. 9·10 Miracidium of *Schistosoma japonicum,* × 460: *o*, Gut opening.—*g*, Gut.—*cg*, Anterior penetration gland.—*lg*, Lateral gland or posterior penetration gland complex with duct (*ld*) and pores (*m*).—*n*, Nerve center.—*nt*, Nerve trunk.—*ge*, Germinal epithelium.—*e*, Germ cell.—*f*, Flame cell.—*et*, Excretory tubule.—*ep*, Excretory pore.—*s*, Sickle-shaped cilium.—*de*, Degenerating germ. (After Faust and Meleney, 1924. Courtesy, *American Journal of Hygiene,* Baltimore.)

closely correspond with *S. haematobium.* The eggs of *S. japonicum* are very different from those of the others, although they possess the same brownish shell. They are smaller, 82–90 × 70–80 μ, with a proportion of length to width of little over 1, against well over 2 in the other species, and there is neither a terminal nor a lateral spine. All that remains is a lateral excrescence in the shape of a little hook.

The egg-laying couples are found within the branches of the superior mesenteric vein that drain the small intestine. The eggs are deposited in the venules of the submucosa or mucosa of the bowel.[35] They are then extruded from the vessels into the perivascular tissues and finally discharged into the lumen of the gut.

The development of *S. japonicum* outside the mammalian host takes place in a number of snails: *Oncomelania nosophora* in Japan and some parts of China, *O. hupensis* in China, *O. formosana* in the island of Formosa, and *O. quadrasi* in the Philippine Islands.

The miracidium, measuring $97 \times 35\ \mu$ (Fig. 9·10), penetrates into the snail, and the sporocysts I develop within the superficial lymphatic cavities. Four weeks after the infection of the snail they have reached a length of $400\ \mu$, then they contain elongate sporocysts II. One week later the latter are discharged into the lymphatic cavities between hepatopancreas and ovotestis, by the rupturing of the mother sporocyst. Eight weeks after infection the second generation of sporocysts have grown to a size of $250 \times 40\ \mu$. They then contain immature cercarias, which grow to maturity in four days. Emission of cercarias begins about nine weeks after infection. Their body has a length of $100–160\ \mu$, their tail of $140–160\ \mu$, and the branches to their tail of $50–75\ \mu$ (Fig. 9·11).[35]

Eight or nine days after piercing the skin of the mammalian host, the young worms arrive in the intrahepatic portal spaces. Sixteen days later they reach maturity, after which the coupled sexes migrate to the intestinal venules. Five weeks after the cercarias enter the skin the females begin to lay their eggs.[9]

As was observed in mansoni infections, the pathological changes the eggs incite in the wall of the bowel (such as miliary abscesslike lesions and cicatricial thickening of the tissues) put an ever-growing obstacle to the normal evacuation of the eggs. As time goes on, an increasing number of eggs are carried into the periportal tissue of the liver, where they provoke the formations of lesions similar to those in the intestinal wall. Another similarity to mansoni infections is the migration of egg-laying worms into the lungs and even into regions beyond the portal and pulmonary circulation. There they continue oviposition, which in turn causes the appearance of similar lesions.

There can be no doubt that *S. japonicum* is a polyxenous species. As a parasite it occurs in a number of alternate hosts besides man. Among these are domestic animals such as dogs, cats, cattle, horses, pigs, sheep, and goats and animals living in close vicinity to man, such as rats. On Lake Lindu (island of Celebes) wild deer have also been found infected.[34]

However, it would be wrong to conclude from this that man is not the principal source of japonicum infection to his fellow man;

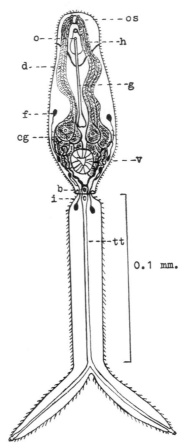

FIG. 9·11   Cercaria of *Schistosoma japonicum,* × 260: *os,* Oral sucker.— *o,* Oral pore.—*n,* Nerve center.—*cg,* Penetration glands.—*d,* Penetration gland ducts.—*f,* Flame cell.—*v,* Acetabulum.—*b,* Excretory bladder.—*i,* Excretory pore.—*g,* Gut.—*tt,* Caudal excretory tubules.—*h,* Head gland. (After Faust and Meleney, 1924. Courtesy, *American Journal of Hygiene,* Baltimore.)

he is the principal source for japonicum just as he is for other schistosomes—in some places, at least.

The fact is that *S. japonicum* does not behave the same everywhere. According to Hsü [36] this is due to the fact that *S. japonicum* is composed of four races that can be distinguished by the shape of their eggs. In this way Chinese, Japanese, Philippine, and Formosan races have been identified. The difference between the last two is conspicuous; the Formosan race can infect man, but it does not produce eggs in man's body; in the cycle of the Philippine race, on the other hand, man is the principal mammalian host. The Chinese and Japanese races occupy a position between the two extremes. They do not need man as a host, but if they enter his body they develop to maturity, i.e. they produce eggs. In Formosa the animal reservoir is no serious danger; in China and Japan, and to a lesser extent in the Philippines, the animal reservoir is a constant menace to man.

There is no immunological response of the human host to infection with S. *japonicum,* if a high rate of infection in children and a lower one in adults are regarded as a criterion for the presence of this response. Pesigan et al.[32] in the Philippines have shown that the rate of infection rises from 5 percent in children under six years of age to 60 percent in children aged 10–14; in the succeeding age groups it remains at about that level. Accordingly, the infection rate of children over 5 years of age is 43 percent and of adults 60 percent.

However, a closer investigation revealed that among the parasite carriers (1) 68 percent showed symptoms of diarrhea, dysentery, or anemia in children over 5 years, and 21 percent in adults; (2) the proportion showing an enlarged liver was 71 percent in children over 5 years of age and 25 percent in adults. Children of 10–14 bore the brunt of the infection, with 73 percent of the parasite carriers showing symptoms.

Thus, in japonicum infection of the Philippine Islands, the comparative frequency of adult and children's infection is proved to be an inadequate gauge of the immunological response of the human host. There actually was such a response, but it revealed its presence in the frequency of asymptomatic carriers.

If the number of parasites per carrier, the so-called "worm load," could have been assessed by the number of eggs discharged in the feces, the worm load in adults would probably have proved less than in children. As a matter of fact, the number of ova discharged by children aged 10–14 was more than twice as high as in adults. Unfortunately, the way schistosomes lay their eggs, and the manner in which the host responds to their presence, render it impossible to accept an evidence which would have been valid in other helminthic infections.

TREATMENT OF BILHARZIASIS
(SCHISTOSOMIASIS)

The principal specific drugs employed are tartar emetic, stibophen (Fuadin), Anthiomaline, and lucanthone hydrochloride (Miracil D, Nilodin). The first three compounds contain trivalent antimony, the fourth does not. The first is administered intravenously, the second and third intramuscularly, and the fourth orally. They are used in the treatment of the three varieties of bilharziasis. Japonicum infection is the most resistant, closely followed by mansoni infection, whereas haematobium infection is on the whole slightly less resistant to therapy.

TARTAR EMETIC (antimonyl tartrate of potassium). H. Most et al.[37] treated japonicum infections by administering the drug in the form of a freshly prepared solution of 0.5 percent in distilled water or saline containing 5 percent of glucose. The intravenous injection was performed with particular care to avoid spilling in the surrounding tissue, and with a speed not exceeding 4 ml of the solution per minute, preferably at mid-morning, or 2–3 hours after a light meal. Ambulatory patients remained recumbent for an hour after each injection.

The solution was injected on alternate days; first five injections of 8, 12, 16, 20 and 24 ml, then 10 injections of 28 ml, to a total of 360 ml (1.8 gm, 648 mg of antimony) over 29 days. Two more injections of 28 ml, prolonging the treatment to 33 days, to a total of 416 ml (2.08 gm, 750 mg of antimony), materially reduced the percentage of failures, i.e. the reappearance of eggs in the feces within three months following the course of treatment. This advantage was gained with hardly any increase in the incidence of the usual side effects.

Most's regimen is a carefully elaborated variant of Christopherson's protracted treatment, as distinct from Alves' and Blair's [37] rapid treatment, which consists of a course of 6–8 intravenous injections, administered within 2 days, of a total of 12 mg of antimonyl tartrate of sodium per kg of body weight. Although Most et al. were treating japonicum infections, their regimen may be expected to be successful in the other forms of bilharziasis that are generally considered to be less resistant to therapy.

Adults with a body weight under 50 kg are given proportionately smaller doses. In children under 14 the maximal single dose is 10 mg of the salt multiplied by the age in years.

Side effects in order of frequency are arthralgia, cough, nausea and vomiting, conjunctivitis. Those requiring interruption of the treatment are serious circulatory disturbances, high fever, and persistent vomiting. Contraindications to therapy are cachexia, myocardial, hepatic, and renal dysfunction and pulmonary diseases. Acute infectious diseases frequently require interruption of treatment.

STIBOPHEN (Fuadin, Neoantimosan), sodium antimony pyrocatechol disulfonate, is supplied commercially in 5-ml ampoules of 6.3 percent solution, 1 ml containing 8.5 mg of antimony. The following dosage is recommended: [38]

(a) *Adults* weighing over 50 kg (110 lb) are given a total of 80–100 ml (680–850 mg of antimony) as follows:

First dose (to test sensitivity to drug) is 1.5 ml intramuscularly in buttock, followed by 5 ml daily for two consecutive days. Thereafter 5 ml is administered three times a week, until 80 to 100 ml is completed. Women are given a total dosage of 70 to 80 ml.

(b) In *children* the same regimen is followed, except that the daily dose varies from 3 to 4 ml, depending upon the child's age, and the total dosage is a little less than 1 ml per lb (0.453 kg) of body weight; e.g. a child weighing 60 lb (27 kg) is given approximately a total dosage of 50 to 55 ml.

In animal experiments stibophen (Fuadin) is less toxic than tartar emetic. Side effects, in order of frequency, are nausea and vomiting, arthralgia, conjunctivitis, and albuminuria. In other words, nausea and vomiting are the most distressing side effects in Fuadin treatment, and arthralgia in tartar emetic treatment.

ANTHIOMALINE, lithium-antimony-thiomalate, in animal experiments is slightly more toxic than tartar emetic and considerably more toxic than stibophen (Fuadin). It is available in ampoules containing a 6 percent solution, with 9.6 mg of antimony per ml. It is administered intramuscularly. Joyeux and Sicé [39] recommend the following regimen: an injection of 1 and 2 ml on the first and second day respectively, followed by daily injections of 5 ml for a period of

10 to 18 days, to a total of 53–93 ml (509–893 mg of antimony). Other authors [40] give no more than 4 ml in a single dose, to a total of 65 ml.

The latest addition to antimony-containing drugs in the treatment of bilharziasis is Friedheim's "TWSb" (α, α-dimercapto-potassium succinate of antimony). It is allegedly less toxic than the others, and appears to have yielded satisfactory results, at least in haematobium bilharziasis.[43] It is administered intravenously or intramuscularly, dissolved just before use in 10–20 ml of pyrogen-free sterile distilled water, corresponding to a total dosage of 1–2 gm of the drug and divided equally into 4–5 daily injections.

LUCANTHONE HYDROCHLORIDE (Miracil D, Nilodin, Miracil R.P.), 1-diethylamino-4-methyl-thioxyxanthone-hydrochloride, is available in tablets of 200 mg, to be taken orally.

In southeastern African haematobium infections Alves [41] recommends a total dosage of 60 mg per kg of bodyweight over 3 consecutive days. He reports a cure rate of 80–90 percent in children and adolescents, after 6 months of observation. In a series of 160 children with S. mansoni infection, Shookhoff [44] reports a cure rate of over 90 percent on an average dosage of 15 mg/kg daily for 7 days. His follow-up period ranged from 1–2 months to more than a year. Nausea and vomiting were frequently encountered but were not troublesome enough to interrupt the treatment.

Others, treating haematobium and mansoni infections, feel the need of larger total doses (100–200 mg per kg) extending over longer periods (up to 12 days), and the results reported are less satisfactory. As was to be expected, mansoni infections are more resistant than haematobium infections. The West African mansoni is less resistant than the Egyptian,[42] an interesting observation in case the American strain should likewise prove less resistant.

The side effects—nausea, vertigo, insomnia, depression, disorientation—are more marked in adolescents than in children; they are said to pass within a week. In Egypt, however, they appear to be more marked.[41] The skin discoloration following the use of this dye varies with different individuals and lasts for several weeks or more.

It should be emphasized that the usefulness of lucanthone hydrochloride in the treatment of bilharziasis has not yet been fully explored.

REFERENCES FOR CHAPTER IX

1. E. BRUMPT. *Précis de parasitologie,* Paris, 1949, Masson & Cie, p. 656.
2. C. H. BARLOW. *J. Parasitol.,* 1949, 35: 205–207.
3. H. VOGEL. *Deut. Tropenmed. Z.,* 1942, 46: 81–91.
4. O. D. STANDEN. *Ann. Trop. Med. Parasitol.,* 1953, 47: 139–145.
5. H. VOGEL. *Zentr. Bakteriol.,* Abt. I, Or., 1941, 148: 29–35.
6. L. OLIEVER. *J. Parasitol.,* 1953, 39: 237–246.
7. H. W. STUNKARD and M. HINCHCLIFFE. *J. Parasitol.,* 1952, 38: 248–265.
8. PH. MANSON-BAHR. *Tropical Medicine,* London, 1957, pp. 702, 714, 721, 729.
9. E. C. FAUST. *Am. J. Trop. Med.,* 1948, 28: 175–199.
10. T. M. AMBERSON and E. SCHWARZ. *Trans. Roy. Soc. Trop. Med. Hyg.,* 1953, 47: 451–502.
11. G. MACLEAN, G. WEBBE, and A. S. MSANGI. *E. African Med. J.,* 1958, 35: 7–22.
12. N. HAMILTON FAIRLEY. *Trans. Roy. Soc. Trop. Med. Hyg.,* 1951, 45: 279–303.
13. H. VOGEL and W. MINNING. *Zentr. Bakteriol.,* Abt. I, Or., 1949, 153: 91–105.
14. J. SCHWETZ. *Ann. Trop. Med. Parasitol.,* 1951, 45: 92–98.
15. A. C. FISHER. *Trans. Roy. Soc. Trop. Med. Hyg.,* 1934, 28: 277–306.
16. A. B. RAPER. *Trop. Diseases Bull.,* 1951, 48: 1010–1011.
17. C. A. KISNER, N. STOFFBERG, and B. DE MEILLON. *S. African Med. J.,* 1953, 27: 357–358.
18. E. C. FAUST and W. A. HOFFMANN. *Puerto Rico J. Public Health,* 1934, 9: 228–282; 10: 1–47.
19. J. A. SCOTT. *Am. J. Hyg.,* 1937, 25: 566–614.
20. P. H. J. LAMPE. *Proc. Roy. Soc. Med.,* 1927, 20: 56–62.
21. W. L. PARAENSE. *Trop. Diseases Bull.,* 1958, 55: 1134.
22. V. S. FILES and E. B. CRAM. *J. Parasitol.,* 1949, 35: 555–560.
23. H. VOGEL. *Trop. Diseases Bull.,* 1942, 39: 563.
24. V. S. FILES. *Parasitology,* 1951, 41: 264–269.
25. T. P. ALMY and J. G. M. HARPER. *J. Am. Med. Assoc.,* 1944, 126: 703–705.
26. O. D. STANDEN. *Ann. Trop. Med. Parasitol.,* 1953, 47: 26–34; *Trans. Roy. Soc. Trop. Med. Hyg.,* 1955, 49: 416–423.
27. J. F. TORREALBA, J. V. SCORZA, and B. C. DAGERT. *Trans. Roy. Soc. Trop. Med. Hyg.,* 1958, 52: 565–569.
28. J. SCHWETZ. *Bull. Soc. Path. exot.,* 1956, 49: 52–56.
29. C. H. BARLOW and H. E. MELENEY. *Am. J. Trop. Med.,* 1949, 29: 74–88.
30. L. B. SENTERFIT. *Proc. Soc. Exptl. Biol. Med.,* 1953, 84: 5–7.
31. J. OLIVER-GONZÁLEZ. *J. Infectious Diseases,* 1954, 95: 86–61.
32. T. P. PESIGAN, M. FAROOG, N. G. HAIRSTON, J. J. JAUREQUI, E. G. GARCIA, A. T. and B. C. SANDOS, and A. A. BESA. *Bull. World Health Organization,* 1958, 18: 345–455.
33. H. VOGEL. *Zentr. Bakteriol.,* Abt. I, Or., 1942, 149: 319–333.
34. E. C. FAUST and C. BONNE. *J. Parasitol.,* 1948, 34: 124–131.
35. E. C. FAUST and H. E. MELENEY. *Am. J. Hyg.,* Monogr. Ser., No. 3, 1924, 339 pp.
36. H. F. and S. Y. L. HSÜ. *Am. J. Trop. Med. Hyg.,* 1958, 7: 125–134.
37. H. MOST, C. A. KANE, P. H. LAVIETES, L. BLUM, B. KATZIN, J. M. HAYMAN, JR., E. F. SCHROEDER, and A. BEHM. *Am. J. Trop. Med.,* 1950, 30: 239–299.
38. M. M. STERMAN. Unpublished data.

39. CH. JOYEUX and A. SICÉ. *Précis de médecine des pays chauds,* Paris, 1950, pp. 297–300.
40. PH. MANSON-BAHR. *Tropical Medicine,* London, 1957, pp. 713–719.
41. W. ALVES. *Bull. World Health Organization,* 1958, 18: 1109–1111.
42. E. G. NAUCK. *Lehrbuch der Tropenkrankheiten,* Stuttgart, 1956, pp. 59–62.
43. R. J. PITCHFORD and W. O. HARRISON. *S. African Med. J.,* 1958, 32: 966–967.
44. H. B. SHOOKHOFF. Unpublished data, 1960.
45. N. R. STOLL. *J. Parasitol.,* 1947, 33: 1–18.
46. *Chronicles World Health Organization,* 1959, 13: 3–19.
47. F. S. BARBOSA. *15th Internat. Congr. Zool.,* London, 1958, 15: 691–693.

CHAPTER X

TREMATODES WITH LARGE NONEMBRYONATED EGGS

This group, characterized by the host passing nonembryonated eggs in his feces, of a length of 80 μ or over, includes four families. Two of them are represented here by one species only, for which reason the section describing them bears their name; the two others are represented by two species, for which reason the respective section bears the name of the family.

PARAGONIMUS WESTERMANI

Paragonimus westermani (Kerbert, 1878) Braun, 1899 (family of Troglotrematidae), is the causative agent of the so-called *endemic hemoptysis* of parts of eastern Asia. Its principal habitat is the lung, where it is found in cavities that communicate with the bronchioles; in that site they often occur in pairs.[1] Autopsies in man have revealed their presence in numerous other organs. In living patients they have been detected in subcutaneous nodules, in the brain and, less often, in the spinal cord.

Besides man, the species parasitizes a number of alternate hosts, such as larger and smaller feline and canine carnivora (including the domestic dog and cat), pigs, and rats. As a consequence, human infection is not dependent on the presence of infected man. It is claimed that not all *P. westermani* are human parasites, but only those belonging to the subspecies *P. ringeri* Cobbold, 1880, and *P. kellicotti* Ward, 1908. However, this makes no difference, as these are also polyxenous.

The existence of numerous alternate hosts obviously increases the chances of human infection. This condition, however, is counter-balanced by the fact that the cercarias leaving the molluscan host do not pierce the human skin, as is the habit of the schistosome cercarias, but enter into the body of certain species of edible crabs.

183

Whatever may be the number of alternate hosts surrounding him, man will not become infected (or rarely so) unless he consumes uncooked crabs.

The adult has the form of a coffee bean (without a groove); it measures 7.5–12 mm in length, 4–6 mm in width, and 3.5–5 mm in thickness. When it is alive it is reddish brown; in a preserved state it has a grayish color, except for the vitelline glands, which show as two brownish lateral fields through the transparent, convex dorsal surface. These glands extend from the anterior to the posterior

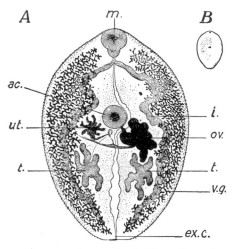

Fig. 10·1   *Paragonimus westermani: A,* Ventral surface × 5½.—*i,* Cecum.—*ov,* Ovary.—*t,* Testis.—*vg,* Vitelline gland.—*ex.c,* Excretory pore, opening of excretory bladder.—*ut,* Uterus.—*ac,* Acetabulum.—*m,* Oral sucker.—*B,* The same, natural size. (After Brumpt, 1922. Courtesy, Masson & Cie, Paris.)

extremity. The suckers are situated on the flat, ventral surface; the oral sucker in a subterminal position, the acetabulum in the middle, slightly anterior to the equator (Fig. 10·1). The genital atrium occupies a position unusual in trematodes, viz., behind the acetabulum, slightly to the right of the midline. The cuticle is covered with minute scales; their shape is characteristic for each of the subspecies. There are two sinuous intestinal ceca, their blind ends almost touching the posterior margin. The excretory bladder extends from the pharynx to the excretory pore, with slight convolutions over the posterior two-fifths of its length. The lobed ovary lies on the left side, posterior to the acetabulum; the uterus, a tightly coiled rosette, occupies a position symmetrical to the ovary. The two testes lie symmetrically side by side in the posterior half of the body; they carry ample lobes.

The eggs (Fig. 8·6:*f*) are nonembryonated when they leave the human body in the sputum (and usually in the feces as the sputum is swallowed). They are filled with vitelline cells surrounding a clear space that represents the fertilized egg cell. The eggs measure 96–112 × 47–61 μ. The yellowish shell bears a flat operculum at one pole; at the opposite pole it is slightly thickened. In water the egg cell develops into a miracidium in the course of three to four weeks, provided conditions as to temperature and aeration are suitable.

The miracidium, emerging from the egg by pushing open the lid, has a size of 81–99 × 36–54 μ.[2] In an appropriate snail (Fig. 10·2:1,

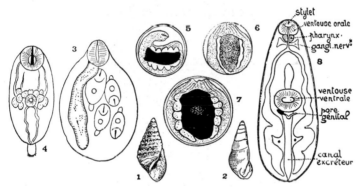

FIG. 10·2 *Paragonimus westermani,* life cycle: 1. *Melania oblique-granosa* and 2. *M. libertina,* molluscan hosts, × ⅔.—3. Redia, × 53.—4. Cercaria, × 150.—5 and 7. Metacercarias, × 53.—6. Young metacercaria, × 53.—8. Free metacercaria: *ventouse orale,* Oral sucker.—*gangl. nerv,* Nerve center.—*ventouse ventrale,* Acetabulum. (After Brumpt, 1936. Courtesy, Masson & Cie, Paris.)

2), in eastern Asia, a species of the genus *Melania* (*Semisulcospira*), the miracidium develops into a sporocyst. The sporocyst produces redias (Fig. 10·2:3) which themselves produce a second generation of redias. The second generation produces cercarias, characterized by the extremely short, knob-shaped tail of 15 × 12 μ (Fig. 10·2:4). They have an average size of 196 × 79 μ and possess the usual suckers, penetration glands, an excretion bladder, and an oral stylet.[3]

The cercarias enter the body of various species of crabs *Potamon dehaani, Sesarma dehaani* and *Eriocheir japonica* (Fig. 10·3) or crayfish (*Astacus japonicus*) and others. As metacercarias (Fig. 10·2: 5–8) they are lodged in various organs, such as the muscles of the legs and the mesothorax, and on the heart. In Formosa [4] the majority of the infected crabs carry the metacercarias in the blood vessels running through the upper median line of the lobes of the gills. There they can be seen, even with the naked eye, as milk-white globules.

The mammalian host becomes infected by eating the crabs or crayfish. The metacercarias are set free in the lumen of the host's bowel; they pierce the gut wall and thus enter the peritoneal cavity, where they are found as early as four hours after the infecting meal. From there they make their way, through the diaphragm, to the pleural cavity, where they arrive four days later. After two weeks they invade the lungs, and there they reach sexual maturity six weeks after entering the body of the definitive host.

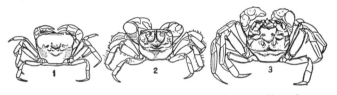

FIG. 10·3   *Paragonimus westermani,* second intermediate hosts, × ⅓: 1. *Potamon dehaani.*—2. *Sesarma dehaani.*—3. *Eriocheir japonica.* (After Brumpt, 1936. Courtesy, Masson & Cie, Paris.)

In the capital of Formosa *P. westermani* has spread among the urban population by the custom, introduced by immigrants from the mainland, of consuming "drunken crab," a delicacy prepared by immersing live crabs in a mixture of rice wine, soy sauce, and various spices.[4] In some parts of Japan no crabs are eaten uncooked. Nevertheless, man becomes infected because the culinary preparation of the crabs requires their being chopped up with a chopping knife. The metacercarias tend to stick to the chopping knife (which is also used for mincing other foodstuffs) or to the fingers of the cook who tries to clean it. In both instances ingestion of the metacercarias becomes almost a certainty.[5]

P. westermani mainly occurs in eastern Asia, notably in Japan, Korea, and Formosa. The rural population in the northern parts of Formosa has been found 73 percent infected. In some areas of Korea human infection is as high as 82 percent, associated with a canine infection of 48 percent.[6] Furthermore, isolated cases have been reported from other countries like India, Australia,[7] North America, Venezuela, Mexico, Peru, and Ecuador.

In some parts of Africa (Cameroons) human infection is far from rare. Among 1100 persons examined, 101 carried the parasite. They were mostly women who were in the habit of eating raw crabs to stimulate fertility.[8] However, African findings must be interpreted with caution because of the existence of a human parasite, *Poikilorchis congolensis,*[9] in retroauricular cysts or abscesses. It lays eggs that greatly resemble those of *P. westermani,* although they are smaller (60–68 × 38–41 μ). So far they have not been found in the lungs, but some day they may be.

Troglotrema (Nanophyetus) salmincola (Chapin, 1926) Wittenberg, 1932, is a very small (about 1 × 0.4 mm) representative of the same family, which, however, lays nonembryonated eggs that are not much smaller than those of *P. westermani* (64–80 × 34–50 μ). Although the parasite (or a very close relative) has been found parasitizing the human intestine in southwestern Siberia,[10] the reason why it is mentioned here is its apparently incomprehensible behavior in dogs and other small carnivora of the western United States and Canada. The second intermediate hosts, in which the parasites live as metacercarias, are fresh water fishes, salmon and trout. Dogs eating infected fish fall ill with an acute intestinal disease ("salmon poisoning") which kills them after seven to ten days. However, those that recover have developed an absolute immunity against the disease.

There was nothing astonishing in trematodes killing their host. But a trematode causing a hyperacute disease, leaving a solid immunity in the survivor, was something altogether new and unexpected, not only in trematodes but in any animal parasitizing man.

The explanation was given by Shope in 1941.[11] The disease is caused by a nonfiltrable pathogenic organism (known, since 1954, as *Neorickettsia helmintheca*).[11a] It is this organism that is the cause of the deadly disease, and it is against this organism that the survivors develop an absolute immunity. The trematode parasite is not directly responsible for either. Indirectly, however, it is; for salmon poisoning is acquired only by consuming fish infected with metacercarias, because the pathogenic agent is lodged within this stage of development of the parasite. It has not been identified in the redias and cercarias within the molluscan host.

Treatment of Paragonimiasis. A combined treatment with emetine hydrochloride and prontosil has been recommended [12] to relieve the symptoms, and to damage or kill the parasites in the lungs. The total dose for adults, administered over 7–17 days, consists of (1) emetine hydrochloride, 12.0–23.5 ml of a 4 percent solution (55–67 mg emetine hydrochloride daily) and (2) prontosil, 60–165 ml of a 2.5 percent solution (214–242 mg prontosil daily) given intramuscularly.

Satisfactory results are also reported from the use of chloroquine, orally, 3–7 tablets daily (0.5–1.0 gm of the base), over a period lasting for several months, to a total of 1.10–2.63 gm of the base per kg of body weight.[13]

THE FASCIOLID FAMILY

The two species of this family parasitizing man can be distinguished by their anterior extremity, which is rounded in *Fasciolopsis,* whereas in *Fasciola* it shows a distinct conical projection.

FASCIOLOPSIS BUSKI

Fasciolopsis buski (Lankester, 1857) Odhner, 1902, inhabits the duodenum and jejunum of man and various alternate hosts, notably pigs. It may be responsible for a disease, *fasciolopsiasis,* which is characterized by intestinal disorder and, in its more advanced stages, by edema and ascites.

The living adult parasite has a rosy hue and is fleshy in appearance. It measures 20–75 mm in length, 8–20 mm in width, and 0.5–0.7 mm in thickness. The anterior extremity tapers slightly. The ventral side carries minute spines, standing close together on the anterior half, and farther apart on the posterior half. The oral sucker has a subterminal position, its diameter is 0.5 mm. The nearby acetabulum has the appearance of a pit measuring 2–3 mm in diameter; just in front of it lies the genital atrium. Immediately behind the pharynx lies the bifurcation of the intestine; the wavy ceca almost reach the posterior extremity. The testes, in the posterior half of the body, are composed of a number of widely ramified branches. The cirrus pouch is of an unusual length, as it reaches a

point halfway the distance between the shell gland and the acetabulum. The ovary is situated in the equator to the right of the shell
gland. The uterus runs in wide convolutions from the shell gland
to the genital atrium. The vitelline glands occupy a lateral position,
and extend from the level of the acetabulum to the posterior extremity of the ceca (Fig. 10·4).

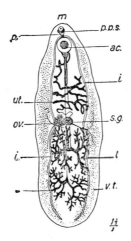

FIG. 10·4 *Fasciolopsis buski,* × 2: *m,* Oral sucker.—*p,* Pharynx.—*ac,*
Acetabulum.—*i,* Intestinal cecum.—*sg,* Shell gland.—*t,* Testis.—*vt,* Vitel-
line gland.—*ov,* Ovary.—*ut,* Uterus. (After Brumpt, 1936. Courtesy,
Masson & Cie, Paris.)

The eggs are voided in the feces in a nonembryonated state. They
are ovoid (Fig. 10·9) or almost spherical in shape, and measure 130–
140 × 80–85 μ. The shell is brownish; it is closed by an inconspicuous operculum.[14] According to Vogel [15] one worm daily produces 21 to 28 thousand eggs, equivalent to 140–280 eggs per 1 gm
of normal feces.

At a temperature of 27°–29° C the miracidium develops within
the egg shell in two to three weeks. The free miracidium measures
108 by 33 μ. It can survive in water for 6 to 9 hours, even up to
52 hours in cool weather.

In China the molluscan host is represented by the snails *Hippeutis
cantori* and *Segmentina hemisphaerula.* The sporocyst retains the
motility and organization of the miracidium from which it developed, so long as it is not yet filled with redias (Fig. 10·5:1, 2). It
grows to a size of 400 × 100 μ or so, reached after 9–10 days. Then

the redias of the first generation (mother redias) leave the body of the sporocyst and reach the ovotestis or the liver within two to three days. There they grow to a size of 600–800 × 100–200 μ (Fig. 10·5:3, 5). Thirteen days after the infection of the snail, redias of the second generation (daughter redias) begin to make their appearance within the mother redias. The daughter redias grow to a still larger size, up to nearly 3 mm (Fig. 10·5:6). After 25–30 days, cercarias commence to leave the daughter redias. They have a size of 195 × 145 μ,

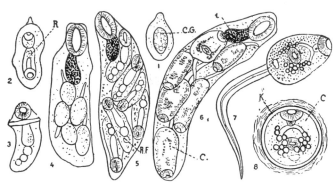

Fig. 10·5   *Fasciolopsis buski,* life cycle: 1, 2. Younger and older sporocysts: *cg,* Germinal mass.—*R,* Redia.—3, 5. Redias with daughter redias. —4, 6. Redias with cercarias: *i,* Intestine of redia.—7. Free cercaria.— 8. Metacercaria (*c*) within cyst wall (*K*). (After Brumpt, 1922. Courtesy, Masson & Cie, Paris.)

with a tail of 498 × 57 μ (Fig. 10·5:7); their skin carries minute spines. By their marked contractility they assume a great variety of shapes (Fig. 8·10).

When the cercaria has left the body of the snail and is moving within the water surrounding the molluscan host, it attaches itself to some water plant and becomes a metacercaria, by shedding its tail and surrounding itself with a cyst wall (Fig. 8·11). This occurs seven weeks after the miracidium penetrates into the snail's body.

The metacercaria has the shape of a disk about 200 μ in diameter. It has a double wall (Fig. 8·11; Fig. 10·5:8). The outer wall with which it is attached to the plant can be broken without difficulty, but the inner wall is very strong. The metacercarias are often attached to the seed pods of the water caltrop (*Trapa natans*), a fruit which is eaten as a delicacy. It is the custom, before eating the fruit, to remove the skin with the teeth and lips. This process suffices to break the outer wall and to detach the metacercarias, which thus gain access to the mouth. But no degree of mastication will succeed in breaking the inner wall, which thus remains available for the protection of the metacerceria when it passes the gastric juice on its way to the duodenum or jejunum.

In certain parts of China this plant is grown in ponds that are fertilized by fresh night soil. The luxuriant vegetation which develops as a consequence offers ideal conditions for the breeding of the molluscan host and its infection with *F. buski,* for the subsequent infection of the water caltrop and, finally, for the infection of man.[14]

Arrived at its destination the metacercaria attaches itself to the duodenal or jejunal mucosa of the mammalian host. After one to three months, eggs are passed in the stools.

F. buski is known as a parasite of man and pigs in a number of countries in southern and eastern Asia. In the Chinese province of Chekiang (to the south of Shanghai) there are villages with a rate of human infection of 80 to 100 percent.[14] However, not all infected persons are ill with fasciolopsiasis. According to Sweet[16] a little under one-half of them are subclinical carriers. Similar conditions were found in the Indian province of Bihar; among 231 infected persons, 82 were subclinical carriers.[17] On the mainland of China man himself is the principal reservoir; pigs are of minor importance; on Formosa the reverse condition prevails.[14]

TREATMENT OF FASCIOLOPSIASIS. This treatment aims at expelling the parasite from the human bowel. Various vermifuges have been used with success. Specially recommended, however, is hexylresorcinol in doses of 0.4 gm for children, and of 1 gm for persons over 12 years of age.[12a]

FASCIOLA HEPATICA

Fasciola hepatica Linnaeus, 1758, a cosmopolitan, polyxenous liver fluke inhabits the bile ducts of the liver of various herbivorous mammals. In one of its hosts, sheep, it is responsible for a disease known as sheep liver rot, but its pathogenic activity is by no means limited to that host.

F. hepatica much resembles *F. buski.* It is somewhat smaller, usually 28–32 × 8–13 mm; but this difference in size is hardly reliable. The eggs are practically of the same size (130–150 × 70–90 μ) and shape (Fig. 10·9). Nevertheless, *F. hepatica* can be distinguished from *F. buski* by the following characteristics: (1) the presence of the *cephalic cone,* the conically shaped anterior extremity that can be easily distinguished from the rest of the body (Figs. 10·6, 10·8); (2) the ramifications of the intestinal ceca (Fig. 10·7); (3) the position of the ovary and the shell gland within the anterior third of the body, and that of the testes within the posterior two-thirds; (4) the relatively short cirrus pouch (Fig. 10·8).

In man the adult worm is believed to live for at least 5 years, but much longer periods are on record, up to 13 years.

FIG. 10·6 *Fasciola hepat-ica,* natural size. (After Leuckart.)

FIG. 10·7 *Fasciola hepatica,* in-testinal ceca with ramifications. (After Leuckart.)

The eggs are nonembryonated when they are passed in the feces of the host. While the eggs are lying in water, a miracidium develops within the egg shell (Fig. 8·7). At a temperature of 22–25° C the miracidium emerges after a fortnight (Fig. 8·8; Fig. 10·11), and penetrates into the body of the first intermediate host. In Europe snails of the genus *Lymnaea (Galba)* are known as such, e.g. *L. truncatula* (Fig. 10·10) and *L. stagnalis,* but every region in the huge area of distribution of *F. hepatica* has its own molluscan host.

Within the snail the miracidium develops into a sporocyst (Fig. 10·12:*c*). Successively are born a second generation of sporocysts and one or two generations of redias (Fig. 8·9; Fig. 10·12:*d*). The redias, in their turn, produce the cercarias (Fig. 8·10; Fig. 10·12:*e*). This development is accomplished within 5–14 weeks.

As in *F. buski,* the cercarias attach themselves to plants and there change into encysted metacercarias (Fig. 8·11). These plants may be true water plants like *Nasturtium officinale,* the water cress, which is consumed by man as a delicacy. In many countries it has been signalized as the principal source of human infection. In France, however, it is dangerous only in its wild state, since the conditions under which it is cultivated by the French rarely permit infection with metacercarias.[18] Other plants on which the metacercarias encyst are blades of grass on temporarily flooded meadows. When the grass is dried, metacercarias have been recovered alive attached to sprigs of hay stacked for over a year.[19] Even apples floating in water have been reported as a source of infection.[20] As time goes on, the encysted metacercarias may become detached from their vegetable substratum.

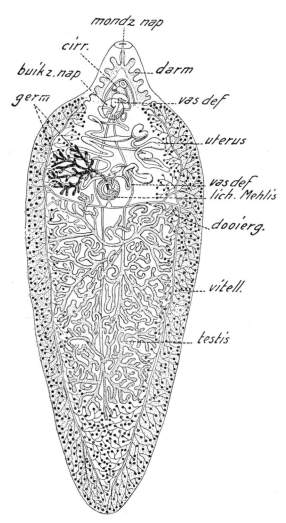

FIG. 10·8 *Fasciola hepatica* × 8: *mondz.nap*, Oral sucker.—*cirr*, Cirrus.
—*darm*, Beginning of cecum (the continuation omitted).—*buikz.nap*, Acetabulum.—*Vas def*, Vas deferens.—*germ*, Ovary.—*lich.Mehlis*, Shell gland.—*dooierg*, Vitelline duct.—*vitell*, Vitelline gland. (After Ihle and Nierstrasz, 1928. Courtesy, Oosthoek & Co., Publishers, Utrecht.)

Then they are washed into ditches, and cattle drinking from that source may acquire an infection.[21]

When the ingested metacercarias have arrived in the duodenum, they leave their shells, pierce the bowel wall, pass through the peritoneal cavity, and thus reach the liver,[20] where they enter the

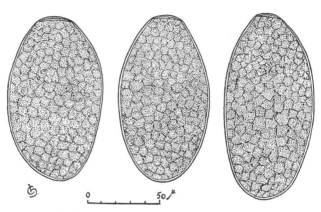

FIG. 10·9   *Fasciola hepatica,* freshly voided eggs. (After Brumpt, 1936. Courtesy, Masson & Cie, Paris.)

bile passages.[20a] An alternative route leads them to the same destination by way of the lymph and blood vessels.[22] Once they are settled in the liver, they attain maturity after a lapse of seven weeks to three months.[23] Eggs make their appearance in the feces of the host 3–4 months after the ingestion of the metacercarias.[24]

FIG. 10·10   *Lymnaea truncatula,* to the right: natural size. (After Leuckart.)

F. hepatica is not a common human parasite. In 1933 Senevet and Lièvre [25] still found it useful to list the 122 cases known at that time. Kourí and Basnuevo,[26] in Cuba, were the first to count them by hundreds. Recently two epidemics were recorded in France; one of 500 cases in the winter of 1956–'57 [27]; the other of 200 cases in 1958.[28] These numbers do not include the subclinical carriers, detected by the intradermal test [29] or by the finding of eggs, in members of the family of persons ill with fascioliasis. In other countries a high rate of infection is found in domestic animals, while human cases are rare. In Holland, for instance, 18 percent of the sheep and 65 percent of the cattle were found heavily infected.[30] In this and similar cases the absence of human fascioliasis might be explained (1) by a failure to establish the correct diagnosis, (2) by a preponderance of subclinical cases, (3) by the existence of several races of *F. hepatica*, some of them strictly limited to animals, others with a

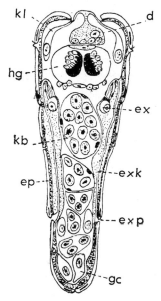

Fig. 10·11   *Fasciola hepatica*, miracidium × 520: *d*, Intestine.—*ep*, Epidermis.—*ex*, Flame cell.—*exk*, Excretory duct.—*exp*, Excretory pore.—*gc*, Germinal cell.—*hg*, Nerve center with pair of eyes.—*kb*, Germinal ball.—*kl*, Penetration gland. (After O. Mattes, 1958, cilia omitted. Courtesy, Gustav Fischer, Jena.)

wider range of adaptability that allows them to include man among their hosts, analogous to what is known in *S. japonicum* and *F. buski*, or (4) by dietary habits preventing infection, analogous to what is known in *Clonorchis sinensis* and *Paragonimus westermani*.

The fact that the metacercarias may reach the liver by way of the blood stream [22] explains the occurrence of the flukes in an *ectopic position*, in abscesses of abdominal muscles, and in deep cutaneous nodules.[31] The trematodes that have been found in the human eye

(*Distomum oculi humani*, Ammon, 1833; *Monostomum lentis*, v. Nordmann, 1882) might have been ectopic *F. hepatica* (unless they were specimens of *Philophthalmus* [32]).

TREATMENT OF FASCIOLIASIS. Emetine hydrochloride administered intramuscularly to adults of 65 kg body weight in daily doses of 40 mg over 8–9 days [26] is recommended by Deschiens.[18] This

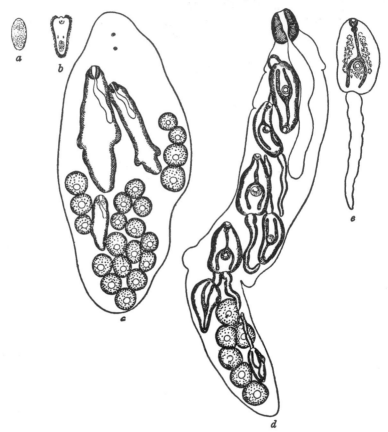

FIG. 10·12   *Fasciola hepatica,* complete life cycle drawn to scale, × 65: *a*, Egg.—*b*, Miracidium.—*c*, Sporocyst.—*d*, Redia.—*e*, Cercaria. (After Blacklock and Southwell, 1944. Courtesy, H. K. Lewis & Co., London.)

author insists on the treatment commencing as early as possible, i.e. during the stage of *larval invasion,* when the metacercarias are still passing through the tissue of the liver on their way to the bile ducts. As no eggs are found in the stools at that stage, the correct time for the initiation of the treatment must be based on the strength of the toxic and pseudotyphoid symptoms of that stage, or of a positive intradermal test.[29]

The morbid condition known as *halzoun* in inhabitants of Lebanon, due to an adult worm adhering to the pharynx, may be caused by *F. hepatica*. Its treatment does not fall within the scope of specific therapy of fascioliasis.

THE ECHINOSTOMID FAMILY

The members of this family are characterized by the possession of a *circumoral disk* surrounding the oral sucker; it carries a collar of spines, the number and arrangement being characteristic of each species. The family contains numerous polyxenous species inhabiting the intestine of fishes and aquatic birds, some of which occasionally infect man. Their cercarias, like all cercarias except those of the schistosomes, require a second invertebrate host for their metacercarial stage. Nevertheless, echinostomid cercarias have been identified as the cause of cercarial dermatitis on the shores of the Lake of Geneva, an example of the unsettled state of the host-parasite relationship obtaining in this family.[33]

Some species, such as *Himasthla muehlensi* Vogel, 1953, *Paryphostomum sufrartyfex* (Lane, 1915) Bhalerao, 1931, *Echinoparyphium paraulum* Dietz, 1909, and *Echinochasmus perfoliatus* (v. Ratz, 1908) Dietz, 1910, have been found once or twice inhabiting the human intestine.

However, the truly human parasites of this family belong to two genera: (1) *Euparyphium,* with a long cirrus pouch, extending to the level of the center of the acetabulum (Fig. 10·14:II, III) and (2) *Echinostoma,* with a short cirrus pouch, the posterior extremity of which does not reach that level (Fig. 10·14:IV).

EUPARYPHIUM (ECHINOSTOMA) ILOCANUM

Euparyphium ilocanum (Garrison, 1908) Tubangui & Pasco, 1933, merits the name of human parasite because it infects numerous members of the tribe of the Ilokanos inhabiting the northwest of Luzon (Philippine Islands), as a consequence of the second host of the parasite, the snail *Pila luzonica* (Fig. 10·13:4, 5), being eaten raw and forming a regular part of their diet.

Sandground and Prawirohardjo [34] found this species parasitizing

16 percent of the patients in a mental hospital at Jakarta (Java). They described it as follows.

The adult measures 4–8 × 0.5–1 mm; its shape is elongated lanceolate (Fig. 10·13:1 and 10·14:II). The anterior two-thirds of the ventral surface are covered with scales; on the dorsal surface they reach no farther down than to the level of the acetabulum. The circumoral disk (Fig. 10·13:2 and 10·14:m) surrounds the oral sucker like a collar. It carries 51 circumoral spines arranged in two concentric circles; each spine is 30–54 μ long. The acetabulum is four times as wide as the oral sucker, from which it is separated by a distance one-sixth of the body length.

Anterior to the bifurcation, the intestinal tract consists of a pharynx and a short esophagus; the bifurcation lies halfway the distance between oral sucker and acetabulum; the two ceca extend as far as the posterior extremity. The large vitelline glands occupy the posterior two-thirds of the body; first they are separated by the uterus, but in the posterior quarter they touch each other; the common vitelline duct is situated equatorially. Two large, slightly lobed testes lie, one behind the other, within the posterior half of the area left unoccupied by the vitelline glands; in front of them, separated from them by the common vitelline duct, the shell gland is situated, and anterior to it the round ovary. Within the area limited by the anterior testis, the two intestinal ceca, and the acetabulum lies the uterus; it forms a number of coils and opens into the genital atrium, situated in front of the acetabulum, slightly to the left of the midline.

The eggs are transparent and pearly white or slightly yellowish. They carry a small operculum, and their average size is 103 × 59 μ. They are passed in the feces in a nonembryonated state (Fig. 10·15:a).

While the eggs are immersed in water, a miracidium of 85 × 35 μ develops within the shell (Fig. 10·13:6), from which it emerges after a lapse of 9–20 days. According to Tubangui and Pasco [35] the first intermediate host in the Philippine Islands is the snail Gyraulus (Anisus) convexiusculus; the same applies to Java.[36] Within this snail a generation of sporocysts is succeeded by two generations of redias. The second generation produces the cercarias which leave the snail 45–50 days after it became infected. The cercaria already shows the circumoral disk characteristic of the family (Fig. 10·13:8); its trunk measures 180–300 × 100–130 μ, its tail 130–150 × 30–50 μ.

The second intermediate hosts, carriers of metacercarias, are also molluscs. *Pila luzonica,* on Luzon, has already been mentioned in

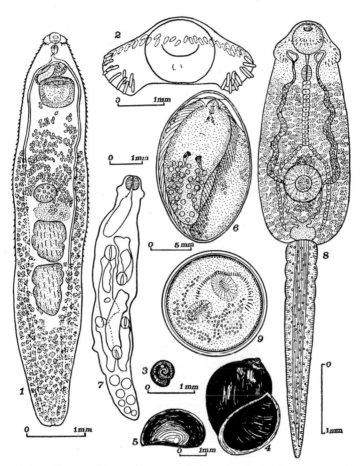

Fig. 10·13   *Euparyphium ilocanum,* life cycle: 1. Adult worm, × 16.— 2. Circumoral disk, with spines, × 100.—3. *Gyraulus convexiusculus,* first intermediate host, × 12.—4. Shell and 5, lid of the shell, of *Pila luzonica,* second intermediate host, × 7.—6. Egg with miracidium, × 400.—7. Redia of first generation.—8. Cercaria, × 400.—9. Metacercaria. (After Brumpt, 1936. Courtesy, Masson & Cie, Paris.)

this respect (Fig. 10·13:4, 5).   On Java the snail *Viviparus javanicus* [37] appears to be of particular importance; but the first intermediate host can also serve as second host.   Man and rats, experimentally

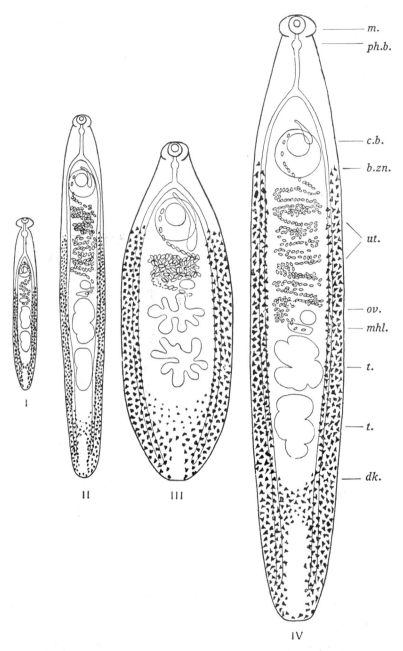

Fig. 10·14   Indonesian echinostomes, × 10: I. *Euparyphium recurvatum.*—II. *E. ilocanum.*—III. *E. malayanum.*—IV. *Echinostoma lindoense* and *E. revolutum: m,* Oral sucker surrounded by circumoral

infected by eating raw snails, passed eggs in their feces 12–20 days after the infecting meal.

Rats are alternate hosts: *Rattus norvegicus* in the Philippine Islands, and *Rattus brevicaudatus* in Java. The last-named rat must be considered the principal host of *E. ilocanum* in that island: more than half of them were found infected. Man is no more than the recipient of the spill-over of the murine infection.

Other members of the same genus found by Bonne in the human intestine are *E. malayanum* Leiper, 1911 (Fig. 10·14:III), in a Batak girl of north Sumatra, and *E. recurvatum* v. Linstow, 1873 (Fig. 10·14:I) in an inmate of the aforementioned hospital at Jakarta.

ECHINOSTOMA LINDOENSE

Echinostoma lindoense Sandground & Bonne, 1940,[38] shows a bright red color when alive. In the preserved state it is whitish, and measures 13–15 × 2.5–3 mm. The circumoral disk carries 37 spines, 70–85 μ in length. The dorsal and ventral surfaces of the anterior extremity carry scales as far down as the level of the acetabulum. Anteriorly the vitelline glands extend to the level of the posterior margin of the acetabulum. The lobes of the testes are fairly well marked. The cirrus pouch does not extend much farther than to the level of the anterior margin of the acetabulum (Fig. 10·14:IV).

The average size of the eggs is 101 × 69 μ (Fig. 10·15:a). The shell is fairly thick. A small operculum occupies one pole; at the opposite pole the shell is thicker than elsewhere. The eggs are passed in the stools in a nonembryonated state.

Lying in water, a miracidium develops within a week; it leaves the eggshell after 12 days. The first intermediate host is the snail *Gyraulus (Anisus) sarasinorum,* in which orange-colored redias of 0.3–1.0 mm develop, situated on the digestive gland. The cercarias carry spines; their trunk measures 0.30–0.46 × 0.14–0.18 mm, their tail 0.32–0.45 × 0.04 mm.

The metacercarias lie within cysts of 0.12–0.13 mm, with a wall of 5 μ. They are found in the second intermediate hosts, the most important of which are the clam *Corbicula lindoensis* and the snail

---

disk.—*ph.b,* Pharynx.—*cb,* Cirrus pouch.—*b.zn,* Acetabulum.—*ut,* Uterus. —*ov,* Ovary.—*mhl,* Shell gland.—*t,* Testis.—*dk,* Vitelline gland. (After Bonne, Bras and Lie Kian Joe, 1949. Courtesy, Editors of *Medisch Maandblad,* Jakarta.)

Viviparus javanicus rudipellis. Man consuming raw infected clams passes eggs in his stools two weeks after the infecting meal. The subject remains infected for more than seven months.[37]

This parasite, which inhabits the jejunum, was found in the center of the island of Celebes, among the inhabitants of the environment of Lake Lindu, who consumed raw corbiculas as part of their regular diet; accordingly 47–53 percent were found infected in the several villages on the shores of the lake.[39] Unlike *E. ilocanum, E. lindoense* is a parasite completely adapted to man. There may exist alternate hosts, but they have not been found among waterfowl, rats, buffaloes,

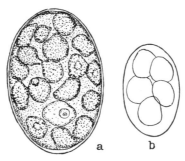

Fig. 10·15   *Echinostoma lindoense: a*, Egg, × 300.—*b*, Egg of *Necator americanus*, to emphasize the large size of *a*. (After Brug and Tesch, 1937. Courtesy, Editors of *Geneeskundig Tijdschrift voor Nederlandsch-Indië*.)

or horses of the Lindu area; however, on the shores of the neighboring Lake Poso a worm indistinguishable from *E. lindoense* has been detected in a rat.[40]

Echinostoma revolutum Fröhlich, 1802, a parasite of ducks and geese, greatly resembles *E. lindoense,* except for the circumoral spines, which are longer, 100–120 μ. Bonne and his co-workers found it once in a boy at Jakarta (Fig. 10·14:IV). Its first intermediate hosts are the snails *Lymnaea rubiginosa* and *Gyraulus (Anisus) convexiusculus;* its second, *Viviparus javanicus* and *Pila conica.*

TREATMENT OF ECHINOSTOMIASIS. Oleoresin of Aspidium, U.S.P. (the extract of the male fern, B.P.) and tetrachlorethylene are considered specific drugs in the treatment of infections with *E. ilocanum, E. malayanum,* and *E. lindoense.*[12]

GASTRODISCOIDES HOMINIS

The general form of the curiously shaped trematode *Gastro-discoides hominis* (Lewis & McConnell, 1876) Leiper, 1913 (*Gastro-discus hominis* [id.] Fischoeder, 1902) (family of Paramphistomidae) is shown in Fig. 10·16:*a, b*. It might be compared to a very shallow bowl with a handle attached to the center of its bottom and directed parallel to its rim. The handle represents the anterior portion of the animal, the bowl the posterior portion. Unlike all other human trematodes, the wide acetabulum is situated at the posterior ex-

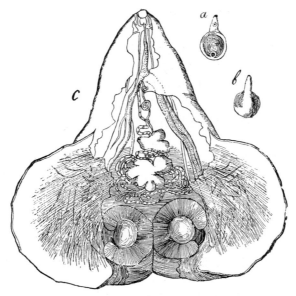

FIG. 10·16 *Gastrodiscoides hominis: a,* Ventral aspect.—*b,* Dorsal aspect, × 2.—*c,* Internal anatomy of the animal opened by a lengthwise, ventral, median cut. (After Lewis and McConnell, 1876.)

tremity of the rim. The small oral sucker has a normal subterminal position, near the tip of the handle; so has the genital atrium, situated on a prominent papilla on the ventral side of the handle, halfway between its tip and the point where the rim of the bowl overlaps it (Fig. 10·16:*a*).

When alive the parasite has a reddish color. The length is 5–10 mm, measured from the tip of the handle to the posterior segment of the rim; the width of the bowl is 4–6 mm; the thickness of the bowl, including the place of insertion of the handle, is about 2 mm; the portion of the handle not hidden behind the bowl is about 2 mm long. The integument has no scales.

The intestine has a short esophagus. At the level of the genital atrium it splits into the wide ceca. There are two wide excretory ducts, situated laterally, with numerous branches; they open into an excretory pore situated on the dorsal surface of the handle. Two deeply indented testes lie near the anterior rim of the bowl; the small ovary lies in the center. The greatly coiled uterus extends from behind the testes to the genital atrium. The vitelline glands are wide but short.

The eggs are passed in the stools in a nonembryonated state. They are operculate, and measure $150–152 \times 60–72 \mu$.

G. hominis is a parasite inhabiting the cecum and ascending colon of its host. The principal host in India and Annam is the pig; in Annam 5 percent of the pigs are infected.[41] In the Malay Peninsula, the "deerlet" or "kanchil," *Tragulus napu,* has been found infected.[42] Nevertheless, man may be a host of importance. In the Indian province of Assam Buckley[43] found an overall rate of infection of 3 percent, rising as high as 41 percent in some villages. So it is not astonishing to find the parasite exported to other countries in the bodies of immigrants from India, as Bonne found it in Surinam; but there are no indications that it has become indigenous in that part of the Guianas.

TREATMENT. Manson-Bahr[12] states that thymol, carbon tetrachloride and tetrachlorethylene are effective anthelmintics.

REFERENCES FOR CHAPTER X

1. MAX WEBER. *Tijdschr. Ned. Dierk. Vereen.,* 1890–92, 3 (2nd Ser.): 83.
2. D. J. AMEEL. *Am. J. Hyg.,* 1934, 19: 279–317.
3. S. YOKOGAWA and S. SUYEMORI. *Am. J. Hyg.,* 1921, 1: 63–78.
4. W. H. HUANG and J. K. CHIU. *Trop. Diseases Bull.,* 1958, 55: 1252–1253.
5. Y. KOMIYA. *Trop. Diseases Bull.,* 1953, 50: 633–634.
6. O. K. KHAW. *Nat. Med. J. China,* 1930, 16: 93–102.
7. G. M. HEYDON. *Trop. Diseases Bull.,* 1928, 25: 453.
8. A. ZAHRA. *Trop. Diseases Bull.,* 1952, 49: 1059.
9. A. FAIN and J. VANDEPITTE. *Ann. soc. belge méd. trop.,* 1957, 37: 251–258.
10. K. J. SKRJABINE and W. P. PODJAPOLSKAJA. *Zentr. Bakteriol.,* Abt. I, Or., 1931, 119: 294–297.
11. R. E. SHOPE. *J. Exptl. Med.,* 1941, 74: 49–68.
11a. C. B. PHILIP, W. J. HADLOW, and L. E. HUGHES. *Exptl. Parasitol.,* 1954, 3: 336–350.

12. PH. H. MANSON-BAHR. *Tropical Diseases,* London, 1957, pp. 794, 937, 945, 957.

12a. O. R. McCoy and T. C. CHU. *Chinese Med. J.,* 1937, 51: 932–944.

13. E. G. NAUCK. *Lehrbuch der Tropenkrankheiten,* Stuttgart, 1956, p. 69.

14. C. H. BARLOW. *Am. J. Hyg.,* Monogr. Ser. No. 4, Baltimore, 1925, 98 pp.

15. H. VOGEL. *Arch. Schiffs- u. Tropen-Hyg.,* 1936, 40: 181–187.

16. W. C. SWEET. *J. Am. Med. Assoc.,* 1921, 76: 1819–1820.

17. L. KANT and K. RAMA. *Trop. Diseases Bull.,* 1955, 52: 177–178.

18. R. DESCHIENS. *Ann. Inst. Pasteur Paris,* 1958, 94: 256–271.

19. M. RAJCEVIČ. *Trop. Diseases Bull.,* 1930, 27: 959.

20. J. EHLERS and H. KNÜTTGEN. *Z. Tropenmed. Parasitol.,* 1949, 1: 364–378.

20a. W. SCHUMACHER. *Z. Parasitenk.,* 1938, 10: 608–693.

21. A. LUTZ. *Centr. Bakteriol.,* 1892, 11: 173–176.

22. H. S. FRENKEL. *Tijdschr. Vergelijk. Geneesk.,* 1921, 6: 292–306 (English summary, 306).

23. W. NÖLLER and F. SCHMIDT. *Sitzber. Ges. naturforsch. Freunde Berlin,* 1927: 96–126.

24. L. MORÉNAS. *Presse méd.,* 1944, 52: 326.

25. G. SENEVET and H. LIÈVRE. *Algérie med.,* Nov. 1933, 7 pp.

26. P. KOURÍ and J. G. BASNUEVO. *Helmintologia humana,* 771 pp., Havana, 1949, Müñiz Hos., pp. 639, 679, 680.

27. J. COUDERT and F. TRIOZON. *Presse méd.,* 1957, 67: 1586–1588.

28. R. MANDOUL, R. SIGALAS, and R. MOURGUES. *J. méd. Bordeaux,* 1958, 185: 665–672.

29. G. LAVIER and J. STEFANOPOULO. *Bull. soc. pathol. exotique,* 1944, 37: 302–307.

30. N. L. WIBAUT. *Mededeel. Vee-artsenijkund. Dienst,* 1944, Jan., 44 pp.

31. H. HEVIA, H. SCHENONE, O. KLEIN, and R. ALARCON. *Bol. chileno parasitol.,* 1958, 13: 57–59.

32. A. S. DISSANAIKE and D. P. BILIMORIA. *J. Helminthol.,* 1958, 32: 115–118.

33. H. GASCHEN, G. MATTHEY, and P. JOMINI. *Bull. soc. pathol. exotique,* 1956, 49: 1172–1177.

34. J. H. SANDGROUND and S. PRAWIROHARDJO. *Geneesk. Tijdschr. Ned. Indië,* 1939, 79: 1497–1503 (in English).

35. M. A. TUBANGUI and A. M. PASCO. *Philippine J. Sci.,* 1933, 51: 581–606.

36. J. H. SANDGROUND. *Geneesk. Tijdschr. Ned. Indië,* 1939, 79: 1722–1734 (in English).

37. C. BONNE and J. H. SANDGROUND. *Geneesk. Tijdschr. Ned. Indië,* 1939, 79: 3016–3034 (in English).

38. J. H. SANDGROUND and C. BONNE. *Am. J. Trop. Med.,* 1940, 20: 511–534.

39. S. L. BRUG and J. W. TESCH. *Geneesk. Tijdschr. Ned. Indië,* 1937, 77: 2151–2158 (English summary, 2158).

40. C. BONNE, A. J. P. BORSTLAP, LIE KIAN JOE, W. J. J. MOLENKAMP, C. E. DE MOOR, and W. NANNING. *Geneesk, Tijdschr. Ned. Indië,* 1942, 82: 13–20 (English summary, 20).

41. M. BRAU and L. BRUYANT. *Bull. soc. pathol. exotique,* 1913, 6: 41–43.

42. M. KHALIL. *Proc. Roy. Soc. Med.,* 1923, 16: 8.

43. J. J. C. BUCKLEY. *J. Helminthol.,* 1939, 17: 1–12.

CHAPTER XI

TREMATODES WITH SMALL EMBRYONATED EGGS

This group, characterized by the host passing embryonated eggs in his feces, of a length under 50 μ, contains three families. The sections in which they are described have been named after the family or after the species according to the rule followed in Chapter X.

THE OPISTORCHID FAMILY

This family is represented here by two genera: *Opistorchis*, possessing lobated testes, and *Clonorchis*, possessing ramified testes.

OPISTORCHIS FELINEUS

Opistorchis felineus (Rivolta, 1884) Blanchard, 1895, a parasite of the bile ducts of the liver, also occurs in the pancreas and was observed in the human lung in Russia.[1] The degree of its pathogenicity largely depends on its numbers.

The adults usually measure 7–12 × 2–3 mm. They are transparent, so that the internal organs can readily be discerned. When alive their color is reddish yellow (Fig. 11·1). The anterior extremity is tapering; the posterior end is rounded. The suckers are about the same size (0.3 mm), and the distance between them is one-fifth of the body length.

The oral pore leads to the pharynx, the short (0.2 mm) esophagus, and the ceca; the latter extend to the posterior extremity. The vitelline glands lie laterally in the middle third of the body. Each gland is composed of nine or more follicles. The transverse vitelline ducts take their origin at the level of the penultimate follicle. The testes are situated in the posterior quarter, one obliquely in front of the other; the anterior testis has four lobes, the posterior, five. There is no cirrus or cirrus pouch. In front of the anterior testis lies a large piriform seminal receptacle associated with Laurer's duct; in front of it, but in the midline, lies the smooth or slightly lobed ovary.

The uterus runs in numerous coils between the ceca; it opens into the genital atrium situated in front of the acetabulum. The excretory bladder passes between the testes in the form of an elongated S and opens into the excretory pore at the posterior extremity.

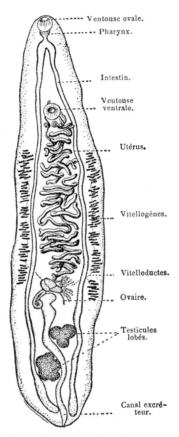

FIG. 11·1 *Opistorchis felineus*, × 12: *Ventouse ovale*, Oral sucker.— *Intestin*, Cecum.—*Ventouse ventrale*, Acetabulum.—*Vitellogènes*, Vitelline gland.—*Vitelloductes*, Transverse vitelline duct.—*Ovaire*, Ovary.— *Testicules lobés*, Lobate testes.—*Canal excréteur*, Excretory bladder. (After Brumpt, 1936. Courtesy, Masson & Cie, Paris.)

The eggs are passed in the feces in a state of embryonation. Their size is 26–30 × 11–15 μ. The shell has a yellowish color. As a rule the operculum is less distinctly differentiated from the rest of the shell than in clonorchis, but there are exceptions. As in clonorchis the part of the shell opposite the operculum sometimes shows a knob-shaped excrescence (Fig. 11·2:1).

In northeastern Europe the first intermediate host is the fresh-water snail *Bulimus* (*Bithynia*) *tentaculatus* (Fig. 11·2:4).[2] The miracidium does not leave the eggshell until the snail has ingested the embryonated egg. The sporocysts mature in the neighborhood of the hindgut, where they reach a length of 1.5 mm (Fig. 11·2:2). The redias which develop inside the sporocyst leave it one month after the snail becomes infected. Skirting the intestinal tract of the host they reach the hepatopancreas. There they grow to a size of 0.5 mm; they have a whitish color and possess a pharynx opening into a short blind-ended intestine (Fig. 11·2:3).

The cercarias emerge from the redia in an immature state, but they reach maturity before leaving the snail. This they usually do about noon. The trunk of the mature cercaria measures 132–172 μ, its tail 440–500 μ. The cuticle has scales and a few long, slender hairs (Fig. 11·2:6). Moreover, the cercaria possesses two pigmented eye spots, a set of penetration glands, and a piercing organ, situated near the mouth, that carries four major and numerous minor denticles. The dorsal and ventral sides of the tail (Fig. 11·2:6) carry a membranous keel (*lophocercous* cercaria).

The second intermediate hosts of *O. felineus* are found among fresh-water fishes of the Cyprinid family, belonging to genera such as *Idus, Tinca, Leuciscus,* and *Chondrostoma.* The cercarias attach themselves to these fishes and pierce their skin, shedding their tail at the same time. Within 12 hours they penetrate into the muscular tissue, where they become encysted. Four weeks later the meta-cercarias have reached a size of 213–280 μ by 147–197 μ (Fig. 11·2:8, 9) and are ready to continue their development in the definitive host.

In young dogs that have ingested infected cyprinid flesh, excysted metacercarias are found in the gallbladder shortly after the infecting meal. After 12 days they are 3 mm long; at that time they are already sexually mature, but it takes another three weeks for the definitive host to pass opistorchis eggs in its feces.

O. felineus is a polyxenous parasite. It has been recovered from domestic animals, cats, and dogs and from wild carnivores, foxes, arctic foxes, and three species of pinnipeds, in several countries of the European continent and Siberia. As a human parasite it is far from rare in certain regions. Winogradoff, in 1892,[3] found *O.*

felineus in over 6 percent of the autopsies he performed in the city of Tomsk. In more recent times, 18 percent of the inhabitants of the Memel delta,[4] and 18–26 percent of those of the lower reaches of the Dnieper, in south Russia [5] have been found infected.

Originally the parasite was recovered at autopsies of persons who had died of a variety of obscure diseases, for the cause of which the parasite offered a ready explanation. Thus the parasite was most

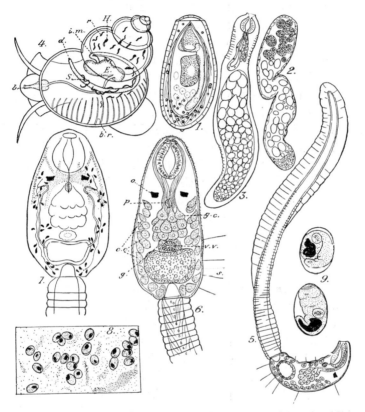

Fig. 11·2 *Opistorchis felineus,* life cycle: 1. Egg with miracidium.— 2. Sporocyst.—3. Young redia.—4. *Bulimus tentaculatus,* the molluscan host.—(b, mouth; S, sporocysts around hind gut; E, stomach; *im,* midgut; r, redia in hepatopancreas H; d, anus).—5. Cercaria in characteristic attitude at the bottom of a jar with water.—6. Trunk of cercaria at higher magnification (o, eye; p, pharynx; *ge,* penetration glands; vv, acetabulum; g, genital cells; cc, germinal cells; s, excretory bladder). —7. The same, showing excretory ducts and flame cells.—8. Muscle of a fish (*Tinca*) with metacercarias.—9. Metacercarias at higher magnification. (After H. Vogel; from Brumpt, 1936. Courtesy, Masson & Cie, Paris.)

naturally associated with disease in the minds of those who performed the autopsies. Neverthless, Rindfleisch,[3] who collected 40 cases examined between 1899 and 1909, found no pathological alterations in the liver of 25 of them. In recent times in Russia, observations have been directed to apparently healthy persons, many of whom have been found infected; however, their worm burden was a light one, no more than an average of five worms per carrier.

Opistorchis viverrini (Poirier, 1886) Stiles & Hassal, 1896. According to the reports this species can be distinguished from *O. felineus* by (1) its slightly smaller size, 6–10 by 1–2 mm, (2) the somewhat greater length of the esophagus, (3) the small distance between the anterior testis and the ovary, (4) the follicles of the vitelline glands being aggregated into a few clusters, and (5) the eggs being slightly shorter and wider (19–29 $\times$ 12–17 μ).

O. viverrini is reported [6] to infect half of the population of northeast Thailand. In children under four years of age it is rare; adults over thirty are most heavily infected. The indigenous inhabitants regularly partake of raw fish; the Chinese inhabitants who do not follow that custom remain uninfected.

Civet cats, domestic cats, and dogs are alternate hosts. They are carrying on the infection in central Thailand, where man, owing to different dietary habits, does not participate in the process.

Opistorchis noverca Braun, 1902. This species (Fig. 8·6:*e*) parasitizes the dog, small carnivores (*Gulo*), and the pig, in India. It has been found in man on two occasions. The eggs are larger than those of the others; their average size is 34 by 21 μ.

In the Western Hemisphere the genus is represented by *Opistorchis* sp. L. F. Gómez and J. D. Rodríguez, 1949, which parasitizes nearly 8 percent of the human population and 3 percent of the dogs in a coastal area 125 miles to the northwest of Guayaquil (Ecuador).[20]

TREATMENT OF OPISTORCHIASIS. Although quite a number of people infected with opistorchis must have been treated in the course of the years, none of the drugs tried, such as gentian violet and Fuadin, have proved satisfactory.

CLONORCHIS SINENSIS

Clonorchis sinensis (Cobbold, 1875) Looss, 1907, inhabits the bile ducts in the liver and occasionally the pancreas of man, cats, and dogs.

Its shape is elongated lanceolate; the posterior extremity is rounded, the anterior extremity tapering. The size varies greatly, from 7 to 20 mm in length and from 1 to 5 mm in width. This variation, together with the presence or absence of pigment, formerly led to the belief of the existence of a large pigmented race (*C. sinensis innocuus*) and a small, unpigmented pathogenic race (*C. endemicus* Baelz, 1883).

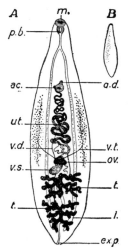

FIG. 11·3   *Clonorchis sinensis: A,* × 4; *B,* natural size: *m,* Oral sucker. —*pb,* Pharynx.—*ac,* Acetabulum.—*ut,* Uterus.—*vd,* Vas deferens.—*vs,* Seminal vesicle.—*t,* Testes.—*ex.p,* Excretory pore.—*i,* Cecum.—*ov,* Ovary. —*vt,* Vitelline gland. (After Brumpt, 1936. Courtesy, Masson & Cie, Paris.)

The color of the parasite is a transparent gray, sometimes yellowish from the absorption of bile. The oral sucker is slightly larger than the acetabulum; the distance between them equals one-third of the body length. The genital atrium is situated just in front of the acetabulum. The cuticle has no spines (Fig. 11·3).

The small pharynx opens into the esophagus, which may be prolonged to a point halfway between the suckers before it bifurcates into the ceca. The latter extend backward to a point near the posterior extremity. The testes are situated in the hindmost third of the body. They carry from four to six long, slender, ramified lobes which extend over the adjacent intestinal ceca. In the middle of the body the vasa efferentia open into a wide seminal vesicle, from which the vas deferens takes its course to the genital atrium. Cirrus and cirrus pouch are absent. The small, faintly lobed ovary is situated in the midline, slightly behind the equator; the much larger seminal receptacle lies behind it. In its course from the ovary to the genital atrium, the uterus keeps its numerous, tightly packed coils well between the intestinal ceca. The vitelline glands are situated laterally, extending from a point at a level just behind the acetabulum to the level of the ovary. The transverse vitelline ducts originate from the penultimate part of each gland. The follicles are either collected into a number of clusters or evenly spread over the whole length of the gland (Fig. 11·3). The former condition was regarded as characteristic of *C. sinensis innocuus,* the latter of *C. endemicus.* The

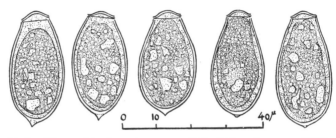

FIG. 11·4   *Clonorchis sinensis,* eggs × 800. (After Brumpt, 1936. Courtesy, Masson & Cie, Paris.)

excretory bladder originates behind the seminal vesicle; a little farther down it is joined by the two main excretory vessels; then it takes an S-shaped course towards the excretory pore at the posterior extremity.

The embryonated eggs are passed in the feces of the host. They measure 27–35 × 12–29 μ. The shell is fairly thick; it has a light yellow-brown color. The operculum is conspicuous because (1) its outline, in the form of an S or of a bow, does not correspond with that of the rest of the shell, (2) it rests on a prominent rim, and (3) the outline of the shell shows a slight contraction below the rim. Opposite the operculum the shell often shows a blunt or pointed prominence (Fig. 11·4). According to Faust and Khaw,[7] the daily egg production of one worm is estimated at 1100–2400.

In the human body the worm can reach a considerable age. In the United States, where infection is practically excluded, persons have been encountered who had left east Asia 13, 20, and 25 years ago and who still harbored *C. sinensis*.[8] In dogs the life of the parasite appears to last for no longer than four years; the production of eggs is terminated after three years.[9]

The miracidia (Fig. 11·5:1), of 32×17 μ, do not leave the shell until the eggs have been ingested by the first intermediate hosts, snails of the genera *Bulimus* (*Bithynia*) and *Parafossarulus*. They penetrate into the tissue around the esophagus and there, after

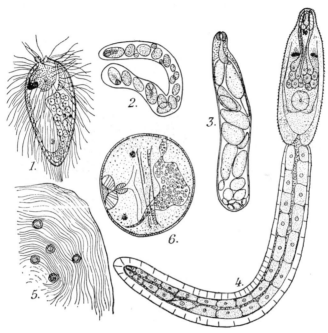

Fɪɢ. 11·5   *Clonorchis sinensis*, life cycle: 1. Miracidium, $\times$ 900.—2. Sporocyst with redias, $\times$ 81.—3. Redia with cercarias, $\times$ 30.—4. Mature cercaria, $\times$ 140.—5. Encysted metacercarias adhering to the scale of a fish.—6. Metacercaria at higher magnification. (After Faust and Khaw, 1927; from Brumpt, 1936. Courtesy, Masson & Cie, Paris.)

twenty days, develop into sporocysts (Fig. 11·5:2) of 90×65 μ.[7] The redias (Fig. 11·5:3) originating from them make their way to the hepatopancreas. They measure 1.73×0.13 mm and show the usual redial organization. Each redia bears about 50 cercarias, which emerge from it when they are still immature.

The mature cercaria (Fig. 11·5:4) has a trunk of $250-275 \times 60-90$ μ; the tail is $630-750$ μ long, with a membranous keel on its dorsal and ventral surface. The cercaria possesses two eye spots and a number of penetration glands; its cuticle is spinose and carries a number of slender hairs. The mouth carries a piercing organ (stylet). The cercarias leave the snail one month after its infection. Their characteristic attitude in water is like that of the cercaria of opistorchis (Fig. 11·2:5).

Numerous species of fresh-water fishes, belonging to various families, serve *C. sinensis* as second intermediate hosts, but every region has one or a few that are more infected than all others, such as *Pseudorasbora parva* in Japan, and the ide *Ctenopharyngodon idellus* in the Canton region. The last-named species is offered unusual opportunities of becoming infected in fish ponds that are prolific breeding areas for the molluscan hosts because of the luxuriant vegetation growing in these ponds, as a consequence of their being fertilized with human excreta.[10] The cercarias penetrate into the muscles of the fish, notably the caudal muscles. In 35 days they develop into encysted metacercarias (Fig. 11·5:6) which have lost the specifically larval organs (viz. the tail, the stylet, and the eye spots) and have shrunken to a size of $140 \times 113 \, \mu$.

When the definitive host, man or dog, ingests living metacercarias by consuming raw fish, the parasites excyst in the duodenum. According to Hsü and Wang[11] they reach the biliary ducts by way of Vater's papilla after four to seven hours. However, D. E. Wykoff and T. J. Lepeš[12] believe that they pass through the blood vessels of the bowel and the portal system to get there. Two weeks after their arrival in the biliary ducts the parasites, grown to adult state, initiate their sexual activity; but it takes another 12 days for the eggs to appear in the stools.

C. sinensis is indigenous to Japan, Korea, China, Formosa, Indochina, and Thailand. In the endemic centers of these countries 50 percent and over of the human inhabitants are infected, the age group of 30–50 more than others.[13] Sometimes the death of the host may reasonably be explained by the pathogenic activity of the parasite. But there are also numerous asymptomatic carriers,[14] many of whom may have forgotten the first days following their primary infection, when metacercarias on their passage through their body caused them a high fever, one month before they commenced passing clonorchis eggs in their feces.[15] Moreover, it should not be forgotten that considerable pathological alterations have been observed in the liver of persons who, during life, hardly complained of any symptoms. In view of the large numbers of carriers, *C. sinensis* is therefore regarded as a pathogenic agent of great importance.

Apart from the endemic centers, smaller numbers of carriers are found in other regions of the same countries. Moreover, they may occur, all over the world, as emigrants from these countries. If the imported parasites find appropriate first and second intermediate hosts in the area of immigration, they may succeed in settling permanently in their new home, as happened in Hawaii.[16] Otherwise the parasite remains a stranger settled only in an alien population as, e.g., in Indonesia.

The alternate hosts, cats and dogs, to which rats are added in Japan, are often more infected than man. Man may even be completely eliminated as a host without any apparent detriment to the parasite. Here China offers an instructive example. In the Canton area 46 percent of the human inhabitants were infected,[13] 44 percent of the dogs, and 72 percent of the cats.[17] In the Shanghai area human infection hardly reached 3 percent,[18] but canine infection amounted to 37 percent and feline to 58 percent. Finally, in the Peking area indigenous human infection was nonexistent, whereas dogs and cats were infected for 25 and 37 percent respectively. The explanation for this apparent lack of correlation between human and animal infection lies in the fact that the higher classes in the south are in the habit of partaking of delicious dishes of well prepared raw fish, seasoned with a great variety of tasty sauces which do not damage the metacercarias.[11] In the north, dishes of this kind are completely unknown.

In Thailand conditions like those in the Canton area prevail in the north of the country, whereas the center is like the Peking area.[6] It may be remembered that in opistorchis infection a corresponding lack of correlation was found between two ethnically different populations inhabiting the same region.

TREATMENT OF CLONORCHIASIS. Experimentally, Faust and Yao [19] have demonstrated that the effect of gentian violet as a clonorchicide, administered orally, is superior to the same drug administered intravenously and to tartar emetic similarly applied. Emetine hydrochloride (intravenous), carbon tetrachloride and mercurochrome (oral) had no effect at all. In practice gentian violet is administered [20] orally as enteric-coated tablets of 60 mg taken three times daily (with meals) for 30 days. If it will not bring about a complete cure in heavy infections, at least it reduces the number of worms. The same appears to apply to chloroquine diphosphate, administered in daily doses of 0.5 gm over 28 days (total dosage 14 gm) or in 3 daily doses of 1 gm, followed by 20 daily doses of 0.5 gm (total dosage 13 gm administered over 23 days).

THE HETEROPHYID FAMILY

The readiness with which all kinds of definitive hosts are accepted is so pronounced in this family that none of its members can be safely regarded as unable to infect man. Other polyxenous trematodes do at least respect the borderline separating the mammals from other warm-blooded vertebrates, but the heterophyids do not. A Japanese scientist tried to infect himself by swallowing the metacercarias of a species parasitizing a Japanese heron—and he succeeded. Another Japanese student tried the same experiment with a parasite of a Formosan heron—and he succeeded in infecting himself not only with that species but also with three others parasitizing the same bird.[21]

For this reason the species to be described have been limited to two, just as were the species of echinostomids, which resemble the heterophyids in the wide range of their hosts. These species are both characterized by the *genital sucker* or *gonotyl,* which in *Heterophyes* is separated from the acetabulum, whereas in *Metagonimus* they have merged into one, to produce a *ventrogenital sucker.*

HETEROPHYES HETEROPHYES

Heterophyes heterophyes (von Siebold, 1852) Stiles and Hassall, 1900, is a small trematode that lives attached to the wall of the small intestine (Fig. 11·6). It is found in Egypt, Greece, Yemen, Palestine, and several foci in the Far East. It measures 1–1.7 mm in length, and 0.3–0.6 mm in width. Both extremities are rounded, but the anterior third of the body is narrower than the posterior two-thirds. The cuticle is covered with small scales, which are shorter on the posterior than on the anterior part of the body; their posteriorly directed margin carries seven to nine minute denticles. The oral sucker is 0.09 mm in diameter, the acetabulum 0.23 mm. On the right posterior border of the acetabulum, and partly hidden by it, lies a third sucker, the *genital sucker* or *gonotyl,* the bottom of which is pierced like the oral sucker—not, however, by the oral aperture, but by the genital aperture (Fig. 11·6:*gr, gp*). Its size is 0.15 mm, and it carries an incompletely closed ring of 60–90 minute spines.

The short pharynx opens into an esophagus of thrice its length. The latter divides into the ceca, the posterior extremities of which are in touch with the testes, and almost so with the excretory bladder. Male and female organs lie crowded within the posterior third of the body; the testes, nearest to the posterior extremity, are situated

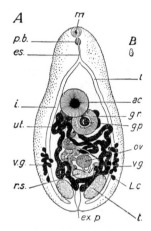

FIG. 11·6 *Heterophyes heterophyes; A,* × 30; *B,* natural size: *m,* Oral sucker.—*i,* Cecum.—*ac,* Acetabulum.—*gr,* Genital sucker.—*gp,* Genital pore.—*ov,* Ovary.—*vg,* Vitelline gland.—*t,* Testis.—*ex.p,* Excretory pore. —*rs,* Seminal receptacle.—*ut,* Uterus. (After Brumpt, 1936. Courtesy, Masson & Cie, Paris.)

symmetrically to the right and left of the excretory bladder; in front of them, but not touching them, lie first the seminal receptacle and then the ovary, both in the midline. The two vasa efferentia, emerging from the testes, form the wide, U-shaped seminal vesicle, which joins the anterior extremity of the uterus to form a common genital duct, opening into the genital atrium at the bottom of the gonotyl. The greatly convoluted uterus winds its coils in a field limited anteriorly by the acetabulum, posteriorly by the testes, and laterally by the intestinal ceca. The small vitelline glands, situated at the level of the ovary and the seminal receptacle, are composed of about fourteen follicles.

The ovoid eggs of 28–30 × 15–17 μ are passed in the feces of the host in a state of embryonation (Fig. 8·6:c). Their shell is light brown and fairly thick, provided with an operculum.

The miracidium does not emerge until the egg has been ingested by the first intermediate host. In Egypt this is a snail of the species *Pirenella conica*. The development within this host comprises one generation of sporocysts and one or two of redias.[22] The cercarias penetrate into the body of various fishes, in Egypt the brackish-water fishes *Mugil cephalus, M. auratus* and others. In the muscles of these fishes they become metacercarias which, after a stay of 15–20 days, are able to resume their life as an intestinal parasite in the mammalian host. There they grow to maturity after another fortnight.[22]

In Egypt 36–88 percent of the schoolchildren are infected with this parasite. The source of infection is the so-called "fessikh," salted fish of the above-named species.[23] Alternate hosts are to be found among domestic animals, cat and dog,[21] animals dependent on man (rats), and wild animals: wild cat, jackal, fox, predatory birds, and, in Yemen,[23] bats.

In the Far East *H. heterophyes* occurs in Japan, where it has been reported to infect 18 percent of the population. Dogs function as alternate hosts, and the mullet *Mugil cephalus* as second intermediate host. However, the Japanese parasites are regarded as different from the Near Eastern ones, and are known as *H. nocens* and *H. katsuradai*.

The same applies to the Philippine Islands, where the local biotype, characterized by its short ceca and esophagus, and by the site of the ovary to the right of the acetabulum, is known as *H. brevicaeca*.[23a]

METAGONIMUS YOKOGAWAI

Metagonimus yokogawai Katsurada, 1912, inhabiting the intestine, has a size of 1.1–1.6 × 0.4–0.7 mm. It differs from the foregoing by the position and shape of the acetabulum: it is not situated in the midline but has been shifted to the right as far as the level of the cecum; its average size is 0.13 by 0.09 mm, with its longitudinal axis at a sharp angle to the midline of the animal; the gonotyl has been incorporated into it, so that the genital atrium is lying within the muscular rim of the acetabulum (Fig. 11·7).

Embryonated eggs are passed in the feces; they measure 26–28

$\times$ 15–17 μ and are hardly to be distinguished from *H. heterophyes*. Like the latter they are ingested by the snail host. According to Stunkard and Willey [24] the molluscan host is *Semisulcospira (Melania) libertina,* in which one generation of sporocysts and two of redias develop in succession. The cercarias are lophocercous (the tail carries a ventral and dorsal membranous keel), their trunk measures 229 $\times$ 85 μ, their tail 286 $\times$ 27 μ. They possess numerous penetration glands and two eye spots; their integument is spinose.

Encysted metacercarias are found on the underside of the scales and in the fins (but not in the muscles) of the oriental trout *Plecoglossus altivelis* [25] and other fishes that serve as food for the popula-

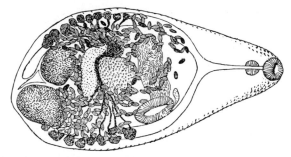

Fig. 11·7 *Metagonimus yokogawai,* $\times$ 50. (After Yokogawa; from Brumpt, 1922. Courtesy, Masson & Cie, Paris.)

tion in Japan and Formosa. The cysts, of a size of 140–160 $\times$ 100–200 μ, possess a thick wall. In young dogs fed on raw trout infected twenty days earlier, the metacercarias in the duodenum emerge from the cyst wall; seven to ten days later the puppies pass the eggs in their feces.

Yokogawa [25] claims that the metacercarias penetrate into the mucosa. They return to the lumen of the bowel as sexually mature adults. This observation has been confirmed for this and other species of heterophyids. However, Stunkard and Willey [24] believe that the parasites do not really penetrate into the tissue but only force their way into the spaces between the villi.

Dogs and cats are the most important alternate hosts of *M. yokogawai,* but it also parasitizes pelicans. It infects man to a rate varying from 2 to 50 percent over a wide area of northeastern Asia. Farther south, in Indonesia, it is found in cats and monkeys, but not in man [26]; three species of heterophyids are known to parasitize man in that country, but neither *Metagonimus* nor *Heterophyes* is among them.[27]

C. M. Africa and his co-workers [27a] in the Philippine Islands have detected various heterophyids in persons who died with acute dilatation of the heart. They were *Heterophyes brevicaeca (v. supra)* and members of the genus *Haplorchis,* characterized by the possession of only one testis, and *Stellantchasmus,* with short ceca and a long esophagus. The eggs of these parasites were found far from the normal site of their parents, viz. in the tissue of the heart and other organs; the concomitant morbid condition was ascribed to this ectopic site. It was assumed that this was due to the parasite penetrating into the tissue of the bowel; it does not succeed in extricating itself from that site and dies. Its eggs, set free by the disintegration of the parent, are passively transported to various organs, the heart among them. It is even possible that the adults are transported in this way, since Deschiens *et al.*[29] found in the Far East *H. heterophyes* encysted in the human brain. Although *Haplorchis* in Indonesia [27] did not behave in this abnormal way, the unsettled host-parasite relationship characteristic of the whole family renders Africa's assumption wholly plausible.

TREATMENT OF HETEROPHYID INFECTION. The specific drug appears to be tetrachlorethylene, available in gelatine globules of 0.5 and 1.0 ml. The adult dosage is 3 ml, for children it is 0.2 ml per year of age.[20] Others [30] recommend thymol and oleoresin of aspidium.

DICROCOELIUM DENDRITICUM

Dicrocoelium dendriticum (Rudolphi, 1818) Looss, 1899 family of Dicrocoeliidae is a transparent parasite inhabiting the biliary ducts of its definitive host. It is lancet-shaped, its size is 8–10 × 1.5–2.5 mm, its integument has no scales or spines. The oral sucker has a definitely ventral position, the wider acetabulum lies one-fifth of the body length farther back, the genital atrium halfway between the two suckers.

The pharynx is spherical in shape. The esophagus divides into the ceca at the level of the genital atrium; these extend to the posterior fifth of the body. Two large, slightly lobed testes lie diagonally, immediately behind the acetabulum; the cirrus pouch lies anteriorly, just behind the bifurcation of the intestine. The ovary is situated behind the posterior testis, to the left of the midline; the small seminal receptacle lies in its close vicinity. The posterior fifth of the body is filled with the coils of the uterus; farther cephalad its coils remain within the area limited by the ceca; from the equator onwards the uterus winds its way between the testes to the genital atrium, with some minor convolutions. The vitelline glands occupy a lateral position in the middle third of the body (Fig. 11·8:*A*).

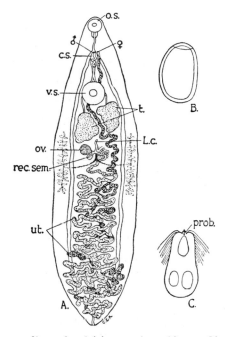

FIG. 11·8 *Dicrocoelium dendriticum, A,* × 10: *cs,* Cirrus pouch.—*L.c,* Laurer's duct.—*o.s,* Oral sucker.—*ov,* Ovary.—*rec.sem,* Seminal receptacle.—*t,* Testes.—*ut,* Uterus.—*v.s,* Acetabulum.—♂♀, Genital atrium.— *B,* Egg.—*C,* Miracidium.—*prob,* Stylet. (After M. W. Jepps, 1936. Courtesy, E. and S. Livingstone, Edinburgh.)

The eggs measure 38–45 × 22–30 μ. Often they are asymmetrical: one side is flat, the other convex. The shell is fairly thick, of a dark yellowish-brown color, with a small operculum (Figs. 11·8:*B* and 11·9). They are embryonated when they leave the host's body in the feces.

The miracidium enclosed within the eggshell carries a piercing organ or stylet at its anterior extremity (Fig. 11·8:*C*). It does not

leave the shell until the egg has been ingested by the first intermediate host. As for no other trematodes, terrestrial snails, of the
genera *Helicella* and *Zebrina,* have taken up this function. Two
generations of sporocysts develop; the second produces large cercarias
with a trunk of 400–700 × 70–200 μ and a tail 450–900 μ long and
almost as wide as the trunk at its base, which gradually tapers to its
slender posterior extremity.

These cercarias, known as *Cercaria vitrina* long before the life
cycle of *D. dendriticum* had been described,[31] carry a stylet in the
anterodorsal portion of the oral sucker. They enter the venous
circulation of the snail and arrive successively in the vena magna

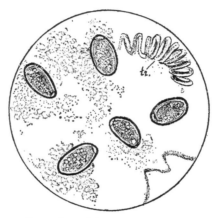

Fig. 11·9 *Dicrocoelium dendriticum,* eggs in feces, × 250: *tr,* Vegetable spiral vessel. (After Brumpt, 1927. Courtesy, Masson & Cie, Paris.)

and the respiratory cavity. In the latter they agglomerate into
spherical slime balls, which in their turn agglutinate into composite
slime balls 3–12 mm in size. The latter are ejected through the
respiratory orifice and become attached to plants. They contain
thousands of cercarias still in possession of their tail, each enclosed
within a separate envelope.

It was formerly believed [31] that sheep become infected by ingesting
the slime balls when they are grazing. Recently, however, Krull and
Mapes [32] have proved that events take a different turn, which brings
them more in line with the life cycle of other trematodes. They
found second intermediate hosts in three species of ants, *Formica
fusca* in New York State, the same species and also *F. rufibarbis* and
F. gagates in Germany.[32a] These insects ingest the slime balls, and

the cercarias become encysted metacercarias in their abdomen after 38–56 days. The mature metacercarias have a size of 243–400 × 200–270 μ; their cyst wall is 16–23 μ thick. If sheep accidentally ingest infected ants they begin to pass eggs in their feces after a lapse of 56–60 days.

D. dentriticum parasitizes sheep and cattle, rabbits, pigs, horses and donkeys, and rarely dogs and cats; in wild life it has been found in deer, hares, boars, and bears. It occurs in Europe, northern and eastern Asia, north and west Africa, and North and South America. As to human infection, between 1925 and 1929 the eggs of *D. dentriticum* were found in 200 inhabitants of European and Asiatic Russia.[33] Sporadic cases have been reported from central Europe and France, northern and central Africa, the Near East, northern Asia, and Java. In assessing the value of these reports it must not be forgotten that the finding of eggs in the feces does not prove the presence of parasites in the intestine; it may be a case of *spurious parasitism* in a person who has consumed (even well-cooked) infected liver, a source of error also signalized with reference to *F. hepatica* and which can be avoided by examining the bile collected by duodenal intubation.

TREATMENT OF INFECTION WITH D. DENDRITICUM. Human infections requiring treatment are too rare to allow evaluation of reports on the administration of drugs such as thymol, fuadin, and even emetine in unusually high doses.

REFERENCES FOR CHAPTER XI

1. O. N. GOLYANITZKAYA. *Trop. Diseases Bull.*, 1950, 47: 382.
2. H. VOGEL. *Arch. Schiffs- u. Tropenhyg.*, 1932, 36: 558–561.
3. M. BRAUN. *Die tierische Parasiten des Menschen*, 608 pp., Leipzig, 1925, Curt Kabitzsch, pp. 212–215.
4. L. SZIDAT. *Zentr. Bakteriol.*, Abt. I, Ref., 1943, 142: 391–392.
5. N. MIRONOWA. *Trop. Diseases Bull.*, 1940, 37: 152.
6. E. H. SADUN. *Am. J. Hyg.*, 1955, 62: 81–115.
7. E. C. FAUST and O. K. KHAW. *Am. J. Hyg.*, Monogr. Ser., No. 8, 284 pp., Baltimore, 1927.
8. D. MOORE. *Public Health Repts.* (*U. S.*), 1924, 39: 1802–1803.
9. M. MUTO. *Japan Med. World*, 1922, 2: 224–226.
10. H. F. HSÜ and C. Y. CHOW. *China Med. J.*, 1937, 51: 341–346.
11. H. F. HSÜ and L. S. WANG. *China Med. J.*, 1938, 52 (Suppl. 2): 385–400.
12. D. E. WYKOFF and T. J. LEPEŠ. *Am. J. Trop. Med. Hyg.*, 1957, 6: 1061–1065.
13. J. H. F. OTTO. *Arch. Schiffs- u. Tropenhyg.*, 1937, 41: 488–493.
14. R. HOEPPLI. *China Med. J.*, 1933, 44: 1125–1141.

15. R. P. KOENIGSTEIN. *Trans. Roy. Soc. Trop. Med. Hyg.,* 1949, 42: 503–504.
16. C. H. BINFORD. *Public Health Repts.,* 1934, 49: 602–604.
17. H. KAWANA. *J. Shanghai Sci. Inst.,* Sect. IV, 1936, 2: 75–85.
18. Y. KOMIYA, H. KAWANA, and S. C. TAO. *J. Shanghai Sci. Inst.,* Sect. IV, 1935, 1: 271–292.
19. E. C. FAUST and YAO KE FENG. *Arch. Schiffs- u. Tropenhyg.,* 1926, 30: 383–391.
20. E. C. FAUST, P. F. RUSSELL, and D. R. LINCICOME. *Clinical Parasitology,* Philadelphia, 1957, pp. 580, 586, 589, 592.
21. E. C. FAUST and M. NISHIGORI. *J. Parasitol.,* 1926, 13: 91–127.
22. M. KHALIL. *Lancet,* 1924 (1): 952, and 1933 (2): 537.
23. W. H. WELLS and B. H. RANDALL. *J. Egypt. Public Health Assoc.,* 1955, 30: 83–86; *J. Parasitol.,* 1956, 42: 287–292.
23a. C. M. AFRICA and E. Y. GARCIA. *Philippine J. Sci.,* 1935, 57: 253–265.
24. H. W. STUNKARD and H. WILLEY. *Am. J. Trop. Med.,* 1929, 9: 117–128.
25. S. YOKOGAWA. *Centr. Bakteriol.,* Abt. I, Or., 1913, 72: 158–179.
26. H. MENGERT-PRESSER. *Mededeel. Burgerlijk. Geneeskund. Dienst Ned. Indië,* 1925, 14: 22–27, Eng. ed.
27. LIE KIAN JOE and G. BRAS. *Documenta Med. Geograph. et Trop. Amsterdam,* 1951, 3: 105–116.
27a. C. M. AFRICA, E. Y. GARCIA, and W. DE LEON. *Philippine J. Public Health,* 1935, 2: 1–22.
28. C. M. AFRICA, W. DE LEON, and E. Y. GARCIA. *Third Intern. Congr. Microbiol.,* New York, 1939, Abstracts, p. 173.
29. R. DESCHIENS, H. COLLOMB, and J. DEMARCHI. *Sixth Intern. Congr. Trop. Med. and Malaria,* Lisbon, 1958, Abstracts, p. 265.
30. PH. H. MANSON-BAHR. *Tropical Diseases,* London, 1957, p. 941.
31. W. NEUHAUS. *Z. Parasitenk.,* 1938, 8: 476–512.
32. W. H. KRULL and C. R. MAPES. *Cornell Vet.,* 1952, 41: 382–432; 42: 253–267, 339–351, 464–489, 603–604; 1953, 43: 389–410.
32a. H. VOGEL and J. FALCÃO. *Z. Tropenmed. Parasitol.,* 1954, 5: 275–296.
33. W. TARASSOW. *Trop. Diseases Bull.,* 1933, 30: 678.

PART THREE

Helminths: Cestodes

CHAPTER XII

CESTODES OR TAPEWORMS

The shape of the common human parasites in this second group of helminths has been compared to a tape. This likeness is produced by numerous flat units, attached to each other in such a way that, together, they form a tape. Each unit is called a *proglottid,* the tape they form, a *strobila.* The length of the proglottids is measured along the longitudinal axis of the strobila, their width in a direction perpendicular to it. The anterior portion of the strobila is thread-like and tapers into an extremity still slenderer than the rest, the *neck,* which is not differentiated into proglottids, but carries a minute knob- or club-shaped structure at its top, the *head* or *scolex.*

Neck and scolex together form one unit; sometimes the name of "scolex" is applied to the whole. It is a most important organ, for two reasons: (1) the neck produces new proglottids, to counter-balance the losses incurred by proglottids withering or being cast off alive at the other extremity of the strobila; (2) the scolex carries the suckers, spines, or hooklets with which the strobila attaches itself to the tissue of the host.

Each mature proglottid carries one set (rarely two) of male and female sex organs, sometimes called the *genital complex.* Neither in scolex and neck nor in the proglottids is there any structure that might be compared with an intestinal tract. The whole strobila absorbs substances present in the intestinal contents of the host, irrespective of their being poisons or nutrients, as may be seen from the yellow color of the taenia expelled by the action of quinacrine and from the diphyllobothrium full of vitamin B_{12} essential for its host.

The structure of the integument resembles that of the trematodes. The muscular system is more complicated; it enables the strobila to move in its totality, and the gravid (egg-bearing) proglottid to move separately when it becomes detached from the strobila.

As in the trematodes, the excretory organs are represented by the terminal organs or flame cells and the associated system of capillaries and ducts. They open into two excretory canals, situated laterally and extending over the whole length of the strobila, without regard to the confines of the separate proglottids. Each canal is first directed anteriorly (ascending canal); as it arrives in the scolex it turns right about to follow the opposite direction (descending canal). Thus, two canals are to be seen in the left and the right side of the strobila.

The human cestodes to be described here fall into two groups. The proglottids of one group, the Pseudophyllidea, have much in common with the trematodes; the genital atrium lies in the midline of one of the flat sides. The uterus has an opening to lay the eggs; it is flanked by two vitelline glands situated laterally. The eggs are operculate. The proglottids of the other group, the Cyclophyllidea, have their genital atrium situated on one of the lateral narrow sides. The uterus has no opening. There is only one vitelline gland to each uterus, and the eggs are nonoperculate.

CHAPTER XIII

PSEUDOPHYLLIDEA

Apart from a number of rare human parasites, this group comprises only one family, the Diphyllobothriidae, with one species inhabiting the human intestine as a sexually mature adult, *Diphyllobothrium latum,* and one (or more) species, belonging to the genus *Spirometra,* inhabiting various human tissues as immature adults.

DIPHYLLOBOTHRIUM LATUM: THE FISH TAPEWORM

Diphyllobothrium latum (Linnaeus, 1758) Lühe, 1910 [*Bothriocephalus latus* (L. 1758) Bremser, 1858; *Dibothriocephalus latus* (L. 1758) Lühe, 1899] is one of the three long tapeworms that commonly parasitize man. The two others (the taenias) are strictly limited to one definitive and one intermediate host. The "broad

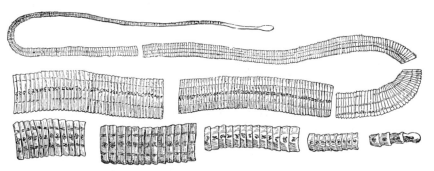

FIG. 13·1 *Diphyllobothrium latum:* Selected portions of the strobila in their natural size. (After Leuckart.)

tapeworm" on the contrary has a wide range of definitive and second intermediate hosts; it is more limited in the choice of its first intermediate host.

The worm can reach a length of 10 or even 12 meters, with 3000 or 4000 or more proglottids. Sexually mature proglottids measure 2–4 mm in length and 10–15 mm in width (Figs. 13·1, 13·4). They are ivory white; the centrally situated uterus, filled with dark-shelled eggs, shows as a black dot on a white background, a feature never seen in the taenias. Another characteristic differentiating the worm from the taenias is the fact that sexual activity and production of eggs are closely associated and are continued for a long time. In the taenias the gravid proglottids (which are filled with mature eggs but have passed the stage of sexual activity) are detached from the strobila. In *D. latum* this happens only to the withered proglottids.

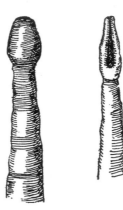

Fig. 13·2   *Diphyllobothrium latum:* Scolex, × 4. Left, aspect of a "flat" side; right, aspect of a narrow side, with bothrium. (After Leuckart.)

The scolex (Fig. 13·2) usually measures 2–3 by 1 mm. It is spatulate or almond shaped, and so it has two flat and two narrow sides. Each narrow side is marked by a deep, longitudinal, slitlike groove or *bothrium* which functions as a sucker. The flat sides have a position perpendicular to the flat sides of the proglottids. The neck of the scolex measures 5–20 × 0.6 mm.

Each sexually mature proglottid carries a genital atrium, situated in the midline, in the anterior quarter of one of the flat sides, which is called the ventral side. The genital atrium is surrounded by a prominent wall. There are two genital pores in this atrium: (1) an anterior or male pore, into which the cirrus opens, enclosed within the cirrus pouch at the anterior end of the vas deferens; (2) a posterior or vaginal pore, into which the vagina opens, a duct unknown in the trematodes. A third genital pore, the *uterine pore,* lies behind the genital atrium, and slightly to the left (Figs. 13·3:1, 13·4).

The numerous testes (Fig. 13·3:2) are situated dorsally in the lateral fields. Their vasa efferentia open into a central seminal vesicle, from which emerges the vas deferens that winds its way to the cirrus pouch. The ovary (Fig. 13·3:1) lies posterior to the

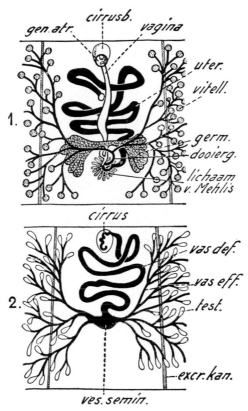

Fig. 13·3 *Diphyllobothrium latum*, median portion of a proglottid (between the excretory canals), schematic: 1. Separate female sexual organs: *gen atr*, Genital atrium.—*cirrusb*, Cirrus pouch.—*vagina* (uterine pore to its left side).—*uter*, Coil of uterus.—*vitell*, Vitelline gland.—*germ*, Ovary.—*dooierg*, Common vitelline duct.—*lichaam v. Mehlis*, Shell gland. 2. Separate male sexual organs: *cirrus*.—*vas def*, Vas deferens.— *vas eff*, One of the vasa efferentia.—*test*, One of the testes.—*excr.kan*, Excretory canal. (After Benham, from Ihle and Nierstrasz, 1928. Courtesy, Oosthoek & Co., Publishers, Utrecht.)

equator. It is dumbbell shaped, the handle lying in the midline. The oviduct, emerging from the center of the ovary, is joined by the vagina; together they form a common duct, sometimes called the "fertilizing duct" because the ova passed on by the oviduct are fertilized here by the spermatozoa admitted by the vagina through the vaginal pore. The fertilizing duct is joined by the transverse vitelline duct, which transports the vitelline cells, the products of the vitelline glands, situated in the lateral fields ventrally to the testes. Then the fertilizing duct terminates by entering the ootype, into which open the numerous shell glands that form the body of Mehlis.

Emerging from the ootype, the uterus (Fig. 13·3:1), in the earlier stages of development, takes a straight course to the uterine pore. While the eggs, collecting within the uterus, are increasing in num-

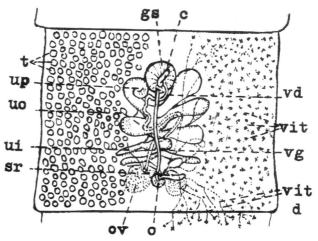

FIG. 13·4 *Diphyllobothrium latum,* sexually mature proglottid, × 17: *c,* Cirrus.—*gs,* Male orifice.—*o,* Ootype.—*ov,* Ovary.—*sr,* Seminal receptacle.—*t,* Testes (drawn only in left field).—*ui,* Inner, *uo,* outer uterine coils.—*up,* Uterine pore.—*vd,* Vas deferens.—*vg,* Vagina.—*vit,* Vitelline follicles (drawn only in right field).—*vit d,* Vitelline ducts. (After Craig and Faust, 1951. Courtesy, Henry Kimpton, London.)

ber, the uterus grows in length, forming coils to the right and the left, which finally are packed into a tight *rosette,* with four or five coils, rarely six, on both sides (Fig. 13·4).

The eggs leave the proglottid by the uterine pore. They are operculate and broadly ovoid (Fig. 13·5), measuring 68–76 × 40–51 μ; their shell has a yellowish color. They are passed in the feces of the host in a nonembryonated condition, i.e. they contain vitelline cells which surround a fertilized ovum that is in an early stage of fission.

If the fertilized egg soon finds its way to clear water (for it is killed by desiccation as well as by putrefaction), it develops into a *coracidium* (Figs. 13·6 and 13·8:*A–C*) after about a fortnight. The coracidium consists of a spherical larva, called *hexacanth larva* or *oncosphere,* which possesses three pairs of hooklets and is enveloped by a cellular membrane carrying cilia. The coracidium pushes open the operculum, emerges from the eggshell, and swims in the surrounding water; in this medium it can survive for no longer than 12 hours.

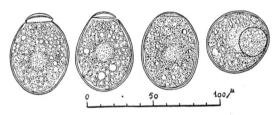

FIG. 13·5   *Diphyllobothrium latum,* eggs, × 350: Right, an egg seen from above; the others, side aspect; the clear central space, the ovum; the granular mass surrounding it, vitelline cells. (After Brumpt, 1936. Courtesy, Masson & Cie, Paris.)

If the coracidium is ingested by certain copepods of the genera *Cyclops* and *Diaptomus,*[1] it sheds the cellular membrane with the cilia when it arrives in the midgut of this first intermediate host (Fig. 13·8:*E*). It pierces the intestinal wall and thus arrives in the hemal cavity. However, not all of the above-named genera of copepods are appropriate hosts. Some are too resistant. They simply refuse the oncospheres admittance to their hemal cavity. Then the parasites remain in the lumen of the midgut, and there they are killed and digested.[2] Others are too little resistant: in their body the oncosphere becomes an aggressor that kills the copepod in two to three days, long before the parasite can develop into its next stage, the procercoid.[3]

However, if the oncosphere finds itself within a copepod of an appropriate degree of resistance, it becomes a larva of the second stage after two to three weeks (Fig. 13·8:*F, G, D*). This larva, the *procercoid,* is about 0.5 mm long. It is characterized by (1) a spinose integument; (2) an anterior invagination at the bottom of which glandular cells are situated; (3) a spherical posterior appendage, called the *cercomer,* that still carries the three pairs of hooklets, thus bearing witness that the procercoid developed from the hexacanth larva, and (4) minute concrements of lime in its interior (Fig. 13·8:*F*, *G*).

Development cannot proceed any further unless the infected copepods are devoured by the second intermediate host, represented by fresh-water fishes of genera such as pike (*Esox*), perch (*Perca*), lawyer (*Lota*) (Fig. 13·8:*H*), trout (*Salmo*) and the ruff (*Acerina*). Then the procercoids are liberated in the intestine of the fish. They pierce the wall of the bowel and make their way to the muscles and

bothrium

FIG. 13·6   *Diphyllobothrium latum:* Coracidium, schematic. (After Benham, from Ihle and Nierstrasz, 1928. Courtesy, Oosthoek & Co., Publishers, Utrecht.)

FIG. 13·7   *Diphyllobothrium latum,*   plerocercoid,   × 7. (After Braun; from Ihle and Nierstrasz, 1928. Courtesy, Oosthoek & Co., Publishers, Utrecht.)

other organs. There they settle down and develop into a third stage, the *plerocercoid* or sparganum, no longer a larva but a very immature tapeworm (Figs. 13·7 and 13·8:*I*), which already possesses a scolex with bothria. It has an initial length of a few millimeters, but it may grow to 30 mm and over. That depends on what happens to the fish in which the plerocercoid is settled. There are three possibilities:

(1) The fish is never killed and eaten; then it dies a natural death, and the plerocercoid dies with it without having attained its full development.

(2) The fish is devoured by another fish. In this case the plerocercoid penetrates into the same organs as those in which it was

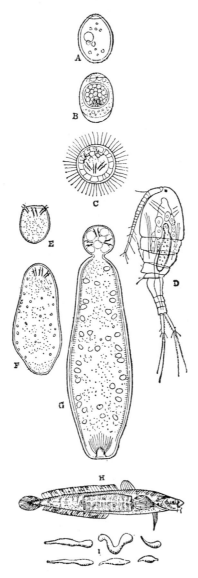

FIG. 13·8 *Diphyllobothrium latum,* life cycle: *A,* Egg.—*B,* Coracidium within egg.—*C,* Free coracidium.—*D,* Cyclops.—*E,* Oncosphere in cyclops, after shedding its cilia-carrying envelope.—*F,* Immature procercoid.—*G,* Mature procercoid showing posterior cercomer (above), anterior invagination in which opens a bundle of glandular cells, interior with concrements of lime.—*I,* Plerocercoids.—*H,* A lawyer, *Lota vulgaris,* in which they were found. (After Brumpt, 1922. Courtesy, Masson & Cie, Paris.)

settled in the first fish; it never stays on in the lumen of the bowel of the second fish, thus remaining what it was before: a plerocercoid. This process of passing from one host to another, without any progress in development (except for growing in length), is called *re-encapsulation*. Theoretically it might go on *ad infinitum*, without the plerocercoid ever becoming a sexually mature tapeworm. In the meantime, predatory fish (e.g. pike), devouring a large quantity of small fry, will collect numbers of plerocercoids of various sizes. If such fish are eventually consumed by man, multiple infection will result, which, as a matter of fact, is of common occurrence in persons infected with *D. latum*.[4]

(3) The fish is consumed by man or devoured by an alternate mammalian host. In this case the plerocercoid remains in the lumen of the bowel; it does not show any inclination to pierce the intestinal wall and to wander to muscles or other organs, which it had invariably displayed during its stay in a succession of fish. Moreover, true development, which had remained in abeyance during the successive re-encapsulations, now progresses rapidly. After two to four weeks the plerocercoid has become an egg-laying tapeworm.[10] But it takes another nine to eleven weeks, at least, to become a full-sized specimen of 7 meters or so.

D. latum, as a human parasite, has an extensive area of distribution in the Northern Hemisphere; the greater part of northern Eurasia, from Sakhalin to Germany, in the Old World; Canada and the northern United States in the New World. In the Southern Hemisphere it has been reported from south Chile, the Australian continent, and Tasmania. Apparently the parasite prefers temperate regions. Although it does not avoid subtropical and tropical countries, such as Spain, Syria, central and south Africa, it nowhere occurs in such profusion as in Siberia and northwestern Russia, where 20–76 percent of the population are infected,[4] a rate which may rise to 80–100 percent in some villages.[5] Finland, with infection rates of 14 percent among the soldiers and of 60 percent among the civilian population,[6] is another example to the same effect; so is the area of the Kurisches Haff and the delta of the Memel River in East Prussia, with a rate of 44 percent.[7] In Germany in the lower reaches of the river Elbe, fishes of the perch and eelpout varieties (*Perca fluviatilis* and *Zoarces viviparus*) have been reported infected with plerocercoids of *D. latum* [8]; but farther to the west of this north European belt no piscine or human infections have been reported (Belgium, northern France, British Isles, and Ireland) or false reports to that effect have been corrected.[9] To the south of this belt, the shores of the French, Swiss, and Italian Alpine lakes show (or showed) considerable human infection, e.g. 15–20 percent on the Lake of Geneva. Cases have also been reported from Poland and Rumania.

North America has its own center of distribution along the Great Lakes. It is assumed that infection was introduced into that area by lumbermen from northeastern Europe. The infection is maintained by the cooperation of various American species of pike and Amerindian dogs that are fed with these fish. From this center infected fish are exported to large cities, such as Detroit, Boston, and New York, where certain classes of the population are in the habit of consuming most appetizing dishes prepared with uncooked fish.[11] Alaska, a most important center, with 30 percent of the Eskimos infected, must be mentioned separately because *D. alascense* (Rausch and Williamson, 1958 [12]) occurs there, and not *D. latum*. The same may apply to the equally important centers of northern Canada.

Among the alternate hosts, such as domestic cats, pigs (in Russia) and bears (in Canada), the dog merits special attention, because man lives in close touch with this animal. In Canada [13] its rate of infection was 30 percent, in East Prussia over 50 percent.[14] However, canine carriers may be of less importance than human carriers as a source of infection, if Essex and Magath [15] are right in their claims that eggs passed by dogs grow coracidia to a smaller percentage than eggs passed by man. Be this as it may, dogs can never be more than a domestic reservoir. In Canada, at least, a sylvatic, or wild, reservoir exists, constituted by the bears. It is worth while speculating whether bears became infected secondarily or whether they were the original definitive hosts in Canada, long before the settlement of the European lumbermen.

There exists some uncertainty as regards the pathogenic effect of *D. latum* on man. Experiments in man [14] have shown that it causes serious symptoms, especially at the time the worm commences to lay eggs. However, the patient quickly recovers; after this initial illness, the parasite is tolerated without any further trouble.[10] If the worm is expelled by anthelminthics, it may be found impossible to reinfect the subject for the next few years, but even a successful reinfection is not accompanied by the serious symptoms that characterized the primary infection.[16]

On the other hand, infection with D. latum may be associated with the symptoms of pernicious anemia. The patient may recover by a therapy specifically directed against that disease, although the worms he harbors have not been dislodged. Conversely, patients suffering from the same disease may die notwithstanding an earlier successful anthelminthic treatment. Moreover, in Finland, where this complication is of comparatively common occurrence, pernicious anemia is met with in one parasite carrier only out of a number of carriers varying between 113 and 136, according to the locality. Thus, the conclusion reached was that no causal association did exist between pernicious anemia and D. latum, or if it did, that it was of the nature of a sensitizing effect of the worm on a patient innately disposed to the disease.

Von Bonsdorff and his associates,[17] however, claim that the worm may be the immediate cause of the disease. Whether it is or is not depends on its site in the human intestine. Usually it is lodged in the ileum, and there it is comparatively harmless. Occasionally, it is lodged in the jejunum, and in that portion of the intestine, especially in its upper reaches and even more in the duodenum, it becomes the cause of pernicious anemia. The reason is that the worm in this particular site absorbs Castle's "extrinsic factor" (vitamin B_{12}). Thus it robs its host of this indispensable nutrient, thereby preventing its association with the "intrinsic factor," the product of the parietal cells in the fundus glands of the stomach. As confirmatory evidence Nyberg et al.[18] have shown that worm carriers excrete much less B_{12} in their urine than normal subjects, and anemic carriers significantly less than nonanemic. Expulsion of the worms was followed by a significant increase in urinary excretion of B_{12}.

TREATMENT OF INFECTION WITH D. latum. As in the treatment of the human taeniases, oleoresin of aspidium is more and more discarded in favor of quinacrine hydrochloride (Atabrine) two tablets every 10 minutes for 4 doses (800 mg) on an empty stomach, together with 0.5 gm of sodium bicarbonate. Saline purgation is prescribed (1 tablespoonful of sulfate of sodium dissolved in a glass of water) if the worm has not been expelled in two hours. The necessity of emptying the intestine before the drug is administered is particularly emphasized.[19]

SPARGANUM MANSONI

Sparganum mansoni Cobbold, 1883, is not the name of a species. It is the immature form (plerocercoid) of one or more species of the diphyllobothriid family. As adults they inhabit the small intestine of feline and canine carnivora; as plerocercoids they parasitize the internal organs of frogs, snakes and birds, as well as mammals—e.g., voles, pigs, and man. It has not yet been decided whether the adult

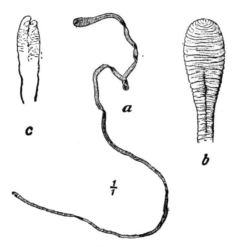

Fig. 13·9 *Sparganum mansoni: a,* Whole worm, natural size.—*b,* Anterior extremity.—*c,* Posterior extremity. (After Sambon, from Brumpt, 1922. Courtesy, Masson & Cie, Paris.)

worm, whose plerocercoid is the human *Sparganum mansoni,* belongs to one species, *D. erinacei,* or to two, *D. erinacei* and *D. mansoni.* However, the adult worms which Bonne,[20] in Indonesia, has grown in cats and dogs, starting from spargana recovered from man, have been identified by Faust [10] as belonging to the species *D. ranarum.* All these species differ from *D. latum* by (1) the smaller size of the strobila, maximal length 2.5 meters; (2) the smaller size of the eggs, 50–66 × 32–37 μ, and their different shape (cf. Fig. 13·10:*A* and *E*); (3) the shape of the uterus, whose coils form a spiral rather than a rosette. For these reasons a separate genus, *Spirometra,*[25] has been created for them.

The spargana parasitize the abovementioned animals in the form of long, flat, often greatly coiled worms (Fig. 13·9). Their size varies from 16 to 35 cm in length and from 0.1 to 1.2 cm in width. They show a distinct transverse striation, but no proglottids. A scolex with bothria has sometimes been observed.

In man spargana have been detected in various internal organs, such as perirenal adipose tissue, urinary bladder, wall of the bowel, pleural cavity and subcutaneous tissue. Bonne and Lie Kian Joe [21] once found a 50-cm-long sparganum in the pulmonary artery. The inhabitants of Indochina often show a sparganum in the immediate vicinity of the eye (*ocular sparganosis*). This peculiar localization owes its origin to the custom of treating various ocular complaints

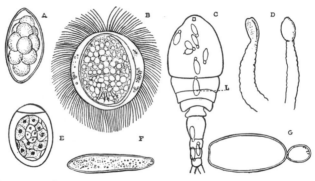

Fig. 13·10 *Diphyllobothrium mansoni,* life cycle: *A,* Egg (as a comparison: *E,* egg of *D. latum*), × 310.—*B,* Coracidium, × 378.—*C, Cyclops leuckarti* carrying procercoids (*L*) 21 days after infection.—*D,* Scolex of *D. mansoni,* frontal and side aspect, × 10.—*F,* procercoid aged 21 days.—*G,* Procercoid aged 8 days, with cercomer, × 125. (After Okumura, from Brumpt, 1936. Courtesy, Masson & Cie, Paris.)

by application to the sick eye of a frog cut open or minced into pulp as a poultice. If the frog was infected, the plerocercoids leave the mutilated carcass and re-encapsulate near the orbit. This process has been reproduced experimentally in rabbits.[22]

Man can become infected without resorting to this kind of treatment and even without ingesting infected copepods or consuming raw or underdone fish or meat of any kind. In Australia pigs are infected with spargana. If their muscles are chopped into minced meat, the spargana stick to the chopping knife. In trying to wipe them off, the cook may inadvertently transfer them to her mouth, like the Japanese cook chopping paragonimus-infected crabs.[23]

Spargana have been found most often in Japan, Indochina, Korea, and Formosa. Sporadic cases were reported in Indonesia, Africa, and Australia.

Sparganum proliferum [24] (Ijima, 1905) Stiles, 1908. This peculiar plerocercoid was found in the groin of a Japanese woman, in cavities of the dermal tissue, of a size of 1–8 mm. In each cavity were lodged one or several plerocercoids, 3–12 mm long; one extremity was very thin, the other had a maximal width of 2.5 mm. No scolex or bothria were seen. The peculiar feature about the worm was its producing buds that became separated from the mother worm and grew to new plerocercoids. Some more cases have been reported in Japan, one in Florida, and one in Europe. Besides the skin, the plerocercoids have been recovered from various internal organs, such as muscles, bowel, mesentery, kidneys, lungs, heart, and brain.[10]

REFERENCES FOR CHAPTER XIII

1. C. Janicki and F. Rosen. *Bull. soc. neuchâtel. sci. nat.*, 1917, 42: 19–53.
2. H. Vogel. *Z. Parasitenk.*, 1930, 2: 629–644.
3. C. H. Li and E. C. Faust. *Proc. Soc. Exptl. Biol., New York*, 1928, 26: 250–251.
4. G. K. Petruschewsky and W. Tarassow. *Arch. Schiffs- u. Tropenhyg.*, 1933, 37: 307–315.
5. W. Tarassow. *Arch. Schiffs- u. Tropenhyg.*, 1934, 38: 477–486.
6. G. Töttermann. *Trop. Diseases Bull.*, 1945, 42: 116–117.
7. L. Szidat. *Zentr. Bakteriol.*, Abt. I, Ref., 1943, 142: 391–392.
8. F. Kühlow. *Z. Tropenmed. Parasitol.*, 1953, 4: 186–202.
9. C. Kerbert. *Ned. Tijdschr. Geneesk.*, 1889, 25: 424–427, 533.
10. G. Z. L. Le Bas. *J. Helminthol.*, 1924, 2: 151–166.
11. M. Barron. *J. Am. Med. Assoc.*, 1929, 92: 1587–1593.
12. R. Rausch and F. S. Williamson. *Z. Tropenmed. Parasitol.*, 1958, 9: 64–72.
13. T. Vergeer. *J. Am. Med. Assoc.*, 1929, 92: 607–608.
14. H. Vogel. *Deut. med. Wochschr.*, 1929, 55: 1631–1633.
15. H. E. Essex and T. B. Magath. *Am. J. Hyg.*, 1931, 14: 698–704.
16. V. Tarassov. *Ann. parasitol. humaine et comparée*, 1937, 15: 524–528.
17. B. von Bonsdorff. *Exptl. Parasitol.*, 1956, 5: 207–230.
18. W. Nyberg, R. Gräsbeck, and V. Sippola. *New Engl. J. Med.*, 1958, 259: 216–219.
19. E. C. Faust, P. F. Russell, and D. R. Lincicome. *Clinical Parasitology*, Philadelphia, 1957, pp. 621, 625, 624.
20. C. Bonne. *Geneesk. Tijdschr. Ned. Indië*, 1930, 70: 1235–1238 (English summary, 1238).
21. C. Bonne and Lie Kian Joe. *Am. J. Trop. Med.*, 1942, 22: 643–645.
22. K. H. Gan. Thesis, Batavia, 104 pp., Soekaboemi, 1941, with English summary.
23. D. F. Sandars. *Med. J. Australia*, 1954 (2nd half): 817–818.
24. J. F. Mueller. *Am. J. Trop. Med.*, 1938, 18: 303–328.
25. J. F. Mueller. *Am. J. Trop. Med.*, 1941, 21: 399–425.

CYCLOPHYLLIDEA I: TAENIIDS AS TAPEWORMS

In the introduction to the cestodes the main characteristics of the Cyclophyllidea, distinguishing them from the Pseudophyllidea, have been shortly enumerated. An amplification of these characteristics follows and refers only to Cyclophyllidea that are common parasites in man.

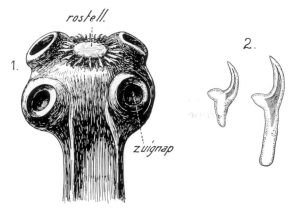

Fig. 14·1 1. Scolex of a taenia: *rostell*, Rostellum.—*zuignap*, Sucker.— 2. Large and small hooklet on rostellum. (1, after Stempell; 2, after Hall; from Ihle and Nierstrasz, 1928. Courtesy, Oosthoek & Co., Publishers, Utrecht.)

(1) The scolex carries four suckers (Fig. 14·1:1). Moreover, its anterior extremity often takes the form of an elevation, the *rostellum*, on which hooklets (Fig. 14·1:2) or spines may be implanted.

(2) The descending excretory canals are united by transverse canals, situated near the posterior margin of each proglottid (Fig. 14·2:*ek, kl*).

(3) In some Cyclophyllidea all proglottids are short, i.e. wider than long, as in the Pseudophyllidea. In others the younger proglottids, nearer the scolex, are short; farther from the scolex they are

square (length equaling width); still further on they are oblong (length exceeding width).

(4) The sexual activity of a proglottid is terminated abruptly by all the eggs it contains reaching maturity almost at the same time. At that moment the proglottid becomes a *gravid proglottid;* its only functioning sexual organ, the uterus, is converted into a sack full of ripe eggs.

(5) The sexually mature proglottid possesses a single vitelline gland, situated behind the bilobed ovary (Fig. 14·2:*Dk*). If the

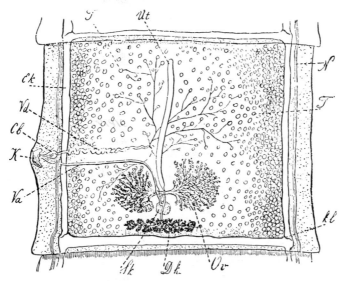

Fig. 14·2 Sexually mature proglottid of *Taenia saginata: Cb,* Cirrus pouch.—*Dk,* Vitelline gland.—*Ek,* Descending excretory canal.—*K,* Genital atrium.—*Kl,* Transverse excretory canal.—*N,* Lateral nerve.—*Ov,* Ovary.—*Sk,* Shell gland.—*T,* Testicular vesicle.—*Ut,* Uterus.—*Va,* Vagina. —*Vd,* Vas deferens. (After Leuckart, from Braun, 1925. Courtesy, Curt Kabitzsch, Leipzig.)

proglottid contains two genital complexes (*Dipylidium*), there are two vitelline glands, one to each complex.

(6) The genital atrium is situated on one of the lateral margins (in dipylidium on both). It comprises a male pore and a vaginal pore (Fig. 14·2:*Cb, Va*). A uterine pore does not exist. The eggs are laid through a rent in the uterus and a corresponding rent in the integument of the proglottid. The genital atria are *unilateral,* i.e. situated on the same side of the succeeding proglottids, or *alternating,*

i.e. one to the right, the next to the left, and so on, with numerous irregularities.

(7) The ovum develops into a larva, the oncosphere (with three pairs of hooklets), while still contained within the gravid proglottid (Fig. 14·4:1–4). The oncosphere is enclosed within a hard shell, the *embryophore,* which is a part of the larva. In its turn, the embryophore is lying within the eggshell proper. The latter may be deciduous (e.g. *Taenia*) or permanent (e.g. *Hymenolepis*). In either case it is nonoperculate (Fig. 14·3).

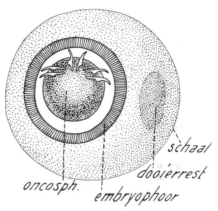

FIG. 14·3 Complete egg of *Taenia solium: schaal,* Egg-shell.—*dooierrest,* Remains of vitelline cell.—*embryophoor,* Embryophore with radial striation.—*oncosph,* Oncosphere with three pairs of hooklets. (After Hall, from Ihle and Nierstrasz, 1928. Courtesy, Oosthoek & Co., Publishers, Utrecht.)

(8) There exists only one intermediate host, a vertebrate in the taenias, an arthropod in the other Cyclophyllidea—insofar as the intermediate host is known. The oncosphere inside the intermediate host develops into a larva which is composed of the scolex and neck of the future tapeworm and of a caudal bladder. This larva bears the general name of *bladder worm.* Various kinds of bladder worms are known, four of which are mentioned here.

(*a*) The *cysticercus* (Fig. 14·4:7) is a thin-walled caudal bladder filled with fluid, into which the scolex and neck are invaginated.

(*b*) In the *cysticercoid* (Fig. 14·4:8) the scolex is withdrawn in its natural position (not inverted) into the interior of the bladder and is surrounded by a double fold of integument whose outer layer represents the caudal bladder, while the inner will become the neck when the scolex arises out of this envelope. Sometimes the caudal bladder has an appendage (Fig. 14·4:8) to which the three pairs of hooklets of the oncosphere may still be adhering.

(c, d) Some bladder worms contain several scolices: *coenurus* and *hydatid* (cf. Chapter XV).

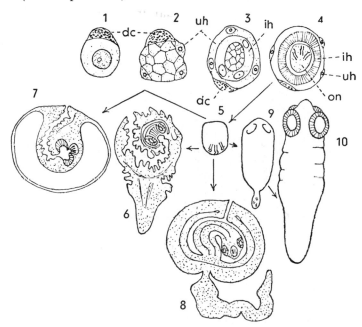

FIG. 14·4 Schematic representation of the development of the Cyclophyllidea: 1–4. Development from egg to oncosphere: *dc*, vitelline cell; *ih*, stages in the development of the embryophore; *on*, oncosphere; *uh*, exterior envelope.—5. Free oncosphere and the various larvas it can produce, viz.: 6. Dithyridium.—7. Cysticercus.—8. Cysticercoid.—9. Procercoid.—10. Plerocercoid. (After Fuhrmann, 1928–1931.)

The general rule that helminths do not multiply within their definitive host (except for oviposition, which does not produce progeny in the same host) does not invariably hold for the cyclophyllids. All the same, in the few cases in which the host is known to subject its parasites to numerical restraint, it appears to do so by preventing reinfection. The observations on this subject have been made in animals; in one case only has it been possible to apply their results to human conditions.

Taenia taeniaeformis (Fig. 14·5:left) is a tapeworm of the cat; it parasitizes the liver of the intermediate host, the rat, in the form of

Cysticercus fasciolaris (Fig. 14·5:right). The rat can be infected by making it ingest the eggs of the tapeworm, which the cat passes in its feces. Once, however, cysticerci have developed within the rat's liver, a repeated infection no longer succeeds.[1] The ability of the rat to prevent reinfection is maintained if the cysticerci in its liver are removed by operation. The residual immunity, left after the removal of the cysticerci, lasts for no longer than two months. At the end of that time the rat can be successfully infected again.[2] Thus,

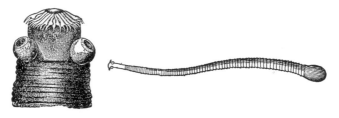

FIG. 14·5   *Taenia taeniaeformis:* Left, scolex, × 15 (after Neumann); right, *Cysticercus fasciolaris,* a so-called proglottiferous cysticercus (after Leuckart).

this state of resistance, dependent on the continued presence of the parasite, has much in common with Sergent's premunition, although it may not be identical with it.

Another tapeworm, *Hymenolepis diminuta,* lives in the bowel of the rat, which, in this case, is the definitive host. If the parasites have been present for no longer than one week, the rat can still be further infected. If, however, they have been resident for two weeks, a reinfection results in the freshly introduced parasites growing to stunted adults or dying before they reach adulthood. If, on the other hand, the original parasites have been removed before fresh ones were introduced, the newcomers meet no obstacle to their development.[3]

The heavy infection from which the rats suffered in their youth caused them to acquire a resistance, which in later life was maintained by constantly repeated infections. These, however, failed to raise the number of worms the adult rats were carrying. As a result, the degree of infection in the adults of a murine population remains far below that in the young ones.

The more common human parasites among the cyclophyllid tape-worms can be tabulated as follows:

(1) The intermediate hosts are mammals ....Taeniid family
    The intermediate hosts—as far as known—are arthropods ....(2)
(2) The gravid uterus stretches in a transverse direction over the whole width of the proglottis ....(3)
    The gravid uterus disintegrates into numerous egg capsules ....(4)
(3) The eggshell and the embryophore are of about the same thickness
                                                          Hymenolepis
    The eggshell is thin; the embryophore is drawn out on one side into a pair of horns, known as the "pyriform apparatus" ..*Bertiella*
(4) Each proglottid contains one genital complex ....(5)
    Each proglottid contains two genital complexes ....*Dipylidium*
(5) Scolex unarmed ....*Inermicapsifer*
(6) Scolex carrying hooklets ....*Davainea*

The important parasites are found in the first group; *Hymenolepis* exemplifies an interesting host-parasite relationship; *Inermicapsifer* is reported to be a common human parasite in Cuba; the others hardly claim any but coventional interest.

In the present chapter, the first part of the Cyclophyllidea, the taeniid family parasitizing man as tapeworms will be discussed, and in Chapter XV the members of the same family parasitizing man as bladder worms; the other cyclophyllids form the subject of Chapter XVI.

The characteristics of the *taeniid family* are the alternating genital atria; the shape of the proglottids, changing from short to oblong as they grow older; the shape of the gravid uterus, viz. a median longitudinal stem carrying a varying number of lateral branches. The eggshell is deciduous; the so-called egg, passed in the feces of the definitive host, is the oncosphere within its embryophore. The latter is very thick; it is radially striated and has a yellow color.

Of the three genera parasitizing man, one (*Taenia*) inhabits the intestine of man as a tapeworm and the connective tissue in the muscles of either cattle or pigs as a cysticercus. Both stages are, on the whole, monoxenous. This genus forms the subject of the present chapter. The two others parasitize man and other mammals as bladder worms; *Echinococcus* as *hydatid*, *Multiceps* as *coenurus*. They will be dealt with in the next chapter.

TAENIA SAGINATA: THE BEEF TAPEWORM

Taenia saginata Goeze, 1782 (*T. inermis* Brera, 1802; *T. medio-canellata* Küchenmeister, 1852) is the most ubiquitous long tapeworm, with its habitat in the human jejunum.[4] As a tapeworm man is its only host; cattle are practically the only host of its cysticercus, named *Cysticercus bovis* or *C. inermis*.

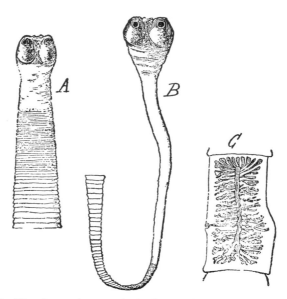

FIG. 14·6 *Taenia saginata: A*, Scolex and anterior proglottids retracted.—*B*, The same, relaxed, × 8.—*C*, Gravid proglottid, × 2. (After Braun, 1925. Courtesy, Curt Kabitzsch, Leipzig.)

Usually the strobila measures 5–10 meters in length, with 700–900 proglottids, but much longer specimens have been observed. On an average the scolex produces 8–9 new proglottids daily. The tapeworm in man has a long life span; Australian experience[5] mentions 83 persons known to have harbored their taenia for an average period of 13 years. Usually man is parasitized by one tapeworm only. Still, multiple infection cannot be rare, at least in Australia, where the average number of worms per carrier is well over two.

The scolex (Fig. 14·6:*A, B*) is cubical, measures 1.5–2 mm in width, and almost as much in thickness. Its apex is flat or slightly concave. The suckers are located at the four upper corners, their diameter is 0.7–0.8 mm; their margin is often pigmented. In a state of relaxation the neck is half as wide as the scolex but much longer (Fig. 14·6:*B*). Halfway down towards the posterior extremity the proglottids are 3–4 mm long, and 12–14 mm wide. Further on they gain in length, but lose in width; thus the gravid proglottids measure 16–20 mm in length and 4–7 mm in width (Fig. 14·7).

The genital atria are situated, irregularly alternating, on one of the lateral margins of the posterior half of each proglottid. The anatomy of the sexually mature proglottid is described in Fig. 14·2. The uterus within the gravid proglottid (Fig. 14·6:*C*) carries 20–25 partly ramified lateral branches on both sides of its longitudinal stem. The apical branches reach the anterior margin of the proglottid; the caudal branches do not reach the posterior margin.

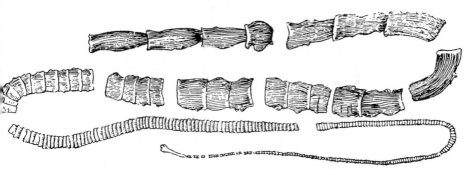

Fig. 14·7 *Taenia saginata:* Several parts of the strobila, natural size. (After Leuckart.)

The gravid uterus contains the complete eggs (Fig. 14·3). They have a very thin deciduous shell; within the shell lies the oncosphere enclosed within its radially striated embryophore. The former measures about 20 μ, the latter 30–40 × 20–30 μ. The egg production of a gravid uterus is estimated at an average of 80,000 oncospheres. About nine proglottids become detached from the strobila daily; thus the total daily output is about three-quarters of a million eggs.

The detached proglottid is alive and motile. When moving about it may contract to 13 × 3.5 mm one moment and expand to 25 × 2.0 mm the next. It behaves like an independent organism and may escape from the jar in which it is kept a prisoner. By its contractions it forces the eggs out of the anterior branches of the uterus. Thus the eggs are actually deposited, although there is no pre-existing uterine pore. Oviposition may take place when the detached proglottid is still within the lumen of the bowel, but usually after leaving the rectum through the anal opening, when it is crawling over the perianal skin, before dropping from the host's body. Thus the eggs may be found in the feces (Fig. 14·8), but also in the material obtained by scraping the perianal skin.[6] Finding eggs in either of these ways yields no information about the species of taenia that

FIG. 14·8   *Taenia saginata:* "Egg" passed in feces, × 450.

produced them, because the eggs of *T. saginata* cannot be differentiated from those of *T. solium*. A definitive diagnosis of the species is made by the examination of a proglottid and observing the number of lateral uterine branches.

Cattle are practically the only animals that serve as intermediate hosts of *T. saginata,* although it is claimed that sheep and goats have been successfully infected. As the eggs are often found in human feces, it is practically certain that man ingests them on occasions. Nevertheless, the occurrence of *Cysticercus bovis* in man is, at best, a rarity.

How bovine infection takes place has not yet been satisfactorily elucidated. According to Le Coultre[7] infection of cattle increases if the grazing grounds are irrigated with water soiled by human excreta, but Swierstra[8] holds that man infects his cattle by direct contact, without the intervention of water, grass or hay. In any case, the eggs can infect cattle weeks (even 159 days[9]) after they have left the human body and have passed the time on completely dry grazing grounds.

The radial striation of the embryophore reflects the presence of large numbers of minute rods held together by a substance which is dissolved by the intestinal secretions. Thus the action of these secretions brings about the disintegration of the embryophore, and the liberation of the oncosphere therein contained.[10] The oncosphere penetrates the intestinal mucosa and enters into its capillaries.

By way of the venous and pulmonary circulation it is transported to the arterial circulation, which carries it to various organs. Finally, it settles in the connective tissue of transversely striated muscles. It is often assumed that there are certain sites of predilection: the pterigoid muscles, psoas, myocardium, the muscles of the upper arm, the thigh, the neck and the tongue. Others, however, deny the existence of muscles of predilection. On rare occasions, the oncospheres have settled in the brain, kidneys, esophagus, and skin.

The oncospheres develop into cysticerci, during which process they become hollow (Fig. 14·9) and grow an inverted scolex, iden-

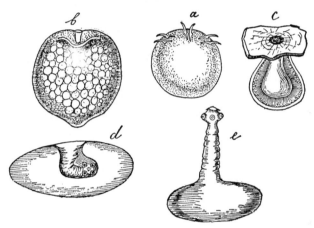

FIG. 14·9 *Taenia saginata: a,* Oncosphere, × 1000.—*b,* Young cysticercus with first trace of future scolex.—*c,* Detail of further development of inverted scolex.—*Taenia solium: d,* Cysticercus with inverted scolex. —The same with everted scolex, × 4. (After Leuckart.)

tical in shape with the scolex of the tapeworm (Fig. 14·10). For this development 3–4 months are required. Fully developed, living cysticerci are ovoid in shape with a length of 6–8 mm. Dead specimens are 2–4 mm long.[10] They are enveloped by a layer of connective tissue, formed by the host's body, which is difficult to separate from the surrounding tissue.

The number of cysticerci found in the bovine is small. In the island of Bali (Indonesia),[7] a country where the chance of infection is uncommonly great, 600 infected heads of cattle were detected in one year, but 92 percent of them carried no more than 1 to 4 cysticerci; only 1 percent carried more than 20, with a maximum of 207.

This low degree of infection is due, not to the small numbers of ingested oncospheres, but to the defense mechanism of the host, which prevents the majority of invading oncospheres from becoming cysticerci. Bovines subjected to heavy infections become so resistant that reinfections with thousands of oncospheres result in the development of no more than a few cysticerci.[11]

This resistance appears to last for years.[8] As yet it is not known whether it represents absolute immunity or relative immunity; in view of what is known in other animal parasites, relative immunity appears to be the likelier alternative. For its maintenance it would

FIG. 14·10   *Cysticercus bovis:* Longitudinal section through inverted scolex. (After Neumann and Mayer. Courtesy, Lehmann's Verlag, Munich.)

require the stimulus of a residual parasite population. At first sight, cysticerci are not able to supply this, for they are too short-lived— nine months at the longest [12]—to maintain a long-lasting relative immunity. Nevertheless, cysticerci settling in small numbers in resistant hosts exposed to heavy reinfections [11] may do so, provided such reinfections follow each other at intervals short enough to substitute fresh cysticerci for dead and dying ones.

Reports of the sanitary meat inspection in many countries show that *Cysticercus bovis* has been detected over the whole world. The percentage of infected bovines ascertained by this inspection depends not only on the actual density of the parasite population but also on the thoroughness of the inspection. The following figures have only a limited value. In Holland, in the years 1951–1953 1.5 percent of adult cattle and 0.8 percent of the calves [13] were found infected. Other European countries report figures of a similar order, but in Yugoslavia they approach 30 percent.[14] In federal-inspected cattle in the United States the figure has become stabilized at about 0.4 percent since 1930.[15]

The incidence of human infection with adult *T. saginata* has been estimated by the number of persons (1) treated for "taeniasis," and (2) passing taenia eggs in their feces (in that case *T. solium* is necessarily included). Examples of the first method are Hemmes' [13] survey, covering various parts of Holland over the three years' period 1951–1953, which yielded an annual incidence of 13 per 100,000; L. J. B. Stuyt's account of 60,000 persons treated for various complaints at the Municipal Hospital of the Hague over the five years' period 1953–1957 yielded an annual incidence of 22 per 100,000; Silverman's [16] estimate of 4 cases weekly in England and Wales amounted to less than 1 per 100,000; and Lepeš [14] found 15 percent of the population in western Yugoslavia suffering from taeniasis. In most countries examined according to the second method the rate of infection did not surpass 1 percent. In the Near East, and in north and central Africa, it varied from 6 to 22 percent; in some areas it rose as high as 33–77 percent.

Differences as to age have been reported in Egypt: 4 percent of egg-passers in children, against 2 percent in adults.[17] Differences as to sex, with a preponderance of adult female over adult male and child infection, have been reported in England and Denmark.[18] On the other hand, white boys were more frequently infected than white girls in the French Cameroons.[19]

The motility of the gravid proglottids may cause them to wander to unusual intestinal localities, such as the appendix, and also to extraintestinal sites, such as the frontal sinus.[20] The whole tapeworm may be affected by the tendency to wander. It has been observed forcing Vater's papilla, and penetrating as far as the pancreas or the gallbladder, or even piercing the wall of the bowel.[21] These, however, are exceptional occurrences. As a rule the pathogenic effect of the tapeworm finds its expression in a state of hypersensitivity of the host to its products of secretion and excretion. This hypersensitivity becomes evident also by a positive intradermal test with an aqueous extract of the tapeworm.[22]

TREATMENT. Treatment with an ethereal extract of the rhizome of the male fern or the oleoresin prepared from it is still practiced with a success largely dependent on the freshness of the rhizome and on its being prepared shortly before use. The oleoresin appears to be more active than the ethereal extract.[6] However, quinacrine hydrochloride [34] appears to be the drug of choice, to be administered in the following manner.

On the day preceding the treatment the patient is put on a liquid diet. A soapsuds enema is given before retiring. The next morning on an empty stomach 2 tablets (200 mg) of quinacrine hydrochloride (Atabrine) are given every 10 minutes, to a total of 8 tablets. For children weighing 40 to 75 pounds, the dose is 0.4 gm, and 0.6 gm for children 76 to 100 pounds. Two hours after the last dose a saline purge of 20 gm of sulfate of magnesia or phosphate of soda is administered in a glass of water.

Nausea and vomiting frequently encountered may be minimized by preliminary sedation with chlorpromazine [33] (Thorazine). If the worm is not expelled after the first bowel movement, a soapsuds enema may be helpful. Occasionally, in cases of persistent vomiting after quinacrine, the drug may be repeated by duodenal tube at a later date. All stool specimens should be saved for 24 hours, and examined for the scolex, or head of the worm.

TAENIA SOLIUM: THE PORK TAPEWORM

As has been said before, the results of mass examination of feces report "taenia eggs," without adding "saginata" or "solium," and rightly so, for the eggs of these species cannot be distinguished one from another. This is a serious defect in mass examination, for in behavior *T. solium* (Linnaeus, 1758) is quite distinct from *T. saginata,* notably in its relation to the human host.

Broadly speaking, the two tapeworms greatly resemble each other. *T. solium* inhabits the anterior half of the small intestine; often several specimens are present, occasionally 40–50.[23] The anterior part of the strobila is filiform; the proglottids turn from short to square, and from square to oblong; the gravid proglottids measure 10–12 × 5–6 mm. The scolex is cubical, with a sucker at each of the four upper corners (Fig. 14·1).

However, there are decisive differences which make it possible to identify even a single specimen.

(1) The (often pigmented) rostellum at the top of the scolex is crowned by a ring of hooklets (Figs. 14·1 and 14·11:*A*); their number may vary considerably, but 22–28 are regarded as normal. Larger hooklets of 160–180 μ alternate with smaller ones of 110–130 μ; accordingly the ring is described as a double one.

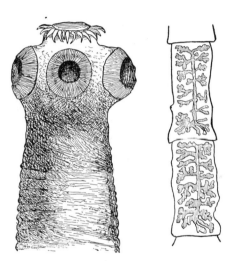

Fig. 14·11   *Taenia solium:* LEFT, Scolex with rostellum and hooklets, × 16.—RIGHT, Two gravid proglottids, × 2. (After Braun, 1925. Courtesy, Curt Kabitzsch, Leipzig.)

(2) The longitudinal stem of the gravid uterus carries 7–13 branches on each side, some of which are strongly ramified (Fig. 14·11:*B*; cf. *T. saginata,* Fig. 14·6:*C*).

(3) The cysticercus, *Cysticercus cellulosae,* develops in the connective tissue of the muscles of the pig; three to four months are required for its completion. The mature cysticercus measures 6–8 × 4–6 mm; larger specimens of 10 × 8 mm have also been recorded. The layer of connective tissue around the cysticercus is transparent and is easily detached from the surrounding tissue. Moreover, the fluid within the cysticercus is also transparent, and the scolex is seen as a white corpuscle on a grayish background. Thus *C. cellulosae* is easier to detect in the muscle than *C. bovis* (Fig. 14·12). Finally, *C. cellulosae* may live for three to six years (*C. bovis,* nine months)

in the body of its host and may survive in its carcass for six weeks (*C. bovis,* two weeks).

(4) The number of *C. cellulosae* in pigs is usually much greater than that of *C. bovis* in cattle. In the island of Bali (Indonesia)[7] only 3 percent of the infected bovines carried more than 10 *C. bovis,* whereas more than half of the infected pigs carried more than 12 *C. cellulosae.*

Fig. 14·12   *Cysticercus cellulosae* in human muscle, × 2. (After Leuckart.)

(5) *C. cellulosae* does not show a well-defined and constant preference for any particular group of muscles. Neither does *C. bovis,* according to some observers. However, there is this difference, that *C. bovis,* with some exceptions, keeps to the muscles, whereas *C. cellulosae* often invades other organs, such as the skin, the brain, and the eye. In Brazil, for example, 98 percent of cysticerci found in cattle were located in various groups of muscles (65 percent in muscles used in mastication, 31 percent in the myocardium, 2 percent in other muscles) and 2 percent in other organs; conversely, 96 percent of cysticerci found in pigs were situated in other organs, and only 4 percent in muscles (0.8 percent in the pterigoids and myocardium, and 3.2 percent in lingual and other muscles).[24]

There is another difference, not yet mentioned; *T. solium* is less strictly monoxenous than *T. saginata* with regard to its intermediate host. Besides the pig, *T. sodium* has at least one other intermediate host, and that host is man. For the well-being of the parasite this is an unfortunate choice, for man is a deadend host if he serves as an intermediate host. To man the choice is equally harmful, because the oncosphere in the human body shows as little discrimination in the selection of its site of development as it does in the pig's body.

Cysticercosis may be acquired by a person who harbors the adult *T. solium* in his intestine or by one who is free from this intestinal infection. In the first case he becomes infected with oncospheres (1) by ingesting the solium eggs passed in his own feces or (2) by solium eggs being transported from his small intestine to his stomach or duodenum as a consequence of reversed peristalsis (internal auto-infection). In the second case he becomes infected with oncospheres by ingesting solium eggs passed in the feces of another person who is a carrier of an adult *T. solium*.

If the oncosphere develops to *C. cellulosae* in the skin or the muscles, no serious consequences are likely to ensue. In the skin,

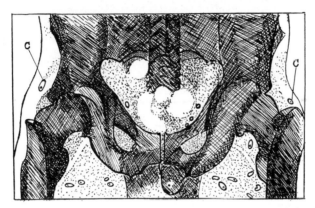

FIG. 14·13   Drawing, after roentgenogram, of human pelvis showing several small, well-defined spots (*c, c*) caused by calcified *C. cellulosae* oriented in the direction of the longitudinal axis of the muscles. (After Marsman, 1936. Courtesy, *Nederlandsch Tijdschrift voor Geneeskunde*, Amsterdam.)

its presence may be readily detected; in the muscles the infection often remains silent and unnoticed. Even a heavy infection of the muscles need not hinder an athlete in his professional activities,[29] and cysticerci may be accidentally detected on a roentgenogram made for an entirely different purpose (Fig. 14·13), as they show up very well after they have become calcified.

Far more serious conditions may develop if the cysticerci are lodged in the brain (Fig. 14·14), e.g. in the wall of the fourth ventricle, the basal meninges, or the eye.[25] The occurrence of epileptiform convulsions in cases where cysticerci have invaded brain tissues has been vividly described by MacArthur[26] and others.[27, 28] In differentiating cerebral cysticercosis from other expanding intracranial lesions a history of tapeworm infection may be of help in arriving at a diagnosis. A peculiar form of *C. cellulosae* in the brain, known as *Cysticercus racemosus,* is particularly suited to block the intracerebral circulation as it floats unattached in the fluid of a cerebral ventricle [30] or the subarachnoidal space. It has the form of a bunch of

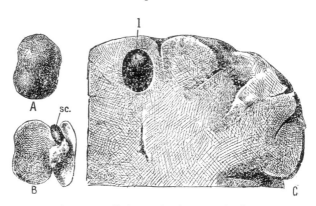

Fig. 14·14 *Cysticercus cellulosae* in human brain, natural size: *C,* Brain.—*l,* Cavity in which the cysticercus is situated.—*A,* Cysticercus extracted.—*B,* The same, opened.—*Sc,* Inverted scolex. (After Brumpt, 1936. Courtesy, Masson & Cie, Paris.)

grapes and may reach a size of 25 cm. As a rule, a scolex is absent; thus it cannot be identified with certainty, since another bladder worm in the human brain, *Coenurus cerebralis,* may assume the same form.[31]

Human infection with adult *T. solium* may be expected wherever porcine infection is prevalent and smoked pork is consumed uncooked. If the transmission from hog to man can be prevented—and this is less difficult than in *T. saginata,* because it is easier to detect infected hogs than infected cattle—then events are repeated that were observed in Germany. There a thorough inspection of pork marked for human consumption first reduced human infection, and, as an inevitable consequence, porcine infection, from 18–32 per 10,000 hogs in the period of 1876 to 1889, to 3 or less in the years 1908–1911.

Human infection with the tapeworm of *T. solium* is usually less frequent than with *T. saginata.* In the Philippine Islands and

Mexico the proportion is as 1 to 7. Various parts of Africa show a fairly low human infection (0.2–0.4 percent). In European and Asiatic Russia percentages of 1–8 are recorded. In the United States it has become very rare.[15]

Porcine infection in Holland is no longer found in indigenous hogs. In Germany and Sweden the rate of infection remains under 3 per 10,000; in the greater part of France, under 7. Moving southeast, the figures increase to 168–321 in Russia and to 500–1200 in the Balkans. Outside Europe numerous infections have been recorded in Siberia, Japan, Bali, South Africa, Madagascar, Tenerife, Chile and other South and Central American Republics.

TREATMENT OF SOLIUM TAENIASIS. Treatment of infections with adult solium tapeworms is the same as that used in saginata infections. However, attempts at an early diagnosis of the species *T. solium* and the immediate institution of therapy cannot be too strongly emphasized in order to avoid as much as humanly possible reinfection by the solium eggs. Internal autoinfection or hand to mouth infection from contaminated feces is too frequent a complication, which may result in cysticercosis and some of its serious clinical manifestations.

Specific treatment with *diethylcarbamazine* of parenchymatous cerebral cysticercosis, in which the cysticercus is deposited in the substance of the cerebral hemisphere, has recently been introduced by H. Collomb and his associates.[32] The results, although not decisive, appear to be encouraging.

REFERENCES FOR CHAPTER XIV

1. H. M. MILLER. *Proc. Soc. Exptl. Biol.* (New York), 1930, 27: 926.
2. H. M. MILLER and E. MASSIE. *J. Prev. Med.*, 1932, 6: 31–36.
3. A. C. CHANDLER. *Third Intern. Congr. Microbiol.*, New York, 1939, Abstracts, 187.
4. R. PRÉVOT, H. HORNBOSTAL, and H. DÖRKEN. *Klin. Wochschr.*, 1952, 30: 78–80.
5. W. J. and H. B. PENFOLD and M. PHILLIPS. *J. Helminthol.*, 1937, 15: 41–48.
6. L. MAZZOTTI, L. RODRIGUEZ, and A. TREVIÑO. *Rev. inst. salubridad y enfermedad trop. Mex.*, 1947, 8: 155–162.
7. A. P. LE COULTRE. Thesis, Utrecht, 248 pp., Utrecht, 1927.
8. D. SWIERSTRA. *Tijdschr. Diergeneesk.*, 1950, 80: 647–655.
9. A. JEPSEN and H. ROTH. *Fourteenth Internat. Veterin. Congr.*, London, 1949, 7 pp.

10. W. J. and H. B. Penfold and M. Phillips. *Med. J. Australia,* 1937, 24 (2nd half): 1039–1042.
11. W. J. and H. B. Penfold. *J. Helminthol.,* 1937, 15: 37–40.
12. H. B. Penfold. *Med. J. Australia,* 1937, 24 (1st half): 579–583.
13. G. Hemmes. *Ned. Tijdschr. Geneesk.,* 1955, 99: 2244–2247.
14. T. Lepeš. *Trop. Diseases Bull.,* 1955, 52: 463–464.
15. E. C. Faust, P. F. Russell, and D. R. Lincicome. *Clinical Parasitology,* Philadelphia, 1957, Lea & Febiger, pp. 649, 640.
16. P. H. Silverman. *Ann. Trop. Med. Parasitol.,* 1955, 49: 429–435.
17. G. Nor Ed Din and I. Baz. *Trop. Diseases Bull.,* 1950, 47: 383.
18. R. B. Griffiths. *Ann. Trop. Med. Parasitol.,* 1950, 44: 357–360.
19. J. M. and M. Doby and S. De Block. *Bull. soc. pathol. exotique,* 1957, 50: 929–936.
20. H. O. Mönnig. *S. African Med. J.,* 1934, 8: 475–476.
21. J. D. Kaan. *Ned. Tijdschr. Geneesk.,* 1941, 85: 1068–1072.
22. W. Kremer. *Ned. Tijdschr. Geneesk.,* 1942, 86: 1901–1904.
23. G. Bugge. *Z. Fleisch- u. Milchhyg.,* 1944, 54: 76–79.
24. M. C. Pardi, G. G. Durarte, and U. F. Roche. *Trop. Diseases Bull.,* 1954, 51: 292.
25. R. H. Elsässer. *Z. ges. Neurol. Psychiat.,* 1944, 177: 323–362.
26. W. P. MacArthur. *Trans. Roy. Soc. Trop. Med. Hyg.,* 1933, 26: 525–528.
27. H. B. F. Dixon and D. W. Smithers. *Quart. J. Med.,* n.s., 1934, 3: 603–616.
28. H. L. Chung and C. U. Lee. *Chin. Med. J.,* 1935, 49: 429–445.
29. R. R. Evans. *Trans. Roy. Soc. Trop. Med. Hyg.,* 1939, 32: 549–550.
30. R. V. Talice and J. Gurri. *Ann. parasitol. humaine et comparée,* 1950, 25: 121–140.
31. J. Wainwright. *J. Pathol. Bacteriol.,* 1957, 73: 347–354.
32. H. Collomb, A. Pruvost, and J. Giraud. *Méd. trop.,* Marseille, 1958, 18: 228–244.
33. H. W. Brown. *Clin. Pharmacol. Therap.,* 1960, 1: 87–103.
34. W. A. Sodeman and R. C. Jung. *J. Am. Med. Assoc.,* 1952, 148: 285–286.

CHAPTER XV

CYCLOPHYLLIDEA II: TAENIIDS AS BLADDER WORMS

This chapter will discuss members of the taeniid family that parasitize man as bladder worms; not, however, as cysticerci, but as bladder worms that show asexual multiplication.

In the genus *Multiceps*, whose bladder worms are called *Coenurus*, asexual multiplication is limited. The coenurus produces numerous scolices. Each scolex represents a new individual, which, however, can develop nowhere but in the body of the definitive host.

In the genus *Echinococcus*, whose bladder worms are called *hydatids*, asexual multiplication is virtually unlimited. Like the coenurus, the hydatid produces numerous scolices, but the scolex can do more than develop into a tapeworm in the body of the definitive host; it can also develop into a *daughter cyst* in the body of the intermediate host in which it was born; and the daughter cyst continues the asexual multiplication its mother, the hydatid, has initiated.

THE GENUS MULTICEPS

The species of this genus that parasitize man may be differentiated according to the site of the coenurus: *M. multiceps* in the central nervous system, *M. serialis* in subcutaneous and muscular connective tissue.

MULTICEPS MULTICEPS

Multiceps multiceps (Leske, 1780) Hall, 1910, as a tapeworm parasitizes the small intestine of dogs and wolves. The worm has a length of 40–60 cm. The scolex has a diameter of 0.8 mm; it carries a double ring of 22–32 rostellar hooklets of two sizes, the larger of 150–170 μ, the smaller of 70–130 μ. The proglottids show the same change in shape, from short to oblong, as is observed in *T. saginata*.

The gravid proglottids, measuring 6–11 × 3–4 mm, have a uterus whose longitudinal stem carries 18–26 slightly ramified lateral branches. They leave the definitive host while still alive. When a dog has become infected by eating the brain of a sheep carrying the bladder worm, the tapeworm grows to maturity in its intestine in the course of three months.

The oncosphere, enclosed within an embryophore of 31–36 μ, must be ingested by an intermediate host in order to develop into the bladder worm, which is called *Coenurus cerebralis*. This development is completed in three months. It usually takes place in the

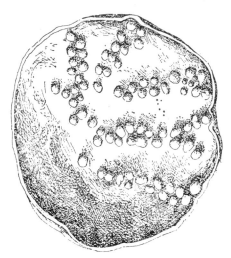

FIG. 15·1 Coenurus of *Multiceps radians*. Internal surface showing numerous scolices. (After Joyeux, Richet and Schulmann, 1922. Courtesy, *Bulletin de la société zoologique de France*, 1922, 47: 181.)

central nervous tissue of the intermediate host. Various herbivores, particularly sheep and exceptionally man, are known to act as hosts.

The difference between the coenurus and the cysticercus has been mentioned already. On the internal surface of the germinal membrane a number of small excrescences can be seen as whitish dots (Fig. 15·1). Each excrescence represents one developing or fully developed (Fig. 15·2) inverted scolex. The racemose degeneration that occasionally affects *Cysticercus cellulosae* when lodged in the brain has also been observed in *Coenurus cerebralis*.

C. cerebralis in the brain of sheep causes a disease known as *gid* (i.e. giddiness) from the locomotor disturbance which characterizes it. In France it has been discovered as a parasite in a lateral cerebral ventricle of a man ill with symptoms resembling those of brain tumor; it contained over 75 scolices.[1] So far, cases have been recorded in France, England, Africa, and the United States.

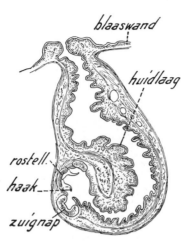

FIG. 15·2 Coenurus of *Multiceps multiceps.* Longitudinal section through inverted scolex: *blaaswand*, Wall of bladderworm.—*huidlaag*, Integument of inverted neck.—*rostell*, Rostellum of inverted scolex.— *haak*, Hooklet of the same.—*zuignap*, Sucker of the same. (After Ihle and Nierstrasz, 1928. Courtesy, Oosthoek & Co., Publishers, Utrecht.)

MULTICEPS SERIALIS

Multiceps serialis (Gervais, 1845) Stiles & Stevenson, 1905, as a tapeworm is an intestinal parasite of dogs, wolves, and foxes. The bladder worm, known as *Coenurus serialis,* differs from *C. cerebralis* in the following points. (1) The intermediate hosts are hares, rabbits, and other rodents. (2) *C. serialis* is usually situated in the connective tissue of muscles or in subcutaneous tissue. (3) The scolices and their necks are three to four times as long as in *C. cerebralis.* (4) *C. serialis* produces external and internal daughter cysts, which also grow scolices; the former are attached with a stalk to the mother cyst; the latter are free, floating in the fluid contained in the mother cyst (Fig. 15·3). (5) The number of rostellar hooklets, 26–32, may be smaller than in *C. cerebralis;* so may the length of the larger hooklets, 132–175 μ, and of the smaller ones, 78–120 μ. (6) The inflated part of the hooklet, situated between the proximal "handle" (inserted in the rostellum) and the distal "blade," is bilobed in *C. serialis,* whereas it is simple in *C. cerebralis.*

C. serialis was found three times as a human parasite in France. Two cases were seen in Nigeria, and one in the Congo. However, the Nigerian coenuri are regarded as a separate species: *M. glomeratus.*[24]

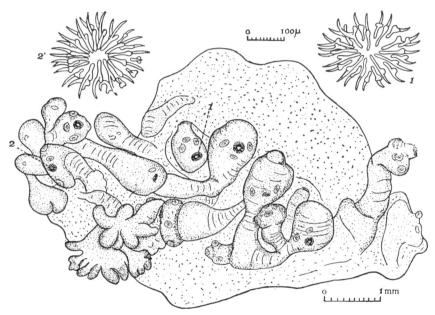

FIG. 15·3 Coenurus of *Multiceps serialis.* External daughter cyst extracted from tissue covering a human hip joint, × 15. *Above:* rings of hooklets, × 100. (After Brumpt, Duvoir and Sainton, 1934. Courtesy, *Bulletin de l'académie de médecine,* 1934, 112: No. 26.)

MULTICEPS BRAUNI

Multiceps brauni Setti, 1897, has a scolex with 30 rostellar hooklets; the larger of 95–140 μ, the smaller of 70–90 μ. According to Fain[2] the bladder worm, *Coenurus brauni,* is less strictly limited to certain classes of tissue than the preceding ones. It has been found in the Congo and in Ruanda-Urundi; it is probably indigenous to other parts of Africa as well.

The intestinal tapeworm parasitizes dogs, the coenurus various wild rodents. The coenurus usually occupies the subcutaneous tissues, but it has also been observed in the pleural and peritoneal cavities, the myocardium, the parotid gland, and the brain. As to human infection, this has been detected in eight children. Seven of them had a subcutaneous infection; the eighth carried the coenurus in the tonsils.

Raper and Dockeray's [3] finds of human coenuri in Kenya and Uganda may perhaps be referred to the same species. They observed five infected persons; in two of them the coenurus was subcutaneous, in two others conjunctival, whereas it was lodged in the vitreous body of the eye of the fifth.

Thus the complex of *M. serialis, M. glomeratus,* and *M. brauni* may eventually turn out to be a not altogether rare sylvatic human parasite in central Africa.

TREATMENT. Not known in diseases caused by coenuri.

THE GENUS ECHINOCOCCUS

There are two species in this genus that parasitize man as hydatids: *E. granulosus* is usually domestic, although it is still sylvatic in at least one country; *E. multilocularis* is known only in a sylvatic cycle.

ECHINOCOCCUS GRANULOSUS

Echinococcus granulosus (Batsch, 1786) Rudolphi, 1801, has a relationship with man that is fundamentally the same as in *Multiceps multiceps.* Dogs are definitive hosts, sheep and man are inter- mediate hosts.

The tapeworm lives in the upper and middle third of the jejunum [4] or in the last third of the duodenum and the first of the jejunum [5] of dogs and some other canine carnivores, with its scolex deeply buried between the villi (Fig. 15·4). The adult worm has an average length of 3.4 mm and is composed of a scolex and three proglottids (Fig. 15·5:*A*); the hindmost, the only gravid one, is somewhat longer and wider than the rest of the body. The greater part of the gravid uterus has a longitudinal stem with several branches. The genital atria are situated in the equator or posterior to it. The average number of testes is 44; 9–22 of them lie anterior to the cirrus pouch. The ovary is composed of two parts, united by a narrow duct. The scolex has a prominent rostellum with 32–38 hooklets in two rings; the average length of the larger hooklets is 37 μ, that of the smaller hooklets 28 μ.[4]

The embryophores measure $38 \times 35\ \mu$, the oncospheres $28 \times 25\ \mu$. They are passed in the feces of the dogs, sometimes accompanied by gravid proglottids.

Various mammals, man among them, serve *E. granulosus* as intermediate hosts. Of particular importance to human society are those that regularly exchange parasites with the dog, for it is from the dog

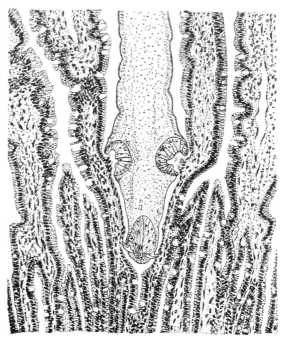

Fig. 15·4   *Echinococcus granulosus.* Scolex of tapeworm fixed between villi in intestine of dog, × 150. (After Dévé, 1949. Courtesy, Masson & Cie, Paris.)

that man acquires his infection. For that reason sheep are the most important intermediate hosts. Cattle and horses are sometimes more heavily infected than sheep, but sheep harbor the most fertile hydatids and consequently are the most important source of infection to dogs.

When the intermediate host has ingested embryophores, their wall disintegrates in the small intestine; the oncospheres are set free and penetrate the intestinal wall, entering the venous circulation. En route to the heart they are filtered out by the hepatic capillaries and, if they should pass that obstacle, by the pulmonary ones. If they are

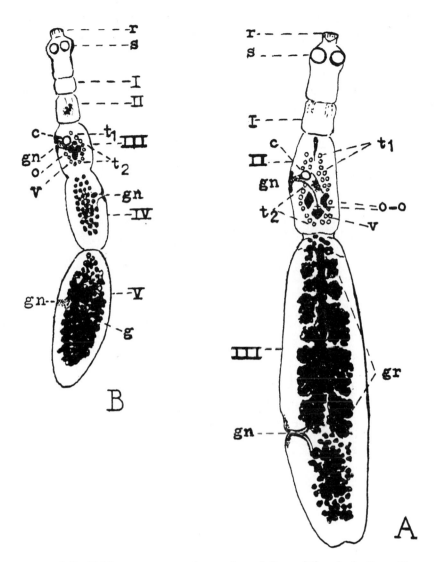

FIG. 15·5 *Echinococcus granulosus, A*, and *E. multilocularis, B*, × 46.
I, II, III, IV, V, proglottids.—*r*, Rostellum.—*s*, Suckers.—*c*, Cirrus pouch.
—*gn*, Genital atrium.—*o*, Kidney-shaped ovary.—*o-o*, Wings of bilobed
ovary.—*gr*, Ramified gravid uterus.—*g*, Gravid uterus without branches.
—*t¹*, Testes anterior to cirrus pouch.—*t²*, Testes posterior to cirrus pouch.
—*v*, Vitelline gland. (After H. Vogel, 1957. Courtesy, *Zeitschrift für
Tropenmedizin und Parasitologie*, Stuttgart.)

held up, this leads to a *primary venous infection* of liver or lung. That is the reason why primary echinococcosis in man and sheep is so often located in one or the other of these organs. Primary human echinococcosis of the liver occurs more frequently than that of the lung. In some countries pulmonary echinococcosis appears to be on the increase; according to Bailenger [6] this is due to increased diagnostic facilities rather than to a real increase in pulmonary infection.

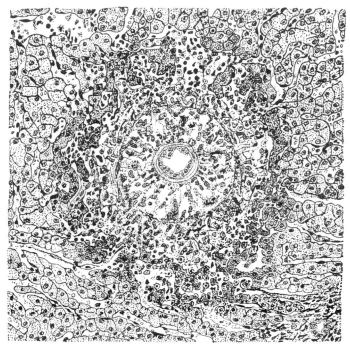

FIG. 15·6   *Echinococcus granulosus.* Hydatid of 7th day in the liver, measuring 60–70 μ, with germinal membrane of 6–8 μ thickness. (After Dévé, 1949. Courtesy, Masson & Cie, Paris.)

According to Dévé [7] the oncospheres reach the systemic circulation in 16 percent of the primary infections. This is the *primary arterial infection,* resulting in the invasion of the spleen, kidneys, eye, brain, and other organs.

It should be added that the word "primary" has been used here to indicate an infection which is the direct result of the ingestion of oncospheres, as distinct from "secondary" infection which is due to elements (vesiculated scolices) emitted from a pre-existing focus of infection.

Retained within the intralobular capillaries of the liver, the oncosphere expands to a size of 30–35 μ in the course of three to five hours. At that time it is still a solid sphere, but after four days a central cavity has been formed, filled with fluid. At the end of the first week the resulting vesicle has grown to a size of 60–70 μ. It is surrounded by a cuticle, inside which lies a layer, 6–8 μ thick, com-

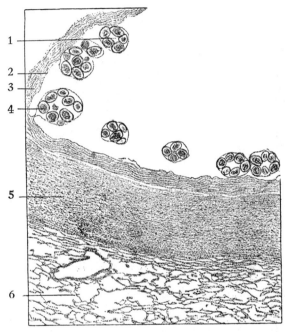

Fig. 15·7   *Echinococcus granulosus.* Section through a part of a fertile hydatid in the lung of sheep: 1, Brood capsule.—2. Germinal membrane. —3. Laminated cuticle.—4. Scolex capsules inside brood capsule.—5. Fibrous capsule.—6. Pulmonary tissue. (After Brumpt, 1922. Courtesy, Masson and Cie, Paris.)

posed of cells containing glycogen: the *germinal membrane.* This membrane is the future site of asexual reproduction (Fig. 15·6). After five months the vesicle has grown to half a centimeter in diameter; that is about the size of the cysticercus, from which it is distinguished by the absence of an invaginated scolex and by the thickness and laminated structure of the cuticle. On its internal surface the cuticle is lined with a thin germinal membrane; on its outer surface it is coated with closely packed fibrous tissue provided by the host: the *fibrous capsule*.

After some months more, the germinal membrane in the vesicle (which from now onward may be designated a hydatid) begins to function by the formation of minute knob-shaped excrescences, or

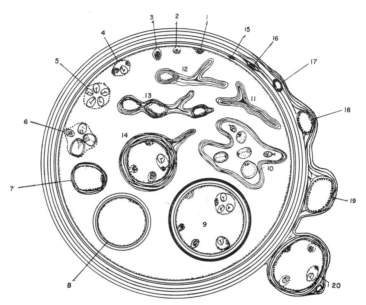

Fig. 15·8 Schematic representation of the formation of brood capsules, scolex capsules, daughter cysts, and granddaughter cysts within the hydatid of *Echinococcus granulosus*: 1–3. Formation of a brood capsule. —4–5. Formation of scolex capsules within the same.—6. Vesiculation of scolex capsules.—7, 8. Sterile daughter cysts, and (9) fertile daughter cysts, developed from scolex capsules.—10. Deformed daughter cyst with scolex capsules vesiculating.—11. Flattened and dead daughter cyst.— 12, 13. Flattened daughter cyst with surviving germinal membrane developing into granddaughter cysts.—14. Fertile granddaughter cyst.— 15, 16. Germinal membrane incarcerated between the lamina of the cuticle.—17. The same, changing to a daughter cyst, which grows into an external daughter cyst (18, 19) and finally into a fertile external daughter cyst (20). (After Dévé, 1949. Courtesy, Masson and Cie, Paris.)

gemmules, that protrude into the lumen of the hydatid. At first these gemmules are solid; soon they become vesicles, their lumen, like that of the hydatid, filled with fluid, their wall of the same cellular substance as the germinal membrane. For some time the gemmule remains attached to its membrane by its stalk. Finally the stalk breaks, and the vesicle now floats in the hydatid fluid. The wall of the vesicle produces a thin cuticle; this does not coat its external surface, but lines its internal surface. These vesicles are called *brood capsules;* their size varies from ¼ to ½ mm.

The wall of the brood capsule, produced by the germinal membrane, shares with that membrane the faculty of growing gemmules on its inner surface. As this is lined with a thin cuticle, the gemmules become coated with it on their outer surface. At the same time they become hollow, and in this way from 10 to 30 minute vesicles are produced inside the brood capsule (Figs. 15·7, 15·8, and 15·9), each covered with a cuticle. They are called *scolex capsules*. When full-

Fig. 15·9   Brood capsule containing 16 scolex capsules, from hydatid in the liver of an ass, × 53.

grown, they resemble miniature cysticerci of a size of $160 \times 115 \mu$, containing an invaginated scolex with four suckers and a double ring of rostellar hooklets (Fig. 15·10).

The scolex capsules are each a potential tapeworm; thus their formation represents an asexual multiplication of great productivity. If the hydatid is carried by sheep, the scolex capsules are likely to reach shepherd's dogs that are fed on the offal of slaughtered sheep. But if the hydatid is carried by man, this chance, under normal conditions, does not exist.

However, the scolex capsule can do more than develop into a tapeworm; it can undergo the process of *vesiculation,* i.e. it can become a vesicle which has lost its scolex and whose living tissue serves as a germinal membrane lining the inner surface of the cuticle and being thus distinguished from a brood capsule (Fig. 15·11). In this way the scolex capsule is metamorphosed to a minuscular hydatid, called the *daughter cyst,* which in the course of time will do all that the hydatid can do, viz. produce a thick laminated cuticle, brood capsules and scolex capsules (Fig. 15·8:9). Initially the daughter cysts are no larger than the scolex capsule that produced them, but they can grow to the size of a marble and more, especially if the hydatid that produced them dies. One or more of the scolex capsules they produce may become vesiculated in turn and develop into a daughter cyst of the second generation, or *granddaughter cyst,*

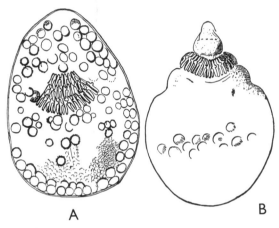

A   B

FIG. 15·10   *Echinococcus granulosus,* scolex capsule, × 400. *A,* Scolex inverted.—*B,* Scolex everted.

which may have to take the place of its dying mother (Fig. 15·8:12–14).

The daughter cysts described here are called *endogenous* because they are formed inside the hydatid. But they can also develop from a portion of the germinal membrane which has become incarcerated between the lamina of the cuticle. Finally they come to lie outside the hydatid (Fig. 15·8:15–20), but still within the fibrous capsule. They are designated *exogenous.*

So long as they remain within the hydatid, vesiculating scolex capsules can only increase its output or take its place when it dies. But they can extend the scope of their activity by giving rise to secondary infection, the origin of *secondary echinococcosis.*[8]   This occurs if scolex capsules escape as a result of a spontaneous rupture of the hydatid or through an artificial opening. They are then transported to various organs, where they develop into secondary hydatids.

As an example, the case of Barnett's [9] New Zealand shepherd may be quoted. His hepatic hydatid ruptured when he was 6 years of age; 33 years later a complex of daughter hydatids was removed by operation, the size of which varied from a cherry to a coconut, with a total contents of 55 liters and a total weight of 29 kg; 16 years after this event two more hydatids the size of an infant's head were removed.

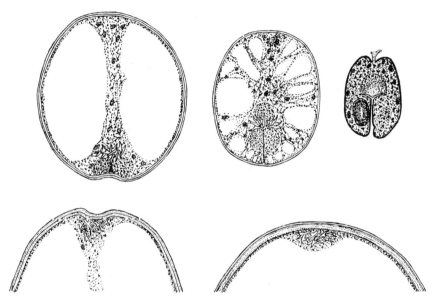

Fig. 15·11   *Echinococcus granulosus,* vesiculation of scolex capsule. *Upper row from r. to l.:* Normal scolex capsule; formation of peripheric vacuoles; vacuoles only leave a central column, and a subcuticular layer, of germinal membrane; hooklets pushed to one pole.—*Lower row from l. to r.:* Central column much reduced in width; central column has disappeared, vesiculation completed; the hooklets still present in a thickening of the subcuticular germinal membrane. (After Dévé, 1949. Courtesy, Masson and Cie and Paul Duval, Paris.)

The cuticle that separates the hydatid from the tissue of the host is not absolutely impermeable. Substances contained in the fluid of the hydatid find their way to the circulation. There they act as antigens that provoke eosinophilia and the formation of antibodies, as evidenced by a positive complement fixation test with hydatid fluid and serum of the host (test of Ghedini and Weinberg) and a positive intradermal reaction of the host following intracutaneous injection of hydatid fluid (Casoni test)—tests which are useful (especially the latter [23]) in establishing the diagnosis. But the intact cuticle is sufficient to prevent the host's body being flooded with antigen. This would result in a serious and sometimes fatal allergic reaction, such as has actually been observed when a considerable quantity of hydatid fluid was poured into the peritoneal cavity after the rupturing of a hydatid. Thus the cuticle must be regarded as a protection of the host as well as a protection of the parasite.[10]

The development of the hydatid as described above may be termed the normal course of events. There exist two main deviations from it:

(1) *The osseous echinococcus,* notably in the vertebrae.[11] The osseous tissue does not respond to the presence of the parasite by the formation of a fibrous capsule. The parasite, in its turn, tardily responds to the contact with the host's tissue by the formation of a cuticle. It begins by producing naked excrescences which penetrate the cavities of the bone. Later on, the excrescences are changed into vesicles that produce a cuticle. To this complex of vesicles Vogel [4] has given the name of *multivesicular echinococcus.* In case one of the excrescences penetrates tissue outside the bone, it changes into a normal hydatid. Thus the unusual qualities of the osseous hydatid do not represent a characteristic inherent in the parasite, but imposed upon it by external conditions.

(2) *The multicystic echinococcus of cattle.* This name has been given by Vogel [4] to a peculiar form of *E. granulosus* in the liver of cattle, characterized by the presence of large numbers of small, cuticularized vesicles. Formerly they were called multilocular echinococcus, as they superficially resemble the species *E. multilocularis (v. infra)* which also has a multicystic hepatic stage. However, the multicystic form shows no tendency to infiltrative or metastatic growth, nor does it stimulate the host's connective tissue to excessive proliferation, followed by central necrosis; in short, it does not behave as a malignant growth. Thus, it is now assumed that the multicystic variety of *E. granulosus* bears no relationship to *E. multilocularis,* and for that reason the old name of multilocular echinococcus has been abandoned in favor of Vogel's new name.

As a rule, man acquires echinococcus infection in his youth; "a hydatid cyst is nearly as old as its host." [12] Dévé [7] has come to the same conclusion on the ground that a hydatid located in a site where it cannot fail to cause early symptoms, such as the eye or the brain, is usually detected in early age. In Iceland, women are particularly exposed to infection from the age of twelve onward, but it is only at the age of 20–40 that they begin to feel the effect of the presence of the parasite.[13] Apart from the danger arising from a particular location or an unusual size, *E. granulosus* may be pronounced a well-adapted parasite. This opinion is supported by a clinician's [14] characterization of hepatic echinococcosis as a disease exhibiting a surprising combination of a conspicuous hepatomegaly and a satisfactory state of health of the patient.

As to the way in which man acquires his infection, two different opinions have been advanced and may be cited.

One, which may be designated the "licking-tongue hypothesis," has little faith in the viability of the eggs of the worm outside the body of the host. It assumes that they are lapped up when the dog is licking its anal region, and transferred to the corners of the dog's lips. Then, while dog and child are exchanging caresses, the child's face is smeared with the dog's saliva and the eggs therein contained.

The other, the "dirty-hands hypothesis," allows for the resistance of the eggs to desiccation. It assumes that they remain alive sticking to the sheep's fleece, soiled with the feces of the shepherd's dogs. From there they are transferred to the hands, and eventually to the mouth, of persons whose occupation forces them to come into close touch with the fleece. In Iceland these persons are of the female sex, because it is the women and girls who take sole charge of the milking of the sheep; and this would explain why the incidence of echinococcosis in the females of that island is threefold that in the males. In Australia and the Argentine, on the contrary, the intimate contact with the sheep's fleece is the prerogative of the butcher trade, and there the incidence of infection in males exceeds that in females.[13]

Human infection with echinococcus has been found in many parts of the world, especially in those which offer diagnostic and surgical facilities. In the United States, where they are well developed, few cases, if any, escape detection.[23] In countries where these facilities are lacking, infections in domestic animals may appear to be far more numerous than in man, as, e.g., in the Punjab, where almost all cattle and one-third of the dogs were infected, whereas the number of known human infections was 26 only.[15]

As a rule, *E. granulosus* is a parasite closely associated with human society. But in Canada it is perfectly independent of man and his domestic animals. As a tapeworm it lives in wolves, as a hydatid in moose and caribou. Miller [16] claims that this association of sylvatic parasitism [17] has existed for centuries, long before man arrived on the scene. Where he did, he added his domestic dog as a fourth to the triad wolf, moose, and parasite, by feeding this animal with the moose's lungs. In this way, man made himself part of the cycle in which the parasite carries on its development; later on he will do the same with his cattle, horses, and pigs. Thus *E. granulosus* will become a domestic parasite, associated with domestic animals and no longer with wild life. That stage, however, has not yet been reached in Canada.[18]

ECHINOCOCCUS MULTILOCULARIS

It has been mentioned already that the thick, laminated cuticle, a characteristic of the normal hydatid even in its earlier stages, protects not only the parasites but the host as well.[10] This protective

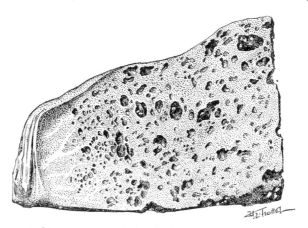

Fig. 15·12 *Echinococcus multilocularis,* in human liver, natural size. (After Brumpt, 1936. Courtesy, Masson & Cie, Paris.)

function becomes apparent by its absence in a particular form of echinococcus characterized by the tardy and defective development of the cuticle and known as *alveolar* or *Bavaro-Tyrolese echinococcus.*[8]

E. granulosus is characterized by its voluminous hydatid, filled with fluid and enveloped by a thick and rigid cuticle which permits it to maintain its spherical shape and to produce scolex capsules and daughter cysts. In the alveolar echinococcus, *Echinococcus multi-locularis* (Leuckart, 1863) Vogel, 1955, entirely different conditions prevail (Figs. 15·12, 13, 14). The cuticle appears much later, and it remains thin and pliable; as a consequence it is easily wrinkled into a mass filling the hollow of the crushed vesicle (Fig. 15·13:1). This condition is detrimental to fertility; one of the characteristics of the alveolar echinococcus is the scarcity of its scolex capsules, which are

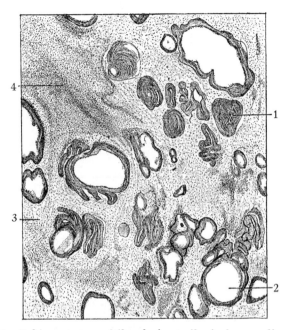

Fig. 15·13 *Echinococcus multilocularis,* sterile, in human liver: 1. Cyst filled with pliable cuticle, tightly pleated.—2. Sterile cyst.—3. Necrotic tissue.—4. Cellular infiltration. (After Brumpt, 1922. Courtesy, Masson & Cie, Paris.)

found in some of the vesicles only (Fig. 15·14:1–3). As a compensation, the germinal membrane develops another activity, entirely alien to its germinal function. No longer does it produce brood capsules, but it proliferates excessively. Unhampered by a restraining cuticle it is free to push forward its excrescences in all directions. These excrescences are naked masses of germinal cells, called *plasmodia,* which penetrate the narrow cavities of the hepatic parenchyma, the blood and lymph vessels (*infiltrative growth*); or they are transported to other organs and there continue the same kind of development (*metastatic growth*). The toxic products, with no cuticle to prevent their diffusion, pass freely into the surrounding tissue, destroy the parenchyma, and stimulate the connective tissue to excessive proliferation before it is killed in its turn. At a later stage the plasmodia are changed into vesicles surrounded by the thin and pliable cuticle mentioned before. This is the origin of numberless, usually sterile, cysts of a diameter of 0.1–0.5 mm that stuff the

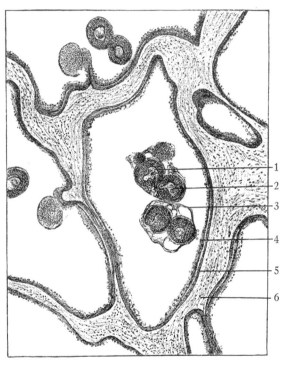

Fig. 15·14   *Echinococcus multilocularis,* fertile, in human liver: 1. Scolex capsule.—2. Hooklets on scolex.—3. Brood capsule.—4. Germinal membrane.—5. Cuticle.—6. Fibrous tissue between cysts. (After Brumpt, 1922. Courtesy, Masson & Cie, Paris.)

affected part of the liver (Fig. 15·12). At its periphery this development continues in the same fashion; in the center the confused mass of cysts and connective tissue dies off (*central necrosis*), leaving a more or less extensive cavity filled with a chocolate-brown mass. In short, the complex behaves in a way strongly reminiscent of a malignant growth.

Thus the relation between the alveolar echinococcus and its host is patently abnormal. It obviously belongs to the class which Leiper [19] once termed *pathologic parasitism,* characteristic of parasites ill-adapted to their host.

Pathologic parasitism is a very unstable foundation for the creation of a new species. Nevertheless, a new species was created for the causative agent of the *Bavaro-Tyrolese echinococcosis,* whose characteristics have been described above. The new (and very doubtful) species was named *Echinococcus multilocularis,* and its creation was further justified by pointing to its curious geographical distribution. In countries with the highest prevalence of *E. granulosus,* such as Uruguay, Argentina, Australia, and New Zealand, the new species was very rare. It is practically confined to certain countries in no way conspicuous for the presence of *E. granulosus,* viz. Southern Germany, the Jurassic and Alpine Mountains, Russia, Siberia, and Alaska.

In recent times, researches in the classical area of Bavaro-Tyrolese echinococcosis, the eastern Siberian islands, and Alaska, have raised *E. multilocularis* to the rank of an undoubted species, on the basis of characteristics much more convincing than its pathologic parasitism, which undoubtedly exists but is not a characteristic of the species.

Rausch and Schiller [20] have found burrowing rodents (*Microtus oeconomus* and *Clethrionomys rutilus* in the Siberian islands, in Alaska also the brown lemming) infected with parasites that cause changes which bear considerable resemblance to the human alveolar echinococcosis. As a tapeworm, this parasite lives principally in arctic foxes, as a bladder worm in the above mentioned rodents. If man (Eskimos) interferes, he adds sledge dogs to the carriers of the tapeworm, and himself to the carriers of the bladder worm. At first Rausch and Schiller regarded this parasite as a separate species, *E. sibiricensis.* At present they admit its close relationship with a parasite rediscovered by Vogel [4] in the Swabian Alps.

In this part of southern Bavaria, in the neighborhood of villages where the Bavaro-Tyrolese human disease is still rife, Vogel found foxes infected with echinococcus tapeworms. They were different from *E. granulosus,* for sheep ingesting their eggs failed to become infected; but infection succeeded when imported field mice of the species *M. oeconomus* swallowed the eggs. The same success was achieved when the experiment was repeated with indigenous field mice (*M. arvalis*). These rodents developed an alveolar hepatic echinococcosis, which thereupon was also detected as a natural disease of field mice in those parts.

The cysts sometimes contained scolices with which dogs could be infected. In their intestine tapeworms developed which proved to be identical with those that, fifty years ago, Posselt,[21] the great champion for the recognition of *E. multilocularis* as a separate species, had reared in dogs from scolex-capsules in a person ill with the Bavaro-Tyrolese sickness. The accompanying table summarizes the points of difference between the two tapeworms (Fig. 15·5:*B*).

The Bavaro-Tyrolese echinococcus retains the name that Leuckart bestowed on it 96 years ago; the Siberian parasite is regarded as a subspecies, *E. multilocularis sibiricensis* Rausch and Schiller, 1956; the name *E. cysticus,* which of late has come to the fore, is no more than a synonym of *E. granulosus.*

Accordingly, *E. granulosus* can no longer be held responsible for the state of pathologic parasitism expressed by the name of alveolar echinococcosis; it is obviously due to *E. multilocularis.*

At an earlier stage of the discussion the opinion was expressed that pathologic parasitism occurs when parasite and host are not adapted to each other. As things are, two questions arise: (1) Are man and *E. multilocularis* not adapted to each other? (2) What is the relation of the parasite to its apparently normal hosts, the field mice? With regard to *E. multilocularis sibiricensis* Rausch and Schiller [22] have answered both questions.

Horses, goats, and pigs are inappropriate hosts; the response of the hepatic tissue to the invading oncospheres is so intense that development comes to an end before it is well on its way. The same applies to man—with this difference, that infection occasionally succeeds and has consequences equally deleterious to host and parasite. In field mice, conditions are different. As a rule the infection is successful; usually it does not take a serious course (but an extensive metastatic diffusion has been met with on occasions). Thus the relation of the parasite to the field mice may be broadly defined as normal, that to man as decidedly abnormal.

TREATMENT OF ECHINOCOCCOSIS. In patients with clinical symptoms and corroborative evidence of a calcified density pointing to the diagnosis of hydatid disease, surgical intervention is the only hope for a radical cure. If the cyst cannot be excised, mar-

STRUCTURAL AND BIOLOGICAL DIFFERENCES BETWEEN

E. multilocularis AND *E. granulosus*

FEATURE	*Echionococcus multilocularis*	*Echionococcus granulosus*
Average length of expanded strobila	2.2 mm	3–4 mm
Size of hindmost proglottid	Shorter than rest of strobila	Longer than rest of strobila
Number of proglottids in dog	Usually four	Three
Location of genital atrium	Anterior to equator	On or behind equator
Average number of testes	22	44
Number of testes anterior to cirrus pouch	No more than 5	9–23
Shape of ovary	Kidney-shaped	Two separate lobes, united by narrow duct
Structure of gravid uterus	Wide pouch without branches	Longitudinal stem carrying a number of branches
Definitive hosts, sylvatic	Foxes	Wolves
Definitive hosts, domestic	Dogs and cats	Dogs
Interval between infecting meal and first passage of eggs in feces	35–47 days	45–61 days
Site of strobilas (in slight infections)	Middle and lower third of small intestine of dog	Upper and middle third of jejunum of dog

supialization is an alternative. The cyst fluid is carefully aspirated so as to avoid spillage. The inner lining of the cyst is then sterilized by the use of a 10 percent formalin solution which is promptly removed. The cyst and its contents are then attached to the adjacent tissues. In complicated lung cysts, lobectomy [26] may be required. In cerebral and pulmonary [26] cysts the use of formalin is hazardous and should preferably be avoided.

Attempts at desensitization with hydatid fluid (especially in inoperable cases or where multiple seeding is suspected) has recently been introduced in Latin American countries. Its effectiveness has not as yet been fully explored.

REFERENCES FOR CHAPTER XV

1. E. BRUMPT. *Précis de Parasitologie,* Paris, 1913, p. 281.
2. A. FAIN. *Ann. soc. belge méd. trop.,* 1956, 36: 679–696.
3. A. B. RAPER and G. C. DOCKERAY. *Ann. Trop. Med. Parasitol.,* 1956, 50: 121–128.
4. H. VOGEL. *Z. Tropenmed. Parasitol.,* 1957, 8: 404–454.
5. A. J. VAN AMERONGEN. *Tijdschr. Diergeneesk.,* 1947, 72: 237–242.
6. J. BAILENGER. *Bull. soc. pathol. exotique,* 1957, 50: 308–314.
7. F. DÉVÉ. *L'Echinococcose primitive,* 362 pp., Paris, 1949, Masson & Cie.
8. F. DÉVÉ. *L'Echinococcose secondaire,* 241 pp., Paris, 1946, Masson & Cie., pp. 1–212, 213–238.
9. L. BARNETT. *Med. J. Australia,* 1944 (2): 511–514.
10. P. DESOIL. *Ann. parasitol. humaine et comparée,* 1925, 3: 151–170.
11. F. DÉVÉ. *L'Echinococcose osseuse,* 236 pp., Montevideo, 1948, Monteverde & Cie.
12. L. BARNETT. *New Zealand Med. J.,* 1945, 44: 304–308.
13. M. EINARSSON. *Ann. parasitol. humaine et comparée,* 1926, 4: 172–184.
14. I. SNAPPER. *Geneesk. Bladen,* 1916, 19: 67–104.
15. M. A. SAMI. *Indian Med. Gaz.,* 1938, 73: 90–94.
16. M. J. MILLER. *Trop. Diseases Bull.,* 1953, 50: 1065–1066.
17. R. W. WOLFGANG and J. B. POOLE. *Am. J. Trop. Med. Hyg.,* 1956, 5: 869–871.
18. G. K. SWEATMAN. *Can. J. Public Health,* 1952, 43: 480–486.
19. R. T. LEIPER. *Proc. Roy. Soc. Med.,* 1933, 27: 127–134.
20. R. RAUSCH and E. L. SCHILLER. *Am. J. Trop. Med. Hyg.,* 1956, 5: 1086–1092.
21. A. POSSELT. *Münch. med. Wochschr.,* 1906, 53: 537–541, 600–609.
22. R. RAUSCH and E. L. SCHILLER. *Parasitology,* 1956, 46: 395–416.
23. M. M. STERMAN and H. W. BROWN. *J. Am. Med. Assoc.,* 1959, 169: 938–940.
24. M. TURNER and R. T. LEIPER. *Trans. Soc. Trop. Med. Hyg.,* 1919, 13: 23–24.
25. H. R. DEW. *Hydatid Disease: Its Pathology, Diagnosis, and Treatment,* Sydney, 1928, Australian Med. Pub. Co., Ltd.
26. N. R. BARRETT. *Thorax,* 1947, 2: 21–57.

CHAPTER XVI

OTHER CYCLOPHYLLIDEA

In this chapter human cyclophyllidea are discussed with arthropods as intermediate hosts and, in addition, species whose intermediate hosts are not known. As far as they are known, the eggs, passed in the stools, are complete; they have a permanent eggshell surrounding an embryophore with an oncosphere. The species to be dealt with here have only short proglottids and a gravid uterus stretching over the width of the proglottid (Hymenolepididae and Anoplocephalidae families); or the mature proglottids are oblong, and the gravid uterus disintegrates into egg capsules, containing a number of eggs each (Linstowiidae, Davaineidae and Dilepididae families).

THE GENUS HYMENOLEPIS (FAMILY OF HYMENOLEPIDIDAE)

HYMENOLEPIS NANA: THE DWARF TAPEWORM

The geographical distribution of the human parasite, *Hymenolepis nana* (v. Siebold, 1852) Blanchard, 1891, suggests a preference for countries with a hot summer. Infection rates of 5 to 33 percent have been recorded in the Mediterranean Basin and southern Russia. In the lower reaches of the river Volga, rates rose to 44 percent. In northern Europe, no systematic survey has been made, except under the abnormal conditions obtaining in collieries (e.g. 80 cases in the Liége area, Belgium). In several parts of Argentina, Chile, the southern United States, and Japan the rates of infection vary from 6 to 12 percent, but in northern China, Indonesia, New Guinea, and Australia even a systematic search revealed the presence of one or a few carriers only. In view of the considerable difference between the rate of infection in adults and children (*v. infra*), and the fact that the age groups are not always kept separate, the figures quoted here cannot be compared with each other.

The strobila inhabits the ileum. Its length is often 15–25 mm, its maximal width 0.5 mm (Fig. 16·1), but a specimen of 6–7 mm may already carry gravid proglottids. The size of the worms is influenced by their number in a given portion of the ileum. If there are only a few parasites they grow to 25 mm or over; if there is overcrowding their length does not exceed 10 mm.[1]

Fig. 16·1   *Hymenolepis nana,* × 18. (After Leuckart, from Braun, 1925. Courtesy, Curt Kabitzsch, Leipzig.)

The scolex has a diameter of 0.19–0.34 mm; it has a retractile rostellum, with a ring of 20–22 hooklets, four round suckers, and a fairly long neck. A full-grown strobila is composed of 110–120 proglottids, all of the short type. Posteriorly, they grow in width, except the hindmost ones; their genital atria have a unilateral position in the anterior half of the proglottid.

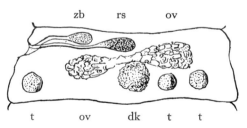

Fig. 16·2   *Hymenolepis nana,* sexually mature proglottid: *t,* Testis.— *ov,* Ovary.—*dk,* Vitelline gland.—*rs,* Seminal receptacle.—*zb,* Seminal vesicle. (After Leuckart.)

The sexually mature proglottid (Fig. 16·2) carries three round testes, close to the posterior margin; two lie close together, near the lateral margin opposite to the genital atrium, the third one near and posterior to that atrium. The bilobed ovary is situated medially; its two lobes are joined together by a narrow median portion, posterior to which lies the vitelline gland. Into the genital atrium open the vagina, provided with a seminal receptacle, and the vas deferens, which possesses a cirrus pouch and a seminal vesicle. When the gravid uterus disintegrates, the eggs fill the whole of the proglottid.

The eggs arc passcd in the feces; they measure 40–57 × 35–47 μ. The eggshell is permanent; it is thin, transparent, and colorless. Inside lies the embryophore, of 25–34 × 22–30 μ; it is also thin, transparent, and colorless, but has the special feature of possessing a minute knob at each pole, from which diverge two, or more, long, thin, much convoluted filaments that encircle the embryophore. Within the latter lies the oncosphere, with a diameter of about 24 μ; it carries the usual six hooklets, almost parallel to each other (Fig. 16·3). Outside the body of the host the eggs are short-lived; stored in water they die in 11 days.[2]

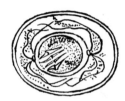

Fig. 16·3 *Hymenolepis nana,* complete egg, × 450, found in fcccs of an inhabitant of New Guinea by Dr. Kleevens.

The development of the oncosphere into a cysticercoid can take place in the body of an arthropod intermediate host (*v. infra*), but also in the mammalian definitive host. The first is called *indirect development,* the second *direct development.* Thc sccond is probably of more common occurrence; therefore it will be discussed first.

Direct development has been observed in *H. nana* as found in rats and mice, often designated by the name of *H. fraterna* Stiles, 1906. It is assumed that it takes the same course in the human body.

Rats and mice, after the ingestion of eggs produced by either the human or murine *H. nana,* eventually harbor adult strobilas in their intestine. This event, unheard of in human cestodes, implies that the infection passes from one definitive host to another by way of direct contact. The explanation is that the oncosphere, having been set free in the lumen of the intestine of the mouse that swallowed the eggs ten hours earlier and having penetrated the tissue of one of the villi of the wall of the third quarter of the small intestine, remains in that site, and does not enter the circulation. There, the oncosphere is changed into a vesicle and becomes surrounded by a cuticle. Four days after the infecting meal a scolex has been developed in the interior of the vesicle (Figs. 16·4 and 16·5). After five days the scolex emerges, dragging the rest of the vesicle behind it (Fig. 16·5:B). It finds its way into the lumen of the bowel and is transferred to the last quarter of the small intestine.[3] Arriving at

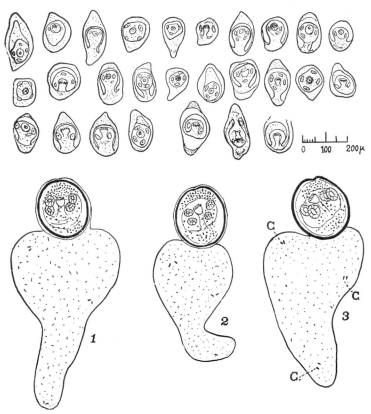

FIG. 16·4   *Hymenolepis fraterna. Above:* Three rows of mature cysticercoids from intestinal villi of mouse.—*Below:* Three cysticercoids aged 36 to 63 days from adult *Tenebrio molitor:* C, Hooklets derived from oncosphere, × 60. (After Brumpt, 1936. Courtesy, Masson & Cie, Paris.)

that site, it settles down between the villi, attached by its suckers and hooklets (Fig. 16·6); it starts growing proglottids eight days after the infecting meal. A fortnight after that date, gravid proglottids are formed; 16–17 days after the same date, eggs are passed in the rat's feces.[4] The oncospheres within these eggs are ready to infect other mice and, with certain restrictions, the mouse that passed them.

Thus, *autoinfection* is possible; but *internal autoinfection,* i.e. infection with an oncosphere from an egg that had not left the host's body, appears to occur as an extremely rare exception.[5]

All this happens with *H. fraterna* in mice and rats. It is not certain that the same happens with *H. nana* in man, but it is probable. The murine and human parasites may not be the same, but they are so closely related that it is possible to infect young rats by feeding them eggs of human hymenolepis, as long as spontaneously infected rats are excluded from the experiment.[6] Conversely, children, but not adults, can be infected by mixing eggs of murine hymenolepis with their food.[7]

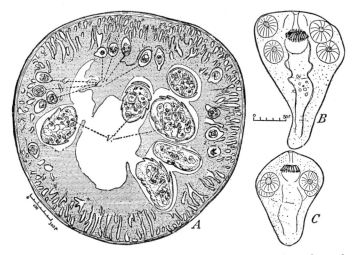

F_IG. 16·5 *Hymenolepis fraterna:* *A*, Transverse section through the last third of ileum of mouse.—*V*, Section through adult worm.—*C*, Through cysticercoids.—*B* and *C*, Scolices emerged from the villi, ready to attach themselves to the intestinal wall, × 180. (After Brumpt, 1936. Courtesy, Masson & Cie, Paris.)

Indirect development has likewise been observed in murine hymenolepis only. Rat fleas and other fleas are the intermediate hosts. They are infected in their larval stage, because it is only in that stage that eggs can be ingested, the adults taking nothing but blood. In the body of the larval flea, the oncosphere develops into a cysticercoid (Fig. 16·4). During metamorphosis, the latter is transferred to the body of the adult flea and therein completes its development.[8] Rats become infected through their habit of eating the fleas that infest them.

Besides fleas, various insects can act as the intermediate host of the murine hymenolepis, among them *Tenebrio molitor,* a beetle, the adult of the meal worm (Fig. 16·4:1–3). However, the adult only is implicated, and not the larva. Beetles have been experimentally infected by making them ingest the eggs of both the murine and human parasite. Both infections were successful, but the beetles were more readily infected with *H. fraterna* than with *H. nana.*[9] Thus, it is not certain that meal beetles are natural hosts of human hymenolepis.

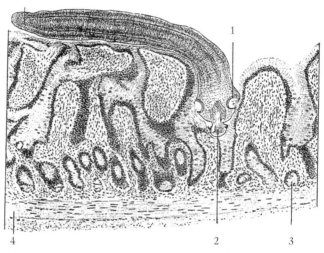

FIG. 16·6 *Hymenolepis fraterna,* attached to intestinal wall with its scolex: 1. Sucker.—2. Rostellum.—3. Intestinal gland.—4. Muscular tissue. (After Brumpt, 1922. Courtesy, Masson & Cie, Paris.)

Assuming that *H. nana* in man behaves like *H. fraterna* in its murine host, i.e. that direct infection is the rule rather than the exception, it follows that man acquires his infection by direct contact, as in *Giardia* infection. Family infection may thus be expected and has actually been observed. As an example De Jongh's [10] case may be quoted. In the Hague, a city in which the parasite has never been heard of before nor since, he observed four carriers in a family of six. The father and two children were asymptomatic; the fourth, an infant, brought the infection to light by its abdominal complaints. Similar observations have been recorded in France [11] and America.[12]

According to Oquiñena [13] the average rate of infection with *H. nana* in children is tenfold that in adults. Observations on the host-parasite relationship in *H. fraterna* can serve to explain this difference between children and adults.

Hunninen [4] has observed that the rate of murine infection with *H. fraterna* greatly decreases after the third month of life of the host, provided it has been exposed to repeated infections during the first three months of its existence. At the end of this period the animal has acquired a resistance insufficient to prevent reinfection but strong enough to prevent the parasite from reaching sexual maturity.

The resistance acquired by the murine host persists for 141 days after the parasites have been expelled from its intestine. Apparently it is not dependent upon a residual parasite population; contrary to what is known in *H. diminuta,* it cannot be classified as relative immunity or premunition.[14]

Whatever may be the nature of this resistance, one thing is certain —that it protects the adults and not the young. Thus it may be assumed that the difference in the adult and child rate of human infection, as pointed out by Oquiñena,[13] also depends on resistance developing as a result of repeated infections experienced in youth.

In rats and mice acquired resistance is diminished or lost under the influence of intestinal bacterial or helminthic (*Strongyloides muris*) infections, malnutrition (protein deficiency), or alcohol poisoning.[15]

If results obtained by observations on *H. diminuta* may be applied to *H. nana,* the pathogenic effect of the latter is due to the parasite entering into nutritional competition with its host. It absorbs carbohydrates and vitamin B_2 from the bowel contents, protein and vitamin B_1 from the tissue of the intestinal wall.[16]

TREATMENT OF HYMENOLEPIS NANA INFECTION. Quinacrine, employed as prescribed in taeniasis, is considered efficacious. It is to be remembered, however, that this anthelmintic does not destroy the cysticercoids lodged in the tissue of the bowel wall. Thus the treatment may have to be repeated after an interval of 8 days, sufficient to allow for the development into tapeworms of cysticercoids left untouched by the first treatment.[18]

Faust et al.[17] recommend never to initiate a more potent treatment before having tried hexylresorcinol crystoids (U.S.P.), available in enteric-coated capsules of 0.1 and 0.2 gm. The drug is given in the morning, before any kind of food has been taken, but without a purge the night before. A saline purge follows two hours after the administration of the drug, and food is withheld for three hours more. The adult dose is 1 to 1.2 gm; for children 0.1 gm for each year of life, up to the age of 10 or 12.[18]

HYMENOLEPIS DIMINUTA: THE RAT TAPEWORM

Hymenolepis diminuta (Rudolphi, 1819) Blanchard, 1891, is a cosmopolitan murine parasite, occasionally found in man, and can be easily distinguished from *H. nana* by its size, 20–60 cm × 3.5 mm (maximal width; Fig. 16·7). Its internal anatomy is the same as that

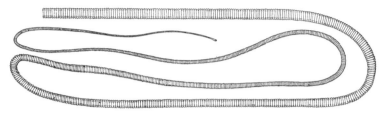

FIG. 16·7 *Hymenolepis dominuta* × ¾. (After Brumpt, 1922. Courtesy, Masson & Cie, Paris.)

of *H. nana*. Its complete eggs (Fig. 16·8) differ from those of *H. nana* by their size, 59–66 μ, the absence of the filamentous appendages of the embryophore, and the differentiation of the space between eggshell and oncosphere into an outer granular and an inner clear zone. Sometimes a granular zone is visible between the embryophore and the oncosphere.[19] Unlike the eggs of *H. nana,* they survive in water for six months.[20]

FIG. 16·8 *Hymenolepis diminuta,* egg, × 750, from feces of child in Amsterdam.

H. diminuta is common in the intestine of rats; nearly half of them may be found infected in some localities. But in man it is much rarer than *H. nana:* one infection of the former to 77–135 of the latter.

Cysticercoids develop only in the arthropod intermediate hosts. Two species of centipedes and 22 of insects can serve this function, including the beetle and the fleas that occasionally serve *H. nana*.

Rats harboring four mature tapeworms in their intestine are resistant to repeated infections.[21]

A Comparison of the Two Members of the Genus Hymenolepis. This comparison raises two points of interest in regard to the relation of the two species to their host.

The first point refers to the kind of definitive hosts.

It may be assumed that both species, *H. nana* and *H. diminuta*, were originally murine parasites, accidentally and rarely invading man. A fundamental change was brought about in this condition when *H. nana* became virtually independent of its arthropod host. Thus it was turned into a parasite transmitted by direct contact. As direct contact is more intimate between man and man than between man and mouse, *H. nana*, accidentally parasitizing man, was more readily transmitted to man than to the mouse. In this way the parasite became isolated from its murine ancestry and was changed into an essentially human strain. This is reflected in the tendency to regard the original murine strain as a separate species. *H. fraterna*.

On the other hand, *H. diminuta* never lost touch with its arthropod host. Thus it never became a parasite transmitted by direct contact; it remained an essentially murine parasite that rarely invades the human body.

The second point refers to the resistance of the host.

It is assumed that resistance to cestode parasites is directed against the tissue-inhabiting stage, the bladder worm; thus resistance is expected to develop in the intermediate host only—and so it usually does. *H. nana* is an apparent exception to this rule because of the resistance developed by the definitive host; but it is apparent only, because this host also carries cysticercoids. *H. diminuta* offers a real exception, the definitive host acquiring resistance without ever harboring cysticercoids.

BERTIELLA STUDERI (FAMILY OF ANOPLOCEPHALIDAE)

In *Bertiella studeri* (Blanchard, 1891) Stiles and Hassall, 1902 [*Bertia satyri* Blanchard, 1891] the proglottids are all of the "short" type, as in hymenolepis, and the uterus stretches transversely be-

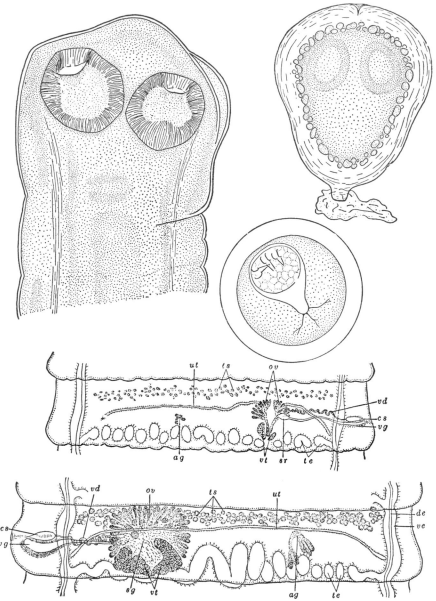

FIG. 16·9 *Bertiella studeri. Above, left:* Scolex, × 110.—*Middle, below:* Young proglottid, × 15.—*Bottom:* Mature proglottid, × 15: *ag*, rudimentary ovary; *cs*, cirrus pouch; *de*, dorsal excretory canal; *ov*, ovary; *sg*, shell gland; *sr*, seminal receptacle; *te*, transverse excretory canal; *ts*, testes; *ut*, uterus; *vd*, vas deferens; *ve*, ventral excretory canal; *vg*, vagina; *vt*, vitelline gland.—*Above, right:* Cysticercoid in *Schelori-*

tween the excretory canals (Fig. 16·9:*ut*); but there are numerous testes (Fig. 16·9:*ts*), the genital pores have an alternating position, and the inner shell of the egg shows the bicornuate protrusion characteristic of the "piriform apparatus" (Fig. 16·9:middle, right).

The strobila inhabits the last two-fifths of the host's small intestine. Its length is about 23 cm, its maximal width about 8 mm. It is composed of 400 proglottids or so, that are detached in chains of 8–10. The scolex is flattened in a dorsoventral direction; the flat side is almost round, with a diameter of about ½ mm (Fig. 16·9:above, left). The suckers are situated laterally on the flat sides; the rostellum is poorly developed and unarmed. The sexually mature proglottids measure 0.5 by 6 mm; their anatomy may be seen in Fig. 16·9.[22] The gravid uterus carries numerous very short branches. The eggs are discharged through one or two openings situated anteriorly to the genital atrium; they are deposited before the gravid proglottid is expelled.

The eggs are spherical, 40–60 μ in diameter. The outer shell (the true eggshell) is transparent and is 6–7 μ thick; the inner shell or embryophore (called here the piriform apparatus) measures 27–35 $\times$ 20–21 μ; it has the form of a bottle with a short neck that carries at its extremity two or three slender protrusions or "horns." The oncosphere, enclosed within the inner shell, measures 17–18 $\times$ 19–20 μ; occasionally it carries more than the usual number of six hooklets. Between the two shells lies the so-called "albuminous mass" which is 40 μ thick (Fig. 16·9:middle, right).

Mites of the family of *Oribatidae* act as intermediate hosts. When they ingest the eggs, the oncospheres develop into cysticercoids (Fig. 16·9:above, right) in the course of two months. They measure 140–160 $\times$ 100–120 μ. Some of them carry a caudal appendage.

B. studeri is a common intestinal parasite in anthropoid apes. On occasions it has been detected parasitizing man (usually children) in the islands of Mauritius, Sumatra, Java, the Philippines,[22a] and the West Indies. Sharma[23] made a systematic search for it among 540 inhabitants of the town of Shillong (Assam, India) and found three of them infected.

---

bates laevigatus, two months old, $\times$ 400.—*Above, middle:* Egg in uterus with two envelopes, and the (punctated) "albuminous mass" in between, $\times$ 700. (After Stunkard, 1940. Courtesy, *American Journal of Tropical Medicine.*)

INERMICAPSIFER MADAGASCARIENSIS (FAMILY OF LINSTOWIIDAE)

Inermicapsifer madagascariensis (Davaine, 1870) Baer, 1956 [*Taenia madagascariensis* Davaine, 1870; *Inermicapsifer arvicanthidis* (Kofend, 1917) Baer, 1925; *Inermicapsifer cubensis* (Kourí, 1938) Baer, 1940], according to Baer,[25] has a strobila with a length of 50–315 mm and a maximal width of 1.5–2.3 mm. The scolex is unarmed; its suckers carry no spines. Proglottids near the scolex are "short"; farther down they become square, 0.8×0.8 mm. Gravid proglottids are oblong, 3 by 2.6 mm. They become detached from the strobila, and are passed in the feces in a form resembling a rice kernel. The genital atria are unilateral, situated in the middle of the lateral margin. The markedly lobed ovary lies in the middle of the proglottid, the vitelline gland on its caudal side, surrounded by testes on both sides and behind. The transversely situated uterus disintegrates into 126–180 egg capsules, filling the whole proglottid. Each capsule contains from four to ten eggs. The eggs have a size of 34–36 μ with an oncosphere of 11 μ; it is not clear whether they are complete eggs or embryophores.

In the islands of Cuba the parasite has been found in over a hundred persons; the majority of them were children under twelve years of age.[26]

Like *Hymenolepis nana, I. madagascariensis* is becoming a human parasite, but for a different reason. The fact is that it has been transported to a new environment where it has lost its definitive rodent host. In East Africa (Kenya, Ruanda-Urundi) it is still in possession of it, in the form of wild rodents of the genus *Arvicanthis,* and members of the suborder of the *Hyracoidea.* The parasite in these surroundings is occasionally encountered in man and was given the specific name of "arvicanthidis." Fain [24] identified it with a human cestode discovered in Cuba by Kourí that bore the specific name of "cubensis." Finally, Baer [25] proved the identity of "cubensis" and "arvicanthidis" with a third cestode, long ago described under the specific name now borne by the species. More important, however, was his tracing of the species to other islands besides Cuba—to Madagascar, the Comoros, and Mauritius—and pointing to the fact that *I. madagascariensis* in all these islands is a purely human parasite, because there are no appropriate definitive hosts among the indigenous rodents.

Intermediate hosts of *I. madagascariensis* are unknown.

TREATMENT. Kourí et al.[26] recommend extract of male fern and carbon tetrachloride.

THE GENUS RAILLIETINA (FAMILY OF DAVAINEIDAE)

Although they belong to different families, *Raillietina* and *Inermicapsifer* resemble each other so much that it is difficult to differentiate them unless a scolex is present showing 80 or more rostellar hooklets (in that case it is a raillietina). The detached

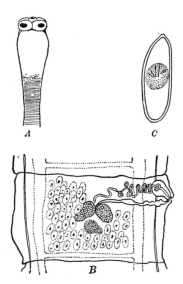

FIG. 16·10 *Raillietina* sp. *A*, Scolex, enlarged.—*B*, Mature proglottid, × 40.—*C*, Egg, × 600. (After Blanchard, Brumpt, and Garrison; from Craig and Faust, 1937. Courtesy, Lea & Febiger, Philadelphia.)

gravid proglottid can be identified only by the position of the unilateral genital atria. In raillietina it is situated in the anterior third of the lateral margin (Fig. 16·10:*B*); in inermicapsifer it is situated in the middle of the lateral margin.

Two well-recognized species [27] are known to use man as a definitive host.

RAILLIETINA CELEBENSIS

Raillietina celebensis (Janicki, 1902) Joyeux and Baer, 1929, has a strobila that varies in length from 16 to 600 cm, with a maximal width of 2.5 mm. The gravid proglottid measures 3×1.5 mm. The scolex carries 80–160 hooklets, 14–26 μ long; its suckers are provided with minute spines. The genital atria are situated in the anterior third of the lateral margin. The cirrus pouch measures 89–180 $\times$ 40–85 μ. Each mature proglottid contains 21–50 testes, and each gravid one, 100–230 egg capsules; the latter contain 1–4 eggs each.

R. celebensis is an intestinal parasite in various species of rats in southeastern Asia, Madagascar, and Queensland. As a human parasite (mostly in children) it has been reported in Japan, Formosa, Bangkok, Jakarta (Java), and perhaps the Philippine Islands.

Intermediate hosts are not known.

RAILLIETINA DEMERARIENSIS

Raillietina demerariensis (Daniels, 1895) Dollfus, 1935, has a strobila 90–120 cm long, with a maximum width of 1.3–1.8 mm. There are 200–300 rostellar hooklets; the suckers are spinose; the size of the cirrus pouch is 180–220 by 80–90 μ; the testes number 50–70, the egg-capsules about 180, and the eggs 8–10 per capsule.

Human infections were found in British Guiana and Honduras,[26] but Ecuador appears to have the highest incidence, with 5 percent of hospital patients infected.

According to Joyeux and Baer,[28] C. Bonne found the howler monkey as an alternate host in Surinam.

Intermediate hosts are unknown.

DIPYLIDIUM CANINUM (FAMILY OF DILEPIDIDAE)

Dipylidium caninum (Linnaeus, 1758) Railliet, 1892 [*Taenia cucumerina* Bloch, 1782] is like inermicapsifer and the raillietinas in that the gravid uterus disintegrates into egg capsules. It differs from them by the proglottids containing two sets of genital organs each, opening into two genital atria situated opposite each other in the middle of the lateral margins.

The strobila has a length of 15–40 cm and a maximum width of 2–3 mm (Fig. 16·11). The proglottids of the posterior half are wider in the middle than at the extremities; thus they reminded Bloch (1782) of cucumber seeds. The proglottids vary in number from 8 to 120; the anterior ones have a width of 0.15 mm. The gravid proglottids measure 8–11 by 1.5–3 mm; they are detached separately or in chains that are often seen protruding from the anal aperture in intertwined strands, which the dog tries to get rid of by rubbing its anal region over the floor; occasionally they leave the human host by way of the nasal cavity.

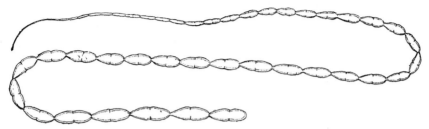

FIG. 16·11 *Dipylidium caninum,* natural size. (After Brumpt, 1936. Courtesy, Masson & Cie, Paris.)

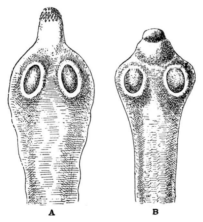

FIG. 16·12 *Dipylidium caninum,* scolex, × 50: *A,* Rostellum protruded. —*B,* Rostellum retracted. (After Blanchard, from Brumpt, 1922. Courtesy, Masson & Cie, Paris.)

The scolex (Fig. 16·12) has a diameter of 350–360 μ. It carries the usual number of suckers, which have an elliptical shape. The club-shaped rostellum is retractile; it carries some rings of hooklets that have the form of spines (Fig. 16·15). When the rostellum is protruded, its basal part is often considerably contracted (Fig. 16·13).

The sexually mature proglottid contains a large number of testes, situated between the meshes of the uterus, which at that stage has the shape of a net (Fig. 16·14). The vasa efferentia of the testes open into two greatly convoluted vasa deferentia. Each vas deferens terminates in a cirrus pouch that opens into one of the genital atria.

There are two ovaries, each one with a vitelline gland behind it. A vagina joins each ovary to the genital atrium of the corresponding side. The gravid uterus disintegrates into 300–400 egg capsules; each capsule contains 8–15 eggs (Fig. 16·18).

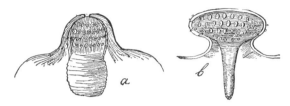

FIG. 16·13 *Dipylidium caninum,* rostellum, × 100: *a,* Retracted.—*b,* Protruded. (After Leuckart.)

FIG. 16·14 *Dipylidium caninum,* proglottid, × 25: *T,* Testes.—*Exb,* Excretory canal.—*U,* Uterus.—*VD,* Vas deferens.—*CB,* Cirrus pouch.— *C,* Cirrus.—*V,* Vagina.—*O,* Ovary.—*Ui,* Expanded portion of oviduct.— *DK,* Vitelline gland. (After Neumann and Railliet; from Brumpt, 1921. Courtesy, Masson & Cie, Paris.)

The egg, measuring 43–50 μ in diameter, has a true eggshell which is thin, colorless, and transparent. There is no more than a narrow space between the eggshell and the equally thin, colorless, and transparent embryophore. The oncosphere, within the embryophore, has a diameter of 25–36 μ and carries the usual six hooklets (Fig. 16·17).

The oncosphere develops into a cysticercoid (or what is usually called by that name) within the body of dog-, cat-, and human fleas.

The larvas ingest the egg; the oncosphere pierces the intestinal wall and takes up a position in one of the posterior segments of the larval insects. There it remains, unchanged, until the second or third day after the metamorphosis of the larva into the adult flea. Then the oncosphere develops into a "cysticercoid" of a length of 300 μ, with an invaginated scolex (Fig. 16·16).

Fig. 16·15 *Dipylidium caninum,* spine on rostellum. (After Braun, from Ihle and Nierstrasz, 1928. Courtesy, Oosthoek & Co., Publishers, Utrecht.)

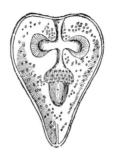

Fig. 16·16 *Dipylidium caninum,* mature cysticercoid, × 120. (After Leuckart.)

The assumption that dogs and cats become infected by eating the fleas is reasonable, but that children swallow fleas that inadvertently get mixed with their food, as has been asserted, appears unlikely. A more acceptable assumption is that cysticerci are squeezed out of the flea when it is crushed between the dog's teeth, and that they stick

Fig. 16·17 *Dipylidium caninum,* egg, × 450.

Fig. 16·18 *Dipylidium caninum,* egg capsule, × 100.

to the corners of the dog's mouth and are transferred to the child's face by the dog's tongue.

In the course of years *D. caninum* has often been observed in man, in most European countries, North America, the Antilles, the Philippine Islands, China, South Africa, and Australia. But its true definitive hosts are dogs and cats.

TREATMENT. Faust et al.[17] recommend the drugs that are found useful in taeniasis.

REFERENCES FOR CHAPTER XVI

1. W. N. F. WOODLAND. *Parasitology*, 1924, 16: 69–83.
2. D. A. SHORB. *Am. J. Hyg.*, 1933, 18: 74–113.
3. C. JOYEUX. *Ann. parasitol. humaine et comparée*, 1925, 3: 270–280.
4. A. V. HUNNINEN. *Am. J. Hyg.*, 1935, 22: 414–434.
5. A. V. HUNNINEN. *J. Parasitol.*, 1936, 22: 84–87.
6. E. ROMAN. *Ann. parasitol. humaine et comparée*, 1939, 17: 12–16.
7. Y. SAEKI. *Trop. Diseases Bull.*, 1921, 18: 112.
8. J. BACIGALUPO. *Ann. parasitol. humaine et comparée*, 1931, 9: 339–343.
9. J. BACIGALUPO. *Compt. rend. soc. biol. Paris*, 1929, 102: 1102–1103.
10. C. L. DE JONGH. *Ned. Tijdschr. Geneesk.*, 1917, 61 (1): 541–547, English summary, 547.
11. F. COUTELEN. *Bull. soc. pathol. exotique*, 1949, 42: 106–111.
12. L. A. SPINDLER. *J. Parasitol.*, 1929, 16: 38–40.
13. F. OQUIÑENA. *Ann. parasitol. humaine et comparée*, 1929, 7: 469–476.
14. J. F. HEARIN. *Am. J. Hyg.*, 1941, 33 (Sect. D): 71–87.
15. J. E. LARSH, JR. *J. Parasitol.*, 1951, 37: 343–352.
16. A. C. CHANDLER. *Am. J. Hyg.*, 1943, 37: 121–130.
17. E. C. FAUST, P. F. RUSSELL, and D. R. LINCICOME. *Clinical Parasitology*, Philadelphia, 1957, pp. 637, 421, 634.
18. E. G. NAUCK. *Lehrbuch der Tropenkrankheiten*, Stuttgart, 1956, pp. 71, 79.
19. F. FÜLLEBORN. *Arch. Schiffs- u. Tropenhyg.*, 1922, 26: 193–202.
20. N. KAMALOV. *Arch. Schiffs- u. Tropenhyg.*, 1931, 35: 606–611.
21. M. PALAIS. *Compt. rend. soc. biol. Paris*, 1934, 117: 1016–1017.
22. H. W. STUNKARD. *Am. J. Trop. Med.*, 1940, 20: 305–327.
22a. C. M. AFRICA and E. Y. GARCIA. *Philippine J. Sci.*, 1936, 56: 1–11.
23. A. N. SHARMA. *Indian Med. Gaz.*, 1930, 65: 200–203.
24. A. FAIN. *Bull. soc. pathol. exotique*, 1950, 43: 434–443.
25. J. G. BAER. *Ann. Trop. Med. Parasitol.*, 1956, 50: 152–156.
26. P. KOURÍ and J. G. BASNUEVO. *Helmintologia humana*, Havana, 1949, pp. 484, 514.
27. J. G. BAER and D. F. SANDARS. *J. Helminthol.*, 1956, 30: 173–182.
28. C. JOYEUX and J. G. BAER. *Acta tropica Bâle*, 1949, 6: 141–144.

PART FOUR

Helminths: Nematodes

CHAPTER XVII

NEMATODES OR ROUNDWORMS

The nonscientific name of the nematodes expresses their most obvious characteristic; roundworms have the shape of organisms that in daily life are called worms.

The integument is composed of a syncytial protoplasmic layer (subcuticular layer) which produces a cuticle that covers its exterior surface. The cuticle is usually marked throughout with a regular series of minute, shallow transverse grooves, or *striations*. During the growth of the young worms, the outer cuticle becomes periodically detached, together with the lining of the mouth, the esophagus, and the rectum. This process is known as *molt* or *ecdysis*. As a rule there are four molts in the course of the development from larva to adult worm.

The subcuticular layer shows four internal thickenings. Two of these thickenings, known as *lateral fields* (Fig. 17·1:zijstr.), run along the sides of the body; they are usually well developed and prominent. The others (Fig. 17·1:rugstr., buikstr.), situated in the middorsal and midventral lines, are less conspicuous. Contained in each lateral field runs a longitudinal canal (Fig. 17·1:excr. kan.), the *excretory canal,* throughout almost the whole length of the helminth. The two canals have a common duct that opens at the *excretory pore.*

The four longitudinal thickenings divide the musculature of the body wall into four sectors. The muscle cells are either numerous and irregularly arranged (*polymyarian* type, Fig. 17·1:spiercel), or the musculature is composed of eight longitudinal rows of flat, rhomboid cells (*meromyarian* type).

The mouth, situated at, or close to, the anterior extremity, may be guarded by liplike structures. A three-lipped condition is of common occurrence (Fig. 17·2); in this, each of the three lips carries on its outer surface one or two of the four or six sensory papillas with which the head may be provided. In other instances there are two lips only, each one carrying three papillas, or no lips at all, in which case the papillas are found in the vicinity of the mouth.

The mouth opens into the buccal cavity and esophagus. Where these two are joined together lies the *nerve ring* (Fig. 17·3:1, slokd. ring). The esophagus is provided with powerful muscular walls,

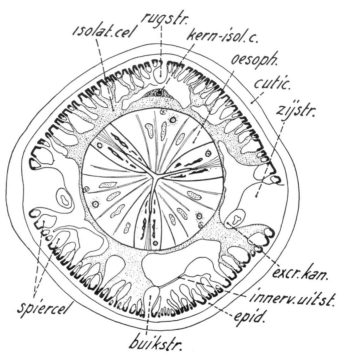

FIG. 17·1 Cross section through *Ascaris* behind nerve ring: *isolat.cel*, Isolating tissue surrounding intestine.—*rug str*, Dorsal thickening of subcuticular layer.—*kern-isol.c*, Nucleus in isolating tissue.—*oesoph*, Esophagus.—*cutic*, Cuticle.—*zijstr*, Lateral field.—*excr.kan*, Excretory canal.—*innerv.uitst*, Extension of muscular elements.—*epid*, Subcuticular layer.—*buikstr*, Ventral thickening of subcuticular layer.—*spiercel*, Muscular elements. (After Braun, from Ihle and Nierstrasz, 1928. Courtesy, Oosthoek & Co., Publishers, Utrecht.)

surrounding a three-sided lumen with a cuticular lining (Fig. 17·1:oesoph.). In many species there is a muscular *bulb* at the posterior end, separated from the esophagus proper by an encircling furrow (Fig. 17·3:1, bulb.). The esophagus leads into the midgut, and this in turn into the rectum, which opens at the anal aperture. In the female the anus is usually situated some distance from the caudal extremity, in the male the rectum has a terminal position. It is termed the *cloaca* as it also allows the exit of the male sexual products (Fig. 17·3:1, anus; 2 cloac. open.).

As a rule, the sexes are separate among the nematodes. The reproductive glands in both sexes are tubular organs, closed at one end and continuous at the other with the ducts by which their products reach the exterior. The female possesses two such tubes, the ovaries; each ovary is continuous with an oviduct, which leads into an uterus (Fig. 17·3:1, ovarium, uter.). The two uteri join in the vagina, which opens at the vulva (Fig. 17·3:1, gesl. open.).

Fig. 17·2   *Enterobius vermicularis,* showing the three lips, each with two sensory papillas. (After Chitwood and Wehr, 1934.)

The male possesses one tube, the testis, which leads into the vas deferens, continuous with an ejaculatory duct which opens at the cloaca. In connection with the cloaca there often is a sheath or a pair of sheaths, each containing a chitinoid copulatory organ called the *spicule* (Fig. 17·4:*sp*). Sometimes there is another chitinoid structure, formed as a thickening of the dorsal wall of the cloaca, which is called the *gubernaculum* or *accessory piece*. The caudal end of the male is usually provided with a number of special papillas. A male structure peculiar to the strongyloids is the caudal *bursa,* a cuticular expansion surrounding the posterior extremity of the male. This membranous expansion is supported by a number of *rays*. During copulation the male embraces with its bursa the vulvar region of the female and attaches the bursa to the integument of that region by means of the secretion of the *cement glands* (prostate glands), which open into the ejaculatory duct.

Often the nematodes leave the host in the form of eggs (Fig. 17·5).

The development of the parasites outside the human body is accomplished in the soil, in intermediate hosts, or in alternate hosts. The time required for extrahuman development may be reduced to a

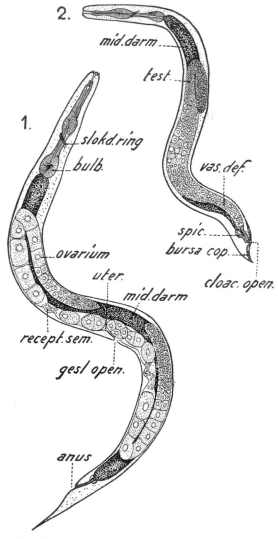

FIG. 17·3 *Rhabditis aberrans,* a free-living nematode: 1. Female: *slokd. ring,* nerve ring; *bulb,* esophagal bulb; *ovarium,* ovary; *uter,* uterus; *mid.darm,* intestine; *recept.sem,* seminal receptacle; *gesl.op,* vulva; *anus,* anal aperture.—2. Male: *test,* testis; *vas.def,* vas deferens; *spic,* spicule; *bursa cop,* bursa; *cloac.op,* cloaca. (After Eva Krüger, from Ihle and Nierstrasz, 1928. Courtesy, Oosthoek & Co., Publishers, Utrecht.)

few hours or less; in that case the parasite is practically transmitted by contact.

As a rule, not without exceptions, nematodes do not multiply in the human body. Thus the host can impose numerical restraint by no other means than by (1) prevention of reinfection or (2) inhibition of the development of parasites that have already penetrated the host. Both defense mechanisms have been directed against several nematodes, with the result that a moderate infection was attained with advancing age.

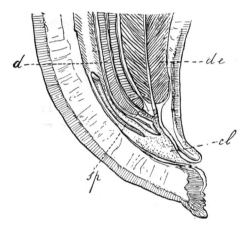

Fig. 17·4 *Ascaris lumbricoides,* male; median longitudinal section through posterior extremity: *cl,* cloaca; *d,* intestine; *de,* ejaculatory duct; *sp,* spicule. (After Leuckart.)

In some instances the working of this mechanism appears to be fairly well understood, especially in a small murine nematode *Nippostrongylus muris.*[1] Its eggs are passed in the rat's feces. Outside the host, larvas hatch from the eggs. At first they are nonparasitic, but after two molts they resume their parasitic mode of life, as manifested by their tendency to enter the host's body by piercing its skin. If they succeed in this effort, they pass through the venous circulation and the right heart to the lungs, and from there by way of the air passages to the intestinal tract. One week after their entrance through the skin they reach sexual maturity, as becomes apparent by eggs being passed in the feces. After a period hardly exceeding one week, the majority of the worms are expelled as a result of the increasing antiparasitic activity of the host.

Often repeated moderate infections greatly intensify the defensive activity of the host. Initially, the adult worms in the intestine are the ones to be affected; but after repeated infections, the migrating larvas on their way from the skin to the lungs are affected as well. They become sluggish and undersized; it takes them much longer than usual to complete their course, and many die in the pulmonary tissue. As a consequence, only a minority of the larvas that entered the host's body reach their intestinal destination. Although they become sexually mature, the number of eggs they produce remains far below the normal average; it is further reduced by the

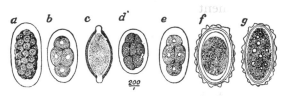

Fig. 17·5   Eggs of various nematodes: a, Trichostrongylus.—b, Ancylostoma.—c, Trichuris.—d, Strongyloides in uterus.—e, Necator.—f, Ascaris.—g, Ascaris, nonfertilized. (After Manson, from Brumpt, 1922. Courtesy, Masson & Cie, Paris.)

fact that the life of the adults is shortened. The general result is a very moderate worm load, not only in the rats that were already infected, but also in those exposed to infection for the first time, because their chance of infection is decreased by the reduced egg production of the parasite carriers.

The resistance described here is explained by the presence of antibodies which cause voluminous precipitates to appear around the oral, anal, and excretory apertures of the larval worm and on its cuticle. These precipitates are supposed to be harmful by interfering with the locomotion of the larvas and with the ingestion of their food. Beside this humoral activity of the host, there is a cellular activity which manifests itself by fibroblasts accumulating and proliferating around the larvas. This has been observed at the starting point of the larval migration, the skin of the host, and at its termination, the lungs. Thus minute fibroid nodules form around the larvas; they first impede, then prevent, their progress, and eventually kill them. Similar cellular activities have been observed in the tissue of the bowel wall. These, however, were not directed against the larvas but against the adults attached to the intestinal wall. Fibroid foci of proliferation interfered with the mechanism of attachment and thus provoked an early expulsion of the worms.

The state of resistance, as described here, lasts for a short time only, unless it is stimulated to continued activity by the uninterrupted presence of small numbers of worms in the body of a host that is exposed to repeated infections.[2] Even if this condition is fulfilled, the state of resistance cannot be maintained if vitamin A is absent from the food of the host.[3] It would be incorrect, however, to conclude from this observation that a deficient nutrition is always detrimental to the maintenance of resistance. Chickens infected with the nematode *Ascaridia galli* lose their ability to keep the parasites in check if put on a diet deficient in pteroyl-glutaminic acid; but a diet deficient in a vitamin closely related to B_{12} does not show that effect, because it causes as much harm to the parasite as to the host.[4]

Systematic helminthology arranges the nematodes in such a way as to bring out their taxonomic affinities while disregarding their ecological (epidemiological) affinities. Here they will be arranged according to the last-named criteria, in other words, according to the methods by which they commonly pass from one host to another. Thus the nematodes to be discussed will be divided into the following groups.

(1) Nematodes transmitted directly from one human host to another, either by contact or after passing a compulsory term outside the human body.

(2) Nematodes man acquires only from animals, practically never from other men, the animal acting either as an alternate host or as an intermediate host.

REFERENCES FOR CHAPTER XVII

1. W. H. Taliaferro. *Am. J. Trop. Med.,* 1940, 20: 169–182.
2. W. H. Taliaferro and M. P. Sarles. *J. Infectious Diseases,* 1942, 71: 69–82.
3. E. G. Riley. *J. Infectious Diseases,* 1943, 72: 133–141.
4. E. H. Sadun. *Am. J. Hyg.,* 1950, 51: 279–291.

CHAPTER XVIII

NEMATODE INFECTIONS THAT PASS FROM MAN TO MAN IN THE FORM OF EGGS

The nematodes belonging to this group leave the human body through the anal aperture in the form of larvas, or eggs. No infection takes place if man ingests the larvas or the eggs in the state they found themselves in on being deposited. They must serve a term of development outside the human body (the "nonparasitic period") before they can resume their parasitic way of life, i.e. before they reach a stage which, on being ingested (or taken up in some other way), results in man becoming infected. The following types may be distinguished.

(1) The nonparasitic period is passed by the eggs adhering to the skin of the human body. During this period, lasting a few hours only, the eggs change from a state of semiembryonation to one of complete embryonation. Thus the resulting infection is practically equivalent to contact infection. This type is represented by *Enterobius vermicularis.*

(2) The nonparasitic period is passed by the eggs in the soil; during this time they change from nonembryonated to fully embryonated eggs. As the period lasts for a fortnight or longer, there is no contact infection. This type is represented by the genera *Ascaris, Trichocephalus,* and allied species.

(3) During the nonparasitic period, passed in the soil, the eggs first change from nonembryonated to embryonated eggs. Then nonparasitic larvas are hatched which, after two molts, become parasitic larvas. They enter the human body either by piercing its skin (hookworms) or by being ingested (*Trichostrongylus, Ternidens*).

(4) No eggs are passed in the stools, but nonparasitic larvas. During the nonparasitic period in the soil, these larvas change to nonparasitic males and females which in their turn produce a second generation of nonparasitic larvas. Finally, the latter, after one molt,

are metamorphosed into parasitic larvas that pierce the human skin. There are several variations on this theme, some of them so far-reaching that the parasite becomes one transmitted by autoinfection. The type is represented by *Strongyloides stercoralis*.

TRANSMISSION BY CONTACT: ENTEROBIUS VERMICULARIS

Enterobius vermicularis (Linnaeus, 1785) Leach, 1853 [*Oxyuris vermicularis* (Linnaeus, 1785) Lamarck, 1816], is an elongate, spindle-shaped, whitish "pinworm" or "seatworm" inhabiting the cecum, the vermiform appendix, and the adjoining parts of the

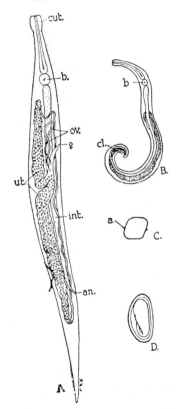

FIG. 18·1 *Enterobius vermicularis.* *A*, Female, × 10: *cut*, bladderlike expansion; *b*, bulb; *ov*, ovary; ♀, vulva; *ut*, uterus; *int*, intestine; *an*, anus.—*B*, Male, × 10: *b*, bulb; *cl*, cloaca.—*C*, Cross section through female, × 10: *a*, keel.—*D*, Egg with tadpole larva, × 230. (After M. W. Jepps, 1936. Courtesy, E. and S. Livingstone, Edinburgh.)

ileum and the colon, the males and the young females attached to the mucosa with their heads. From this site the egg-bearing or gravid females are transported to the anus; the males may remain in their original habitat, but they also may be encountered in the stools.

The span of life of the adult worms is reported to vary from six weeks to three months. The period during which eggs are deposited lasts no longer than one hour.[1] The gravid female leaves the host's body through the anus, deposits all its eggs on the perianal and perineal skin, and then dies.[2]

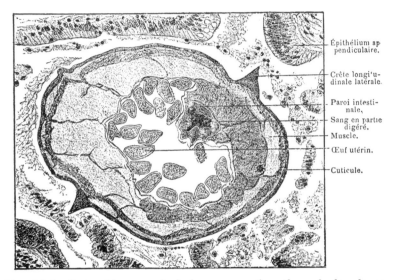

Épithélium appendiculaire.

Crête longi'udinale latérale.

Paroi intestinale.

Sang en partie digéré.

Muscle.

Œuf utérin.

Cuticule.

FIG. 18·2 *Enterobius vermicularis,* cross section through female attached to mucosa of appendix: *crête longitudinale latérale,* keel. (After Brumpt, 1936. Courtesy, Masson & Cie, Paris.)

The male (Fig. 18·1:*B*) measures 3–5 × 0.1–0.2 mm; its caudal extremity is short, strongly curved ventrally. The cuticle of the dorsal and ventral sides of the head shows a bladderlike, transversely striated expansion (Fig. 18·1:*A*, cut). A cuticular keel, triangular on cross section, runs along the lateral fields over the whole length of the body (Fig. 18·2, "crête longitudinale latérale"). The oral aperture is surrounded by three lips (Fig. 17·2). The esophagus terminates in a conspicuous bulb (Fig. 18·1:*A*, *b*). There is one spicule, 70 μ long; its extremity is S-shaped. The caudal extremity shows a narrow membranous extension at both sides, the *caudal alas,* anteriorly supported by a pair of sessile papillas. There are four other pairs of postanal papillas.[3]

The female (Fig. 18·1:A) is longer, 9–12 × 0.3–0.6 mm; the caudal part is slender and pointed; its length, measured from the anus, is one-fifth of the body length; it is as transparent as glass, sharply contrasting with the dull, opaque white of the rest of the body. One third of the body length separates the vulva from the head. The paired ovaries, oviducts, and uteri of the young female lie in the second and third quarters of the body; the uterus of the gravid female fills the whole body, with the exception of the caudal portion. The cuticular expansions, described in the male, are also present in the female, except for the caudal ones.

The way the gravid female disposes of its some 11,000 eggs has already been recorded. Eggs may be found in the stools, if they are rubbed off from the perianal skin during the passage of a scybalum. No viable eggs are laid inside the bowel; eggs found in the intestine at autopsies or operations never contained a "tadpole" larva (Fig. 18·1:D).[4]

The eggs, of 50–60 × 20–30 μ, deposited between the creases of the perianal skin and on the perineum, all show the same stage of development, viz. the *tadpole stage* (Fig. 18·1:D). They are asymmetrical in shape; one side is more convex than the other. The shell is transparent and colorless; it is composed of an inner shell, the eggshell proper, separated by a narrow fissure from the outer shell, also called the "albuminoid envelope," which is the product of the uterine wall. Inside the shell lies the tadpole larva, an ovoid with a short and slender caudal appendage pressed against its ventral side.

Under the influence of the relatively high temperature and moisture prevailing at the site where they have been deposited, the tadpole larvas inside the eggs complete their development within six hours and become infective larvas of a size of 140 μ (Fig. 18·3:2, 3). If eggs containing such larvas are ingested, infection is the consequence.

The albuminoid envelope is adhesive; thus the infective eggs adhere to each other and to the perianal or perineal skin; but they become separated by an excess of water and by the complete desiccation of the outer shell.

As a rule the gravid females move over the perianal skin in the evening. This often causes severe itching, which may grow intolerable if numerous worms are present. In the rural area east of Amsterdam, one-fifth of the parasite carriers had such complaints,[5] but in Brazil,[6] much higher rates (75 percent) were recorded. Scratching, the natural consequence of severe itch, causes the eggs to adhere to the finger nails, where they have been detected in about one-third of the parasite carriers.[7] From there they are transported to the mouth, thus causing autoinfection, or they are passed on to other persons, which causes infection by contact.

Infective enterobius eggs are highly resistant to a number of adverse conditions, such as putrefaction, desiccation, and disinfecting agents, although they quickly die when immersed in water. This explains their being detected in the dust on the window sills in class-rooms and adjoining lavatories of schools with numerous parasite

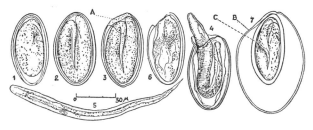

FIG. 18·3 *Enterobius vermicularis,* eggs, × 340: 1. With tadpole larva. —2. With complete larva.—3. As 2: *A,* place where shell will be rup-tured.—4. The larva hatching.—5. Hatched larva.—6. Empty shell.—7. Egg in acetic acid, the two shells separated. (After Brumpt, 1922. Courtesy, Masson & Cie, Paris.)

carriers among the pupils. What is more important, these dust-carried ova not only have a normal appearance, with larvas hatching from them (Fig. 18·3:4), but they also prove viable by the infection of persons who ingest them.[8]

Five to seven weeks after the ingestion of infective eggs, the ova of the next generation are detected for the first time in the anal region of the subject. There they continue to be found for the next two to four weeks. Accordingly, the span of life of the individual worm varies from seven to eleven weeks.

The ingestion of infective eggs originating from a person's own body is one way of producing autoinfection, i.e. of prolonging the existence of a parasite population that otherwise would have died out as a consequence of the short life of the worms. It is possible that there exists another form of autoinfection. Larvas have been observed to hatch from eggs adhering to the perianal skin; these may re-enter the host's body through the anus and reach the cecum by following the route their parents took a few days earlier—but in an opposite direction. This mode of infection has been termed *retrofection*.[9]

Under favorable conditions, *E. vermicularis* may become the most common of all nematodes parasitizing man. During World War II 98 percent of the children of some schools in Amsterdam were found infected,[7] and 85 percent of the adults belonging to the same socioeconomic classes.[10] Thus there was hardly any difference in the rate of infection between children and adults. This, however, is not the rule. In Czechoslovakia [11] the rate of infection was highest among older children (75 percent) and adolescents (64 percent); these rates decreased with advancing age to 20 percent in younger adults and 15 percent in older adults; in young children they varied from 26 to 42 percent. In Holland the socioeconomic position did not appear to have any appreciable influence on the rate of infection.[5] In the United States the rate of infection of the white population is seven times as high as in negro population.[12]

Apart from the physical and psychic effects of itching, the pathogenic significance of *E. vermicularis* depends upon two peculiarities in its behavior:

(1) The tendency to wander, exhibited by the females, causes them to take an abnormal course, such as ascending the intestinal tract as far as the stomach, esophagus, nose, and mouth; or ascending the female genital tract, starting from the perineum, as far as the vulva, vagina, uterus, and peritoneal cavity. The latter course is supposed to be taken by the gravid females. This is an unlikely supposition, considering the shortness of their life span. More probably, it is taken by larvas hatched on the perineum. In that case the invasion of the female genital tract is to be regarded as an unsuccessful attempt of the larvas to re-enter the anus, i.e. to cause retrofection.

(2) An aberrant habit of some larvas causes them to penetrate the wall of the cecum or vermiform appendix and not to reappear until they have become adults.[13] This larval activity supports the view that regards *E. vermicularis* as one of the primary causes of appendicitis.[14] Supposing that the larvas, behaving in this abnormal way, do

not succeed in finding their way back to the lumen of the bowel by
the time they have grown to adulthood, this would explain the finding of large numbers of adult males and females in the tissue of the
wall of the cecum, the colon and the rectum (Fig. 18·4).[15] Similar
findings in the tissue of the uterine wall, the fallopian tubes, and the
male genital organs (prostate glands) might be explained by larvas,
intent on retrofection, having missed their way.[16]

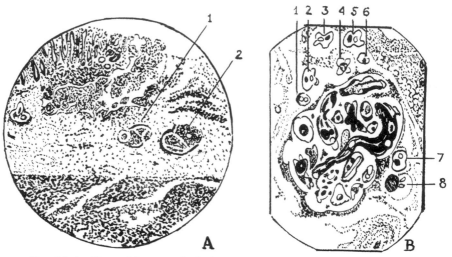

Fig. 18·4   *Enterobius vermicularis* in tissue of intestinal wall: *A*, Section of an ulcus with undermined edge; under the bottom of the ulcus
two small abscesses, 1 and 2, 1, containing an enterobius (× 29).—*B*,
Section of a bundle of enterobius surrounded by a sheath; some (1–8)
are lying outside (× 59). (After J. Bijlmer. Courtesy, *Journal of Parasitology*.)

TREATMENT OF ENTEROBIASIS. According to H. W.
Brown,[71] the drugs of choice are the piperazine salts, the citrate
(Antepar), phosphate (Antepar, Piperazate), or the adipate (Entacyl).
They are available in a palatable syrup, each milliliter containing
100 mg of the drug or in tablets 0.5 gm each. These compounds are
most effective when given in one dose daily on an empty stomach,
followed by a glass of water. The treatment is continued for 7 days
with dosage based on weight, as follows: infants up to 15 pounds are
given 2.5 mg (½ teaspoonful); 16–30 pounds, 5.0 ml (1 teaspoonful);
children 31–60 pounds, 10 ml (2 teaspoonfuls) or 2 tablets (1.0 gm);
over 60 pounds and adults, 20 ml (4 teaspoonfuls) or 4 tablets (2.0

gm). Few side effects, such as occasional nausea, vomiting, abdominal cramps, or rarely an urticarial rash, have been reported.

Recently, pyrvinium pamoate (Povan), a cyanine dye, has been employed by Beck [72] and his co-workers with excellent results. The drug is available in a palatable suspension, and is administered in dosage of 2 mg/kg per day for 7 days. The suspension is also employed in a single dose schedule of 5 mg/kg with a reported cure rate of 96 percent and comparatively few side effects, such as an occasional nausea and vomiting.

Gentian violet was in use for many years before the introduction of piperazine and the cyanine dyes (such as pyrvinium and dithiazanine), with fairly good results. It is administered in enteric-coated tablets (65 mg), for adults, one tablet three times daily with or after meals; children are given 10 mg daily for each year of life. The course of treatment is 7–10 days, repeated after an interval of one week. Nausea, vomiting, loose stools, and abdominal pains are frequently encountered.

In the treatment of enterobiasis it is often advisable to administer the drug to the entire household, particularly when two or more members of the group are found infected or when the proper use of the scotch tape swabs by the patient is questionable. Since the drugs currently used are not too disturbing to patients, this additional precaution will very often prove rewarding. In addition, patients should be instructed in routine hygienic measures. It should be an integral part of the therapeutic regimen, regardless of the type of drug employed.

INFECTION WITH EGGS THAT BECOME EMBRYONATED IN THE SOIL

Infection with the worms discussed in this section cannot be classified as contact infection, because embryonation does not take place in eggs adhering to the human skin but in free nature. A whole family may be infected, and a person living with that family for some time (e.g. during the summer holidays) may also acquire the infection, but he will not transmit it to others once he has rejoined his own family. When treating a person ill with ascariasis there is no reason to treat asymptomatic carriers at the same time, as there is when dealing with enterobiasis.

The two worms to be described here, *Ascaris lumbricoides* and *Trichocephalus trichiurus,* have nothing in common from a taxonomic point of view. Ecologically they are constant and almost inseparable associates.

ASCARIS LUMBRICOIDES

Ascaris lumbricoides Linnaeus, 1758, inhabits the jejunum. It is elongate cylindrical in shape; its anterior extremity is more tapering than the posterior one (Fig. 18·5); living, its color is reddish or

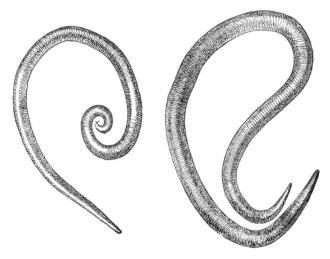

FIG. 18·5   *Ascaris lumbricoides,* natural size: *Left,* male; *right,* female. (After Brumpt, 1936. Courtesy, Masson & Cie, Paris.)

yellowish gray. The mouth is surrounded by three lips (Fig. 18·7); their base is separated from the rest of the body by an encircling furrow (Fig. 18·8); the inner margins of the lips carry numerous minute denticles, of 4–5 by 4 μ; the larger lip, situated dorsally, carries two sensory papillas; the two smaller ones carry one papilla each. The cuticular striations are conspicuous over the whole length of the body.

The adult male measures 15–31 cm $\times$ 2–4 mm. It can be identified by its caudal extremity being strongly curved ventrally. It carries numerous pre- and postanal papillas. A much convoluted testicular tube is situated in the posterior half of the body. There are two pointed spicules that often protrude from the cloaca of dead worms; they are 2–3 mm long.

The adult female measures 20–35 cm in length (and over) and 3–6 mm in width. The vulva is separated from the head by a distance equal to one-third of the body length. The short vagina is joined by the two uteri that are situated, side by side, in the middle and last third of the body. They are continuous with the ovarian tubes, whose length is tenfold of the worm.

In Japanese prisoners not exposed to reinfection, the worms survived for a period varying from one to two years.[18]

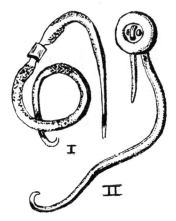

FIG. 18·6 *Ascaris lumbricoides,* natural size: I. Attempting to pass through a glass bead.—II. Entangled in two holes of a button. (After Neveu-Lemaire, 1922. Courtesy, *Bulletin de la société zoologique de France.*)

The eggs (Fig. 18·9:*a*) measure 45–75 by 35–50 μ. They have two envelopes. The inner one, the eggshell proper, is fairly thick, colorless, and smooth. The outer one, the "albuminoid envelope," a product of the uterine wall, is brownish yellow and is coarsely mammillated on its outer surface; sometimes it is ruptured, leaving the inner shell exposed (Fig. 18·9:*b, e*). The inner shell contains the fertilized ovum, with a granular protoplasm and a clear central nucleus. Other eggs, measuring 88–93 $\times$ 38–44 μ, are barrel-shaped (Fig. 18·9:*d, e*); the inner shell is thin and contains a granular mass, but no ovum; these are unfertilized eggs. The production of eggs by one female is estimated at 200,000 daily, or 2000 per gram of feces of normal consistency. Assuming that the two sexes are equal in number, 1000 eggs in 1 gm of normal feces represent one worm in the small intestine.[19]

The eggs that are passed in the feces are not embryonated; hence they are not infectious. To become so they must stay some time in porous earth, not too moist to impede the circulation of the air, and at a temperature of over 15° C. If these conditions are fulfilled, the

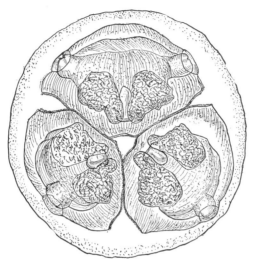

FIG. 18·8   *Ascaris lumbricoides,* oral lips, × 80. Aspect from ventral side. (After Leuckart.)

FIG. 18·7   *Ascaris lumbricoides.* Oral lips, frontal aspect; with four sensory papillas, and denticles on inner margin. (After Leuckart.)

eggs become embryonated after one to three weeks (Figs. 18·9.*c* and 18·10:*x, y*); it takes them another three weeks to become infective.[20] This additional time the larvas probably need to molt once or twice within the eggshell.[21] If these conditions are not fulfilled, no embryonation takes place, but the egg remains alive and ready to start development at a more propitious moment.

Immature eggs, as well as embryonated ones, are said to survive for a long time; in water and in the soil for over a year.[22] This, however, is a rule not without exceptions. According to Voûte [23] the eggs survive for no longer than two months of a summer in Holland. Apart from the length of survival, the eggs are resistant to various disinfectants, to desiccation (provided temperature remains below 30° C) and to low temperatures, which must drop to − 30° C to be able to kill the eggs.[24]

If the host ingests embryonated eggs, he begins to pass eggs in his stools from 10 to 12 weeks after the infecting meal. If these are fertilized eggs, this proves that he harbors at least one female and one male ascarid in his intestine, both sexually mature. During the first two weeks of the period the following events occur.

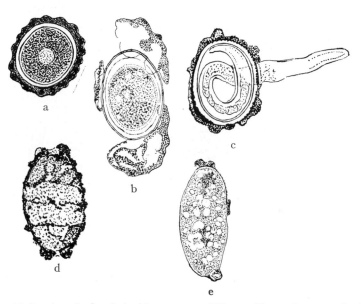

FIG. 18·9   *Ascaris lumbricoides,* egg, × 300. *a,* Nonembryonated.—*b,* outer shell rubbed off.—*c,* embryonated, larva hatching.—*d,* Nonfertilized.—*e,* Nonfertilized, outer shell rubbed off.

The eggs pass the stomach unchanged. Arriving in the jejunum, they hatch into larvas (Fig. 18·9:*c*). These larvas, of a size of 260 × 12–13 μ, do not remain in the lumen of the bowel. They penetrate the tissue of the gut wall and thus arrive in the venous circulation of the abdomen. Most of them reach the liver between the second and the fifth day, and the lung between the sixth and the eighth day.[25] Arriving in the lung, they escape from the capillaries into the lumen of the pulmonary alveoli. On the eighth day they have advanced as far as the trachea; and one to four days later, by way of the larynx, the pharynx, the esophagus, and the stomach, they have returned to the place from which they started 9 to 12 days earlier. This excursion may be termed the *visceral migration.* During this migration, the larvas have molted twice and have considerably increased in length, from a ¼ mm to 1.3–2 mm on the tenth day, and to 1.7–2.4 mm on the fifteenth day.[26]

Some larvas do not reach their destination, because they fail to leave the circulation when they reach the lungs; so they are carried to the left heart, and from there to various organs, such as the brain, the kidneys, and even to the unborn offspring in the uterus. They become encapsulated by the tissue of the host, but they do not die.[27] This deviation from the normal course may be termed *aberrant visceral migration.*

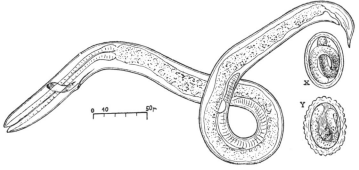

Fig. 18·10   *Ascaris lumbricoides,* larva in lung, 8 days old, × 280. X and Y, embryonated eggs, drawn to scale. (After Brumpt, 1922. Courtesy, Masson & Cie, Paris.)

The details described here have not been observed in the body of man but in experimental animals, rats and guinea pigs. In these small rodents the larvas of ascaris can perform the visceral migration. However, once they have returned to the lumen of the small intestine, they are unable to complete their development to adult worms; they are expelled by the host, which thereby reveals itself as an "incompatible host."

However, evidence is available to prove that the larvas of ascaris in the human body follow the same route. Koino [28] ingested 2000 embryonated ascaris eggs of human origin. From the sixth until the thirteenth day after the infecting meal he was ill with symptoms resembling pneumonia. The sputum he raised contained ascaris larvas from the ninth until the sixteenth day, to an approximate total of over a thousand. Finally, on the fiftieth day, an anthelmintic treatment expelled over 600 immature ascaris, varying from 3 to 8 cm in length.

S. Yoshida's experiment [29] completed Koino's. He ingested the larvas that had passed through a guinea pig's lung, thus avoiding their passing through his own lung. The result was that ascaris eggs were found in his stools 75 days after the infecting meal. In this case the guinea pig had acted as an intermediate host, preparing the parasite for an uninterrupted life in the human intestine.

Although ascaris has no intermediate hosts under natural conditions, it can be forced to accept them. Mice can be infected with a species of ascaris naturally parasitizing dogs. Those that return to the intestine, after passing through liver and lungs, are expelled. But those that lose their way and get caught in the kidneys or other organs remain there alive, encapsulated by the host's tissue. Dogs fed with these organs become infected with mature ascaris in their normal, intestinal habitat.[30]

Thus the life cycle of ascaris appears to include three stages; (1) a nonparasitic stage, passed in nature, but protected by the eggshell; (2) an initial parasitic stage inhabiting various tissues of a number of hosts, including man; (3) a subsequent parasitic stage, inhabiting the human intestine.

As a rule, human infection with ascaris is more prevalent in rural than in urban surroundings. In Amsterdam and its suburbs the rate of infection among school children was 1 percent or less; in the rural areas in their vicinity it reached 45 percent. Moreover, socioeconomic conditions influence this rate; in residential areas of the same district the rate of infection was 3 percent among the children of the well-to-do, and 26 percent among those of the poorer classes.[5] As to the explanation of this difference, opinions are still divided.

There are, however, exceptions to this rule. In Sydney (Australia), the small, heavily infected plots behind the houses in overcrowded poor quarters are the foci of an urban ascaris infection.[31] The city of Marrakech (Morocco), with its well-watered palm groves, is more infected than the desert villages of its environs.[32] Finally, the place where the eggs become embryonated may be located inside the human habitation, on a moist and moldering wooden floor, soiled with fecal matter.[33]

Ascaris infection in the succeeding age groups reaches its maximum in younger, sometimes in older schoolchildren, occasionally at the preschool age. If only the rate of infection is considered, there is no great difference between adults and children. In heavily infected Puerto Rico it is 59 percent in boys aged from 5 to 10, less than fourfold that in males older than 20 (17 percent). However, the difference becomes better marked if the "worm load" is taken into account, i.e. the average number of worms harbored by the carriers in each age group. It is expressed by the number of thousands of eggs in 1 gm of normal stools, every thousand representing one worm. In the above example the worm load of the boys was 37, against 0.75 in the male adults, a ratio of 49 to 1.[34]

According to Cort [35] the high worm load in children, contrasting with the low-grade infection in adults, is due to the habits of children rendering them more prone to infection, rather than to a resistance acquired by adults as a consequence of heavy infections passed in childhood. Others, however, claim that resistance to ascaris does exist. They base this claim on the results of animal experiments. Ascaris-infected pigs actually acquire a resistance to reinfection, dependent on a residual parasite population. Worms left over from an earlier infection stimulate the tissue of the intestinal wall to a cellular reaction that prevents young worms from attaching themselves to the gut wall after their passage through the lung.[36] Another form of resistance, affecting the migrating larvas, has been induced in "incompatible hosts," such as mice and guinea pigs, by repeated exposure to infection.[37] Cats infected with the feline ascaris *Toxocara cati* possess a marked resistance to reinfection. It affects the worms in the intestine as well as the migrating larvas. Moreover, every attempt at reinfection unfavorably influences the pre-existing parasite population.[38]

Ascaris does not as a rule penetrate the intestinal wall; it does not attach itself with sharp teeth or cutting edges; it does not suck blood, but feeds on the contents of the lumen.

Nevertheless, it shows certain forms of behavior that render it more or less pathogenic. Some of them are always in evidence; others show only on occasions.

Of the forms of behavior that are always in evidence, the visceral migration of the larvas is the most important. It is well known that larvas of ascaris passing through the lungs of an "incompatible host" often cause its death, provided they are present in large numbers.[39] Normal hosts, pigs, likewise feel the effect of the migrating larvas [40]; so does man, if exposed to massive infection, as results from Koino's [28] experiment. Even if the infection is carried out with small numbers of embryonated eggs, 45 or so, it causes a transient infiltration of the lungs, appearing from 9 to 12 days after the infecting meal and associated with eosinophilia which bears a close resemblance to the so-called "Löffler phenomenon." Other effects the migrating larvas may produce are rare because they are associated with aberrant migration, which may take them as far as the brain.[41]

Another normal function, secretion and excretion, tends to sensitize the host to the products of this activity. As these products are set free in unusual quantities at the death of the worm, it is advisable to take steps quickly to eliminate the worms killed by an anthelmintic drug.[42]

Of the peculiarities that show only on occasions, the first to be mentioned is the effect of large numbers of adult worms in the bowel. This may be the cause of acute obstruction of the small intestine, usually near the ileocecal valve, or more rarely of intussusception or volvulus.[43] The effect of obstructions caused in this way may be aggravated by the administration of vermifuges, particularly santonin.[44]

Another incidental form of behavior of the worms is their tendency to wander, which may be stimulated by certain vermifuges.[45] It is not dangerous if it causes them to leave the host's body by way of the anus or, more unusual, through the nose; but it may aggravate a pre-existing morbid condition if the worm, leaving through the urinary aperture, has reached this exit by way of an enterovesical fistula and the urinary bladder.

Closely associated with this tendency in the worm is its inclination to enter all kinds of natural or artificial narrow passages. It is of little importance if this affects foreign bodies in the intestine, such as a glass bead through which the worm attempts to pass; or a button with four holes, in two of which the worm is caught (Fig. 18·6).[46] It may have more serious consequences if the narrow passages to which the worm feels attracted are Vater's papilla, the pancreatic or fallopian duct, a sutured lesion, a lachrymal duct or a pulmonary artery; if they become impacted in an inflamed appendix or in Meckel's diverticulum; or, finally, if many of them are lured into entering the biliary ducts, which may result in an accumulation of worms in the liver.[73]

The geographical distribution of ascaris can best be described by saying that it occurs wherever people look for it. Temperate regions are no less infected than many tropical countries. In the island of Terschelling (Holland) Stekhoven [47] found a rate of infection of 50 percent in children and 27 percent in adults. However, in some tropical countries rates are registered, such as 94 percent in the district of Ruhengiri in the Congo,[48] with which no temperate region can compete.

TREATMENT OF ASCARIASIS. On the strength of investigations by Brown and Sterman [49] and others,[49a] Faust et al.[12] recommend a 7-day course of piperazine citrate, as prescribed for enterobiasis. This drug (available commercially as Antepar, in syrup or tablets), has also been found effective in a two-day course of treatment [50] administered in larger doses, once daily as follows: children weighing 31–60 lb (14–27 kg) are given 10 ml or two tablets (1.0 gm); those weighing 60–100 lb (27–45 kg) 20 ml or four tablets (2.0 gm); and those weighing 101 lb (45 kg) and over, and adults are given 25 ml or five tablets (2.5 gm) in a single dose. The same dose is repeated on the following day.

Piperazine citrate has also been successfully used by Peña-Chavarria [74] and his co-workers in a series of cases of typhoid fever, complicated by ascarid infection.

Hexylresorcinol has been employed for many years,[75] with good results. It is available in 0.1- and 0.2-gm hard gelatin capsules (Crystoids). The drug is administered on an empty stomach, 1.0 gm to adults, 0.8 gm to children 6–10 years, and 0.6 gm to those under 6 years of age. The pills should be swallowed whole; if chewed they will cause a burn of the mouth.

Recently, Goodwin [76] and co-workers and others [77] have reported on the efficacy of bephenium hydroxynaphthoate (Alcopar), a quaternary ammonium compound in the treatment of multiple helminth infections; Hsieh [78] and collaborators have employed this compound in Taiwan in combined heavy roundworm, hookworm, and whipworm infections in doses of 2.5 gm of the base, twice in one day, in a group of 20 children 10–15 years of age. With this schedule the authors obtained a cure rate of 65 percent and an egg reduction of 91 percent in the rest of the children in the ascaris infection, and a higher cure rate in the associated hookworm infection (v. infra). They are of the opinion that the drug is useful in combined infections with ascaris and ancylostoma, the hookworm predominant in that area.

ANIMAL ASCARIS

(1) Ascaris of pigs is known as *A. suum* Goeze, 1782, or *A. suilla* Dujardin, 1845. Both names are regarded as synonyms of *A. lumbricoides,* and the porcine variety is not recognized as a separate systematic unit, although Rachman and Lie Kian Joe [51] claim that the two can be differentiated by the size and the shape of the labial denticles. Nevertheless, pig ascaris does not appear to be well adapted to the human host. As a rule it becomes sexually mature much too early, after 25–29 days, instead of the normal period of 67–73 days, and often it is spontaneously expelled after 5–11 days.[52]

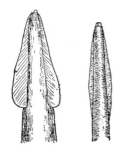

FIG. 18·11 *Toxocara canis,* head with cervical alas. (After Leuckart.)

FIG. 18·12 *Toxocara* sp. Egg, × 300, in bile collected by duodenal intubation.

(2) The genus *Toxocara* contains (among others) two species, with males of a length of 4–6 mm, females of 6–12 mm, and eggs (Fig. 18·12) that measure 70–85 × 65–75 μ, with a brown, pitted outer shell and a much smaller inner shell. Both species show broad cervical alas (Fig. 18·11). One species parasitizes dogs (*T. canis*), the other cats (*T. cati*). In Holland toxocara eggs have been detected in the bile of a child recovered by duodenal intubation. Similar findings, specifically referring to *T. cati,* have been reported from other countries.

With regard to *T. canis,* man is supposed to be an incompatible host. His relation to this parasite is like that of mice or guinea pigs to *A. lumbricoides.* Thus it may be expected that the larvas of *T. canis* perform the ordinary or the aberrant visceral migration in the human body, but do not survive in the intestine.

Toxocara larvas, or at least nematode larvas (for it may be impossible to identify them in a specimen removed by biopsy [53]), have actually been found in miliary granulomas of the liver, less frequently in other organs such as lungs, brain, eye, kidneys, of children suffering from a disease characterized by persistent hypereosinophilia, hepatomegaly, hyperglobulinemia, and often pneumonitis, which P. C. Beaver [79, 80] has identified as a clinical entity, termed *visceral larva migrans.* Accordingly, the larvas of *T. canis* and of other nematodes, including *A. lumbricoides,* are regarded as the causative agents of this disease.

Mice are also incompatible hosts of toxocara. The larvas often lose their way and are caught in other organs, particularly the brain. Unless they are numerous in that site, they appear to cause little damage. Nevertheless, even small numbers of them may be dangerous in the presence of certain neurotropic viruses, latent in the brain, which they are able to stimulate to renewed activity.[54]

(3) *Lagocheilascaris minor* Leiper, 1909, has been found as an adult in an abscess of the mastoid and the neck,[55] in human inhabitants of Surinam. Human infection has also been observed in Trinidad. The normal hosts are feline carnivores, in which the parasite inhabits the intestine.

The male measures 9×0.4 mm, the female 15×0.5 mm. The three lips are separated from the neck by a deep furrow; each lip has a conspicuous vertical cleft. Along the lateral fields runs a keel, triangular on cross section. The eggs resemble those of toxocara.

TRICHOCEPHALUS TRICHIURUS (TRICHURIS TRICHIURA)

Trichocephalus trichiurus (Linnaeus 1771, Blanchard 1895) [*Trichuris trichiura* (Linnaeus, 1771) Stiles, 1901 *Trichocephalus dispar* Rudolphi, 1802], the whipworm, inhabits the cecum, less frequently the ascending colon and the appendix. In heavy infections whipworms also occupy the terminal portion of the ileum.[56] Worms apparently identical with the human parasite have been found in the intestine of pigs, monkeys, and lemurs. For the present, however, these animals cannot be classified as alternate hosts of the parasite discussed here.

The anterior portion of the body (the "whipcord") is threadlike, the posterior portion (the "handle") much wider. The former contains the long esophagus; on its ventral side it is accompanied by a series of large cells. The anus in both sexes lies at the posterior extremity (Fig. 18·13:*A*).

The male measures 30–45 mm; its whipcord is three-fifths of this length. The caudal extremity is curved (Fig. 18·13:*B*). There is a single lanceolate spicule situated within an inverted pouch; when the pouch is everted it is seen to carry numerous minute spines on its bulbous extremity, through which the spicule protrudes. The internal male organs consist of one long testicular tube, a seminal vesicle, and a long and muscular ejaculatory duct.

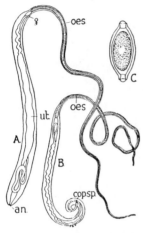

FIG. 18·13 *Trichocephalus trichiurus*. *A*, Female: *oes*, esophagus; ♀, vulva; *ut*, uterus; *an*, anus.—*B*, Male: *oes*, esophagus; *copsp*, spicule.—*C*, Egg. *A* and *B* × 4; *C* × 500. (After M. W. Jepps. Courtesy, E. and S. Livingstone, Edinburgh.)

FIG. 18·14 *Trichocephalus trichiurus*, male with its whipcord buried in mucosa. (After Leuckart, from Brumpt, 1922. Courtesy, Masson & Cie, Paris.)

The female measures 35–50 mm; its whipcord is two-thirds of this length. The vulva is situated where the whipcord joins the handle. The internal female organs consist of a single greatly coiled ovarian tube, continuous with a uterus that opens into a short vagina.

Both sexes have their whipcords buried in the superficial layer of the mucosa (Figs. 18·14, 18·15), parallel to the surface; their handles, occasionally their heads, emerge from this substratum.

The eggs (Fig. 18·13:*C*) measure 50–54 × 22–23 μ; they are described as "barrel-shaped." The outer shell is yellowish brown and fairly thick; the inner shell is very thin and colorless. The outer shell has an opening at both poles; these openings are closed with a colorless plug. The eggs are passed in the stools in a nonembryonated state. The number of eggs per gram of normal feces, believed to represent a single worm in the bowel, varies from 15 to 50 and to 120, according to different investigators.

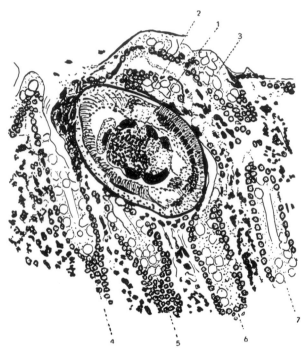

Fig. 18·15　*Trichocephalus trichiurus.* Section through mucosa of the colon of a child: 1. Cross section through worm.—2 and 3. Flattened Lieberkühr glands covering worm.—5 and 6. The same on both sides of worm.—4 and 7. The same normal. (After Hartz, 1953. Courtesy, *Documenta,* Amsterdam.)

As in ascaris, the eggs passed in the stools are not infective. They have to pass a stage in moist well-aerated soil to become so. It is generally accepted that this takes them twice as long as the eggs of ascaris; 2–3 and even 6–12 months. But in Panama they mature as quickly as ascaris, in two weeks.[57]

On the whole, trichocephalus eggs appear to be less resistant to desiccation than ascaris eggs; hence the prevalence of trichocephalus in dry areas is less than that of ascaris. In moist areas the prevalence of the two may be equal,[58] or trichocephalus may be in the majority.[47]

Four weeks after ingesting embryonated trichocephalus eggs, man passes eggs of the next generation in his feces.[59] The larvas hatch 20 hours after ingestion.[60] Unlike ascaris, there is no visceral migration; the larvas remain in the gut. The larvas of a related canine species, *Trichuris depressiusculus*, are known, after hatching, to penetrate the intestinal wall and to remain there for the next 48 hours; then they return to the lumen and pass on to the cecum, where they arrive 24 hours later. In this permanent habitat they develop into egg-laying females at the end of 36 days.[61] It is not known whether *T. trichiurus* behaves in the same way.

The rate of infection with trichocephalus in children and adults is much the same as that with ascaris. In the island of Puerto Rico,[34] the boys were 82 percent infected, with a worm load of 8000 eggs per gram of feces, a rate which was almost double and a worm load which was eightfold those found in adults. In the island of Terschelling (Holland) [47] the child rate was 73 percent, the adult rate 37 percent; the adult worm load was almost one-third that in children.

Like ascaris, trichocephalus is a rural parasite. East of Amsterdam, schoolchildren of the suburban areas were infected for 3–4 percent, those in the rural areas 26 percent.[5] As to its geographical distribution, it is said to be more common in warm, moist regions. The high incidence in the island of Terschelling, where the climate is admittedly moist but far from warm, shows that the above statement must be accepted with some reserve.

The way the parasite is attached to the mucosa, its blood-sucking habits [56] (which are doubted by some authors [62]), the massive infections it may cause, its possible association with appendicitis, and the ineffectiveness of anthelmintics,[45] explain why the pathogenicity of the parasite is rated higher than that of ascaris. In Indonesia cases of very heavy infections have been described which left little doubt in the investigator's mind as to the part played by the parasite in bringing about the fatal issue. Kourí and Díaz,[63] in Cuba, are convinced that massive infections, involving not only the cecum and appendix but also other parts of the colon (hepatic, splenic and sigmoid flexure, and rectum) and the terminal portion of the ileum, cause the death of numerous children between 1 and 5 years of age.

However, a careful histological analysis of fatal cases of this description has led Hartz [62] to conclude that trichocephalus is responsible for a disturbance of the coordinating function of the intramural nervous elements of the mucosa of the colon, only in children suffering from the effects of gross malnutrition or concomitant bacterial infections. In young children heavy infections of the lower sigmoid and rectum associated with marked tenesmus and bloody diarrhea have been observed. Not infrequently, this condition has resulted in prolapse of the rectum.

On the other hand, there exist numerous asymptomatic carriers of trichocephalus. No doubt it is due to carrying only small numbers of parasites that they suffer little or no ill effect from their presence; but it is not known whether it was by mere chance that they were so lightly infected or whether humoral and cellular reactions contributed to bring about this result.

TREATMENT OF TRICHOCEPHALIASIS. Mention has been made of the ineffectiveness of vermifuges in trichocephaliasis. This is not to be taken literally. It means that the better anthelmintics remove many trichocephalus, but not all. In enterobiasis this would be serious; for a partial result, in this case, means continued auto-infection, which would soon repair the losses. In trichocephaliasis this is of no concern, and the removal of part of the worms may convert an intolerably heavy infection into a tolerable light infection.

Under these circumstances Faust et al.[12] recommend a treatment with tetrachlorethylene and oil of chenopodium. The night before the administration the patient is given a saline purge, followed by a high-retention enema of tepid water. The next morning 2.7 ml of tetrachlorethylene and 0.3 ml of oil of chenopodium are administered on an empty stomach, followed by the usual saline purge two hours later.

Recently, Swartzwelder [64] and associates, following the experimental work of McCowen [81] and collaborators and the clinical studies of Frye [82] and co-workers, have reported favorably on the use of dithiazanine iodide (Delvex), 3,3'-diethyldicarbo-cyanine iodide, for the treatment of trichocephaliasis. The drug is available in enteric-coated tablets of 50, 100, and 200 mg. The recommended dose is 20 mg per pound (0.454 kg) of body weight with a maximum of 600 mg per day, given in divided doses 3 times daily for 5 to 7 days. Nausea and vomiting were frequently encountered, but were usually not troublesome enough to interrupt the treatment. In patients showing a secondary anemia, the use of iron is indicated.

CAPILLARIA HEPATICA

Capillaria hepatica (Bancroft, 1893) Travassos, 1915 [*Hepaticola hepatica* (Bancroft, 1893) Hall, 1916], which has also been given the generic name of *Thominx* (Dujardin, 1845) resembles trichocephalus. Its eggs (Fig. 18·16) have the same general structure; but they differ by the great number of narrow canals that pierce the outer shell, and by their larger size, 51–67 × 30–35 μ.

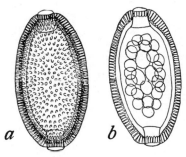

FIG. 18·16 *Capillaria hepatica,* eggs in human feces, × 700: *a,* Surface view.—*b,* Cross section with larva in the stage of a morula. (After Faust and Martinez, 1935. Courtesy, *Journal of Parasitology.*)

Its life cycle, however, is so different from that of trichocephalus that its incorporation into the ecological group forming the subject of this chapter seems hardly justified, as may be gathered from the following description.

Capillaria parasitizes the liver of various rodents, rats among them, wild hogs, monkeys, and other mammals. The eggs reach the soil in a way to be described below, and there they become embryonated after 25–28 days at a temperature of 33–34° C.[65] If a rat ingests these eggs, the larvas hatch in its cecum; then they penetrate the tissue of the gut wall and reach the liver by way of the abdominal venous circulation. So far, events are in complete accordance with the accepted scheme. From now onward, however, they take a different course; the larvas may get as far as the lungs,[66] but as a rule they stay in the liver. There they grow to maturity, and there the females lay their eggs. These eggs are not evacuated through the bile ducts; they stay in the rat's body,[67] and they do not become embryonated.

The rat must die for the eggs to be set free and to become embryonated. This death may be brought about by the parasites killing their host within five days, provided they are numerous; however, it is doubtful whether the eggs survive for any length of time in a putrefying carcass. A much surer way for the eggs to leave the host is by some carnivore devouring the rat. The carnivore will not become infected, for the eggs are not embryonated; it will evacuate the eggs in its feces, thereby acting as a "liberating intermediate host." It is the only way, in case the parasites do not kill their host.

Fig. 18·17   *Capillaria hepatica,* egg situated within a giant cell of human liver. (After G. F. Otto et al., 1954. Courtesy, *Bulletin of the Johns Hopkins Hospital,* Baltimore.)

Of course there would be no need for a liberating host if the parasites had selected the lung as a site to reach sexual maturity in; for then there would be ample opportunity for the eggs to be coughed up with sputum. This has actually happened once in a human infection; but the parasite involved was identified as *Capillaria aerophila* Creplin, 1839.[68]

In Ituri (in the Congo) Fain [69] has found a truly natural host of capillaria. It is a rat, *Mastomys coucha.* In that region eight other rodents and a species of *Dendrohyrax* have been found infected. All of them suffer greatly from the severe liver lesions caused by the parasite, except mastomys, for that rodent tolerates the infection without exhibiting any pronounced pathological reactions. As far as mastomys is concerned, the eggs would never leave the host but for the intervention of a liberating intermediate host—unless it chose to follow *C. aerophila*'s example, by extending its visceral migration as far as the lungs.

Apart from *C. aerophila,* human interest in capillaria was chiefly roused by the fact that almost one-tenth of the inhabitants of the Chagres Valley (Panama) passed the eggs of the parasite in their feces. However, the interest quickly waned when the case turned out to be an example of "spurious parasitism" due to the people consuming the well-cooked liver of wild hogs and monkeys infected with capillaria.[70]

Nevertheless, some interest remains, for true infection with *C. hepatica* has been observed in man on five occasions: once in an adult in India, and four times in children, three in the southeastern United States (Fig. 18·17) and one in South Africa. No specific treatment is known.

REFERENCES FOR CHAPTER XVIII

1. G. L. LANGHANS. *Arch. Kinderheilk.,* 1926, 77: 27–38.
2. E. B. CRAM. *Trop. Diseases Bull.,* 1942, 39: 191; 1943, 40: 618, 619.
3. H. F. HSÜ. *Chinese Med. J.,* 1933, 47: 1290–1291.
4. N. WUNDT. *Münch. med. Wochschr.,* 1924, 71: 546–548.
5. L. R. HUMMELEN. Thesis, Amsterdam, 91 pp., Zutphen, 1945, Brink & Co., English summary, 91.
6. M. L. ANTUNES. *Trop. Diseases Bull.,* 1948, 45: 629.
7. W. A. P. SCHÜFFNER and N. H. SWELLENGREBEL. *Ned. Tijdschr. Geneesk.,* 1943, 87: 1363–1366, English summary, 1366.
8. W. A. P. SCHÜFFNER and N. H. SWELLENGREBEL. *Ned. Tijdschr. Geneesk.,* 1946, 90: 762–764, English summary, 764.
9. W. A. P. SCHÜFFNER, N. H. SWELLENGREBEL, and J. BOOL. *J. Parasitol.,* 1949, 35: 138–146; 1950, 36: 391–393.
10. F. H. SMALT. *Ned. Tijdschr. Geneesk.,* 1944, 88: 483–485, English summary, 485.
11. O. JIROVEC. *Zentr. Bakteriol.,* Abt. I, Or., 1952, 157: 539–546.
12. E. C. FAUST, P. F. RUSSELL, and D. R. LINCICOME. *Clinical Parasitology,* Philadelphia, 1957, pp. 406, 411, 410, 421, 422, 344.
13. F. D. JORDA. *Arch. Disease Childhood,* 1957, 32: 208–215.
14. M. STRAUB and J. SCHWARTZ. *Ned. Tijdschr. Geneesk.,* 1940, 84 (2nd half): 1627–1634, English summary, 1634.
15. J. BIJLMER. *J. Parasitol.,* 1946, 32: 354–366.
16. W. ST. C. SYMMERS. *J. Pathol. Bacteriol.,* 1957, 73: 549–555.
17. PH. H. MANSON-BAHR. *Tropical Diseases,* London, 1957, p. 983.
18. B. HOBO. *Trop. Diseases Bull.,* 1956, 53: 1255.
19. H. W. BROWN and W. W. CORT. *J. Parasitol.,* 1927, 14: 88–90.

20. N. R. Stoll. *J. Parasitol.*, 1933, 20: 126.
21. E. Brumpt. *Précis de parasitologie,* Vol. I, Paris, 1949, p. 838.
22. G. Müller. *Zentr. Bakteriol.,* Abt. I, Or., 1953, 159: 377–379.
23. A. D. Voûte. *Ned. Tijdschr. Geneesk.,* 1956, 100: 2790–2792, English summary, 2792.
24. C. R. Bakker. *Tijdschr. Vergelijk. Geneesk.,* 1924, 10: 275–280, English summary, 280.
25. F. H. Stewart. *Brit. Med. J.,* 1916 (2nd half): 486–488, 753–754.
26. F. H. Stewart. *Parasitology,* 1918, 10: 189–195.
27. F. Fülleborn. *Beih. Arch. Schiffs- u. Tropenhyg.,* 1925, 29: 557–562.
28. S. Koino. *Trop. Diseases Bull.,* 1923, 20: 235–236.
29. S. Yoshida. *Trop. Diseases Bull.,* 1921, 17: 79.
30. F. Fülleborn. *Arch. Schiffs- u. Tropenhyg.,* 1921, 25: 367–375.
31. T. C. Backhouse and A. J. Bearup. *Med. J. Australia,* 1951 (2nd half): 595–596.
32. J. Gaud and M. Chédécal. *Trop. Diseases Bull.,* 1957, 54: 623–624.
33. F. A. Lentze. *Veröffentl. mediz. Verwalt.,* 1932, 37: 76.
34. P. Kumaran-Nair. *Puerto Rico J. Public Health,* 1935, 11: 118–138.
35. W. W. Cort. *Am. J. Trop. Med.,* 1940, 20: 183–198.
36. E. de Boer. *Tijdschr. Diergeneesk.,* 1935, 62 (No. 18), English summary.
37. O. Wagner. *Z. Immunitätsforsch.,* 1933, 78: 372–382.
38. M. P. Sarles and N. R. Stoll. *J. Parasitol.,* 1935, 21: 277–291.
39. F. Fülleborn. *Klin. Wochschr.,* 1922, 1: 984–988.
40. B. Schwartz and J. Alicata. *J. Parasitol.,* 1932, 19: 17–25.
41. W. Beautyman and A. Woolf. *J. Pathol. Bacteriol.,* 1951, 63: 635–647.
42. R. Deschiens. *Ann. inst. Pasteur Paris,* 1948, 75: 397–410.
43. N. Fernando. *J. Trop. Pediat. London,* 1958, 4: 61–70.
44. L. C. J. van Rensburg and A. E. Kark. *Med. Proc. Johannesburg,* 1958, 4: 522–536.
45. E. C. Faust. *J. Am. Med. Assoc.,* 1941, 117: 1332.
46. M. Neveu Lemaire. *Bull. soc. zool. France,* 1922, 47: 39–41.
47. J. H. Schuurmans Stekhoven. *Ned. Tijdschr. Geneesk.,* 1931, 75: 859–873, English summary, 873.
48. L. Clément. *Ann. soc. belge méd. trop.,* 1938, 18: 347–349.
49. H. W. Brown and M. M. Sterman. *Am. J. Trop. Med. Hyg.,* 1954, 3: 750–754.
49a. C. Swartzwelder, J. H. Miller, and R. W. Sappenfield. *Am. J. Trop. Med. Hyg.,* 1955, 4: 326–331.
50. M. M. Sterman. Unpublished data.
51. A. Rachman and Lie Kian Joe. *Documenta Med. Geograph. et Trop. Amsterdam,* 1954, 6: 342–344.
52. I. Takata. *Trop. Diseases Bull.,* 1952, 49: 423–424.
53. R. L. Nichols. *J. Parasitol.,* 1956, 42: 349–399.
54. H. Mochizuki et al. *J. Infectious Diseases,* 1954, 95: 260–266.
55. W. E. F. Winckel and A. E. Treurniet. *Documenta Med. Geograph. et Trop. Amsterdam,* 1956, 8: 23–28.
56. A. da Matta. *Bull. soc. pathol. exotique,* 1917, 10: 932–941.
57. H. W. Brown. *J. Parasitol.,* 1927, 14: 1–5.
58. L. A. Spindler. *Am. J. Hyg.,* 1929, 10: 476–496.
59. B. Grassi. *Centr. Bakteriol.,* 1887, 1: 131–132.

60. F. FÜLLEBORN. *Arch. Schiffs- u. Tropenhyg.*, 1923, 27: 421–425.
61. T. HASEGAWA. *Arch. Schiffs- u. Tropenhyg.*, 1924, 28: 337–340.
62. PH. H. HARTZ. *Documenta Med. Geograph. et Trop. Amsterdam,* 1953, 5: 303–313.
63. P. KOURÍ and V. DÍAZ. *Trop. Diseases Bull.,* 1953, 50: 54.
64. J. C. SWARTZWELDER et al. *Am. J. Trop. Med. Hyg.,* 1958, 7: 329–333.
65. M. NISHIGORI. *Trop. Diseases Bull.,* 1926, 23: 260.
66. F. FÜLLEBORN. *Arch. Schiffs- u. Tropenhyg.,* 1924, 28: 48–61.
67. D. A. SHORB. *J. Parasitol.,* 1931, 17: 151–154.
68. K. J. SKRJABINE. *Trop. Diseases Bull.,* 1940, 37: 662.
69. A. FAIN. *Ann. soc. belge méd. trop.,* 1953, 33: 107–117.
70. A. O. FOSTER and C. M. JOHNSON. *Trans. Roy. Soc. Trop. Med. Hyg.,* 1939, 32: 639–644.
71. H. W. BROWN. *Clin. Pharmacol. Therap.,* 1960, 1: 87–103.
72. J. W. BECK, D. SAAVEDRA, G. J. ANTELL, and B. TEJEIRO. *Am. J. Trop. Med. Hyg.,* 1959, 8: 349–353.
73. R. CESPEDES. *Rev. Biol. Trop.,* 1953, 1(2): 197–221.
74. A. PEÑA-CHAVARRIA, C. LIZANO, and H. XIRINACHS. *Am. J. Trop. Med. Hyg.,* 1957, 6: 388.
75. H. W. BROWN. *Am. J. Hyg.,* 1932, 16: 602–608.
76. L. G. GOODWIN, L. G. HAYEWARDENE, and O. D. STANDEN. *Brit. Med. J.,* 1958, 2: 1572–1576.
77. N. AHMAD and G. RASOOL. *J. Trop. Med. Hyg.,* 1959, 62: 284–285.
78. HSIEN-CHEN HSIEH, H. W. BROWN, MARCIA FITE, LIEN-PIN CHOW, CHIN-SUN CHENG, and CHIN CHUAN HSU. *Am. J. Trop. Med. Hyg.,* 1960, 9: 496–499.
79. P. C. BEAVER. *Exptl. Parasitol.,* 1956, 5: 587–621.
80. P. C. BEAVER, C. H. SNYDER, G. M. CARRERA, J. H. DENT, and J. W. LAFFERTY. *Pediat.,* 1952, 9: 7–19.
81. M. C. McCOWEN, M. E. CALLENDER, and M. C. BRANDT. *Am. J. Trop. Med. Hyg.,* 1957, 6: 894–897.
82. W. W. FRYE, J. C. SWARTZWELDER, R. LAMPERT, S. H. ABADIE, and C. B. CARSON, JR. *Am. J. Trop. Med. Hyg.,* 1957, 6: 890–893.

CHAPTER XIX

NEMATODE INFECTIONS THAT PASS FROM MAN TO MAN IN THE FORM OF LARVAS

As in Chapter XVIII, in the present chapter it is the soil that conditions the nonparasitic stage to resume the parasitic mode of life. But in the worms to be discussed in this chapter it is a free-living larva, in one instance a free-living adult, that has to be prepared for a renewed parasitic life. The soil is thus an intermediate host rather than an inanimate breeding place. The nonparasitic stage enclosed within an egg shell is much less dependent on external conditions than the nonparasitic free-living larva; therefore the worms to be dealt with here are limited to subtropical and tropical countries or to areas in temperate regions specially adapted to provide for their needs.

The free-living nonparasitic stage may be a larva or an adult; it is called the *rhabditiform stage*. The stage, still free-living but ready to resume parasitic life, is always a larva; it is called the *filariform stage*.

The parasites leave the human body as larvas or as eggs; both are passed in the stools. The eggs of the nematodes discussed in the preceding chapter could nearly always be readily identified. This is not the case with the eggs of the present group. They all possess a single, thin, transparent, colorless shell; in freshly passed stools they already contain a varying number of blastomeres; their size differs somewhat from one species to another, but not sufficiently to allow of a reliable identification.

Ecologically these nematodes fall into two groups, the first of which comprises two subgroups:

(1) The rhabditiform stage is represented by larvas only; they develop to filariform larvas which (*a*) are ingested by man, or (*b*) make their way into the human body by penetrating its skin.

(2) Characteristically, the rhabditiform stage is represented by larvas that develop into adult males and females. Their progeny are

rhabditiform larvas of the second generation. They develop to filariform larvas that behave as in subgroup 1 (*b*).

NEMATODES WHOSE FILARIFORM LARVAS ARE INGESTED BY MAN

THE GENUS TRICHOSTRONGYLUS

Trichostrongylids often parasitize man. Their eggs greatly resemble hookworm eggs, and the adults are difficult to dislodge with vermifuges; thus an apparently unsuccessful antihookworm treatment has more than once been administered to subjects who did not harbor hookworms but trichostrongylus.[1] This is the main point of interest offered by this genus.

The following description mainly applies to *T. colubriformis* (Giles, 1892) Ransom, 1911, as described by Lie Kian Joe.[2] Wherever necessary, other species will be taken into account.

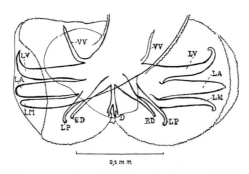

Fig. 19·1 *Trichostrongylus colubriformis,* bursa. *D,* Dorsal rays.—*ED,* Externodorsal, *LP,* posterolateral, *LM,* mediolateral, *LA,* anterolateral, *LV,* lateroventral, *VV,* ventroventral ray (cf. bursa of Ancylostoma, Fig. 19·9, and Necator, Fig. 19·13). (After Bonne and Lie Kian Joe, 1939. Courtesy, *Geneeskundig Tijdschrift voor Nederlandsch Indië.*)

At autopsies in Jakarta (Java) the worms were mainly attached to the wall of the duodenum and the anterior portion of the jejunum; they were rare in the stomach and the lower levels of the intestine. One in every two or three Indonesians was found infected, and one in every five Chinese. In the latter, *T. colubriformis* was the only species detected; Indonesians also harbored *T. axei* (Cobbold, 1879) Mönnig, 1934. The average number of worms per carrier was nine *T. colubriformis* and three *T. axei,* with a maximum of 73 and 8 respectively.

The living worms have a reddish color; the males measure 4–7.5 mm × 76–102 μ, the females 4.5–8.5 mm × 76–114 μ. The anterior third of the body is more slender than the rest. There is no buccal capsule; the mouth is surrounded by three inconspicuous lips.

In the male, the ventroventral and lateroventral rays (Fig. 19·1:*VV* and *LV*) of the bursa are lying far apart. The brown spicules are flat and twisted, their extremity is a slender, tapering, separate structure (Fig. 19·2:*A*); their length is 124–144 μ. They are accompanied by

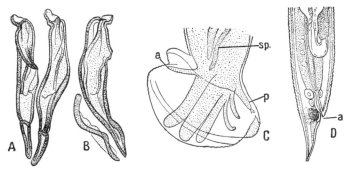

Fig. 19·2   *Trichostrongylus colubriformis: A,* Spicules, ventral view.— *B,* Spicules, side view, with gubernaculum.—*C,* Bursa.—*a,* Ventroventral ray.—*p,* Dorsal ray.—*sp,* Spicules.—*D,* Posterior extremity of female.— *a,* Anus. (After Looss, from Brumpt, 1922. Courtesy, Masson & Cie, Paris.)

an equally flat and twisted gubernaculum (Fig. 19·2:*B*). In the female the vulva is situated a short distance behind the middle, the anus near the posterior extremity (Fig. 19·2:*D*).

The eggs (Fig. 19·3) measure 72–99 × 36–46 μ. They have a single, colorless, thin shell. In freshly deposited stools they contain at least 16 blastomeres; often they are too numerous to be distinguished.

In the soil rhabditiform larvas hatch after one day. In 3 to 4 days and after two molts they develop into filariform larvas, enclosed within a "sheath," i.e. the skin of the last molt. The filariform larvas are particularly resistant to desiccation. Lie Kian Joe [3] did not succeed in infecting man by depositing numerous filariform larvas on the skin of the subject, but he readily brought about human infection by making the subject ingest the larvas of *T.*

colubriformis. This does not imply, however, that the larvas on arriving in the intestine develop into adults without performing a visceral migration; *T. orientalis* Jimbo, 1914, in Japan, is reported actually to carry out the development after its arrival in the bowel.[4] This development takes place in a short time; 21 days after the ingestion of the larvas, the subject commences to pass eggs in his stools.

In Java, *T. colubriformis* commonly parasitizes sheep and goats, less commonly monkeys and rabbits. *T. axei* is found in sheep, goats, and cattle. Man is no more than an incidental host; he is somewhat refractory to infection, very much so to infection with *T. axei.*

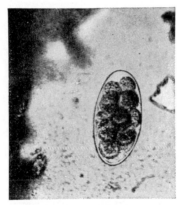

Fig. 19·3   *Trichostrongylus colubriformis,* egg in freshly passed feces, × 285. (After Bonne and Lie Kian Joe, 1939. Courtesy, *Geneeskundig Tijdschrift voor Nederlands Indië.*)

Trichostrongylids are common to fairly common human parasites in Syria, Armenia, Iran (Abadan), India, Japan, Korea, China, Mauritius, and the Congo; further, they are far from rare in Russia, Iraq, and Egypt, and they have been reported from the United States and Australia.

The parasites are not readily expelled by the common anthelmintics.

TERNIDENS DEMINUTUS

Ternidens deminutus Railliet and Henry, 1909, is mentioned here for the same reason as justified the discussion of trichostrongylus. In some parts of Africa (South Africa, Southern Rhodesia, Nyasaland, Mozambique, Katanga) and neighboring islands (Comoros, Mauritius) it is fairly common in man, with rates of infection ranging from 3 to 59 percent. The eggs, measuring 70–94 × 47–55 μ, have a single, colorless, thin shell and can be distinguished from hookworm eggs only by their slightly larger size and their more advanced development (numerous blastomeres) in freshly deposited stools.

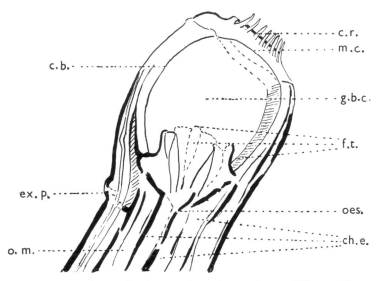

FIG. 19·4   *Ternidens deminutus,* buccal capsule, × 260: *cr,* Corona radiada.—*mc,* Collar.—*cb,* Wall of capsule.—*gbc,* Lumen.—*ft,* Teeth at bottom of capsule.—*exp,* Excretory pore.—*oes,* Esophagus.—*che,* Lining of esophagus.—*om,* Muscles of esophagus. (After Amberson and Schwarz, 1952. Courtesy, *Annals of Tropical Medicine and Parasitology,* Liverpool.)

The usual forms of antihookworm treatment are only moderately effective against ternidens, and so it is desirable to avoid confusion with hookworms.

The usual hosts of ternidens are monkeys, not only in central Africa, but also in India, Indochina, and Indonesia. In these animals the worms inhabit the intestine from the duodenum to the colon.[5] There they stay, probably during their larval life, embedded in cystic nodules (cf. Fig. 19·6).

Anteriorly the so-called *buccal capsule* is situated, a subglobose capsule in whose bottom the esophagus opens (Figs. 19·4 and 19·5). It is directed anteriorly (in hookworms it is slightly shifted in a dorsal direction) and is guarded by a double crown of stout bristles, the *corona radiata* (Fig. 19·4:*c.r.*), absent in hookworms. On the bottom of the cavity stand three bifurcate teeth (Fig. 19·5:*f.t.*) arising from the wall of the esophagus.

The females measure 12–16 × 0.6–0.8 mm, with a vulva just anterior to the anus.

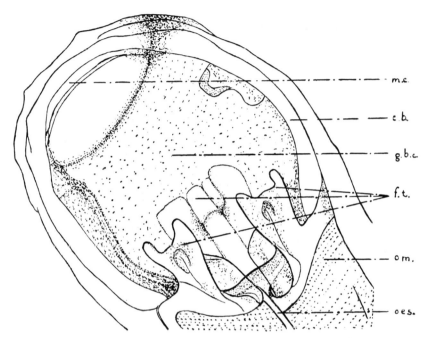

FIG. 19·5   *Ternidens deminutus*. Like Fig. 19·4. Corona radiata is not visible, but the teeth at the bottom of the buccal cavity (*ft*) are better in view, × 450. (After Amberson and Schwarz, 1952. Courtesy, *Annals of Tropical Medicine and Parasitology*, Liverpool.)

The males measure 9.5 × 0.6 mm. The bursa is characterized by the dorsal ray being branched, each branch terminating in two short ramifications, and by the partial fusion of the posterior and median lateral rays and of the latero- and ventroventral rays (cf. Fig. 19·1). The spicules measure 1.3 mm in length and 31 μ in width. A gubernaculum is present, measuring 107 μ in length, with a maximal width of 53 μ; proximally it is narrow and thick, distally it is broad and thin.[6]

When the eggs have passed 48 hours in the soil, rhabditiform larvas are hatched. They molt after a period lasting 1 to 6 days.

Filariform larvas are produced by a second molt, on the eighth to tenth day. The skin shed at the second molt continues to envelop them as a sheath. The filariform larvas are highly resistant to desiccation; even if they are completely dry and wrinkled and have lost their sheath, they still are viable.

Human infection does not succeed, unless filariform larvas are ingested. Fifty days after the infecting meal eggs are passed in the stools.[7]

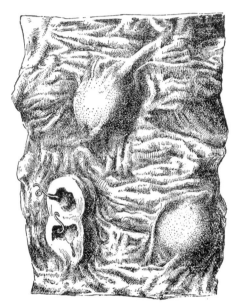

FIG. 19·6 Nodules in the tissue of the wall of the colon of an inhabitant of East Africa, caused by "Oesophagostomum brumpti," natural size. (After Brumpt, 1922. Courtesy, Masson & Cie, Paris.)

THE GENUS OESOPHAGOSTOMUM

The members of this genus resemble ternidens by the *corona radiata* they carry at the anterior margin of the buccal capsule. At the base of the leaf-like bristles composing this structure stands a ring of much smaller excrescences, the *corona interna*. The male bursa differs from ternidens by the two branches of the dorsal ray terminating in two ramifications of unequal length. The teeth at the bottom of the buccal cavity are much less conspicuous than in ternidens.

In normal hosts (domestic animals, monkeys) infection takes place by the ingestion of the third-stage (filariform) larvas, occasionally by their penetrating the skin. On arrival in the colon or cecum, the larvas penetrate the submucosa, where they provoke the formation of fibrous nodules (Fig. 19·6). Within the nodules they grow and molt and become larvas of the fourth stage. After ten days they return to the lumen of the intestine. There they molt for the adult stage, and on the thirtieth to fortieth day eggs appear in the feces. The eggs measure 60–72×36–$40\,\mu$ and closely resemble hookworm eggs.

Excluding cases in which only eggs were found, eight cases of oesophagostomum infection in man are known. Man is definitely an unsuitable host, for the following reasons. (1) The worms stay in the nodules up to the stage of immature adulthood. As the worms are pathogenic only as long as they stay in the nodules, this retarded emergence increases their harmful effect. (2) The adults returning to the intestinal lumen are undersized. (3) In one of the eight human cases, the worm has been found in an extraintestinal site—a subcutaneous tumor of the abdomen.

According to Chabaud and Larivière [8] oesophagostomes found in man belong to three species: (1) *Œ. stephanostomum* Stossich, 1904, found in Africa (including the variety *thomasi* of Brazil), characterized by a corona radiata of 38–40 leaf-like bristles; (2) *Œ. bifurcum* Creplin, 1849, also found in Africa (syn. *Œ. brumpti* and *Œ. apiostomum* of some authors), characterized by a corona radiata of ten bristles and by spicules less than 1.15 mm long, with a non-alate extremity of $20\,\mu$; (3) *Œ. aculeatum* v. Linstow, 1879, found in Asia (syn. *Œ. apiostomum* of other authors), with the same corona radiata, but spicules longer than 1.15 mm with a non-alate extremity of $40\,\mu$.

According to Faust et al. [9] carbon tetrachloride is an efficient anthelmintic.

THE HOOKWORMS

The nematodes forming the subject of this section differ from those discussed in the preceding one by the way man acquires his infection. The filariform larvas do not enter his body by being ingested, but by penetrating his skin. In this way they resemble the parasites dealt with in the next section. They differ, however,

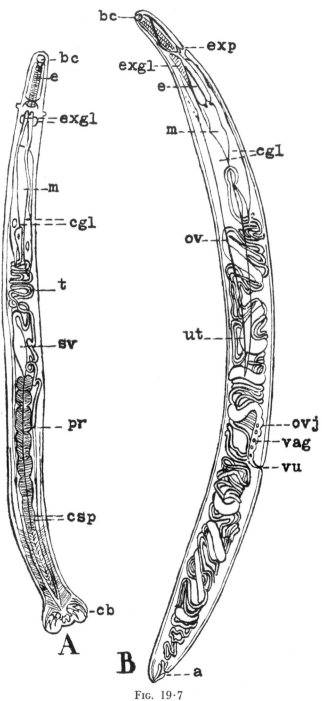

Fig. 19·7

by the simple life cycle of their free-living nonparasitic phase of development.

The human hookworms are closely related to certain carnivore hookworms, *Ancylostoma braziliense, A. ceylanicum,* and *A. caninum.* The following is a description of the human species.

THE HUMAN HOOKWORMS

Ancylostoma duodenale (Dubini, 1843) Creplin, 1845, inhabits the human jejunum with its head firmly attached to the mucosa. It is cylindrical in form, tapering anteriorly, the females tapering at both extremities (Fig. 19·7). Living worms are rosy to yellowish white in color. The cuticle shows the usual transverse striation and two

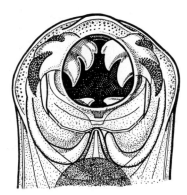

FIG. 19·8 *Ancylostoma duodenale.* Frontal view of buccal capsule with two pairs of teeth. (After Looss, 1911. Courtesy, *Records of the School of Medicine,* Cairo.)

cervical papillas at 0.4 mm from the anterior extremity. The buccal capsule (Fig. 19·8) carries two pairs of large curved teeth at its anterior ventral margin. Two long, unicellular glands, the *cephalic glands,* open at the base of the teeth. Two other glands, the *cervical glands,* open at the excretory pore situated near the anterior extremity.

FIG. 19·7 *Ancylostoma duodenale,* adults, lateral view, × 20: *A,* male; *B,* female: *a,* Anal pore.—*bc,* Buccal capsule.—*cb,* Bursa.—*cgl,* Cephalic glands.—*csp,* Spicules.—*e,* Esophagus.—*exgl,* Excretory gland (above them in male, cervical papillas).—*exp,* Excretory pore.—*m,* Midgut.—*ov,* Ovary. —*ovj,* Ovejector.—*pr,* Prostate (cement) gland.—*sv,* Seminal vesicle.—*t,* Testis.—*vag,* Vagina.—*vu,* Vulva. (After Faust et al., 1957. Courtesy, Lea & Febiger, Philadelphia.)

The male (Fig. 19·7:*A*) has a length of about 10 mm; its average weight is 1.3 mg.[10] A single, greatly coiled testicular tube opens into the seminal vesicle situated in the middle of the body. The latter is continued in the ejaculatory duct that opens at the cloaca and is partly hidden behind the large *prostate* or *cement glands*. Laterally from these lie the spicules, almost 1 mm long; their distal extremity is pointed, but carries no special differentiations; they are extruded through the cloaca (Fig. 19·9). The bursa is characterized by the single dorsal ray (Fig. 19·9:*p*) that carries two short ramifications at its distal extremity, and by the partly fused lateroventral and ventroventral rays (Fig. 19·9:*a*).

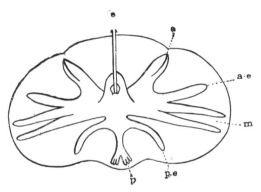

Fig. 19·9 *Ancylostoma duodenale,* bursa, rays: *p*, Dorsal; *pe*, externodorsal; *m*, postero-lateral and medio-lateral; *ae*, antero-lateral; *a*, partly fused latero- and ventro-ventral; *s*, spicules, basal portion. (After Brumpt, 1922. Courtesy as Fig. 19·2).

The female (Fig. 19·7:*B*) is about 12–13 mm long; its average weight is 2.68 mg.[10] The posterior extremity has the shape of a short cone, whose apex carries a minute, tapering rod-shaped excrescence, or *mucron*, which arises from the deeper layer of the cuticle and pierces the superficial layer. The vulva lies at a distance of two-thirds of the body length from the mouth. Two uteri emerge from the common vagina; the portion of the uterus joining the vagina has a strong muscular wall, and functions as an *ovejector*. Each uterus continues in a seminal receptacle, followed by a long, greatly coiled ovarian tube. One of the uteri is situated in the median third of the body, the other in the terminal third. When the sexes meet, the male bursa embraces the female at the level of the vulva, then the bursa is fixed to the female skin with the secretion of the cement glands, and the male coils itself around the female.[11]

The eggs (Fig. 19·11) have an average size of $60 \times 40\,\mu$; their shell is thin, transparent, and colorless. *In freshly deposited* stools

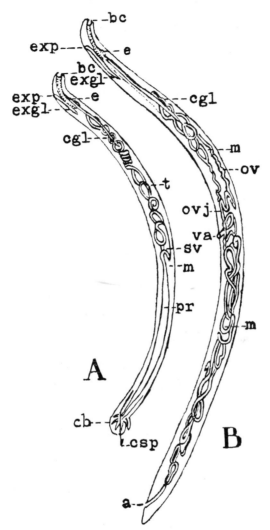

FIG. 19·10 *Necator americanus*, adults, lateral view, × 18. *A*, male; *B*, female. *a*, anal pore; *bc*, buccal capsule; *cb*, bursa; *cgl*, cephalic glands; *csp*, spicules; *e*, esophagus; *exgl*, excretory gland; *exp*, excretory pore; *m*, midgut; *ov*, ovary; *ovj*, ovejector; *pr*, prostate (cement) gland; *sv*, seminal vesicle; *t*, testis; *va*, vulva. (After Faust et al., 1957. Courtesy, Lea & Febiger, Philadelphia.)

the majority of them contain four blastomeres; but if some hours pass before they are examined, the number of blastomeres quickly increases, and then they look like small-sized newly laid eggs of trichostrongylus or ternidens. The daily production of eggs by one female is estimated at 5000 to 7000; but some authors raise this estimate to 22,000.[12, 13]

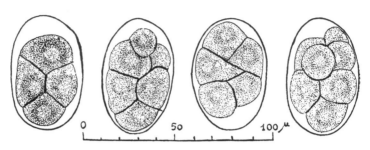

FIG. 19·11   *Ancylostoma duodenale,* eggs in freshly passed human feces with 4, 6, 5 and 7 blastomeres. (After Brumpt, 1936. Courtesy, Masson & Cie, Paris.)

A. duodenale is supposed to parasitize man exclusively; Lane's [14] report on its occurrence in a tiger and other findings of that nature probably refer to *A. paraduodenale* Biocca, 1951.

The geographical distribution of the species will be discussed under *Necator americanus.*

Necator americanus (Stiles, 1902) Stiles, 1906, differs from the foregoing in the following characteristics.[10] The worms are smaller; the males measure about 7–10 mm, with an average weight of 0.64 mg [10]; the females measure about 9–11 mm, with an average weight of 1.45 mg.[10] At the upper margin of the buccal cavity there are no teeth, but four sharp-edged plates, two dorsal and two ventral ones (Fig. 19·12:*dpl, vpl*). When hookworms are killed in 80 percent alcohol they are bent in the shape of a bow; in *A. duodenale,* the head and the tail are bent in accordance with the curvature of the body; in *N. americanus,* they are bent in a direction opposed to it (Fig. 19·10).

In the female the vulva is situated halfway the distance between head and tail, or a little nearer the head. The rodlike excrescence, or mucron, at the posterior extremity is absent.

In the male the dorsal ray of the bursa (Fig. 19·13:p) is bifid, each branch closely associated with the adjacent externodorsal ray (Fig. 19·13:pe); the position of the partly fused latero- and ventroventral rays is different (Fig. 19·13:a). The distal extremities of the spicules are loosely joined together; one spicule terminates in a hooklet which fits into the base of the triangular extremity of the other spicule.

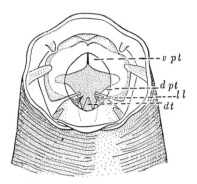

FIG. 19·12 *Necator americanus,* frontal view of buccal capsule with ventral (*vpl.*) and dorsal (*dpl.*) sharp-edged plate. (After Craig and Faust, 1951. Courtesy, Henry Kimpton, London.)

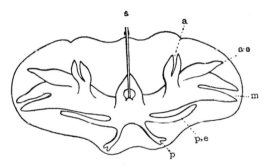

FIG. 19·13 *Necator americanus,* bursa, rays: p, Dorsal (bifid).—pe, Externodorsal.—m, Postero- and mediolateral.—ae, Anterolateral.—a, Partly fused latero- and ventroventral.—s, Spicules, basal portion. (After Brumpt, 1922. Courtesy, Masson & Cie, Paris.)

The eggs measure 64–76 × 36–40 μ; they are slightly longer, but not wider, than those of *A. duodenale.*

Necator produces half as many eggs as ancylostoma [12]; but the comparative fertility of the two species is about equal because necator weighs half as much as ancylostoma. All the same, necator needs no more than one-sixth of the quantity of blood required by ancylostoma for its daily egg production.[15] If the pathogenicity of the worms depends on their voracity, that of necator may be rated lower than that of ancylostoma. Finally, Schüffner [11] observed that the susceptibility of necator to anthelmintics is higher than that of ancylostoma.

N. americanus is a human parasite. However, it has been reported as parasitizing monkeys, rhinoceroses, anteaters, and a species of tree porcupine. Moreover, an allied species parasitizing swine, *Necator suillus* Ackert and Payne, 1922, has been experimentally transmitted to man.[16] The parasite reached sexual maturity, produced eggs, and maintained itself in the foreign host for a period of four months.

The areas of geographical distribution of the two species partly overlap. In the Western Hemisphere necator rules practically undisputed, although ancylostoma has been reported in Maracaibo.[17] So it does in Polynesia. Necator prevails over ancylostoma in central and south Africa, southern Asia, and Melanesia. *A. duodenale* is the only representative of human hookworms in Europe, including the Mediterranean Basin, and in central and northern Asia; it prevails over necator in China and Japan and even in some few localities of Indonesia, such as the island of Flores, and in certain districts of central Java. Elsewhere in Indonesia necator is the only hookworm, except in foreigners newly arrived from China.

HOOKWORMS OF CARNIVORES

Ancylostoma braziliense de Faria, 1910 and *A. ceylanicum* Looss, 1911,[72] parasitize the intestine of cats, dogs, and other small carnivores in America and Asia respectively, but have often been found in man. Stoll in 1947 [18] recorded nearly 200 human infections, from the United States to Brazil in the New World and from Bengal to Fiji in the Eastern Hemisphere.

These species differ from *A. duodenale* by their buccal armature; of the four teeth situated at the upper margin of the buccal cavity the lateral ones are unusually long, the median ones are inconspicuous (Fig. 19·14:left). The bursa is practically the same in both species, except that the two apical ramifications of the single dorsal ray are somewhat longer (Fig. 19·14:middle).

When the filariform larvas penetrate the human skin, they often miss their way to the blood and lymph vessels, and continue to wander in the hypodermal tissue. Thus they become the cause of an affection of the skin which constantly changes its place and is known as *creeping eruption* or *dermal larva migrans*. It is well-known on the Atlantic coast of the United States from New Jersey to Florida [19] and has also been observed in other parts of the world, in the Western Hemisphere (the Guianas) as well as in the Eastern (Philippine Islands, western New Guinea).

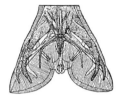

FIG. 19·14   *Ancylostoma braziliense. From left to right:* Frontal view of buccal capsule, with two lateral teeth; bursa, ventral view; bursa, side view. (After Brumpt, 1936. Courtesy, Masson & Cie, Paris.)

If the larvas succeed in entering the circulation, they may get lost in the internal organs, thus contributing to the causation of visceral larva migrans. Even if they reach the intestine, they may still continue to behave abnormally by penetrating the mucosa and laying eggs in the tissue, from which rhabditiform larvas may hatch.[20]

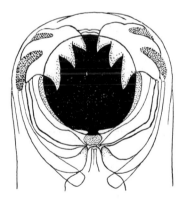

FIG. 19·15   *Ancylostoma caninum.* Frontal view of buccal capsule with three pairs of teeth. (After Looss, 1911. Courtesy, *Records of the School of Medicine,* Cairo.)

Ancylostoma caninum (Ercolani, 1859) Hall, 1913, a parasite of dogs and cats, is about the size of *A. duodenale,* from which it differs in the teeth on the anterior margin of the buccal cavity, which number six instead of four (Fig. 19·15). The eggs measure 64

$\times$ 40 μ; in some strains they are larger, 74–84 $\times$ 48–54 μ. The latter strain accidentally infected a human being in Amsterdam; eggs were evacuated for a few weeks. Lie Kian Joe and Bras,[21] in Java, found a single human infection in many hundreds of post-mortem examinations. Similar observations were made in China and the Philippine Islands, but experimental infection did not succeed in man.[22]

Thus *A. caninum* cannot be called a human parasite. Nevertheless, it is listed here, because its study has greatly contributed to clarifying the host-parasite relationship in hookworm infections.

DEVELOPMENT OF LARVAL HOOKWORMS OUTSIDE THE HUMAN HOST

In undiluted feces of normal consistency and at a temperature of 27° C, hookworm eggs become embryonated after 24 hours (Fig. 19·16). A temporary fall of the temperature to 21° C prolongs this period to 36 hours and over. In semifluid fermenting feces, also in water, many eggs die.[23] The larvas emerge from the eggshell; thus they can be found in stools passed 24 hours previously.

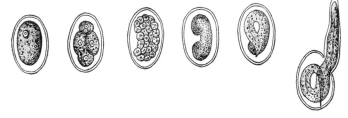

FIG. 19·16 *Ancylostoma duodenale.* Development of larvas in eggs passed in feces (temperature of 27°C.). *From left to right:* 1 and 2, In freshly passed stools.—3. After 12 hours.—4. After 18 hours.—5 and 6. After 24 hours. (After Brumpt, 1936. Courtesy, Masson & Cie, Paris.)

These larvas measure 300 $\times$ 20 μ or so (Fig. 19·17:*A*). They are of the *rhabditiform* type; they have an esophagus with a thick wall, and a well-differentiated bulb. The buccal cavity is 10 μ long, terminating in a globose expansion; it is lined with a chitinoid membrane which shows as two parallel, highly refractive rods (Fig. 19·18:*B, bc*). The larvas are motile, but their locomotion has no fixed direction; it does not get them anywhere.

In the same fecal environment and at the same temperature, the larvas pass a first molt on the second or third day. This second-stage

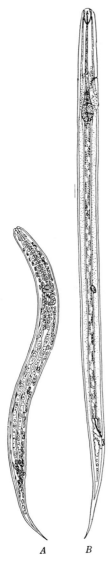

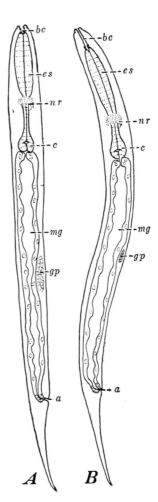

FIG. 19·17 *Ancylostoma duodenale.* A, Rhabditiform larva, × 310.—B, Filariform larva, × 160. (After Craig and Faust, 1951. Courtesy, Henry Kimpton, London.)

FIG. 19·18 Rhabditiform larvas of A, *Strongyloides stercoralis* and B, *Necator americanus,* × 400: *a,* Anus. —*bc,* Mouth.—*c,* Bulbus.—*es,* Esophagus.—*nr,* Nerve ring.—*gp,* Genital primordium.—*mg,* Midgut. (After Craig and Faust. Courtesy, Henry Kimpton, London.)

rhabditiform larva measures $480 \times 30 \mu$ or so. Its locomotion is as little purposeful as that of its predecessor.

On the fifth day the larvas molt again. The resulting third stage has grown in length, 650–700 μ, but not in width, 25–27 μ (Fig. 19·17:B). It differs from the preceding stages by the presence of a sheath, i.e. the skin, shed at the last ecdysis, loosely enveloping the emerging larva. Moreover, the third-stage larvas differ from the first and second stages by the way they behave. They are very active, and their motility is purposeful. Thus, they are able to leave the fecal surroundings which appeared to suit the first and second rhabditiform larvas, but which have become intolerable to the third stage, the *filariform larvas*. On the other hand, water, which killed the first and second stages, is quite acceptable to the third stage; it survives in water for three months, if well aerated.[24] However, the most suitable environment of the filariform larvas is not water, but moist, loose earth.

The filariform larvas have returned to the parasitic way of life; their principal aim is to enter the human body. But a long time may pass before they are offered an opportunity to do so. Thus a discussion of the behavior of the hookworms outside the human host ought to include the life of the filariform larvas in their temporary environment.

This life exposes the filariform larvas to all the vicissitudes of a sojourn in free nature, especially to low temperatures and lack of water, air, or food. A temperature under 20° C prevents development and inhibits the motility of the fully developed filariform larvas. Thus hookworms, as a general rule, are indigenous in tropical and subtropical countries. In temperate regions they can survive only under the special conditions that obtain in collieries where the temperature constantly stays above 20° C. This close association with coal mines explains why hookworms are sometimes called "mine worms" in western Europe. This rule is not without exception. Even in a very temperate country like Holland, hot summers occur on occasions, and it was during one of them that hookworm infection was detected for the first time; not, however, in miners, but in kilnmen.[25]

Even in tropical countries, filariform larvas do not occur indiscriminately in any kind of soil. In the rubber and tobacco plantations in Sumatra (Indonesia) the principal source of infection is the moist earthen floor in the laborers' homes [26]; in the silk-cultivating regions of China, it is the soil at the foot of the mulberry trees [27]; in other regions of China the sweet potato fields [28]; in Puerto Rico and Trinidad the cacao and coffee plantations [29]; in Morocco the phosphate mines.[30]

The degree of infestation of the soil greatly depends on shade; shaded soil is more heavily infected with filariform larvas than soil fully exposed to the rays of a tropical sun.[31] It also depends on the customs of the population; if they are in the habit of defecating in a river with a strong current, soil infestation is practically excluded; the habit of defecating on the soil obviously promotes it.[32]

The longevity of the filariform larvas is influenced by the physical and chemical properties of the soil; humus is much more favorable than clay; a high salinity actually destroys the larvas. The fact that filariform larvas take no food, but depend for their nutrition on the food stored in the epithelial cells that line the midgut, renders them particularly vulnerable to any influence that forces them to take too much exercise, i.e. to overdraw the limited fund of energy represented by these stored nutrients. Such an influence is supplied by a succession of wet and dry periods which causes the level of the subsoil water to rise and to fall. The filariform larvas closely follow the oscillations of this level, a tendency which may cause them to cover comparatively long vertical distances, up to 90 cm.[33] If this goes on for too long, the stored food supply is exhausted, and the larvas die of inanition.

The various conditions enumerated here render it impossible to measure accurately the maximal span of life of the filariform larvas. Nine weeks or so [34] is probably a fair estimate, but in East Africa and India it has been raised to a year [14] and in Sumatra to half a year.[26]

The vertical migration is practically the only locomotion of the larvas. An active horizontal displacement in the soil is not known; passively they can be transported by water, by particles of earth adhering to human or animal limbs, and by pigs ingesting eggs prior to their hatching and depositing them unchanged in some other place.

The above applies only to larvas in the soil. There is no reason to doubt that the soil is their normal habitat, but it is not exclusively so. In the hospital in Guam, Loughlin and Stoll [35] collected large numbers of filariform larvas on unwashed laundry. On cotton blankets they moved in a horizontal direction over distances of 20 cm and more. It has not yet been ascertained how long eggs and larvas stay alive in unwashed underwear; thus it is not known whether autoinfection can result from neglecting to have one's dirty linen regularly laundered.

ENTRANCE OF THE FILARIFORM LARVAS INTO THE HUMAN BODY

The filariform larvas reach the jejunum of the host either passively, by being ingested, or actively, by penetrating the skin. The first way is open to the larvas because they are able to resume their life in the intestine without a preparatory passage through the lungs.[36] The supposition that the first way is the exception, and the second the rule, is universally accepted.

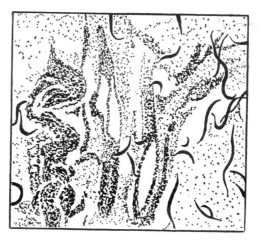

Fig. 19·19 *Ancylostoma* larvas in cutis. (After photograph in possession of Royal Tropical Institute, Amsterdam.)

The occurrence of human infection through the skin has been proved by Looss's human and animal experiments.[37] Shedding the sheath that envelops them, the larvas penetrate the cutis (Fig. 19·19), where they enter the capillaries, either vascular or lymphatic. By way of the lymphatic system or through the venous circulation they reach the right heart. Through the pulmonary artery they enter the lungs, where they leave the capillaries and pass through the alveoli, the bronchioles, the bronchi, the trachea, and the larynx. Here they leave the respiratory tract to enter the digestive tract, taking the route of the pharynx, the esophagus, the stomach, and the duodenum to the jejunum, where they eventually settle down, to grow into adult worms.

The visceral migration of the hookworms, from the skin to the jejunum, takes much less time than that of ascaris, from the intestine back to the intestine. It may be completed in 24 hours, although the majority of the larvas need more time to achieve it.[38]

As in ascaris, the migrating larvas may miss their way out of the circulation when arriving in the lung. In that case the systemic circulation carries them to various organs. This explains the prenatal infection of puppies born by dogs infected with *A. caninum*,[39] a parasite which is therefore regarded as a potential causative agent of visceral larva migrans in man.

Looss [24] divides the period of intestinal growth of the filariform larvas into four stages: (1) During the first week after their arrival in the jejunum, the filariform larvas, born in free nature, retain their original form unchanged. (2) At the end of this week they molt and now change to fourth-stage larvas, no larger than the filariform larvas. But these fourth-stage larvas possess developing sexual organs and a provisional buccal capsule that lacks the marginal teeth but is provided with two teeth at its bottom. This stage, which also lasts a week, is terminated by another molt from which emerges (3) the young adult, a fortnight after the settlement in the jejunum. Initially this stage measures 2 mm and develops a definitive buccal capsule with marginal teeth; but another four or five weeks are needed for the worms to develop into sexually mature individuals, for the females to be fertilized, and for the first eggs to be passed in the feces.[40]

Thus the whole course of development from the larvas entering the human body through the skin to the eggs leaving it through the anus ought to be achieved within eight weeks. L. C. Brumpt,[41] treating patients ill with *polycythaemia vera* by infecting them with hookworms, saw the eggs appear in the feces in less time than that, viz. 38–41 days after the larvas penetrated the skin. But it may take much longer, 10 or 11 weeks, not only in experimental infections but also in natural infections which the observer has had the good fortune to follow from the very beginning.[42]

THE HOST—PARASITE RELATIONSHIP IN HOOKWORM INFECTION

Adult hookworms attach themselves to the intestinal mucosa by sucking a portion of the tissue into their buccal capsule (Figs. 19·20 and 19·21). When they become detached, that portion of the tissue remains visible as a bleeding pinprick. When numerous worms are attached close together, the surface of the intestinal wall is covered with a layer of mucus mixed with blood.

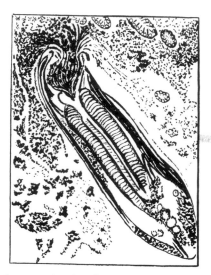

FIG. 19·20 *Ancylostoma duodenale.* Longitudinal section through buccal capsule and esophagus of worm attached to the mucosa of the intestine; a portion of the tissue has been drawn into the buccal capsule. (After photograph in possession of Royal Tropical Institute, Amsterdam.)

Ancylostoma caninum has been proved to suck blood by the observation of living worms attached to a living loop of the intestinal tract. The quantity of blood imbibed in 24 hours by a single worm may be as much as 0.2 ml.[43]

In human infections Foy et al.[44] recorded an average daily fecal blood loss of 12 ml (40 mg of iron) per 1500 hookworms. In some cases it rose to 35 ml; but higher losses have been reported, and the wide variations in the amount of fecal blood lost in different individuals carrying the same number of worms is explained by (1) migratory browsing habits of the worms, (2) persistence of bleeding points in the mucosa.

Whatever the explanation may be, there can be no doubt but that the loss of iron, consequent upon the loss of blood, is one of the main causes of anemia in hookworm infections; the lost blood may be reabsorbed by the intestinal mucosa, but the iron it contains is not.[15] In severe hookworm infections the disturbance of the iron balance of the patient's body may assume such proportions that a so-called "sup-

FIG. 19·21   Half-schematic representation of the object of Fig. 19·20, showing the buccal teeth. (After Brumpt, 1936. Courtesy, Masson & Cie, Paris.)

portive treatment," [9] including, among other measures, the administration of suitable iron-containing drugs, must precede the specific anthelmintic treatment. This has to be done, notwithstanding the fact that the parasites have been damaged by the patient's intense anemia, which retarded the growth of the young parasites and lowered the fertility of the adult females; thus they are to profit by the effect of the supportive treatment. However, this side effect will be neutralized by the specific treatment following after some weeks.[45]

The paragraph above does not imply that *A. duodenale* and *N. americanus* in the human body are ill-adapted parasites that destroy their host and are saved from the consequences only by taking refuge in the soil. On the contrary, the parasites are well-adapted; there are more asymptomatic carriers than sick individuals.

This became apparent in the antihookworm campaign in the collieries of northwest Europe during the last decades of the nineteenth century. Initially it was deemed sufficient to treat the patients in order not only to cure them, but also to eliminate any source of fresh infection. However, when Grassi and Parona's discovery [46] that the worms in the bowel could be identified by the eggs in the stools was put to practical use 21 years later, it was found that, though one-eighth of the labor force in the collieries were suffering from ancylostomiasis, another fourth of them were asymptomatic carriers who constituted a source of infection to their fellow workers as long as treatment was restricted to the actually ill. [47]

Most investigators agree that the asymptomatic carrier harbors a small number of worms in his intestine and that the sufferer from hookworm disease harbors numerous worms, although the limit which can be tolerated varies from 50 to 200 worms, according to different authors. Still, the question remains to be answered why it is that some people harbor many worms and others only a few. Is this due merely to chance, or is it due to the host resisting reinfection? The relationship existing between the dog and its hookworm, A. caninum, answers this question as far as the results of animal experiments can be applied to human conditions. [48]

Dogs, like man, become infected with hookworms by the filariform larvas penetrating their skin. This occurs under natural conditions and also under experimental conditions. Puppies are especially suitable for such experiments. They can be infected once, and they can also be infected several times in succession. If they are, the number of hookworms in their intestine steadily increases. Eventually, this causes them to suffer from severe anemia, and many of them die. Others, however, survive; the quantity of hemoglobin in the blood begins to increase; numerous worms are spontaneously evacuated from the intestine, and finally the hemoglobin content is restored to a normal level. In this way the sick carrier of numerous worms has become an asymptomatic carrier of a much smaller quantity of worms.

If the asymptomatic carrier is exposed to a renewed infection, with a number of filariform larvas so high as to warrant the death of any unprotected puppy, it tolerates this infection without any apparent ill effect; what is more, the reinfection hardly causes any appreciable rise in the number of hookworms settled in the intestine.

The defense mechanism of the asymptomatic carrier can break down. If the puppies are kept for a long time on a diet sufficient as to quantity but deficient as to the essential nutrients, they are rendered as defenseless to the parasites as they were before the experiment started.

The residual hookworm population that the puppy continues to harbor responds to the changed conditions their host is exposed to. Of course they cannot do so by increasing in number; that would be possible only if the puppy were exposed to repeated infection, which it is not, at this stage of the experiment. They respond with an increased production of eggs. Thus the host becomes a much more important source of infection than it was before it was exposed to malnutrition.[49]

If the puppy is exposed to a moderate reinfection at this particular stage, the effect is markedly different from that following the earlier attempt. The number of hookworms steeply increases, and the puppy is soon suffering from a serious disease which it has little chance to survive. If it does, supported by a timely change of diet, recovery is again accompanied by a spontaneous diminution of the worm load to a level comparable to that which existed before the second part of the experiment was started.

These experiments in dogs are in accordance with Heilig and Visveswar's [50] observations on the pathogenic effect of even a small worm load on persons suffering from malnutrition; they explain the differences of opinion of various investigators regarding the size of the tolerated worm load [51]; and they confirm Cort and Otto's [52] opinion that the serious effects of hookworm disease are due to the combined effect of the activity of the worms and of malnutrition or other debilitating conditions, rather than to the helminthic infection alone.

In the human population of tropical countries, with all age groups, classes, and sexes equally exposed to infection, heavy infection acquired in youth ought to result in a low infection rate or at least a low worm load in the older age groups—provided resistance to hookworm infection can be acquired by man. There is no clear evidence to this effect; the rate of infection increases up to the age group of 15–19; thereafter it may slowly decrease,[53] but it may also maintain the same level up to the age group of 50 and over.[28]

Starting from the undeniable fact that man may carry hookworms for a succession of years, some authors argue that this by itself proves the absence of any resistance to reinfection, because the parasites do not survive in man's body for more than a few months. Thus an apparent survival for years must be the result of an uninterrupted series of reinfections.[54] Whatever may be the truth about resistance to hookworms, this argument, at any rate, does not disprove its existence, for L. C. Brumpt [41] ascertained the persistence of hookworms for 2 to $3\frac{1}{4}$ years in persons who never left Paris during that time, and similar observations are on record which even prolong the period of survival from five to fourteen years.[55]

TREATMENT OF HOOKWORM INFECTIONS

All cases of hookworm infection should have a hemoglobin determination before specific therapy is begun. In cases showing an anemia it is advisable to give some form of iron, such as ferrous carbonate or ferrous gluconate, before the administration of an anthelmintic. Occasionally, in cases of severe anemia and malnutrition, one or more blood transfusions may be required.

Specific Therapy. Thymol, oil of chenopodium and carbon tetrachloride had been used for many years, but have been largely replaced by more efficacious and less toxic drugs, such as the following.

TETRACHLORETHYLENE, U.S.P., is available in soft gelatin globules of 0.5 ml. The dose for an adult is 3.0 ml and for children 0.2 ml for each year of life, and is given in the morning on an empty stomach, followed in two hours by a saline purge of one ounce of sodium sulfate or buffered phosphosoda. Food is withheld for two hours more to avoid adverse effects, such as nausea, vomiting, or dizziness.

Following the work of Carr [75] and associates, the more recent practice has been to omit the post-treatment saline purge and to give larger doses of tetrachlorethylene at the rate of 0.05 to 0.06 ml per pound of body weight. Adults are given 4–5 ml and children in proportionate doses with a maximum of 4.0 to 4.5 ml. Patients are advised to abstain from fatty food for several days, take a light meal the evening preceding the treatment, and no food in the morning the drug is administered.

With this regimen the authors claim to have eliminated the side effects that were encountered when the post-treatment purge was used, and obtained a marked increase in the efficacy of this drug.

HEXYLRESORCINOL, U.S.P., is available in hard gelatin capsules (Crystoids) of 0.2 gm. The adult dose is 5 capsules (1.0 gm); children under six years of age are given 3 capsules (0.6 gm), and six to twelve years of age 4 capsules (0.8 gm). The drug is given on an empty stomach and food is withheld for three to four hours. A post-treatment purge may be given if desirable. The treatment may be repeated after three days. This drug is useful in combined hookworm and ascarid infections, but is less effective than tetrachlorethylene (cf. treatment of ascariasis, p. 326).

DITHIAZANINE IODIDE (Delvex, Telmid; cf. *Ascaris* and *Trichocephalus*) has been recently introduced in multiple helminth infections in doses of 200 mg three times daily for five days. It is less effective against hookworms than against trichocephalus, strongyloides, and enterobius infections.

BEPHENIUM HYDROXYNAPHTHOATE (Alcopar), a quaternary ammonium compound, has recently been shown by Goodwin [76] and associates and others [77] to be effective against hookworms as well as against ascarids, but less effective against whipworms, in doses of 2–3 gm of the base once, or 2–3 times in one day. Hsieh [78] and co-workers treated a group of 23 children aged 10–15 in Taiwan with 2.5 gm of the base twice in one day in combined heavy hookworm, roundworm, and whipworm infections. They obtained a cure in 74 percent of the cases with a total egg-count reduction of 99 per cent. Similar, but less striking results, were obtained in the roundworm infection. They maintain that this drug is more effective than tetrachlorethylene in hookworm disease, especially in ancylostoma infections.

STRONGYLOIDES STERCORALIS

The way man becomes infected with *Strongyloides stercoralis* (Bavay, 1876) Stiles and Hassall, 1902, is exactly the same as with hookworms. The reason why it is discussed in a separate section is twofold: (1) Its nonparasitic stage of development is represented by free-living adult males and females; their progeny will resume the parasitic mode of life, but they themselves remain free-living worms till the end of their life. (2) Occasionally, it completely abandons

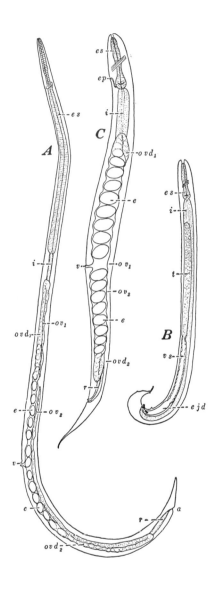

FIG. 19·22   *A–C, Strongyloides stercoralis: A,* Parasitic female, × 75.—
B, Free-living male, × 160.—*C,* Free-living female, × 160: *a,* anus; *e,*
eggs; *ejd,* ejaculatory duct; *ep,* excretory pore; *es,* esophagus; *i,* midgut; *ov* 1, *ov* 2, ovaries; *ovd* 1, *ovd* 2, oviducts; *r,* rectum; *t,* testes; *v,*
vulva; *vs,* seminal vesicle. (After Craig and Faust, 1951. Courtesy,
Henry Kimpton, London.)

the free-living stage of its life cycle; then it becomes a parasite causing autoinfection.

The free-living generation of this worm is characterized by a short, thick esophagus with a conspicuous bulb (*rhabditiform generation*) (Fig. 19·22:*B, C*), the parasitic generation by a long esophagus without a bulb (*filariform generation*).

The adults of the filariform generation inhabit the duodenum and upper jejunum of man. They occupy the lumen of Lieberkühn's glands and often penetrate the glandular tissue. Their length is little over 2 mm, their width about 30 μ. They are typically filariform; the esophagus has a length of 0.6 mm, one-fourth of the body length; it continues into the midgut without a bulb (Fig. 19·22:*A*). The anterior quarter is more slender than the rest of the body; the anus is situated close to the conical posterior extremity, which terminates in a point or a knob; the vulva lies at a distance of one-third of the body length from this extremity. The oral aperture is surrounded by three lips.

Adults A and C are females, for they possess two uteri filled with eggs. The eggs measure 50–58 $\times$ 30–34 μ; they have a thin, colorless, transparent shell and are far advanced in development. Consequently, the adults that produced them were fertilized females, but there is no unanimity of opinion as to how they became fertilized. Some regard them as females that produce their eggs by parthenogenesis; others believe that the parasitic adults are not females but hermaphrodites; still others insist that they are females that have been fertilized by parasitic males when both were staying in the trachea.[57]

Whatever their nature may be, the parasitic adults lay some tens of eggs daily, either in the lumen or in the tissue of Lieberkühn's glands, and in these situations larvas are hatched. If they are hatched in the lumen of the gland, they penetrate the surrounding tissue; if they are hatched in the tissue, they stay there, without, however, penetrating the muscles of the mucosa.[58] Eventually they return to the lumen of the bowel and are passed in the feces.

Thus the carrier of parasitic adults is identified, not by finding eggs, but by finding larvas in the freshly passed stools (Fig. 19·18:*A*; Fig. 19·23:*A*). These larvas measure 200–300 $\times$ 14–16 μ; they are of the rhabditiform type, for they have a thick, short esophagus with a bulb at its proximal end. A large genital primordium (Fig. 19·18:*A, gp*) is situated at one-third of the distance from the anus to the mouth (Fig. 19·18:*A, a* and *bc*). The posterior portion is tapering; it measures one-sixth of the body length, and the anus lies at its proximal end. The buccal cavity is short; it lacks the two parallel

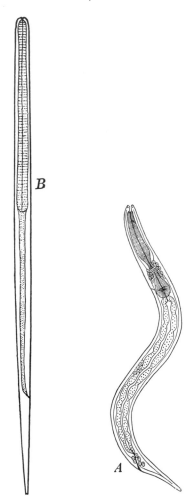

FIG. 19·23 *Strongyloides stercoralis. A,* Rhabditiform larva, × 310.— *B,* Filariform larva, × 120. (After Craig and Faust, 1951. Courtesy, Henry Kimpton, London.)

lines that characterize the buccal cavity in the rhabditiform larvas of the hookworms (Fig. 19·18:*A, bc; B, bc*).

If the feces are deposited on moist earth at a temperature of 20° C or over, the rhabditiform larvas, after four molts, change to free-living adult males or females (Fig. 19·22:*B*, *C*), a stage which they reach after 30 hours. The males live to a maximum of 9 days, the females of 12 days. Unlike the parasitic adults (Fig. 19·22:*A*), the anterior portion of the body differs little in width from the rest; the esophagus and the bulb are of the rhabditiform type; the oral lips are inconspicuous; the posterior portion of the body is tapering, and the anus lies at its proximal end.

The free-living males have a size of 0.7 mm × 35 µ or so. Their posterior end is strongly curved. They possess two curved spicules and a gubernaculum.

The free-living females exceed 1 mm in length; their width is about 50 µ. At first the uteri contain some 30 or 40 yellowish eggs of an average size of 70 × 45 µ and with a thin, transparent shell. Later on, larvas emerge from the eggs while they are deposited in the soil.

The larvas born from the free-living females are still of the nonparasitic, rhabditiform type, but of the second generation. In strongyloides of monkeys the rhabditiform larvas of the second, the third, and of still later generations are known to develop to free-living males and females.[59] But in strongyloides parasitizing man no more than one complete free-living generation is known. Although the second generation starts as a nonparasite, it does not continue so. After a single molt, the rhabditiform larva (Fig. 19·23:*A*) changes to a filariform larva (Fig. 19·23:*B*) which remains enveloped by the skin shed by the preceding stage, the so-called sheath. This larva measures about 540 × 14–15 µ; its esophagus is almost half as long as the whole body and it is continued into the midgut without an intervening bulb.

The filariform larvas can survive in the soil for some time, but they are parasites all the same, and if they get the chance they will enter the human body. They do so by penetrating any part of the human skin that touches the soil, and they perform a visceral migration in the course of which they pass through the bronchioles and the bronchi. In this respect they behave exactly like filariform hookworm larvas.[60] But unlike hookworm larvas, they continue to develop during that passage. Thus the last molt may take place in the trachea, and the emerging mature females may penetrate the tracheal mucosa and lay their eggs in this unusual environment. The shifting back of the site of development from the intestinal to the pulmonary tract may go so far that the worms never reach the jejunum and that the rhabditiform larvas are evacuated with the sputum.[61]

However, these are exceptions. As a rule, the larvas reach the duodenum prior to their last molt, and there they change to mature parasitic females, an event which becomes apparent by rhabditiform larvas being passed in the feces. In dogs experimentally infected with canine strongyloides, larvas appear one week after infection; in man they appear after 17 days.

The course of events described above is known as *indirect development*. It is not the only possible course. A far from uncommon deviation is the so-called *direct development*. It is characterized by the complete disappearance of free-living males and females. The rhabditiform larvas evacuated by one host become filariform larvas after a single molt. Thus they are ready to infect the next host, without having to pass an adult free-living stage and a rhabditiform stage of the second generation. Some authors explain this simplification of the free-living stage by the influence of temperature; others regard the tendency to perform a direct development as a racial characteristic.[62]

It makes no difference whether man is infected by indirectly or by directly developed filariform larvas. In both cases he acquires his infection from the soil. But there is another deviation from the conventional course which makes a considerable difference in this respect. It is a variety of the direct development characterized by an accelerated metamorphosis of rhabditiform to filariform larvas. It takes place, not in the soil, but on the perianal and perineal skin of the host, and the resulting filariform larvas penetrate this skin, thus giving rise to what Napier[63] has termed *exo-auto-infection* of the host.

The accelerated metamorphosis mentioned above may affect the rhabditiform larvas while they are still in the lumen of the bowel of the host. In that case the filariform larvas resulting from the metamorphosis penetrate the intestinal wall somewhere lower down. This form of autoinfection of the host Napier[63] has termed *indirect endo-auto-infection*.

Finally, the rhabditiform larvas having just emerged from the eggs embedded in the glandular tissue may be subjected to accelerated metamorphosis. In that case neither the rhabditiform larvas nor the filariform larvas born from them will ever reach the lumen of the duodenum or jejunum. The resulting autoinfection has been called *direct endo-auto-infection* by Napier.[63] Faust,[64] who discovered this phenomenon, called it *hyperinfection*. According to him, the filariform larvas resulting from the accelerated metamorphosis are of an unusually small size.

Whatever variations may occur in the life cycle of strongyloides, one phase of it never changes: the passage through the lungs. Filariform larvas may be born in the soil, on the perianal skin, in the lumen of the intestine, or in the intestinal wall—they all have to perform a visceral larval migration. Some of them will have to pass the liver, and there they may be identified as visceral larva migrans; others will not; but all, eventually, reach the lung. Most of them will leave the capillaries to enter the alveoli on their way to the trachea. A few will miss this chance; the systemic circulation will carry them to various organs, the kidneys among them.[60]

Strongyloides parasitizing dogs, cats, rats, and monkeys are difficult to differentiate from the human parasite or cannot be distinguished from it. Dogs can be infected with human strongyloides; to puppies it is highly pathogenic; older dogs show an asymptomatic infection.[65] This, however, does not apply to rats; they can only be infected with their own parasite, *S. rati*.[66] Thus the assertion that all strongyloides belong to one species cannot be correct. Moreover, it is refuted by cross-breeding experiments between strains of strongyloides from different animal sources; they produce hybrid eggs that are not viable, a fact which proves the existence of a genetic difference between the strains.[59]

As was the case in hookworms, strongyloides is limited to tropical and subtropical countries and to special localities in temperate regions, because the free-living stage renders the species particularly vulnerable to unfavorable climatic conditions.

Autoinfection does not make any difference in this respect. Undoubtedly, it enables the parasite and its progeny to maintain themselves in the body of a person even if he should inhabit arctic regions. But autoinfection does not necessarily imply that the filariform larvas born on the perianal skin or evacuated in the stools can be successfully passed on to other persons. They might be; but for the moment no evidence is available to prove that they are, or that strongyloides spreads by contact. If it does not, no autoinfection can relieve the species of its dependence on climatic conditions.

The cases of heavy worm loads often associated with endo-auto-infection, which Faust [64] appropriately termed "hyperinfection," are always serious. They can leave no doubt as to the high pathogenicity that strongyloides can display if large numbers of them are infecting the human body.[73] On occasions, however, such cases may leave a certain doubt as to the exact part played by the parasites in the causation of the morbid condition. This doubt arises when the patient afflicted with hyperinfection is suffering at the same time from the effects of malnutrition or intestinal bacterial invasion.[67]

On the other hand, very slight infections are far from rare in persons returning from the tropics. If left untreated, they remain infected for years, with no other symptoms than a persistent eosino-philia.[62] As external infection can be excluded and as strongyloides do not survive for more than a year,[68] the persistent parasitism must be due to autoinfection which, in this case, cannot be termed hyperinfection.

Sheldon [69] has shown that animals repeatedly exposed to infection with strongyloides eventually develop a certain degree of resistance; it is insufficient to eradicate the parasites, but it enables the host to keep them at a low level. The low-grade human infections referred to in the preceding paragraph perhaps owe their origin to a similar cause. It is not known, however, whether partial resistance is maintained after the complete eradication of the residual parasite population.

TREATMENT OF STRONGYLOIDIASIS. (1) METHYLROSANI-LINE CHLORIDE (*medicinal gentian violet*) is generally recommended as a useful but not altogether satisfactory drug, more effective in recent infections than in those of long standing. It is available in enteric-coated tablets containing 0.065 gm (1 grain) of the drug. Adults and older children take 3 tablets daily, one hour before meals, for 16–17 days, to a total of 3.25 gm. Young children take 0.010 gm daily for every year of life. Nausea, vomiting, abdominal cramps and diarrhea are frequently encountered with the use of this drug.

The drug is also administered by duodenal intubation of a 1 percent aqueous solution. According to different authors the quantity to be intubated is 2.5 ml,[56] 25.0 ml,[9] or 50–100 ml instilled over a long period in the form of a succession of droplets.[70]

Finally E. D. Palmer is reported[9] to have achieved satisfactory results in hospitalized patients by intravenous administration of a 0.5 percent solution of gentian violet in triple-distilled water, filtered three times; 20 ml of the solution is injected daily for 20 days.

(2) DITHIAZANINE IODIDE (Telmid or Delvex—Lilly, cf. *Ascaris* and *Trichocephalus*) has been recently recommended in doses of 200 mg three times daily over a period of 14 to 21 days.[74]

(3) PYRVINIUM CHLORIDE (Vanquin—Parke Davis & Co.), a cyanine dye, has been recently tried in strongyloidiasis, with favorable results, in doses of 50 mg three times daily for seven days. The side effects encountered—some nausea, abdominal pain, and some diarrhea—were not of serious import.[71]

REFERENCES FOR CHAPTER XIX

1. I. S. STEWART. *Brit. Med. J.,* 1949 (2nd half): 737–738.
2. LIE KIAN JOE. *J. Parasitol.,* 1947, 33: 359–362.
3. LIE KIAN JOE. Thesis, Jakarta, 120 pp, Sukabumi, 1941, English summary.
4. H. KOINO. *Trop. Diseases Bull.,* 1927, 24: 190.
5. T. M. AMBERSON and E. SCHWARZ. *Ann. Trop. Med. Parasitol.,* 1952, 46: 227–237.
6. H. F. HSÜ. *China Med. J.,* 1933, 47: 1289–1290.
7. J. H. SANDGROUND. *Ann. Trop. Med. Parasitol.,* 1929, 23: 23–31.
8. A. G. CHABAUD and M. LARIVIÈRE. *Bull. soc. pathol. exotique,* 1958, 51: 384–393.
9. E. C. FAUST, P. F. RUSSELL, and D. R. LINCICOME. *Clinical Parasitology,* Philadelphia, 1957, pp. 393, 389, 390, 362.
10. W. A. P. SCHÜFFNER. *Arch. Schiffs- u. Tropenhyg.,* 1926, 30: 534–544.
11. W. A. P. SCHÜFFNER. *Arch. Schiffs- u. Tropenhyg.,* 1912, 16: 700–703.
12. F. L. SOPER. *Am. J. Hyg.,* 1927, 7: 542–560.
13. D. L. AUGUSTINE et al. *J. Parasitol.,* 1929, 15: 45–51.
14. C. LANE. *Indian J. Med. Research,* 1917, 5: 210–216, 350–358.
15. M. ROCHE et al. *J. Clin. Invest.,* 1957, 36: 1183–1192.
16. J. J. C. BUCKLEY. *Brit. Med. J.,* 1933 (1st half): 699–700.
17. B. PEÑA-GARCÍA. *Arch. venezolanos patol. trop. y parasitol. méd.,* 1954, 2: 245–254.
18. N. R. STOLL. *J. Parasitol.,* 1947, 33: 1–18.
19. J. W. BURNS and F. A. J. KINGERY. *Southern Med. J.,* 1956, 49: 1290–1292.
20. C. BONNE. *Am. J. Trop. Med.,* 1937, 17: 587–594; 1942, 22: 507–509.
21. LIE KIAN JOE and G. BRAS. *Documenta Med. Geograph. et Trop. Amsterdam,* 1950, 2: 288.
22. G. W. HUNTER and C. B. WORTH. *J. Parasitol.,* 1945, 31: 366–372.
23. A. LOOSS. *Centr. Bakteriol.,* Abt. I, 1896, 20: 865–870.
24. A. LOOSS. *Centr. Bakteriol.,* Abt. I, 1897, 21: 913–917, 917–926.

25. V. Dubois. *Ned. Tijdschr. Geneesk.*, 1886, 22 (1st half): 268–270.
26. G. Baermann. *Geneesk. Tijdschr. Ned. Indië*, 1917, 57: 579–669, English summary, 669.
27. W. W. Cort. *Am. J. Trop. Med.*, 1940, 20: 183–198.
28. C. C. Tang. *Am. J. Hyg.*, 1949, 50: 236–262.
29. W. W. Cort. *Am. J. Hyg.*, 1925, 5: 49–89.
30. J. Gaud. *Maroc méd.*, 1958, 37: 486–487.
31. J. H. and A. W. Schuurmans Stekhoven and M. Soeradji. *Geneesk, Tijdschr. Ned. Indië*, 1921, 61: 650–706, English summary, 706.
32. W. A. P. Schüffner. *Geneesk. Tijdschr. Ned. Indië*, 1904, 44: 321–334.
33. F. K. Payne. *Am. J. Hyg.*, 1923, 3: 40–58, 584–597.
34. D. L. Augustine. *Am. J. Hyg.*, 1923, 3: 420–443.
35. E. H. Loughlin and N. R. Stoll. *Am. J. Hyg.*, 1947, 45: 191–203.
36. S. Yokogawa and T. Oiso. *Am. J. Hyg.*, 1926, 6: 484–497.
37. A. Looss. *Centr. Bakteriol.*, Abt. I, 1901, 29: 733–739; 1903, 33: 330–343.
38. J. F. Kendrick. *Am. J. Trop. Med.*, 1934, 14: 363–379.
39. L. M. Yutuc. *J. Parasitol.*, 1949, 35: 358–360.
40. A. Looss. *Sixth Intern. Congr. Zoolog.*, Berne, 1904: 225.
41. L. C. Brumpt. *Ann. parasitol. humaine et comparée*, 1952, 27: 237–249.
42. P. B. van Steenis. *Geneesk. Tijdschr. Ned. Indië*, Mem. Vol., 1936: 655–663, English summary, 663.
43. T. Gerritsen et al. *Science*, 1954, 119: 412–413.
44. H. Foy et al. *E. African Med. J.*, 1958, 35 (No. 11).
45. L. C. Brumpt and Ho-Thi-Sang. *Compt. rend. soc. biol. Paris*, 1953, 147: 1064–1066.
46. B. Grassi and C. Parona. *Atti soc. ital. sci. nat.*, 1878, 21: 53.
47. H. Bruns. *Münch. med. Wchschr.*, 1904, 51 (1st half): 657–662, 715–717.
48. W. W. Cort. *J. Parasitol.*, 1932, 19: 142–147; *Am. J. Trop. Med.*, 1940, 20: 183–198.
49. A. O. Foster and W. W. Cort. *Science*, 1931, 73: 681–683.
50. R. Heilig and S. K. Visveswar. *Indian Med. Gaz.*, 1943, 78: 578–583.
51. N. H. Swellengrebel. *Documenta Med. Geograph. et Trop. Amsterdam*, 1957, 9: 306–308.
52. W. W. Cort and G. F. Otto. *Gastroenterology*, 1940, 7: 2–11.
53. J. A. Scott. *Am. J. Trop. Med.*, 1946, 26: 331–337.
54. A. C. Chandler. *Indian J. Med. Research*, 1926, 13: 625–634.
55. E. D. Palmer. *Am. J. Trop. Med. Hyg.*, 1955, 4: 756–757.
56. Ph. H. Manson-Bahr. *Tropical Diseases*, London, 1957, pp. 807–810, 981.
57. E. C. Faust. *Am. J. Hyg.*, 1933, 18: 114–132.
58. A. J. F. Oudendal. *Arch. Schiffs- u. Tropenhyg.*, 1926, 30: 510–520.
59. D. L. Augustine. *Am. J. Hyg.*, 1940, 32 (Sect. D): 24–32.
60. F. Fülleborn. *Beih. Arch. Schiffs- u. Tropenhyg.*, 1914, 18: 182–236.
61. A. A. Laptev. *Trop. Diseases Bull.*, 1946, 43: 50–51.
62. H. Galliard. *Compt. rend. soc. biol. Paris*, 1949, 143: 686–688.
63. L. E. Napier. *J. Trop. Med. Hyg.*, 1949, 52: 23–30, 46–48.
64. E. C. Faust. *Am. J. Trop. Med.*, 1940, 20: 359–375.
65. H. Galliard. *Compt. rend. soc. biol. Paris*, 1939, 130: 413–416.
66. Sri Oemijati. Thesis, Jakarta, 1956, 170 pp., English summary, 128–131.
67. Ph. H. Hartz. *Arch. Pathol.*, 1946, 41: 601–611; *Documenta Med. Geograph. et Trop. Amsterdam*, 1954, 6: 61–68.

68. H. GALLIARD. *Ann. parasitol. humaine et comparée,* 1951, 26: 201–227.

69. J. S. SHELDON. *Am. J. Hyg.,* 1937, 25: 53–64.

70. E. C. NAUCK. *Lehrbuch der Tropenkrankheiten,* Stuttgart, 1956, p. 83.

71. H. W. BROWN and M. M. STERMAN. Unpublished data abstracted in *Am. J. Trop. Med. Hyg.,* 1958, 7: 255–256.

72. E. BIOCCA. *J. Helminthol.,* 1951, 25: 1–10.

73. H. W. BROWN and V. P. PERNA. *J. A. M. A.,* 1958, 168: 1648–1651.

74. J. C. SWARTZWELDER, W. W. FRYE, J. P. MUHLEISEN, J. H. MILLER, R. LAMPERT, A. PEÑA-CHAVARRIA, S. H. ABADIE, S. O. ANTHONY, and R. W. SAPPENFIELD. *J. A. M. A.,* 1957, 165: 2063–2067.

75. H. P. CARR, M. E. PICHARDO SARDA, and N. A. NUÑEZ. *Am. J. Trop. Med. Hyg.,* 1954, 3: 495–503.

76. L. G. GOODWIN, L. G. JAYEWARDENE, and O. D. STANDEN. *Brit. M. J.,* 1958, 2: 1572–1576.

77. N. AHMAD and G. RASOOL. *J. Trop. Med. Hyg.,* 1959, 62: 284–285.

78. HSIEN-CHEN HSIEH, H. W. BROWN, MARCIA FITE, LIEN-PIN CHOW, CHIN-SUN CHENG, and CHIN-CHUAN HSU. *Am. J. Trop. Med. Hyg.,* 1960, in press.

CHAPTER XX

NEMATODE INFECTION MAN ACQUIRES VIA ALTERNATE HOSTS

As has been explained in Chapter I, a parasite in an alternate host behaves and develops in exactly the same way as it does in man. For the present, *Trichinella spiralis* is the only nematode of this category.

TRICHINELLA SPIRALIS

Trichinella spiralis (Owen, 1835) Railliet, 1895 (*Trichina spiralis* Owen, 1835) inhabits the first quarter of the small intestine as adult male and female intestinal worms; immature worms, direct descendants of the former, live in the sarcolemma of the fibers of striated muscles of the same host ("muscle worms"). The muscle worms cannot leave their host unless they are devoured by the next host; in the intestine of the latter they develop to mature worms. As *T. spiralis* is a polyxenous parasite, the two succeeding hosts may belong to different species. Man acquires trichinella infection by consuming inadequately cooked infected pork, in the same way as he acquires taenia infection. There are two differences, however: (1) *Taenia solium* has no choice; it must pass from hog to man and *vice versa,* whereas *Tr. spiralis* need not. (2) In *T. solium* porcine infection depends on human infection; in *Tr. spiralis* it does not.

Intestinal worms develop from muscle worms if man consumes infected pork or pork products. Assuming that events follow the same course as in rats [1] the muscle worms are freed from their capsule by the digestive action of the gastric juice. They penetrate the mucosa of the proximal quarter of the small intestine, but they do not remain there longer than 24 hours. They then return to the lumen of the bowel and develop into mature males or females within the next two or three days.

The males (Fig. 20·1:*A*) measure 1.4–1.6 × 0.04 mm; the anterior part is slender, the posterior half is stout. A conspicuous string of round cells accompanies the intestine until near the middle of the body. The cloaca, flanked by two conical appendages, has a terminal position. The vas deferens opens into the cloaca; it can be evaginated, thus serving as an organ of copulation (Fig. 20·2). The testicular tube measures ½ mm; it is continued in the vas deferens.

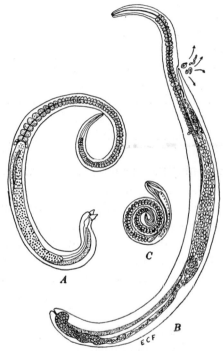

FIG. 20·2 *Trichinella spiralis*, posterior extremity of male with two conical appendages and evaginated vas deferens. (After Leuckart.)

FIG. 20·1 *Trichinella spiralis*. *A*, Adult male, × 90.—*B*, Adult female, × 90.—*C*, Muscle worm, × 660. (After Craig and Faust, 1951. Courtesy, Henry Kimpton, London.)

The females measure 2.2–3.6 × 0.06 mm. Their anterior quarter is slender, their posterior three-quarters stout. The round cells accompanying the esophagus are smaller than in the male and do not reach farther than the anterior third of the body (Fig. 20·1:*B*). The anus is situated posteriorly, the vulva one-fifth of the body length from the mouth. A single ovary continues in a seminal receptacle and an oviduct. The mature eggs measure $30 \times 40 \mu$. Larvas emerge from them while they are still lying within the uterus; thus the female worm gives birth to living larvas that leave its body through the vulva.

Prior to the birth of the first larva the female has left its original position, the lumen of the glands in the mucosa of the small intestine, and has penetrated the villi and the lymphatic ducts of the submucosa.[2] Thus the larvas ("blood worms") are born directly in the lymphatics. From there they reach the circulation, where they can stay from the seventh to the twenty-first day after the infection [3] as larvas measuring 80–120 $\times$ 6 μ.

By way of the veins, the right heart, the pulmonary circulation, and the left heart, they reach the systemic circulation, which carries them to various groups of striated muscles. There they settle down from the ninth or tenth day onward. There appears to exist a certain preference for masticating, lingual, intercostal, diaphragmatic, laryngeal, and ocular muscles, but other highly active muscles, such as those of the upper arm or the calf, may harbor more muscle worms than the diaphragm.[4]

Occasionally circulating larvas do not reach their normal destination, but get lost in various organs, such as the brain, the liver, the kidneys, the spleen, the wall of the urinary bladder or aorta. In pregnant animals Roth [4a] found them in the tissues of the unborn offspring. Among these abnormal sites the myocardium deserves special attention because it is composed of striated muscles. Nevertheless, larvas settling there are as quickly destroyed as in any other abnormal site.[4] The destruction of these worms is particularly harmful to the host if they occur in the brain or the heart.

In the striated muscles, the infected muscular fiber shows signs of degeneration; the striation disappears, and the fiber assumes a granular structure; by growing in width it becomes spindle-shaped, and the nuclei increase in size and number. The larvas contained within the fibers grow from 80–120 $\times$ 6 μ into immature adults of 900–1280 $\times$ 40 μ (Fig. 20·3:a, b), among which the males and females can be identified.[5] At this stage they already possess the string of round cells that accompanies the esophagus (Fig. 20·1:C). The size of the immature worm forces it to adapt itself to the small space assigned to it by coiling itself into a spiral (Fig. 20·3:e). This process of growth, development, and coiling is accomplished in approximately five weeks. In the fourth to the sixth week it is associated with and followed by a cellular reaction engendered by wandering cells of the host that penetrate the affected fiber. After three months this process results in the formation of a capsule that completely envelops the immature worm. Notwithstanding the small size of the capsules (200–500 × 80–300 μ) they can be detected without magnification when they become calcified,[6] a process which is initiated in the third to the sixth month and is completed after a year or so. The immature

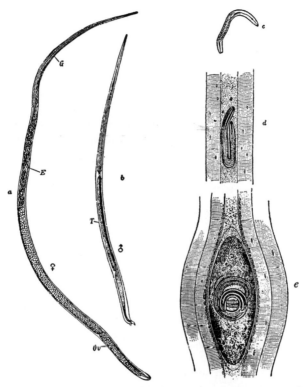

FIG. 20·3   *Trichinella spiralis: c,* Blood worm.—*d,* Young muscle worm in muscle fiber.—*Underneath,* fully developed muscle worm. (After Claus, from Braun. Courtesy, Curt Kabitzsch, Leipzig.)

worm within the capsule may die and then also becomes calcified; but it may also survive for years and retain its ability to grow to maturity in the next host.

Man is not a suitable host for trichinella because his resistance is too weak, as evidenced by the unduly prolonged period of sexual activity of the intestinal worms, which may last for 54 and even 87 days.[7, 8] It causes an overproduction of muscle worms, to the detri-

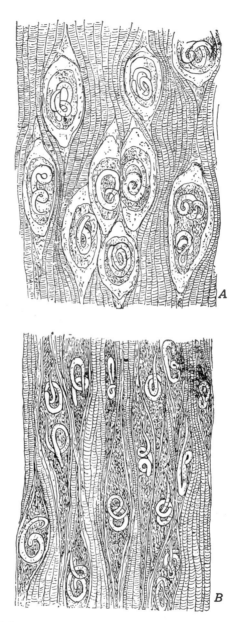

Fig. 20·4 *Trichinella spiralis.* *A*, Muscle worms in completed capsules, × 70.—*B*, Muscle worms aged seven weeks, not yet encapsulated. (After Leuckart.)

ment of the human host, who, moreover, is put at a disadvantage by his suffering more severely from the parasitic invasion than other mammals.[9]

The guinea pig, although the intestinal worms continue their sexual activity for four to eight weeks,[10] is in a slightly better position because it tolerates the effect of infected meat containing 1000 worms per gram of muscle, a dose which may prove fatal to man.[11]

However, the perfect host-parasite relationship in trichinella can only be appreciated by turning to the association of cats or dogs and rats. In adult dogs [12] or cats [13] the intestinal worms produce larvas for a short time only; as a consequence, a correspondingly small number of muscle worms is developed. Thus the mammal succeeding the dog or the cat as a host is not exposed to heavy infection. This is important, since the host alternating with the dog or the cat often is the sewer rat, *Rattus norvegicus,* which devours their carcass [14] and often succumbs to heavy infections.[15] However, it does very well as a host, wedged in between dogs, cats, and other small carnivores such as foxes or badgers.[16] This association of carnivorous and rodent hosts offers the parasite the best chances of a permanent survival with a minimum of risk from the untimely death of one of the participating hosts.

The rat is the weak link in the chain of infections, although it is well adapted to its task; for it does not allow the sexual activity of the intestinal worms to last for longer than two weeks. However, for means to enforce numerical restraint on the parasites residing in its body, it depends on the food it ingests. Rats nourished on a diet deficient in vitamin A are unable to limit the period of sexual activity of the intestinal worms.[17] The same effect can be obtained by treating the rats with cortisone, which allows adult trichinellas to stay on in the rat's intestine for periods of 8 to 14 weeks.[18]

If wild or domestic swine join the association of carnivores and rodents, they need not destroy the well-balanced host-parasite relationship. Nevertheless, they often do so, by causing man to enter the circle of hosts, for that means the joining in of a dead-end host, which is as fatal to trichinella as it is to echinococcus. It ought to be admitted, however, that man to some extent counterbalances the deleterious effect of his interference by feeding his pigs on offal of infected slaughtered pigs,[19] thereby perpetuating the infection.

Guinea pigs, although highly susceptible to trichinella infection, are able to develop some degree of resistance to it. A series of light infections, carried out by making them ingest a few hundred muscle worms at a time, engender a state which allows them to support without serious effects a dose of 2000 muscle worms which would be fatal to nonconditioned guinea pigs. Resistance thus acquired is directed against (1) the intestinal worms and the larvas they bear, and (2) the muscle worms. The first form of resistance manifests itself (a) by an intensified peristalsis and mucoid excretion expelling the still immature worms,[20] and (b) by the blood serum of the host causing precipitates to appear at the mouth, the vulva, and the anus of the mature females, which are supposed to shorten their life by interfering with the birth of the larvas and with nutrition. Resistance to muscle worms becomes apparent by the blood serum of the host causing precipitates at the oral level, accompanied by the immobilization and the eventual death of the young worms.[21]

None of these activities engender an absolute immunity: reinfections are always possible. But the parasites are kept at a low level, and thus they are prevented from endangering (1) the life of the host harboring them, (2) the life of the individual that is to be their host when it has devoured the first one, and (3) their own existence. Whether the acquired relative immunity persists after the disappearance of the last muscle worm is a question that cannot be answered for the present.

It is possible that a similar relationship exists between trichinella and man. The blood serum of the human carrier, like that of the guinea pig, provokes precipitation around the mouth of muscle worms.[21] On the other hand, in the United States among 12,000 human corpses selected at random, 1933, or 16 percent, were found infected. The number of larvas rose with the age of the subjects examined. Thus, successful reinfections must have been of common occurrence. However, as no less than 1656 of the infected subjects carried from one to ten muscle worms per gram of muscle tissue and offered no history of overt trichinosis during their lifetime,[23] it is possible that this condition was partly due to the resistance developed by this group which had been sufficient to limit the parasitic invasion of the muscles to a level compatible with good health.

This extensive but mild infection has been explained by the special conditions which usually govern the distribution of pork throughout the United States. They offer for consumption a mixture of heavily infected, lightly infected, and uninfected pork, averaging a light dose of muscle worms for almost every inhabitant, part of whom could be traced after death. Small worm loads are also distributed in Poland [24] through the medium of heavily infected pork which is cooked, but not sufficiently to expose every part of the meat to a temperature of 58° C.[25] It may be a matter of speculation whether countries like Holland, with a rate of infection of 0.2 percent established in the same fashion as in the United States and Poland,[26] would not be worse off than the latter countries if they should be suddenly exposed to heavy infection.

T. spiralis is widely distributed. Its occurrence in man wholly depends on the dietary habits of the population with regard to the consumption of pork. In Europe trichinosis is (or was) fairly common in Germany and Poland. In Russia, Sweden, and England, cases are not infrequently observed; in Austria, Finland, Denmark, Holland, Belgium, and France they are rare. The United States has already been mentioned in this respect; cases have been reported in Algeria, Egypt, Syria, India, Indonesia, China, Hawaii, West Africa, and South America.

In Canada's Northwestern Territory,[27] Spitzbergen and Greenland,[28] and northern Norway,[29] *T. spiralis* parasitizes wild life not associated with man, such as polar bears, arctic foxes, and a species of seal. However, infection likewise occurs in the human inhabitants of these regions and their domestic animals. Thus it is impossible to decide whether this infection of wild life is an example of sylvatic parasitism or merely an escape from domesticity. The same doubt exists with regard to wild-life infection in central Europe affecting wild swine, foxes, and badgers.

Apart from asymptomatic or subclinical infections with relatively mild manifestations due to (1) the ingestion of a few muscle worms or to (2) the host preventing them from reaching maturity or at least from producing a heavy infection, *T. spiralis* must be regarded as a pathogenic organism of great importance. It causes a gastrointestinal disorder during the first week after the infecting meal, followed by signs and symptoms of a generalized systemic infection known as trichinosis. This condition is characterized by fever, generalized intense muscle pains and tenderness, sweating, swelling of the eyes and face ("periorbital edema"), conjunctival injection and chemosis, a transient maculopapular rash, difficulty in chewing and swallowing (involvement of tongue and masseter muscles), respiratory embarrassment, and a number of other symptoms. In moderately heavy infections these symptoms may last two to eight weeks with a drop in temperature by lysis. In severe infections evidence of toxemia and myocardial insufficiency may supervene and the individual may succumb to this disease. Moreover, the parasite may cause additional harm by spreading or activating a cerebral virus, the causative agent of lymphocytic choriomeningitis.[30]

A clue to the diagnosis is the rising eosinophilic leukocytosis which generally appears during the second week of the disease. The insidious onset of periorbital edema and congestion of the eyes in a case of unexplained fever and generalized muscle pains in the presence of eosinophilia is good presumptive evidence for the diagnosis of trichinosis. The recovery of trichinella larvas from the unused infective meat is often very helpful in confirming the diagnosis.

A positive intradermal skin test [34] and the finding of a rising titer of antibodies by the complement-fixation technique are good confirmatory evidence. Likewise, a positive hemagglutination, flocculation and/or precipitin test are useful tools in the establishment of the diagnosis, particularly when the clinical picture is not characteristic.

In man, the parasite is of little help in the diagnosis during the early course of the infection. The adult trichinellas are rarely recovered from the feces. Likewise, only on rare occasions have the larvas been found in the sediment of the centrifuged blood or spinal fluid obtained during the second and third weeks of the disease. However, the findings of living, nonencapsulated larvas or immature worms, on muscle biopsy by the compression or digestion techniques, are final proof in the diagnosis.

No specific therapy for this disease is known.[32] Cases diagnosed early may benefit from piperazine citrate as in some of the other nematode infections. The use of steroids, especially ACTH (adrenocortico-tropic hormone),[33] have been found very useful in relieving some of the symptoms in the more severe forms of this infection and have occasionally proved lifesaving.

REFERENCES FOR CHAPTER XX

1. O. F. GURTSCH. *J. Parasitol.,* 1949, 35: 19–26.
2. M. ASKANAZY. *Centr. Bakteriol.,* 1894, 15: 225–227.
3. M. C. HALL. *Public Health Repts.,* Washington, D. C., 1937, 52: 539–551.
4. W. E. KERSHAW et al. *Ann. Trop. Med. Parasitol.,* 1956, 50: 355–361.
4a. H. ROTH. *Acta Pathol. Microbiol. Scand.,* 1935, 12: 203–215.
5. G. BUGGE. *Arch. Tierheilk.,* 1934, 68: 24–32.
6. H. SPAETH. *Deut. med. Wchschr.,* 1942, 68: 912–916.
7. W. STRYKER. *Trop. Diseases Bull.,* 1948, 45: 457.
8. J. R. CARTER. *Trop. Diseases Bull.,* 1949, 46: 766.
9. H. NEVINNY. *Virchows Arch. pathol. Anat. u. Physiol.,* 1927, 266: 185–283.
10. H. ROTH. *J. Parasitol.,* 1938, 24: 225–231.
11. H. ROTH. *Am. J. Hyg.,* 1939, 29 (Sect. D): 89–104.
12. D. A. DE JONG. *Centr. Bakteriol.,* Abt. I, Or., 1911, 59: 417–423.
13. I. SCHAAF. *Berlin. u. Münch. tierärztl. Wochschr.,* 1941: 131.
14. M. HOBMAIER and J. C. GEIGER. *Am. J. Public Health,* 1938, 28: 1205–1211.
15. R. LEHMENSICK and P. SENADISAYA. *Z. Parasitenk.,* 1941, 12: 340–361.
16. H. W. Schmidt. *Münch. med. Wochschr.,* 1941, 88: 449–453.
17. O. R. McCOY. *Am. J. Hyg.,* 1934, 20: 169–180.
18. E. K. MARKELL. *J. Infectious Diseases,* 1958, 102: 158–161.
19. B. SCHWARTZ. *Third Internat. Congr. Microbiol.,* New York, 1939, Abstracts, 171.
20. O. R. McCOY. *Am. J. Hyg.,* 1940, 32 (Sect. D): 105–116.
21. J. OLIVER-GONZÁLEZ. *J. Infectious Diseases,* 1941, 69: 254–270.
22. H. ROTH. *Nature,* 1945, 155: 758–759.
23. W. H. WRIGHT. *Public Health Repts.,* Washington, D. C., 1944, 59: 669–681.
24. Z. KOZAR et al. *Zentr. Bakteriol.,* Abt. I, Or., 1958, 172: 164–174.
25. G. F. OTTO and E. ABRAMS. *Am. J. Hyg.,* 1939, 29 (Sect. D): 115–120.
26. G. VAN DER MEER et al. *Ned. Tijdschr. Geneesk.,* 1941, 85: 4710–4716, English summary, 4716.
27. M. BROWN et al. *Can. Public Health J.,* 1949, 40: 20–21.
28. H. ROTH. *Nature,* 1949: 163.
29. T. FLATMARK. *Trop. Diseases Bull.,* 1959, 56: 80.
30. H. MOCHIZUKI et al. *J. Infectious Diseases,* 1954, 95: 260–266.
31. P. C. KORTEWEG et al. *Ned. Tijdschr. Geneesk.,* 1910, 54 (2nd half): 1354–1397, 1507–1525, English summary, 1525.
32. E. C. FAUST, P. F. RUSSELL, and D. R. LINCICOME. *Clinical Parasitology,* Philadelphia, 1957, pp. 984, 985, 338.
33. M. A. LUONGO et al. *New England J. Med.,* 1951, 245: 757–760.
34. D. L. AUGUSTINE and H. THEILER. *Parasitology,* 1932, 24: 60–86.

CHAPTER XXI

NEMATODE INFECTIONS MAN ACQUIRES
VIA BLOODSUCKING INSECTS

Unlike the ecological groups of nematodes discussed in the preceding chapters, the present one coincides with a systematic unit, the family of the Filariidae (or superfamily of Filarioidea). The human parasites among them live in man's body as adults and as larvas to which the adults give birth. These larvas bear the general name of *microfilarias*. Microfilarias of various species differ from each other in the following morphological or biological characteristics: (1) some are "ensheathed," i.e. enveloped within the eggshell stretched beyond recognition; others are naked; (2) in some the nuclei reach the end of the body, in others the caudal extremity carries no nuclei; (3) some microfilarias occur in the peripheral circulation at night, during daylight, or irrespective of the time of day; others do not occur in that site. As the adults live in lymphatics, body cavities, or subcutaneous tissues, the following classification is mainly based on the microfilarias which can be readily demonstrated in the blood or in the tissue fluid of the skin.

(1) Microfilarias in the peripheral circulation ....(2)
Microfilarias in cutaneous and subcutaneous tissue ....(5)
(2) Microfilarias ensheathed ....(3)
Microfilarias naked ....(4)
(3) The adults usually living in lymphatics ....*Wuchereria*
The adults living in connective tissue, in and below the skin
Loa loa
(4) Microfilarias with a pointed tail, lacking nuclei
Mansonella ozzardi
Microfilarias with a blunt tail, containing nuclei
Acantocheilonema perstans
(5) Microfilarias with a tail lacking nuclei ....*Onchocerca volvulus*
Microfilarias with a tail containing nuclei
Acantocheilonema streptocerca

WUCHERERIA

The filarias of this section have mosquitoes as intermediate hosts. They belong to two species, of which one, *W. bancrofti,* is widespread in the tropics, whereas the other, *W. malayi,* is limited to southern Asia.

WUCHERERIA BANCROFTI

Wuchereria bancrofti (Cobbold, 1877) Seurat, 1921 [*Filaria nocturna* Manson, 1891], often in pairs of opposite sex, inhabits abdominal lymphatics, such as those associated with the aorta, the inferior vena cava, the kidneys, the epididymis, the spermatic cord, and enlarged lymph nodes. The parasites may occur in large numbers in the adipose tissue between the skin and the superficial fascia

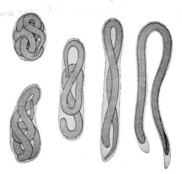

Fig. 21·1   The eggshell changed to the larval sheath by the decoiling and stretching of the larva. (After Looss.)

of the limbs.[1] Adults have been found in the anterior chamber of the eye[2] and the upper eyelid.[3] Their color is whitish; when still fresh they are as stiff as horse hair.

The male measures 28–38 × 0.108–0.120 mm.[4] The caudal part has the shape of a spiral with three windings and a blunt extremity; near the anus two narrow lateral keels are situated, the caudal alas; they are supported by 6–10 pairs of pedunculate papillas, followed by 4–5 pairs of sessile papillas. The cloaca lies at a distance of 0.14–0.18 mm from the posterior extremity. One spicule is 0.5–0.6 mm long, the other 0.2 mm; they are accompanied by a small U-shaped gubernaculum.

The female measures 71–82 × 0.17–0.19 mm. The head is globose, provided with eight perioral papillas arranged in two circles. The

neck is slender. The anus is situated at a distance of 0.22–0.25 mm
from the posterior extremity, the vulva 0.65–0.84 mm from the
anterior extremity. The distal portion of the vagina lies coiled
within a muscular pouch of $175 \times 75 \mu$. The two uteri occupy the
greater part of the space within the body; they are filled with eggs,
carrying developing larvas within their shell. The eggshell is not
ruptured, but stretched to fit the size of the growing larva (microfilaria); accordingly the latter leaves its mother's body enclosed
within the eggshell, which is now termed a "sheath" (Fig. 21·1).
In the form of "ensheathed" microfilarias they pass into the lymphatics and the peripheral circulation (Fig. 21·2).

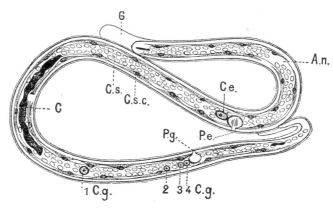

Fig. 21·2   *Microfilaria bancrofti (nocturna)*. G, Sheath (to the right:
cephalic patch).—*An*, Nerve ring (anterior patch).—*Pe*, Excretory pore
(V-patch).—*Ce*, Excretory cell.—*Csc*, Subcuticular cells.—*Cs*, Somatic
cells.—*C*, Central viscus.—1, 2, 3, *Cg*, Genital cells.—4, *Cg*, Anal cell.—
Pg, Anal pore (caudal patch). (After Brumpt, 1936. Courtesy, Masson
& Cie, Paris.)

If the infected human subject leaves the area where he was
exposed to reinfection, microfilarias continue to appear in his
peripheral circulation for a period which may last seven years and
a half.[6] However, the adult filarias in his lymphatic system do not
live as long as that, for the microfilarias often survive their parents
two years.[5] After death the adults become calcified; thus their
presence can be demonstrated by X-ray examination, a finding
which may be of practical importance if it leads to the detection of
living worms beside the calcified remnants.[1]

The microfilarias of *W. bancrofti*, known as *Microfilaria nocturna*

(Fig. 21·2), have a length usually varying from 270 to 290 μ, and a width of 6 to 8.5 μ; the sheath may be considerably longer. After appropriate fixation and staining, the body of the larva appears to be filled with numerous nuclei, separated one from another by narrow unstained spaces, except for the tapering tail, which is devoid of nuclei. In front of and within the column of nuclei, four empty spaces may be discerned, viz. (1) the cephalic patch, which is inconspicuous because of its shortness (Fig. 21·2:to the right of G); (2) Manson's anterior patch, or nerve ring (Fig. 21·2:*An*); (3) Manson's V-shaped patch, or excretory pore (Fig. 21·2:*Pe*); (4) Manson's caudal patch, or anal pore (Fig. 21·2:*Pg*), which in *Mf. nocturna* is inconspicuous. Between the excretory and anal pore lies a mass which, in successful preparations, stains deeply with Giemsa's solution and is known as Manson's central viscus or Fülleborn's internal body (Fig. 21·2:*C*). Moreover, certain more or less conspicuous cells may be discerned, viz. the excretory cell (Fig. 21·2:*Ce*), the genital cells (Fig. 21·2:*Cg*, 1–3), and the anal cell (Fig. 21·2:*Cg*, 4) which in *Mf. nocturna* is inconspicuous.

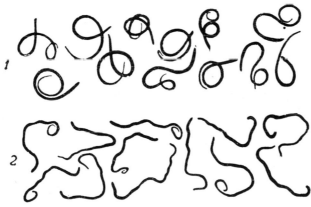

Fig. 21·3   *Microfilaria bancrofti* (1), and *Microfilaria loa* (2). (After P. Manson. Courtesy, Cassell & Co., London.)

Apart from the presence of a sheath, the relative position of the patches, and the absence of caudal nuclei, *Mf. nocturna* is also characterized by the graceful, sweeping curves it shows in quickly dried, not too thin blood films (Fig. 21·3:1).[7]

An important characteristic of *Mf. nocturna,* from which its name is derived, is not related to its form but to its behavior; the microfilarias are absent from the peripheral circulation during the day, and only to be found there at night. The following observation of the number of microfilarias in 20 cubic mm of blood may be quoted as an example of this *nocturnal periodicity*.[8] At 12 noon and 3 P.M., no larvas; 6 P.M., 2 larvas; 9 P.M., 36 larvas; 12 midnight, 73 larvas; 3 A.M., 44 larvas; 6 A.M., 41 larvas; 9 A.M., 4 larvas; 12 noon, no larvas. Some authors express the nocturnal periodicity as the proportion between the number of larvas found at midnight and noon.[9] In *Mf. nocturna* this proportion is at least 100.

Abnormal conditions may cause the nocturnal periodicity of *Mf. nocturna* to be converted to a diurnal one.[10] When the host has a fever, periodicity may be disturbed or completely lost.[11]

The fundamental cause of the periodicity is still unknown. As to its immediate cause, there is general agreement that Manson was right when he explained the periodic disappearance of the microfilarias by their retention in the capillaries of the lungs,[12] the heart, and the liver.[13]

Microfilarias are occasionally transmitted by blood transfusion. In the new host they may survive two years [5] and may even grow to an unusual size, but in the human body they can never develop to a more advanced stage (unless Faust et al.[14] are right, who claim that they can). Outside the human body they cannot survive except in one milieu, the body of certain mosquitoes, in which they can grow and develop to a stage which enables them to resume life in the human host. These mosquitoes transmit *W. bancrofti* from man to man, in the double function of a preparatory intermediate host (as the crabs are to paragonimus) and a transporting intermediate host (as anopheline mosquitoes are to plasmodia).

Manson's observation,[15] that microfilarias die in water, but do not if they have passed some ten days in the body of a mosquito, has been confirmed. But his conclusion, that man becomes infected by drinking water that harbors these resistant forms, is no longer tenable, since James [16] proved that the same mosquito that receives the parasite from man returns it to man some 12 days later.

A well-known intermediate host of *W. bancrofti,* although by no means the only one, is *Culex fatigans,* the *urban vector* of the parasite over large stretches of the tropical and subtropical world. There also exist mosquitoes transmitting the parasite in rural areas, such as species of the genus *Mansonia,*[17] *Culex annulirostris,*[8] *C. bitaenior-*

hynchus,[18] *Aëdes kochi,*[19] *Anopheles farauti,*[20] *A. darlingi,*[21] *A. gambiae,* and *A. funestus.*[22]

Mf. nocturna is ingested with man's blood by the mosquito vector. On arriving in the insect's midgut, they move about aimlessly no longer, but take a definite direction, viz. towards the proximal portion of the wall of the midgut immediately behind the esophagus,[23] thereby shedding their sheath. They pierce the wall, enter the hemocele, and make their way to and penetrate the muscles of the thorax,[24] where they settle down. In this site they first become

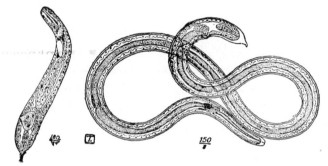

FIG. 21·4 *Microfilaria bancrofti* in thoracic muscles of *Culex fatigans:* Left, "sausage" stage, × 180.—*Right,* advanced stage, × 150. (After Brumpt, 1936. Courtesy, Masson & Cie, Paris.)

short, stout, and sluggish (Fig. 21·4:left)—the so-called "sausage" stage. After five days or so they regain their activity and resume their growth (Fig. 21·4:right). After nine to eleven days they are full grown (Fig. 21·5).

At this stage they leave the thoracic musculature and go wandering through the hemocele of various organs of the mosquito, such as the legs and the abdomen.[25] On their way they pass through the neck and the head of the mosquito; thus they approach a particular organ, the *labium* or lower lip of the mosquito's proboscis. The labium is a flexible sheath which envelops the piercing and sucking parts of the proboscis. As its hemocele is continuous with that of the head, the larvas, once they have reached the head, easily find their way into the hemocele of the labium and back into the head, the neck, and the thorax, a route they may pass back and forth repeatedly. However, if the infected mosquito settles on man's skin and begins to bite, the warmth the skin radiates stimulates the larvas to a better directed activity. They pass the whole length of the labium, and pierce the membrane between the two apical appendages, the *labella,* that are pressed to the skin (Fig. 21·6). Thus they find themselves on the surface of the human skin,[26] which they penetrate; the exact mechanism of this action is not yet fully understood.[27] The development described above is dependent upon certain climatic conditions; the optimum is 26° C and 90 percent humidity.[28]

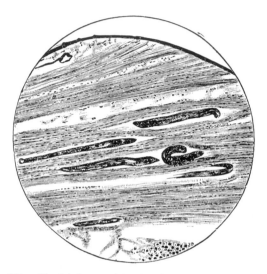

FIG. 21·5 *Microfilaria bancrofti.* Section through thorax of *Culex fatigans,* with microfilarias, 12 days after infection. (After Brumpt, 1936. Courtesy, Masson & Cie, Paris.)

In certain subjects who could be observed from the initial stages of infection onward, the larvas, after penetrating the skin, first reached the peripheral lymph ducts and subsequently the larger lymphatics. They developed into sexually mature adults in the regional lymph glands, and there the sexes copulated. Two months after the primary infection, egg-bearing females were found in extirpated lymph nodes. Two years after that date the subjects were removed from the filarious region where they had been stationed, but an observation continued for four years never revealed the presence of microfilarias in the peripheral circulation. The period of exposure (two years) had been too short to bring about this effect.[5]

W. bancrofti is indigenous in south and southeast Asia, including the city of Jakarta, Java. (*W. malayi* is prevalent in other Indonesian islands, such as Sumatra, Borneo, and Celebes.) Furthermore *W. bancrofti* occurs in Micronesia and Melanesia, the Near East (Lebanon), north and central Africa, and the tropical regions of the Western Hemisphere.

Wuchereria pacifica Manson-Bahr and Muggleton, 1952. This human parasite, whose rank as a species is not universally recognized,

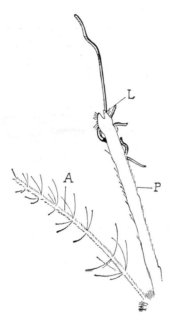

Fig. 21·6   Mature larvae of *W. bancrofti* leaving the apical extremity (*L*) of the proboscis (*P*) of *Culex fatigans.—A*, antenna. (After microphotograph made by Dr. H. de Rook.)

differs from *W. bancrofti* by three biological characteristics. They are the following.

(1) *A complete lack of periodicity.* (2) *A different intermediate host, Aëdes polynesiensis (A. scutellaris auct.),* a rural mosquito that bites man in the daytime and in the open when he is working in the fields, far from his habitation. As a consequence, adult male agricultural laborers are far more exposed to infection than their wives and children. This discrimination as to age, sex, and occupation, particularly noticeable in the island of Samoa,[29] is not known in *W. bancrofti* transmitted by rural vectors. In New Caledonia *Aëdes vigilax* is the vector. (3) *A different geographical distribution,*

which limits the parasite to an area in the Pacific situated to the east of a line that runs the following course; west of the Gilbert Islands; east of the Ellice Islands; west and south of the New Hebrides; north and east of New Caledonia. The same line separates the western, malarious part of the Pacific from the eastern, non-malarious part.

WUCHERERIA MALAYI

The adult males of *Wuchereria malayi* (Brug, 1927) Rao and Maplestone, 1940, differ from *W. bancrofti* by possessing only five pairs of adanal papillas; the spicules are shorter, 0.35 and 0.12 mm,

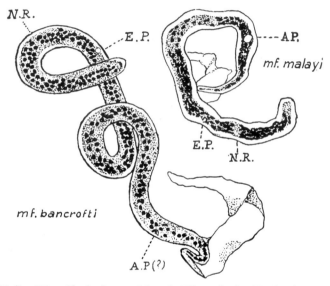

FIG. 21·7   *Microfilaria bancrofti* and *Mf. malayi: AP,* Anal pore.—*EP,* Excretory pore.—*NR,* Nerve ring. (After Brug, 1931. Courtesy, Publisher of *Proceedings of the Royal Society of Medicine,* London.)

with a well-developed center section in the left one. The microfilarias can be distinguished more readily by the following characteristics (Fig. 21·7).[9]

(1) The nuclei lie so close together that they form a mass in which it is difficult or impossible to discern the individual elements. (2) In quickly dried, fairly thick blood slides the microfilarias show stiff coils with secondary kinks; they do not show the smooth coils of the microfilarias of *W. bancrofti.* (3) The cephalic patch is conspicuous

because of its length. (4) The anal pore is conspicuous. (5) The caudal extremity narrows down suddenly to a threadlike appendage with two nuclei at the tip of the tail. (6) The length of the microfilarias of *W. malayi* usually varies from 186 to 201 μ, that of *W. bancrofti* from 270 to 290 μ. (7) The nocturnal periodicity is not so marked

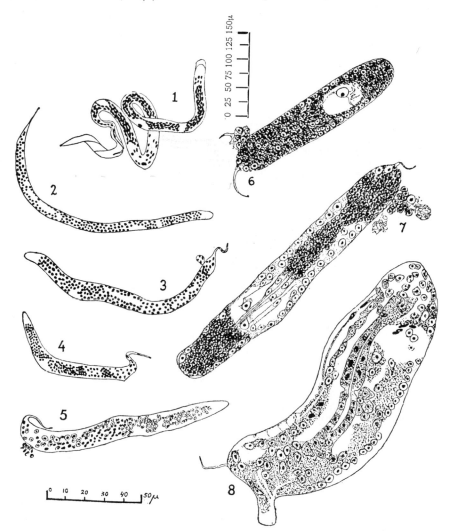

FIG. 21·8 *Microfilaria malayi:* 1. In blood.—2–8. In thoracic muscles of *Mansonia longipalpis* and *M. annulatus*, from 12 hours to 4½ days after the infection. 1–5, × 500; 6–8, × 150. (After Brug, 1931. Courtesy, Publisher of *Proceedings of the Royal Society of Medicine*, London.)

as in *W. bancrofti;* the proportion of night to day is as 22 to 1 or so; in *W. bancrofti* it is well over 100 to 1.

The development of *W. malayi* in its intermediate host, *Mansonia longipalpis* or *M. annulatus,*[9] is essentially the same as that of *W. bancrofti* in *C. fatigans.* Twelve hours after ingestion, unchanged microfilarias are found in the midgut of the mosquito, with or without a sheath (Fig. 21·8:1), and short microfilarias in the thoracic muscles (Fig. 21·8:2). The latter are still in possession of the slender caudal appendage with the two nuclei characteristic of *W. malayi.* In the next five days the short larvas grow more in width than in

FIG. 21·9   As Fig. 21·8: Five days and a half after the infection, × 440.

length ("sausage" stage); the caudal appendage does not participate in this growth (Fig. 21·8:5–8; Fig. 21·11:1½d–5½d). In the meantime an intestinal tract develops in the interior of the larva (Fig. 21·8:7–8; Fig. 21·9). From the sixth day onward, the larva no longer gains in width and may grow more slender (Fig. 21·11:10½d, 12½d), but it continues to add to its length (Fig. 21·10; Fig. 21·11:6½d–

FIG. 21·10   As Fig. 21·8: Six days and a half after the infection, × 150.

12½d). During the sausage stage the motility of the larva had been reduced to a minimum, but it begins to increase on the sixth day, and it is most lively on the tenth. Full-grown larvas, of 1.8–1.9 mm by 33 μ, may make their appearance as early as the eighth day; but it is only on the eleventh that they become numerous.

The mosquitoes that transmit *W. malayi* are none of them essentially urban, as is *C. fatigans.* Accordingly, malayi infection is never of the urban type so characteristic of bancrofti infection in some parts of the world.

As far as is known, man is the only definitive host of *W. bancrofti*. In the Malay Peninsula, *W. malayi* has at least one other natural definitive host, the domestic cat.[30] It is probable that wild monkeys, lemurids, and carnivores are natural definitive hosts in the Malay Peninsula, and that they constitute a sylvatic reservoir from which

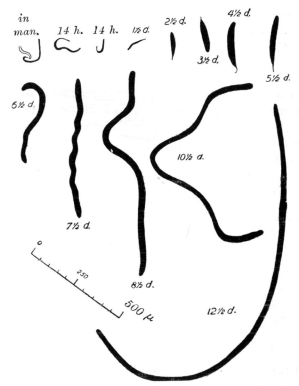

FIG. 21·11 Diagram representing the progress of the development of *Mf. malayi* in *Mansonia longipalpis* and *M. annulatus*. (After Brug, 1931. Courtesy, *Proceedings of the Royal Society of Medicine*, London.)

human infection stems. For the moment, however, this point is not yet clarified; it is even possible that the infection of the domestic cat is a spill-over from human infection.[31]

W. malayi was discovered in Sumatra (Indonesia). Its easternmost extension in Indonesia is the island of Ceram (Moluccas). It has also been found in the Malay Peninsula, Indochina, China, Korea, southern India, and Ceylon.

The preceding paragraphs refer to what might be called Indonesian *W. malayi*. In the Malay Peninsula it occurs in the freshwater tree-grown swamps of east Pahang. But in the same peninsula another human parasite occurs in the coastal rice fields and open swamps of Kedah, which differs from Indonesian malayi in the following points.

(1) It shows a marked nocturnal periodicity; (2) it does not develop readily in *Mansonia longipalpis,* but is highly infective to *Anopheles barbirostris;* (3) it does not develop well in domestic cats, and this animal is rarely found naturally infected.[32] *W. malayi* of western Celebes (Indonesia), which heavily infects *A. barbirostris,*[32a] probably belongs to this variety.

Furthermore two malayi-like filarias parasitize mammals, but not man. They are (1) *W. pahangi* Buckley and Edeson, 1956, in dogs and cats in the Malay Peninsula; man has been infected experimentally;[73] (2) *W. patei,* Buckley, Nelson and Heisch, 1958, in dogs, cats, and genet cats in Pate Island, Kenya (E. Africa).

The two varieties of the human malayi, together with those parasitizing animals, have been placed in a separate genus, *Brugia* Buckley, 1958.

HOST—PARASITE RELATIONSHIP IN WUCHERERIA INFECTION

In endemic regions, where exposure occurs repeatedly from early childhood to old age, the youngest child showing microfilarias was 5 months old[33] in bancrofti infection, and 109 days old[35] in malayi infection. However, according to Jachowski and Otto[34] microfilarias do not become visible, as a rule, till after the fourth year—a rule which is not universally applicable, certainly not in malayi infections.[35] The percentage of manifest carriers of microfilarias gradually rises, till it becomes stabilized when adult age is reached. This level is maintained through the succeeding years. The percentage may show a tendency to drop in the age group of 50–60 years,[20] but it need not do so.[36] Consequently, an uninterrupted exposure to infection does not lower the carrier rate in the course of the years. Perhaps it can reduce the worm load of the carriers, but the worm load of the succeeding age groups can only be estimated by the average microfilaria count of each group, and this estimate is invalidated by the fact that the microfilaria count in the later stages of infection of a subject ceases to be a reliable index of the number of adult worms he is harboring; microfilarias may be altogether absent from the peripheral blood of a patient ill with elephantiasis.

Nevertheless, this lifelong exposure has a definite influence which becomes apparent when a comparison is made between the indigenous population and adult immigrants in a highly endemic area. In malayi-infected Vietnam, for instance, foreigners (French and Algerian) fall ill with lymphadenitis (axillary, cervical, epitrochlear, inguinal), bronchopulmonary symptoms, and eosinophilia from six to eight months after the initial exposure, but without microfilarias in the peripheral circulation. In the autochthonous population these serious adenopathies are not observed, not even in children; if they occur among the latter, they must run such a mild course that they are overlooked. This relative immunity to the earlier stages of the disease does not protect the autochthonous population against the later stages, notably not against elephantiasis.[37]

In areas of bancroftian or pacific filariasis, foreign soldiers fell ill with lymphadenitis, associated with funiculitis, orchitis, and epididymitis, but without microfilarias in the peripheral circulation. In the autochthonous population this initial stage is passed in childhood, often unnoticed. The resulting relative immunity protects the adults against this stage of the disease, but not against the later stages.[38]

A Javanese settlement in the island of Celebes with a high malayi endemism afforded another opportunity of the same kind, this time a comparison between Javanese born in Java and Javanese born in the settlement, the former exposed to infection for the first time as young adults, the latter as infants. Unlike the examples quoted above, the relative immunity enjoyed by those born and bred in the settlement actually engendered a partial protection against elephantiasis, notwithstanding their higher parasite rate. Their average sick rate due to elephantiasis was 6 percent, against 19 percent in those born in Java; their average microfilaria rate was 26 percent, against 16 percent in those born in Java.[35]

For the earlier stages, particularly of malayi filariasis, the microfilarias are partly responsible, provided they are arrested in their course and destroyed in the lymph glands. Under these conditions, they may provoke the clinical triad of adenopathy, eosinophilia, and bronchopneumonic symptoms known in Sumatra [37] and other malayi-infested regions.

However, this morbid condition is not wholly dependent on *W. malayi,* for in regions of exclusively bancroftian filariasis analogous observations have been made.[40] This abnormal relationship between host and parasite, which prevents the microfilarias from reaching their natural destination, is peculiar to persons who are foreigners in the wuchereria-infested region. It may explain the absence of microfilarias in the peripheral circulation of such persons.

The younger and older adult worms cause acute disturbances in the lymphatic system, either directly or by the host becoming sensitized to the products of their excretion. The symptoms characterizing the later stages, elephantiasis among them, are regarded as the consequences of the lymphatic circulation being blocked by cellular activity of the host, as a response to the presence of dead and dying worms. Some authors believe this to be a sufficient explanation of the lymph varices, chyluria, and other symptoms in the lymphatic system, while others claim that the acute, recurrent erysipeloid reaction encountered in elephantiasis, at least, is due to the intervention of hemolytic streptococci.

TREATMENT OF WUCHERERIAN FILARIASIS

DIETHYLCARBAMAZINE (Hetrazan, Banocide, Nothézine), 1-diethyl-aminocarbamine-4-methylpiperazine, in the form of citrate, is regarded as a specific drug, since it causes a rapid disappearance of the circulating microfilarias by promoting their phagocytosis by elements of the endothelial system.[41] Eventually the death or at least the sterilization of the adult females is brought about.

The recommended dose is 2 mg per kg of body weight three times daily, administered orally after meals. The administration is to be continued for two to three weeks in mild cases, and for three to four weeks in severe cases.[41]

The treatment favorably influences filarial lymphangitis and, to some extent, hydrocele, but it has no effect on symptoms which are caused by the blocking of the lymphatic circulation.[42]

The side effects—headache, nausea, fever, and inflammatory reaction of the lymphatic system, particularly of the inguinal glands— are supposed to be allergic reactions provoked by the products emanating from dead parasites. As a rule they subside after a few days.[42] They are said to be more severe in malayi filariasis.[41]

Suramin (*v.* Onchocerciasis) does not affect the adults.[42]

LOA LOA: THE EYE WORM

Loa loa (Cobbold, 1864) Castellani & Chalmers, 1913 [*Microfilaria diurna* Manson, 1891] resembles wuchereria in that its microfilarias have a sheath. The internal structure of the microfilarias greatly resembles that of *W. malayi*. Otherwise loa has little in common with wuchereria; its periodicity is diurnal, its adults live in the subcutaneous tissue of their host, its vectors are horseflies, it occurs in central Africa only, and it causes no elephantiasis.

The parasite occurs in the rain forests of west and central Africa, from 8° N. lat. to 5° S. lat., and from the West Coast to 30° E. long. Its head is conical in shape; there are three pairs of perioral papillas. Its cuticle carries numerous bosses that look like minute droplets; they are absent from the cephalic and caudal extremities of the male.

The males measure 30–34 mm in length, and 0.35–0.43 mm in width; they may be called stout for a filaria. The caudal extremity is curved and carries two minute lateral keels supported by eight pairs of papillas five pairs of larger club-shaped ones and three pairs of small ones; the cloaca is subterminal. One spicule measures 176–190 μ. It is abruptly bent in the middle and terminates in two points. The other is 110–115 μ long and terminates in a hooklet.

The female is more slender, 50–70 × 0.4–0.5 mm. The vulva lies 2.5 mm from the cephalic extremity, the anus 0.17 mm from the caudal extremity.

The microfilarias measure 250–330 × 6–8.5 μ. They are enveloped by a sheath, the greatly stretched eggshell.[43] In quickly dried, fairly thick blood films (Fig. 21·3:2), it resembles malayi in its wrinkles and secondary kinks as also by the presence of caudal nuclei; but the caudal extremity tapers gradually, and its nuclei form an uninterrupted continuation of the series of nuclei in the rest of the body. The genital primordium (Fig. 21·12, 1 *C.g.*) is conspicuous, and the anal pore well developed (Fig. 21·12:*Pg*). The diurnal periodicity is less influenced by the habits or bodily condition of the host than is the case in *W. bancrofti*. Nevertheless, Külz,[44] sailing from west to east (Hamburg to Melanesia), observed that *Mf. diurna* reached its daily maximum in the peripheral circulation at 3 P.M. by the ship's clock; thus the interval between two maxima was less than 24 hours.

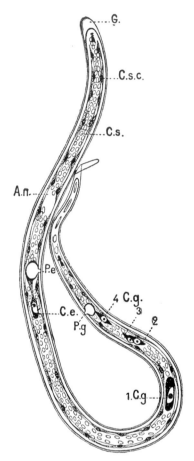

Fig. 21·12 *Microfilaria loa (diurna)*, × 1000: *G*, Sheath.—*Csc*, Sub-cuticular cells.—*Cs*, Somatic cells.—*An*, Nerve ring.—*Ce*, Excretory cell. —*Pe*, Excretory pore.—1–3, *Cg*, Genital cells.—4, *Cg*, Anal cell.—*Pg*, Anal pore. (After Brumpt, 1936. Courtesy, Masson & Cie, Paris.)

The transmission from man to man is carried out by certain tabanid flies, members of the genus *Chrysops* (Fig. 21·13). They are bloodsucking insects that bite in the daytime, unlike the mosquitoes transmitting urban *W. bancrofti* that bite at night; moreover, they are very voracious, imbibing large quantities of blood.[45]

In the midgut of the fly the microfilarias shed their sheath; after six hours thcy pierce the wall of the gut and penetrate the enocytes of the fat body, thus becoming intracellular parasites.[46] After the fourth day (Fig. 21·14), on which longitudinal growth has set in, the larvas lie in the abdomen, coiled between the ovarian follicles and around the salivary glands. On the seventh day the larva has grown from 240 × 22 μ to 1500 × 40 μ. At that time commences the wandering through or along various organs; but the majority of larvas are to be found in the subcutaneous tissue, and some in the

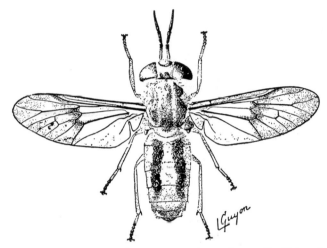

Fig. 21·13 *Chrysops dimidiata*, vector of *Loa loa*, × 5. (After Brumpt, 1936. Courtesy, Masson & Cie, Paris.)

thoracic muscles. On the ninth day the larvas have grown still longer, but more slender, 1800 × 27 μ. They make their way to the large hemocelic space in the head, either along the esophagus or through the wide, ventral hemocelic canal. For a time they may settle in the muscular tissue behind the eyes; but on the twelfth day they penetrate the proboscis at a spot situated between the root of the labium (Fig. 21·15:*Lb*) and an adjoining organ, the hypopharynx (Fig. 21·15:*hy*). They have now become "mature larvas" (Fig. 21·14:10) and measure 2000 × 25 μ, eight times their length on the second day, but hardly more than their width on that day.

There exists a delicate membrane, the *labiohypopharyngeal membrane,* which is reflected from the root of the labium on to the ventral side of the hypopharynx. Probably by the rupturing of this membrane [46] the mature larvas finally liberate themselves, stimulated to this effort by the warmth of the human skin when the fly settles down to take blood and presses the distal part of its labium, the labella (Fig. 21·15:*Lbl*), against the skin. At that moment large numbers of larvas emerge, in groups of 20 or 30 at a time. This, apparently, disturbs the fly, for it retracts its proboscis and tries to clean off the larvas with its front legs. With larvas still adhering to its legs, it resumes its former activity, and thus the larvas are deposited on the skin.[47]

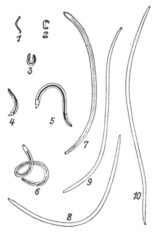

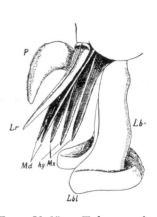

Fig. 21·14 Diagram (the larva "1" has a length of 150 μ) representing the progress of the development of *Mf. loa* in *Chrysops*. The figures 1–10 indicate the number of days after the infection of the fly. (After Connal, 1922. Courtesy, *Transactions of the Royal Society of Tropical Medicine and Hygiene,* London.)

Fig. 21·15 *Tabanus bovinus,* composing parts of the proboscis: *Lb,* Labium.— *Lbl,* Labella.—*Lr,* Labrum-epipharynx.—*hy,* Hypopharynx.—*Md,* Mandibles.—*Mx,* Maxils.—*P,* Palp. (After Grünberg. Courtesy, Gustav Fischer, Jena.)

One year after the host has become infected in the way just described, adult worms may appear under the skin or on the conjunctiva, but microfilarias are not detected till five months after that.[47] Post-mortem examinations of subjects who had permanently left the loa-infested area 6, 7, and 13 years before their death have revealed the presence of parasites which, all that time, had caused no appreciable symptoms [47]; worms that did cause trouble have been recovered even after 24 years.[48]

The relationship of loa to its human host much resembles what is known to exist in the wuchererias. The youngest child with microfilarias in its peripheral circulation was four years of age. From that age onward the rate of infection steadily increases, up to a certain level which is maintained for the remainder of the host's life, without any sign of abating in old age.

However, in loa infections the worm load can be assessed by the number of diurnal microfilarias, because the obstacles which prevent the wuchereria larvas from reaching the circulation in the later stages of the infection are not markedly operative against loa microfilarias. It is therefore of particular importance that Gordon,[45] although

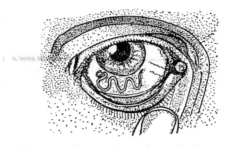

Fig. 21·16 Adult *Loa loa* passing through the conjunctiva. (After Fülleborn; from Brumpt, 1936. Courtesy, Masson & Cie, Paris.)

confirming that the rate of parasite carriers remains high through life in loa regions of high endemism, has found the majority of the adults carrying no more than a light infection. Consequently, *L. loa* in the human body is subjected to numerical restraint, a restraint which does not become apparent by the percentage of carriers diminishing with age, but by the worm load showing a decrease associated with age.

Those who have not acquired the ability to impose numerical restraint by an association with the parasite dating from the first days of life are likely to suffer from loaiasis as adults. Apart from the rare cases of subacute or chronic encephalitis associated with loa microfilarias in the brain,[49] the most distressing symptoms are (1) the localized and transient edemas of the skin, called *Calabar swellings,* often affecting the dorsal side of the hand and wrist, and (2) the pruriginous symptoms, both of an allergic nature; (3) the passage of the adult worm through the conjunctiva (Fig. 21·16) and

(4) the sensation caused by the adult worm passing through the skin, especially near the knee joint.

In the Cameroons *L. loa* is found in monkeys as well as in man. The simian microfilarias are slightly longer (262–270 μ) than the human of the same region (247–250 μ). Moreover, their periodicity is more or less nocturnal, and their vectors are *Chrysops langi* and *C. centurionis,* which bite at dusk, whereas the vectors of human loa, *C. dimidata* and *C. silacea,* bite during the day. The first two bite high up in the tops of the trees of the rain forest. So there is little likelihood of man becoming infected with the simian strain. The reverse does occur, although rarely.[50]

TREATMENT OF LOAIASIS. DIETHYLCARBAMAZINE (Hetrazan) is recommended,[41] either in daily doses of 6 mg per kg of body weight, or in daily doses of 400 mg for male adults, and 300 mg for female adults, continued for 10 to 21 days. An antihistaminic (Benadryl, Anthisan) is prescribed to counteract the allergic symptoms, which are encountered during the first 3 or 4 days of the treatment.[42] Attempt should be made to remove surgically the adult worms, especially when they cross the corneal conjunctiva or the bridge of the nose.

SHEATHLESS MICROFILARIAS IN THE PERIPHERAL CIRCULATION

The filarias belonging to this group often parasitize man in Africa and South America. They have little or no public health importance and are probably to be classified as commensals, although little is known about their relationship to their human host.

ACANTHOCHEILONEMA PERSTANS

Acanthocheilonema perstans (Manson, 1891) Railliet, Henry and Langeron, 1912 [*Dipetalonema perstans* (Manson, 1891) Yorke and Maplestone, 1926] is prevalent in Africa; in some areas half of the population is infected [51]; it also occurs in South America, e.g. among the Amerindians of Surinam.[52] The adults are usually situated in the peritoneal cavity. They are unusually slender, even for filarias— about as long as *W. bancrofti* and half as wide.

There are three pairs of oral papillas. The caudal part is curved in both sexes; it terminates in two triangular cuticular appendages

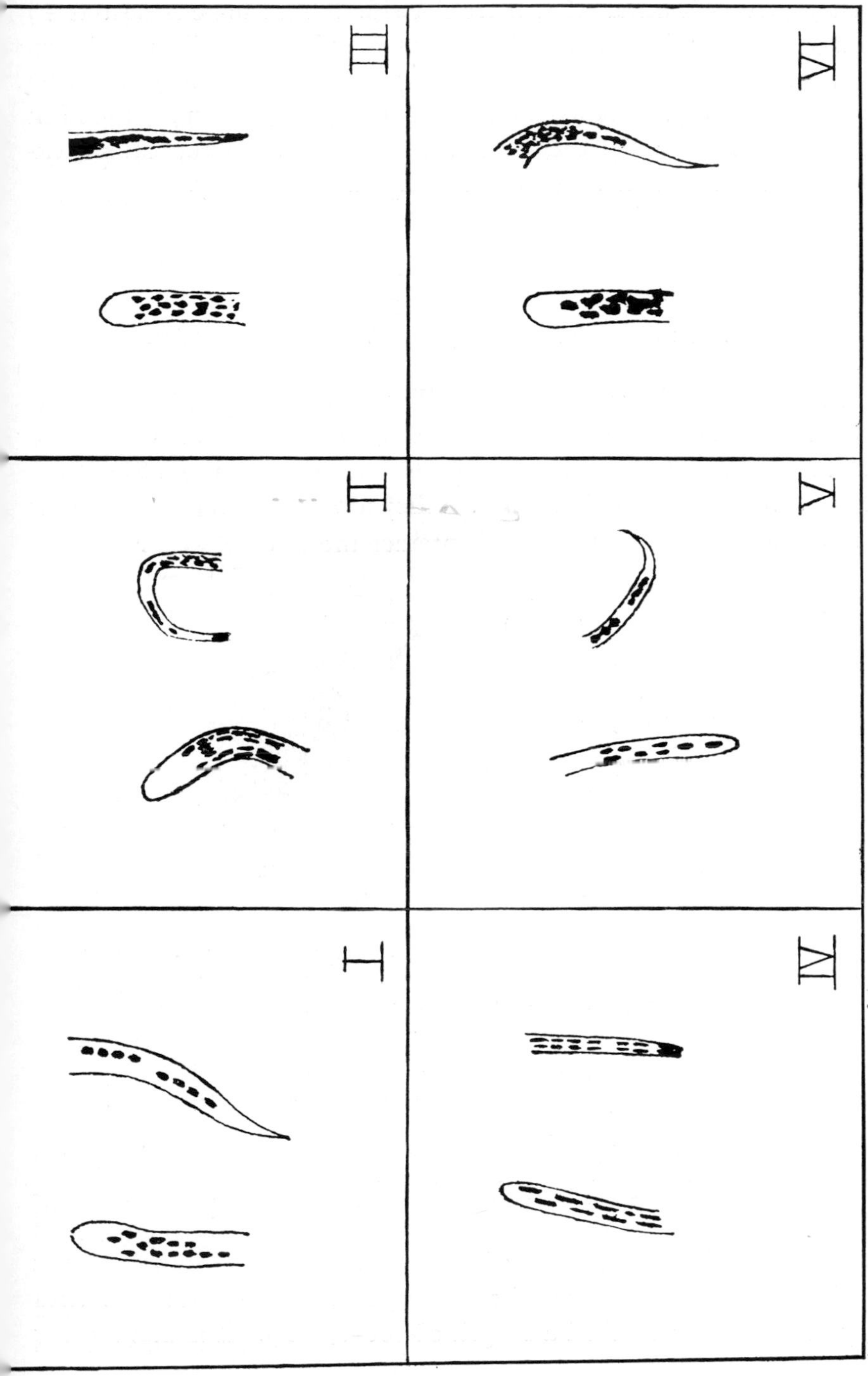

Fig. 21·17 Cephalic (*left*) and caudal (*right*) extremity of I, *Mf. bancrofti*; II, *Mf. malayi*; III, *Mf. loa*; IV, *Mf. perstans*; V, *Mf. ozzardi*; VI, *Mf. volvulus*: × 5C0.

that touch each other with their flat sides. The male measures 45 mm × 60–80 μ; it possesses five pairs of adanal papillas and two spicules, one half as long as the other; the cloaca lies 90 μ from the caudal extremity. The female measures 70–80 × 0.12 mm; the neck is slightly constricted; the anus lies 0.15 mm from the caudal extremity, the vulva 0.6 mm from the cephalic extremity.

Fig. 21·18   Caudal extremity of *Mf. streptocerca,* × 500.

The microfilarias are sheathless. They measure 200 × 4.5 μ, varying from 160–200 × 5–6 μ to 90–110 × 4 μ.[53] The position of the nuclei in the cephalic and caudal parts may be seen in Fig. 21·17:*IV*. They show no periodicity; perhaps they are slightly more numerous at night.

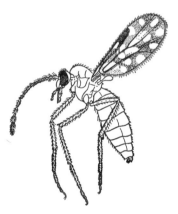

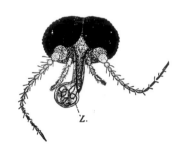

Fig. 21·20   *Culicoides austeni.* Head of female, with labrum-epipharynx from which bulges a pouch (*Z*) filled with larvas of *A. perstans.* (After Brumpt, 1936. Courtesy, Masson & Cie, Paris.)

Fig. 21·19   *Culicoides austeni.* Female, side view, × 25. (After Brumpt, 1936. Courtesy, Masson & Cie, Paris.)

The vectors are little gnats, members of the genus *Culicoides,* such as *C. austeni, C. milnei,* and *C. grahami* (Fig. 21·19). The sausage-shaped sluggish stage of the development of the microfilaria is lodged in the thoracic musculature of the gnat. After the fourth day it begins to grow in length, and its motility is regained. On the seventh day the larva has reached a length of 600–1,000 μ. It makes its way through the head to the proboscis on the eighth day. Unlike the larvas of wuchereria, it does not enter the hemocele of the lower lip of the insect, but that of its upper lip, the *labrum-epipharynx*. Like the lower lip, it is part of the proboscis and consists of an upper and a lower chitinous piece which, together with a thin lateral membrane, form a hollow organ in whose cavity the cephalic hemocele opens. When the larvas enter this cavity, the lateral membrane bulges outside the labrum-epipharynx (Fig. 21·20) and finally it is ruptured.

The microfilarias have been seen in the blood of young children. This may be interpreted as a sign that they do not meet the obstacles to their entry into the circulation encountered by the larvas of the wuchererias and loa during the initial stages of the infection, an interpretation which is in agreement with the apparently harmless nature of the parasite.

Filarias indistinguishable from *A. perstans* have been found in anthropoid apes of Africa.

Diethylcarbamazine does not destroy the microfilarias.[38]

MANSONELLA OZZARDI

Mansonella ozzardi (Manson, 1897) Faust, 1929 [*Filaria demarquayi*, Manson, 1897] is limited to the Western Hemisphere, where it occurs in various parts of tropical South America such as Surinam [52] and in some of the Antilles.

The adult male is incompletely known. The female measures 65–80 by 0.2–0.3 mm. Its caudal extremity is curved and carries a pair of subterminal appendages.

The sheathless, nonperiodic microfilarias have an average length of 250 μ. The absence of nuclei from the cephalic and caudal extremity distinguishes them from those of *A. perstans* (Fig. 21·17:*D*).

According to Buckley [54] development in *Culicoides furens* is completed in eight days. In Surinam *Culicoides guttatus* appears to be the vector.[55]

McCoy,[56] who found about half of the Amerindians in the Republic of Panama carrying ozzardi microfilarias, regarded the parasite as harmless; Biagi [57] in heavily infected Yucatan could not detect any clear-cut symptoms for which it might be held responsible.

Diethylcarbamazine does not destroy the microfilarias.[38]

SHEATHLESS MICROFILARIAS IN THE SKIN

The two species belonging to this group have nothing in common except that their sheathless microfilarias occur in the human skin. Thus both may be found in so-called "skin snips." As one of them is the microfilaria of an unimportant human parasite (*Acantocheilonema streptocerca*) and the other of a very important one (*Onchocerca volvulus*), it is necessary to distinguish one from the other in Africa. In the Western Hemisphere the former does not occur, and so there cannot arise confusion.

ACANTOCHEILONEMA STREPTOCERCA

Acantocheilonema streptocerca (Macfie and Corson, 1922) Faust, 1949, except for adult worms recovered from 'African monkeys, which are claimed to represent this species, is known as a human parasite only by its sheathless microfilarias in the skin of inhabitants of West Africa and the Congo.

The microfilarias have an average size of $221 \times 3 \mu$.[58] Their tails are curved in the form of a hooklet; the distribution of the nuclei in the caudal part of the larvas is illustrated in Fig. $21 \cdot 18$, which also shows how they differ from the microfilarias of *Acantocheilonema perstans* (Fig. $21 \cdot 17:IV$). As to those of *Onchocerca volvulus,* also occurring in the skin in regions of Africa in which *A. streptocerca* is prevalent, confusion between them is excluded because onchocerca larvas have no nuclei in their caudal extremity, which, moreover, is not curved (Fig. $21 \cdot 17:VI$).

Culicoides grahami and *C. austeni,* both vectors of *A. perstans,* have been identified as vectors of *A. streptocerca,* in which the microfilarias grow to maturity in seven days; they have reached a size of $574 \times 21 \mu$ when they appear in the proboscis.[58] There exists some doubt whether *C. grahami* is a vector of both species of acantocheilonema; it has been claimed [59] that this gnat transmits *A. streptocerca* only. However, there can be no doubt that *C. austeni* [60] and *C. milnei* [61] are vectors of *A. perstans*.

The parasite is held responsible for causing certain cutaneous lesions. The microfilarias are reported to be destroyed by diethylcarbamazine.

ONCHOCERCA VOLVULUS

Onchocerca volvulus (Leuckart, 1893) Railliet and Henry, 1910, inhabits the lymphatic vessels of the subcutaneous tissue of inhabitants of central Africa from Senegal to Tanganyika, Central America, Chiapas and Oaxaca in southern Mexico, and northeastern Venezuela. It causes the appearance of granulomatous nodules, and lichenification and atrophy of the skin. The greatly convoluted worms lie in the fibrous nodules (Fig. 21·21) together with their

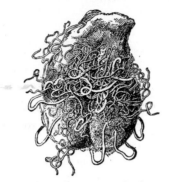

FIG. 21·21 Tumor with *Onchocerca volvulus* cut open, × 2. (After Brumpt, 1922. Courtesy, Masson & Cie, Paris.)

progeny, the microfilarias, which rarely appear in the blood (Fig. 21·22).

The cuticle of the adult worm carries unusually distinct transverse striations. There are two rings of perioral papillas; an inner circle of four small ones and an outer circle composed of four small and two large ones.

The male measures 20–45 by 0.13–0.20 mm; the caudal part is wound in a spiral or a tight curve. The number and position of the caudal papillas may vary from three to five pairs near the cloaca, and from two to three pairs at the posterior extremity. One spicule is 0.17–0.23 mm long, with a blunt proximal extremity and a pointed distal extremity; the other spicule, of 0.07–0.10 mm, has a club-shaped distal extremity.

The female is considerably longer than any other insect-borne filaria: 230–700 × 0.30–0.45 mm; the vulva is situated 0.4–1.1 mm from the cephalic extremity.

As has been pointed out already, the sheathless microfilarias are usually found in the skin and not in the blood; they differ from those of *A. streptocerca* by the absence of nuclei from the caudal extremity (Fig. 21·17:*VI*). They occur in two sizes—a large one of 285–368 × 6–9 μ and a small one of 150–287 × 5–7 μ.[62]

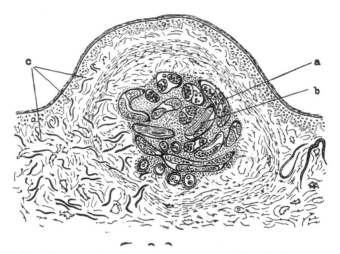

FIG. 21·22   Cross section through tumor caused by *Onchocerca volvulus: a,* Bundle of intrauterine larvas.—*b,* Cross section through female worm.—*c,* Free larvas. (After Geigy and Herbig, 1955. Courtesy, Verlag für Recht und Gesellschaft, Basel.)

In Africa the vectors of *O. volvulus* are small black flies, *Simulium damnosum,* and other members of that genus [63] (Fig. 21·23).   The way the larvas develop in the thoracic musculature of the fly follows in broad lines the pattern of the wuchererias.   The final stage, of a

FIG. 21·23   *Simulium reptans,* × 10. (After Brumpt, 1922. Courtesy, Masson & Cie, Paris.)

size of 657–760 × 23 μ, is found in the labium of the proboscis (Fig. 21·24) from the seventh day onward.

In the Western Hemisphere *O. volvulus* (here called *O. caecutiens* Brumpt, 1919) is indigenous to a certain region of Guatemala and

the adjacent part of Mexico and has also been reported in northeastern Venezuela. The insect vectors are different species of the same
genus, such as *S. avidum, S. ochraceum,* and *S. mooseri.* The development of the larvas resembles that occurring in *S. damnosum,*
but the final stage may be considerably longer, up to $1160 \times 25\ \mu$.[64]

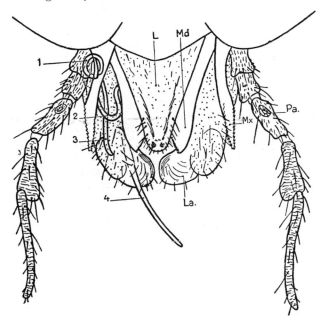

GIG. 21·24 *Mf. volvulus,* matured within the body of *Simulium damnosum,* leave (1–4) the labium (*La*) of the insect: *L,* Labrum.—*Md,*
Mandible.—*Mx,* Maxils.—*Pa,* Palps. (After Blacklock, from Brumpt,
1922. Courtesy, Masson & Cie, Paris.)

The host-parasite relationship in *O. volvulus* depends on various
factors:

(1) *The stage of development of the worm.* The young and
mature adults are the cause of the fibrous nodules, lichenification,
and atrophy affecting the skin. The microfilarias, by penetrating the
cornea from the bulbar conjunctiva or by traversing the adventitial
sheaths of the perforating blood vessels at the limbus or the
equator,[65] become lodged below the conjunctiva, outer sclera, cornea,
iris, retina, and the sheath of the optic nerve. Thus they become the
cause of keratitis, iritis, and chorioiditis, which may terminate in
blindness. Ocular onchocerciasis occurs in Africa as well as in

Central America; however, it seems to be more prevalent in the New World.

(2) *The site of the onchocercal tumors.* In the New World they are predominantly located on the scalp or elsewhere near the eye, whereas in Africa they are uncommon in that site. This is regarded as an explanation of the greater prevalence of ocular onchocerciasis in Central America. However, this difference is not considered to represent a specific characteristic of the New World "Onchocerca caecutiens"; rather it is due to a characteristic of New World simuliums, which are said to be in the habit of biting at a level higher above the ground than their African relatives.[38]

(3) *The period of exposure to infection.* In onchocerca-infested countries, the degree of infection in the succeeding age groups is measured by the percentage of persons carrying, not microfilarias, but rather onchocercal tumors. In the Congo two-thirds of the older children and four-fifths of the adults carry nodules[66]; thus it is evident that the symptoms do not abate with advancing years and that no relative immunity is acquired by an exposure lasting from early childhood (two-month-old children have been found carrying nodules[67]) to old age. Similar conditions obtain in Kenya[68] and Venezuela.[69]

However, the exclusive attention paid to the nodule carriers obscures the fact that there are parasite carriers without nodules, or whose nodules have been removed at least one year earlier without the reappearance of fresh ones, and who, accordingly, have become tolerant of the presence of parasites in their skin.[64] The onchocercal nodules thus appear to be the result of hypersensitivity to the metabolites of the worm.[70] In a population whose hypersensitivity has been subdued, a high infection rate, coinciding with a low nodule rate, will give the correct measurement of the degree of tolerance acquired.[71]

TREATMENT OF ONCHOCERCIASIS. Enucleation of the onchocercal tumors is recommended as a preliminary to the administration of specific drugs and as a preventive of ocular involvement. The presence of worms in healthy portions of the skin does not appear to detract from the usefulness of this surgical intervention.[72]

In onchocerciasis allergic reactions to Hetrazan are more severe than in other filariases. It is therefore recommended[41] that the 21 days' course of treatment be modified from 6 mg daily per kg of body weight, to a course in which 2 mg per kg of body weight is administered on the first day, 4 mg on the second, and 6 mg on the third and succeeding days. In alarming allergic conditions, the course is to be interrupted for several days; in this interval an antihistaminic drug is administered.

In view of the fact that adult onchocerca is more resistant to Hetrazan than other adult filarias, the above course of treatment must be repeated when microfilarias reappear, i.e. in about six months' time [42]; or it must be supplemented by a course of suramin, in the form of a 10 percent aqueous solution, administered intravenously, 1 gm weekly, for five weeks.[38] According to some authors [42] the course of Hetrazan, preceding that of suramin, may be reduced to eight days. Others, however, prolong it to 3–6 weeks and administer the suramin concomitantly weekly for eight weeks.[41]

REFERENCES FOR CHAPTER XXI

1. F. W. O'Connor. *Am. J. Roentgenol. Radium Therapy,* 1930, 23: 494–502.
2. S. E. Fernando. *J. Trop. Med. Hyg.,* 1935, 38: 17–18.
3. W. E. F. Winckel et al. *Documenta Med. Geograph. et Trop. Amsterdam,* 1953, 5: 343–346.
4. A. Fain. *Ann. parasitol. humain et comparée,* 1951, 26: 228–244.
5. L. T. Coggeshall. *Ann. N. Y. Acad. Sci.,* 1948, 50: 27–170.
6. H. C. Conn and F. S. Greenslit. *Am. J. Trop. Med. Hyg.,* 1952, 1: 474–476.
7. F. Fülleborn. *Arch. Schiffs- u. Tropenhyg.,* 1914, 18: 232–234.
8. H. de Rook. *South Pacif. Comm., Tech. Paper,* No. 105, Noumea, 1957: 1–19.
9. S. L. Brug. *Proc. Roy. Soc. Med., Sect. Trop. Diseases & Parasit.,* 1931, 24: 23–33.
10. G. W. Hunter and V. G. Warren. *J. Parasitol.,* 1950, 36: 164–168.
11. L. C. Feng and F. Yao. *China Med. J.,* 1935, 49: 61–81.
12. F. Hawking and J. P. Thurston. *Trans. Roy. Soc. Trop. Med. Hyg.,* 1951, 45: 329–340.
13. A. Rowlands. *Trans. Roy. Soc. Trop. Med. Hyg.,* 1956, 50: 563–564.
14. E. C. Faust et al. *Am. J. Trop. Med. Hyg.,* 1952, 1: 239–249.
15. P. Manson. *Proc. Linnean Soc., Zool.,* 1879, 14: 304.
16. S. P. James. *Brit. Med. J.,* 1900 (2nd half): 533–537.
17. W. J. O. M. v. Dijk. *Documenta Trop. & Geograph. Med., Amsterdam,* 1958, 10: 21–33.
18. J. Bonne-Wepster. *Documenta Med. Geograph. et Trop. Amsterdam,* 1956, 8: 375–379.
19. T. C. Backhouse and G. H. M. Heydon. *Trans. Roy. Soc. Trop. Med. Hyg.,* 1950, 44: 291–296.
20. H. de Rook. *Documenta Med. Geograph. et Trop. Amsterdam,* 1957, 9: 197–212.

21. G. Giglioli. *Am. J. Trop. Med.,* 1948, 28: 71–85.
22. F. Hawking. *Bull. World Health Organization,* 1957, 16: 581–592.
23. F. W. O'Connor and H. Beatty. *Trans. Roy. Soc. Trop. Med. Hyg.,* 1936, 30: 190–194.
24. M. O. T. Iyengar. *Parasitology,* 1936, 28: 190–194.
25. C. F. A. Bruyning. *Documenta Med. Geograph. et Trop. Amsterdam,* 1953, 5: 333–338.
26. S. S. Rao and M. O. T. Iyengar. *Indian J. Med. Research,* 1932, 19: 941–943.
27. T. B. Menon and B. Ramamurti. *Indian J. Med. Research,* 1941, 29: 393–401.
28. B. C. Basu and S. S. Rao. *Indian J. Med. Research,* 1939, 27: 233–240.
29. Ph. H. Manson-Bahr. *Trans. Roy. Soc. Trop. Med. Hyg.,* 1955, 49: 127–131.
30. J. F. B. Edeson and R. H. Wharton. *Trans. Roy. Soc. Trop. Med. Hyg.,* 1958, 52: 25–38.
31. J. S. K. Boyd. *Trans. Roy. Soc. Trop. Med. Hyg.,* 1958, 52: 44.
32. T. Wilson et al. *Trans. Roy. Soc. Trop. Med. Hyg.,* 1958, 52: 480–481.
32a. S. L. Brug. *Geneesk. Tijdschr. Ned. Indië,* 1937, 77: 1462–1470, English summary, 1470.
33. P. Jordan. *Trans. Roy. Soc. Trop. Med. Hyg.,* 1952, 46: 207.
34. L. A. Jachowski and G. F. Otto. *Am. J. Hyg.,* 1955, 61: 334–348.
35. J. W. Tesch. *Geneesk. Tijdschr. Ned. Indië,* 1937, 77: 1434–1461, English summary, 1460.
36. I. Guicherit et al. *Documenta Med. Geograph. et Trop. Amsterdam,* 1951, 3: 368–372.
37. H. Galliard. *Bull. World Health Organization,* 1957, 16: 601–608.
38. E. C. Faust, P. F. Russell, and D. R. Lincicome. *Clinical Parasitology,* Philadelphia, 1957, pp. 455, 456, 473, 475, 468, 472.
39. F. M. Meyers and W. Kouwenaar. *Geneesk. Tijdschr. Ned. Indië,* 1939, 79: 853–873, English summary, 873.
40. Ph. H. Hartz. *Documenta Med. Geograph. et Trop. Amsterdam,* 1950, 2: 170–175.
41. Ph. H. Manson-Bahr. *Tropical Diseases,* London, 1957, Cassell & Co., pp. 767, 768, 174, 175, 782.
42. E. G. Nauck. *Lehrbuch der Tropenkrankheiten,* Stuttgart, 1956, pp. 96, 104, 99.
43. L. Nattan Larrier. *Bull. soc. pathol. exotique,* 1911, 4: 710–720.
44. L. Külz. *Arch. Schiffs- u. Tropenhyg.,* 1914, 18: 248–250.
45. R. M. Gordon. *Ann. Trop. Med. Parasitol.,* 1955, 49: 98–105.
46. M. M. J. Lavoirpierre. *Ann. Trop. Med. Parasitol.,* 1958, 52: 103–121.
47. R. M. Gordon et al. *Trans. Roy. Soc. Trop. Med. Hyg.,* 1950, 44: 11–41.
48. H. Ziemann. *Act. Conv. tert. trop. Morb.,* Amsterdam, 1938, 1: 247–276.
49. L. van Boogaert et al. *J. Neurol. Psychiat.,* 1955, 18: 103–119.
50. B. O. L. Duke and D. J. B. Wijers. *Ann. Trop. Med. Parasitol.,* 1958, 52: 158–175.
51. N. A. D. Sharp. *Trans. Roy. Soc. Trop. Med. Hyg.,* 1928, 21: 371–396.
52. E. van der Kuyp. *Documenta Med. Geograph. et Trop. Amsterdam,* 1950, 2: 357–358.
53. E. Brumpt. *Précis de Parasitologie,* Paris, 1949, Masson & Cie.
54. J. J. C. Buckley. *Trans. Roy. Soc. Trop. Med. Hyg.,* 1934, 28: 1.

55. C. F. A. Bruyning. *Documenta Med. Geograph. et Trop. Amsterdam,* 1957, 9: 169–172.

56. O. R. McCoy. *Am. J. Trop. Med.,* 1933, 13: 297–310.

57. F. F. Biagi. *Trop. Diseases Bull.,* 1957, 54: 465–466.

58. M. Chardome and E. Peel. *Ann. soc. belge méd. trop.,* 1949, 29: 99–119.

59. C. Henrard and E. Peel. *Ann. soc. belge méd. trop.,* 1949, 29: 127–143.

60. C. A. Hopkins and W. L. Nicholas. *Ann. Trop. Med. Parasitol.,* 1952, 46: 276–283.

61. B. O. L. Duke. *Ann. Trop. Med. Parasitol.,* 1958, 52: 123–128.

62. C. F. Craig and E. C. Faust. *Clinical Parasitology,* London, 1951, pp. 421–430.

63. D. B. Blacklock. *Ann. Trop. Med. Parasitol.,* 1926, 20: 203–218.

64. R. P. Strong et al. *Onchocerciasis,* 234 pp., Cambridge, Mass., 1934, Harvard Univ. Press; *Am. J. Trop. Med.,* 1938, 18, Suppl. No. 1: 1–136.

65. F. C. Rodgers. *Trans. Roy. Soc. Trop. Med. Hyg.,* 1959, 53: 138–141.

66. M. d'Hooghe. *Ann. soc. belge méd. trop.,* 1935, 15: 159–195.

67. F. Fülleborn. *Kolle and Wassermann, Handbuch pathogener Mikroörganismen,* 1929, 6: 1043–1224.

68. J. J. C. Buckley. *J. Helminthol.,* 1949, 23: 1–24.

69. L. González et al. *Trop. Diseases Bull.,* 1950, 47: 645.

70. M. Wanson. *Ann. soc. belge méd. trop.,* 1950, 30: 667–863.

71. R. Kirk. *Ann. Trop. Med. Parasitol.,* 1947, 41: 357–364.

72. M. S. Israel. *Trans. Roy. Soc. Trop. Med. Hyg.,* 1959, 53: 142–147.

73. J. F. B. Edeson et al. *Trans. Roy. Soc. Trop. Med. Hyg.,* 1960, 54: 229–234.

CHAPTER XXII

NEMATODE INFECTIONS MAN ACQUIRES VIA NONBLOODSUCKING HOSTS

In this chapter two parasites will be discussed, sufficiently well known to be of interest, *Dracunculus* and *Gnathostoma*. The others are mentioned cursorily.

DRACUNCULUS MEDINENSIS: THE GUINEA WORM

Dracunculus medinensis (Linnaeus, 1758) Gallandant, 1773, known as the guinea worm, was formerly counted among the filarias. It differs from them (1) by the larvas being born in an advanced state of development, with an intestinal tract (Fig. 22·1); (2) by their leaving the human body immediately after birth and meeting their intermediate host in free nature. Worms supposed to be identical with the human parasite have been reported in wild and domestic carnivores, horses, bovines, and monkeys.

Fig. 22·1 *Dracunculus medinensis,* uterine larva, × 153. (After Brumpt, 1936. Courtesy, Masson & Cie, Paris.)

The male is imperfectly known, since only one specimen has been collected from the human body. However, it has been observed in experimentally infected dogs.[8a] The length of the female varies from 32 to 120 centimeters, its width from 0.5 to 1.7 mm. The posterior extremity is provided with a hook-shaped appendage. The head bears a cuticular "shield." The mouth is surrounded by eight papillas (Figs. 22·2 and 22·3). The intestine of the gravid female is pushed aside by the voluminous uterus which, at that stage, is full of larvas ready to be born (Fig. 22·4). These larvas measure 500–750 × 15–25 μ; they are characterized by the slender, tapering tail, whose length is nearly one-third of the whole larva (Fig. 22·5).

The connective tissue of the mesentery is probably the place where the worms reach maturity.[1] The fertilized female is supposed first to make its way to the nearest subcutaneous tissue available. Proceeding along that tissue, it ultimately reaches the lower legs. Arrived at that site, the host responds to the presence of the parasite by a cellular reaction which culminates in the formation of a fibrous sheath around the worm,[2] a response which, in its later stages, is accompanied by allergic reactions. These are manifested by a rise in temperature and edema of the face and hands. They are frequently associated with nausea, vomiting, diarrhea, and other symp-

FIG. 22·2 *Dracunculus medinensis*, anterior extremity with papillas, side aspect. (After Leuckart.)

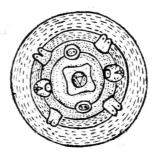

FIG. 22·3 *Dracunculus medinensis*, anterior extremity, frontal aspect. (After Craig and Faust, 1951. Courtesy, Henry Kimpton, London.)

toms and the clinical entity is known as *dracontiasis*. A high eosinophilia is found at this stage. Finally the worm pierces the internal layers of the skin, without, however, touching the epidermis. Nevertheless, the superficial layers of the skin, still covering the head of the worm, become inflamed, and a blister is produced which on rupturing after a few days leaves an ulcer with a minute opening in its bottom through which the head of the worm may occasionally be seen. If the skin around the affected spot is cooled with water, a filament, clear as glass, emerges from the aperture at the bottom of the ulcer. Immediately after its appearance it turns milky white and then ruptures, pouring its contents, a milky fluid, over the bottom of the ulcer. This fluid is a sample of the contents of the uterus; it is milky because of the innumerable larvas suspended in it. The filament, according to Manson, is the distal portion of the uterus evaginated from the worm's body, as a response to the stimulus afforded by the cooling of the skin. There are other explanations to account for the phenomenon, but all agree as to the result; a batch of larvas is evacuated. This evacuation is repeated over and over again, and the whole uterus is emptied after a fortnight or so.

FIG. 22·4   *Dracunculus medinensis,* cross section through gravid female, the uterus full of larvas; to the right, what is left of the intestine. (After Leuckart.)

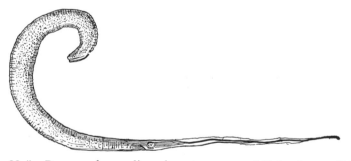

FIG. 22·5   *Dracunculus medinensis,* outer aspect of living larva. (After Leuckart.)

The guinea worm shows a tendency to turn downward on its way through the subcutaneous connective tissue, thereby reaching the surface of the skin of one of the legs in 82 percent of the cases.[3] This must be regarded as an adaptation of vital importance; for the legs are the extremities that get in touch with water, at least in hot countries. The association of the wetting of the skin and the evacuation of the larvas must be seen in the same light, for the larva must get into water, if it is to develop; only in that medium will it have a chance to meet its intermediate host. There are female worms that select another spot to arrive at the surface and to set free their brood; but such exceptions often confirm the rule that they select the spot that offers the larvas the best chance of reaching water. Apparently much depends on the habits of the human host, as was the case with

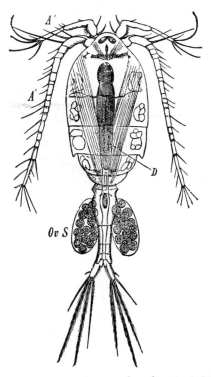

FIG. 22·6   *Cyclops coronatus*, ovigerous female: *A, A,* Two pairs of antennas.—*D*, Intestine.—*OvS*, Egg pouches. (After Brumpt, 1936. Courtesy, Masson & Cie, Paris.)

the worms that preferred the skin of the shoulders and head of their host to that of his legs; for that host was in the habit of carrying leaking water bags on his shoulders, and dripping jars on his head.[4]

Water by itself is not the medium the larvas stand in need of; on the contrary, they die in water after three days.[5] What they need are copepods of the genus *Cyclops*, already known as the first intermediate hosts of *Diphyllobothrium* (Fig. 22·6). The copepod becomes infected by ingesting the larvas [6]; arriving in the lumen of the intestine, the larvas pierce the wall of the bowel and thus arrive in the body cavity of the cyclops, where they are highly motile during the first days.[7] After one week they molt and thereby shrink from 600 to 400 μ. At the end of the second week the caudal extremity is reduced from 70 to 45 μ, but this loss is compensated by an increase in length of the rest of the body.[8] These larvas constitute the final stage of the development in cyclops. They are characterized by a strongly developed nerve ring, a string of brown granules in the posterior half of the body, two lobate appendages at the caudal

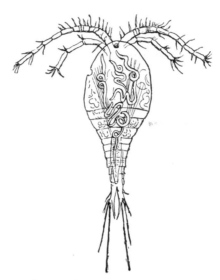

FIG. 22·7   *Dracunculus medinensis,* larvae in body of Cyclops. (After Neumann and Mayer. Courtesy, Lehmann's Verlag, München.)

extremity, and a reduced motility.[9] These larvas do not show any further change (Fig. 22·7) until the moment man ingests infected cyclops by drinking grossly contaminated water. Then the copepods are killed by his gastric juice, but the larvas regain their activity. They pierce the body wall of their intermediate host and lodge in the lumen of the human intestinal tract.

What happens next is imperfectly known, except for the final result, set forth clearly by Powell's [10] observation, which has the value of an experiment. A hunting party from Bombay composed of sixteen Europeans and five servants passed two days in an area where half the population were carrying gravid dracunculus. They admitted having drunk unfiltered water. After a period varying from 345 to 435 days, an average of about one year, seven of the Europeans and one servant produced together nineteen worms.

This "experiment" shows that a person who ingests mature larvas in the course of a certain year, produces a brood of fresh larvas during the same season of the succeeding year. That season ought to be excessively dry [11]; for dracunculus needs an environment allowing the production of fresh broods of larvas at a moment when man's fastidiousness in the choice of water and the quantity of that commodity available have both been reduced to a minimum.

Tropical countries with moderately dry seasons do not fulfil this condition. Western Indonesia is an example of this kind, where dracunculus has been imported uninterruptedly in the course of many years, where there is no lack of appropriate intermediate hosts, and where the transmission to definitive hosts, anthropoid apes, has been successfully carried out.[9] But there undoubtedly indigenous cases have never been detected.[7] Surinam is another such region; in the past, dracontiasis was common enough among the slaves on the sugar plantations; it was kept up by constant importation from West Africa. But unlike schistosomiasis, it never succeeded in getting a foothold in the country, and thus it disappeared with the slave trade.

Among the regions where dracunculus is flourishing, some are excessively dry at certain seasons, such as Arabia, Asia Minor, Iran, Turkistan, the Deccan and Rajputana (India), and West Africa. However, around Lake Chad (central Africa) the period of infection coincides with the rainy season because it is then that the people use the readily contaminated pools, whereas in the dry season they use deep wells which are naturally protected from contamination.[5] In regions where even the rainy season does not materially relieve the drought, the period of infection coincides with the hot season.[3]

In the heavily infected Deccan (India), infections are as common in adults up to the age of 35 as in children. In adults 35 to 55 years of age the rate of infection drops to one-third and in those over 55 years of age to one-tenth of the standard set by children and younger adults. Thus it would seem that some resistance to infection develops with advancing age.[3]

The pathogenic activity directly exercised by dracunculus is limited to the allergic reaction of the host before the worm makes its appearance at the surface of the skin and to the ulcer associated with this appearance. Indirectly, the pathogenic effect may be of greater importance, viz. an invasion of pyogenic cocci as the result of the parasite being ruptured during an injudicious attempt to remove it from its subcutaneous hiding place. Popular medicine long ago invented a method to prevent the rupturing—extracting the worm very slowly, each day one turn of the little stick around which the whole worm is gradually wound (Fig. 22·8).

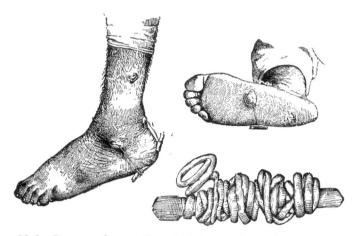

Fig. 22·8 *Dracunculus medinensis* being extirpated from the human foot by the popular method of winding it around a little stick. *Below,* the whole worm wound around the stick. (After Brumpt, 1936. Courtesy, Masson & Cie, Paris.)

Cyclops, the intermediate host, appears to suffer more than man—at least the Nigerian representative of the genus does so, *Themocyclops nigeriensis,* for it dies within two days after a heavy infection. The larvas in its body also die long before they could reach maturity; for it takes them a fortnight to attain the final stage of development. So cyclops has to survive the infection for at least two weeks if it is to be an efficient intermediate host. It can do so only if it has ingested no more than a few larvas. Even if that requirement has been met, infected cyclops are so enfeebled after a fortnight that they are unable to rise more than 10 cm above the bottom of the pool in which they are living. However, they have no occasion to, since in the dry season the pool is hardly likely to reach that depth.[12] Inefficient cyclops are also known in the life cycle of *Diphyllobothrium,* but they are not the rule; maybe themocyclops is not the rule either.

TREATMENT OF DRACONTIASIS. At present no generally accepted chemotherapy is known.

GNATHOSTOMA SPINIGERUM

The normal definitive hosts of *Gnathostoma spinigerum* Owen, 1838, are dogs, cats, and various wild carnivores in south and east Asia. The worms live in tumors within the wall of the stomach of these animals.

The main characteristic of the adults is a swollen anterior extremity, the *head bulb,* that carries eight rings of hooklets; another is the stumpy form of the worm, the males measuring 10–25 × 1–2 mm, the females 9–31 × 1–2.5 mm; a third is the presence of denticulate scales over two-thirds of the body. The male possesses four pairs of large pedunculate caudal papillas and two or more pairs of small sessile ones; moreover, a spicule of 1–2.6 mm and one of 0.4–0.8 mm. In the female, the vulva is situated at 4–8 mm from the posterior end. The nonembryonated eggs measure 65–70 × 38–40 μ; they are transparent, their shell is superficially pitted and closed at one pole with a plug (Fig. 22·9).

The eggs are passed in water and the larvas hatch after 20 days. They penetrate certain species of the genus *Cyclops,* in whose body cavity they undergo a further development. Within a period of 10 days or a fortnight they grow to larvas that already possess a head bulb.[13] These copepods are devoured by various fresh-water fishes of the genus *Clarias, Ophiocephalus,* and *Glossogobius.* If infected copepods are among them, the gnathostoma larvas become encapsulated in the muscles of the fish, which thus function as second intermediate hosts. The larvas they harbor are in the third stage of development.

In Japan, one of the countries in which gnathostomes occur, various other animals may serve as second intermediate hosts, such as frogs, grass snakes, black-eared kites, and pigs. They become infected, either by swallowing infected cyclops or by devouring a second intermediate host, e.g. pigs fed with offal of fish. In the last case the third-stage larvas, which had been encapsulated in the muscles of the fish, are encapsulated anew in the muscles of the pig, without any further advance in their development. Following the terminology used in describing the life cycle of *Diphyllobothrium* or

Sparganum, this passage from one second intermediate host to another may be called *re-encapsulation.*

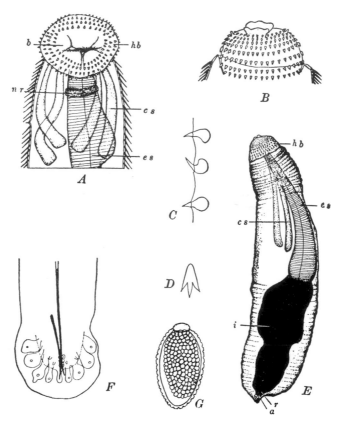

Fig. 22·9   *Gnathostoma spinigerum. A,* Anterior portion of immature worm ventral, × 100.—*hb,* Head bulb with four rings of hooklets.—*cs,* Salivary glands.—*nr,* Nerve ring.—*es,* Esophagus.—*B,* Head bulb of mature worm, lateral view, with eight rings of hooklets, × 100.—*C,* Cephalic hooklets.—*D,* Body spine, at higher magnification.—*E,* Immature worm, lateral view, × 40: *hb,* Head bulb.—*es,* Esophagus.—*cs,* Salivary glands. —*i,* Gut.—*r,* Rectum.—*a,* Anus.—*F,* Posterior portion of male, ventral side, with papillas and spicules, × 40.—*G,* Egg in feces of cat, × 333. (After Craig and Faust, 1951. Courtesy, Henry Kimpton, London.)

If a definitive host, such as a cat or a dog, devours a second intermediate host, the following events occur. The third-stage larvas pierce the wall of its stomach or duodenum. Thereupon they make their way to the liver, various muscles, or connective tissue, but without becoming encapsulated in any of them. In these surroundings the gnathostomes resume their course of development till they approach maturity. At that stage they return to the wall of the stomach or other parts of the intestinal tract. By their presence they stimulate the surrounding tissue to proliferative activity, resulting in the formation of small tumors, each containing several worms of both sexes. Finally the females are fertilized, and eggs are deposited, an event which becomes apparent by the passage of eggs in the feces of the dog or the cat, 148 to 195 days after the infecting meal.[14]

In the life cycle of gnathostoma, man is neither a second intermediate nor a definitive host. If man consumes raw fish with encapsulated third-stage larvas, the parasites fail to re-encapsulate in his muscles, as they would do in the second intermediate host; but they also fail to return to the tissue of the intestinal wall, as they would do in the definitive host. Instead of this, they keep on wandering aimlessly through the subcutaneous connective tissue (sometimes the eye, the omentum, or the lung [15]), thereby causing eruptions that continuously change their site ("creeping eruption") or a migrating edema known in China as "Yangtze edema." [16] During its wandering through the human body, the young worm may almost reach maturity, with a head bulb carrying eight rings of hooklets and a far advanced sexual differentiation [17]; but eggs are never evacuated from the human body, which thus is shown to be a dead-end host.

Human infections with gnathostoma have been observed in Bengal, the Malay Peninsula, Indochina, China, Japan, the Philippines, and Indonesia,[18] but nowhere in such numbers as in Thailand, where 34 cases were reported between 1889 and 1947, 31 of them in women.[17]

In the state of Georgia (U.S.A.) adult gnathostomes have been recovered from stomach tumors of a raccoon, and larvas from the peritoneum of an aquatic moccasin snake. Human infection has not yet been recorded.[18a]

According to Daengsvang [17] there exists no chemotherapy effective against the infection.

OTHER ARTHROPOD–BORNE NEMATODES

(1) *Dioctophyma renale* (Goeze, 1782) Stiles, 1901, is one of the largest of parasitic nematodes; the male measures 140–450 × 4–6

mm, the female 200–1000 × 5–12 mm. Alive its color is red. It inhabits the renal pelvis of fish-eating carnivores, dogs particularly, and occasionally of horses and cattle. Often the worm finds its way to the peritoneum, after having caused extensive destruction in the kidney; but in dogs it has also been found in that site without involvement of the kidneys. This, probably, represents the normal parasitism.[19]

The male is characterized by the muscular oval bursa not supported by rays, and a single spicule of 5–6 mm. The female has a vulva situated 14–75 mm from the anterior extremity; it possesses a single uterus.

Nonembryonated eggs are passed in the urine. They are brownish yellow and broadly spindle-shaped and measure 64–68 × 40–44 μ. The shell is very thick; its surface is pitted, except at the poles, where it is smooth. Outside the host they become embryonated after a lapse of six weeks. They then contain a larva of 240 × 14 μ. According to A. E. Woodhead [20] the larvas hatch when the eggs have been ingested by a certain species of leech. In this first intermediate host the larvas grow and become encapsulated. When the leech is devoured by a second intermediate host, certain species of freshwater fishes, it is again encapsulated. Within the capsule it becomes a third-stage and subsequently a fourth-stage larva, which is infective to carnivores that devour the fish raw. But if this event does not occur at the right moment, the infective larva may reach a "preadult" stage in the second intermediate host. The development is completed in the course of two years.

In mammals the parasite has been found in Europe, America, and Asia. As to human infection, Vuathier, in 1933,[21] listed ten cases and added an eleventh fatal case. Since then a twelfth has been reported.[22] No chemotherapeutic treatment is known.[20]

(2) *Gongylonema pulchrum* Molin, 1857, usually inhabits the mucosa of the esophagus of sheep, goats, cattle and pigs. In man it has been found in tunnels and cavities of the mucosa and submucosa of the mouth, from which the worms could be extracted. In man they may become almost 6 cm long; in their natural host they may grow to more than double that size.

The worms are characterized (Fig. 22·10) by the anterior end being covered with bosses arranged in eight longitudinal rows. The eggs have also been recovered from cases of human infection; they measure 50–70 × 25–37 μ; they have a fairly thick, transparent shell, and they are embryonated.[23]

The intermediate hosts, cockroaches and coprophagous beetles, ingest the eggs. The larvas hatch in their intestine and become encapsulated in the body cavity.[24] The definitive host is supposed to acquire the infection by devouring the insect or drinking water contaminated with larvas previously liberated by the death of the insect.

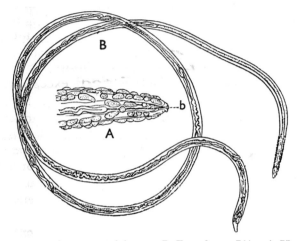

FIG. 22·10   *Gongylonema pulchrum*. B, Female, × 7½.—A, Head showing cuticular bosses.—b, Mouth. (After Brumpt, 1922. Courtesy, Masson & Cie, Paris.)

Faust et al.[20] listed 18 cases of human infection, viz., 6 from Europe, 9 from the United States, 1 from Ceylon, and 2 from China.

(3) *Physaloptera caucasica* von Linstow, 1902 (*Ph. mordens*, Leiper, 1907), originally recorded from man in the Caucasus, is far from rare in the indigenous population of central Africa [30] and in African monkeys. The worms parasitize the esophagus, the stomach, and the jejunum with their heads buried in the mucosa. The male measures 14–34 × 0.7–1 mm, the female 22–100 × 1–2.8 mm. Thus they resemble young ascarids, from which they may be distinguished by their possessing two lips, each provided with dental processes. Moreover, the male carries two conspicuous caudal alas, four pairs of long pedunculate papillas, besides a number of sessile papillas and two spicules, one of 3–5.5 mm, the other of 0.5 mm. The eggs

measure 45–62 × 32–45 mm; they have a thick smooth shell and are embryonated when passed in the feces.

Nothing is known of its life cycle outside the definitive host. The larvas of a related species, *P. maxillaris,* not recorded in man, develop in cockroaches.[25]

Faust et al.[20] suggest that carbon tetrachloride or tetrachlorethylene might be effective in eliminating the parasite.

(4) *Thelazia callipaeda* Railliet and Henry, 1910, is whitish, threadlike, the males measuring 4–13 × 0.2–0.7 mm, the females 6–17 × 0.3–0.8 mm. The cuticle is composed of rings which overlap one another; thus the contour of the worm is serrate.[26] The mouth is surrounded by a thick, barrel-shaped ring, which forms a shallow cavity provided with an inner ring of six papillas and an outer ring of four pairs of papillas.[27]

When deposited, the eggs are embryonated; their size is 54–60 × 34–37 μ, and their shell is thin. In water the egg becomes greatly distended; the greater part of its inside is empty and keeps the egg floating, the larva of 400 × 13 μ having retired to a separate compartment.[28] It is regarded as certain that the embryonated egg is not infective, but the subsequent fate of the larva contained within its shell is unknown. Supposing it is the same as that of its relative, *Oxyspirura parvovum,* parasitizing the eyes of chickens, cockroaches serve as intermediate hosts.

According to Lee and Parmelee[29] thelazia frequently occurs on the conjunctiva of dogs, rabbits, and deer and has been reported nine times parasitizing man in Asia (predominantly in China) under the name of *Th. callipaeda,* and three times in North America (to which they add three more cases) under the name of *Th. californiensis.* The worms glide across the surface of the conjunctiva, and not under it, with a serpentine movement, causing lachrymation, conjunctivitis, corneal scarring, opacity, and occasionally blindness. The worms can readily be removed with an eye forceps after the conjunctiva is anesthetized by the instillation of 1 percent cocaine solution.

(5) *Eustoma rotundatum* Rudolphi, 1819, is a species not systematically related to the worms mentioned in this chapter. They belong to the superfamily of the Spiruroidea, whereas *E. rotundatum* is an ascaroid. The species is listed here because it passes its adult life in the bowels of definitive hosts (marine predaceous fishes, probably rays and sharks) and its larval life in the peritoneum of inter-

mediate hosts (various marine fishes, such as herrings). If the intermediate host is devoured by another species of fish acting as intermediate host, the larvas contained in the first pierce the stomach
wall of the second and become settled in the peritoneal cavity. If
man ingests the larvas by consuming uncooked infected herrings,
the parasite behaves abnormally by penetrating, but not piercing,
the wall of the distal or middle portion of the ileum, occasionally
the jejunum. The intestinal tissue of the host responds abnormally
by producing a phlegmonous infiltration composed exclusively of
eosinophilic leukocytes, at the site of penetration. This is associated
with intestinal obstruction that requires immediate surgical intervention, the result of which is rendered doubtful because the sutures
passing through the eosinophilic infiltrate show a tendency to cut
through the tissue. The larvas have a length of 2 cm or so; the
cuticle shows transverse striations. The head has three lips, a large
one and two smaller ones; the large lip has two large papillas; the
smaller lips have one large and one small papilla each; one of the
lips carries a toothlike structure; interlabia are absent; the constric-
tion behind the lips is shallow. At their posterior extremity some
larvas carry a conical cuticular excrescence, or *mucron,* devoid of
spines. There is no intestinal cecum or esophageal appendix, although a conspicuous "renette cell," or excretory organ, may masquerade as such. Between the esophagus and the midgut lies a
conspicuous glandular proventriculus, whose length is two-fifths of
the esophagus. The excretory pore is situated at the level of the
periesophageal ganglion.[31]

REFERENCES FOR CHAPTER XXII

1. R. E. MacConell. *J. Trop. Med. Hyg.,* 1914, 17: 337–340.
2. N. Hamilton Fairley and W. Liston. *Indian J. Med. Research,* 1924, 11: 915–932.
3. K. Lindberg. *Bull. soc. pathol. exotique,* 1946, 39: 318–328; 1948, 41: 282–293.
4. V. Harrington. *Brit. Med. J.,* 1891 (1st half): 146.
5. E. Roubaud. *Bull. soc. pathol. exotique,* 1913, 6: 281–289.
6. V. N. Moorthy. *Trop. Diseases Bull.,* 1933, 30: 230.
7. M. Marjitno and W. Essed. *Mededeel. Dienst Volksgezondheid Ned.-Indië,* 1938, 27: 141–146; English ed.
8. V. N. Moorthy. *Am. J. Hyg.,* 1938, 27: 437–460.
8a. V. N. Moorthy and W. C. Sweet. *Indian Med. Gaz.,* 1936, 71: 437–442.
9. S. L. Brug. *Mededeel. Dienst Volksgezondheid Ned.-Indië,* 1930, 19: 162–167; English ed.

10. A. POWELL. *Brit. Med. J.,* 1904 (1st half): 73.
11. R. T. LEIPER. *J. Trop. Med. Hyg.,* 1911, 14: 211–212.
12. S. D. ONABAMIRO. *W. African Med. J.,* 1954, 3: 180–194.
13. S. DAENGSVANG and P. TANSURAT. *Ann. Trop. Med. Parasitol.,* 1938, 32: 137–140.
14. T. IRIE. *Trop. Diseases Bull.,* 1959, 56: 343.
15. B. PRIJYANONDA. *Ann. Trop. Med. Parasitol.,* 1955, 49: 121–122.
16. Y. KOMIYA and S. KONDO. *Trop. Diseases Bull.,* 1952, 49: 1058–1059.
17. S. DAENGSVANG. *J. Parasitol.,* 1949, 35: 116–121.
18. LIE KIAN JOE. *Documenta Med. Geograph. et Trop. Amsterdam,* 1949, 1: 75–80.
18a. B. B. BARBERO and J. R. SHEPPERSON. *Proc. Helminthol. Soc.,* Washington, D. C., 1959, 26: 53–54.
19. G. B. WISLOCKI. *J. Parasitol.,* 1919, 6: 94–97.
20. E. C. FAUST, P. F. RUSSELL, and D. R. LINCICOME. *Clinical Parasitology,* Philadelphia, 1957, pp. 347, 348, 433, 439.
21. N. VUATHIER. *Presse méd.,* 1933 (1st half): 356.
22. A. LISBOA. *Trop. Diseases Bull.,* 1945, 42: 817.
23. E. C. FAUST and W. H. MARTINEZ. *J. Parasitol.,* 1935, 21: 335.
24. H. A. BAYLIS. *J. Trop. Med. Hyg.,* 1925, 28: 413–419; 1926, 29: 194, 346.
25. M. HOBMAIER. *J. Parasitol.,* 1941, 27: 233–235.
26. E. C. FAUST. *Trans. Roy. Soc. Trop. Med. Hyg.,* 1927, 20: 365–369.
27. H. F. HSÜ. *Arch. Schiffs- u. Tropenhyg.,* 1933, 37: 363–369.
28. E. C. FAUST. *J. Parasitol.,* 1928, 15: 75–86.
29. R. D. LEE and W. E. PARMELEE. *Am. J. Trop. Med. Hyg.,* 1958, 7: 427–428.
30. R. T. LEIPER. *J. Trop. Med.,* 1911, 14: 209–211.
31. P. H. VAN THIEL et al. *Trop. geogr. Med.,* Amsterdam, 1960, 12: 97–114.

PART FIVE

Arthropods

CHAPTER XXIII

ARTHROPODS: LINGUATULIDS

The arthropods are characterized by the possession of a rigid exoskeleton, segmented into a number of segments or "somites"; jointed limbs, metamerically repeated, some of which act as jaws; and a modified body cavity, the hemocele.

Arthropods parasitizing man belong to three groups:

(1) The *linguatulids* of obscure affinity and systematic position.

(2) The *Acarina* or *mites,* with four pairs of legs, two pairs of mouth parts, no antennas, and fused body segments.

(3) The *insects,* with three pairs of legs, three pairs of jaws, one pair of antennas, usually two pairs of wings, and a body composed of three parts, head, thorax and abdomen, the first and the second (usually) with fused segments, the third with separate segments.

The definition of "parasite," mentioned in Chapter I, i.e. an animal dependent on man for its dwelling, nutrition, and multiplication, will be applied to the arthropods. It excludes bloodsucking arthropods dependent on man for their nutrition only. However, the discussion will include certain bloodsucking arthropods, collectively called "house vermin," that depend on man's "anatomical" body for their food, but on man's "social" body, i.e. his clothes or his house, for dwelling space and multiplication, as distinct from "body vermin" that depend on man's "anatomical" body for the three functions. Arthropods will also be included that are parasites during a single stage of their development.

LINGUATULIDS OR TONGUE WORMS (PENTASTOMIDA)

Some authors [1] hold that there are undeniable affinities between the Linguatulida and the Acarina, but others reject this opinion. In consideration of the second point of view, the two groups will be discussed in separate chapters.

The linguatulids are polyxenous endoparasites that feed on the body of the host. Their surface shows very conspicuous rings which are not true segments. Legs are absent in the adult. The mouth is flanked by two pairs of claws; each claw can be retracted into a pouch.[1] The anus is situated at the posterior extremity, the vulva anterior to it, and the male aperture near the anterior extremity, both on the ventral side. The ovary lies dorsally from the gut, extending lengthwise over the greater part of the body; anteriorly it splits into two oviducts that embrace the gut, and fuse into a common duct, the uterovagina, on the ventral side. The uterovagina runs backwards and opens into the vulva; in young females it is straight, in gravid females greatly convoluted, embracing the gut with its coils. The eggs have three shells; the inner and middle shell touch each other; between the middle and outer shell there is a space filled with fluid. Within the shell lies a larva with four short limbs, each with a pair of minute claws at its apex.

The linguatulids parasitizing man belong to the genera *Linguatula*, with a dorsoventrally flattened body, and *Armillifer (Nettorhynchus)*, with a cylindrical body showing transverse annular swellings.

LINGUATULA SERRATA

The one species of Linguatula parasitizing man is *Linguatula serrata* Fröhlich, 1789. The adults of this cosmopolitan parasite occupy the nasal cavity of dogs, wolves, foxes, horses, and goats, adhering to the middle concha or the lamina cribrosa. In this position it has been found in man on rare occasions, in India, Italy, and Holland. As a mature larva or nymph, it lives in various viscera of intermediate hosts: rodents, horses, donkeys, cattle, goats, sheep, and pigs; and not infrequently in man.

The adult, when still fresh, has a yellow color. It is spatulate; the anterior half is wide, the posterior half, narrow. Dorsally, in the midline, the body carries a longitudinal crease. The triangular anterior extremity, the "cephalothorax," is smooth; on its ventral side it carries a quadrangular mouth, flanked by the inner pair of claws; the outer pair lies slightly farther backwards. The remainder of the body, the "abdomen," is composed of about 80 "rings" (Fig. 23·1).

The females have a length of 8–13 cm; their maximal width is 8–10 mm, posteriorly tapering to 2 mm. In the males the measurements are 1.8–2 cm, 3–4 cm, and 0.5 mm respectively. The eggs are passed in the nasal mucus;[2] they are yellowish and measure 90 × 70 μ, not counting the outer shell, whose diameter is 200 μ. The

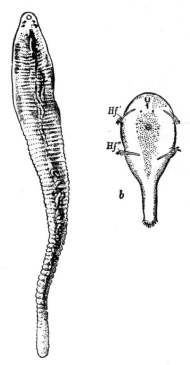

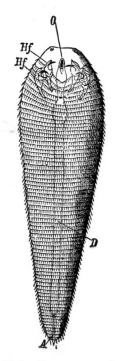

FIG. 23·1 *Linguatula serrata,* natural size: *b,* Newly hatched larva, × 200.—*Hf¹, Hf²,* Anterior and posterior pair of limbs. (After Brumpt, 1922. Courtesy, Masson & Cie, Paris.)

FIG. 23·2 *Pentastoma denticulatum,* larva of *Linguatula serrata,* in intermediate host, × 20: *O,* Mouth.—*Hf,* Two pairs of claws.—*D,* Intestine.—*A,* Anus. (After Brumpt, 1922. Courtesy, Masson & Cie, Paris.)

larva, within the inner shell, measures 90 μ; each one of its four rudimentary "legs" bears a pair of claws; its tail has a blunt ending that carries a number of minute spines (Fig. 23·1:*b*).

The intermediate host acquires its infection by ingesting the eggs. From seven to nine months later the larvas may be detected in various internal organs. During that time they have grown to a size of 4–6.5 × 0.8–1.5 mm[3] (Fig. 23·2), known as *Pentastoma dentic-*

ulatum. They are like miniature adults except for the lack of a tapering tail and the presence of a row of minute spines on every abdominal ring.

The pentastomes, measuring from 2 to 3 mm and bent in the form of a U, are enclosed within thick fibrous capsules produced by the cellular activity of the host's tissues. Thus encapsulated, they

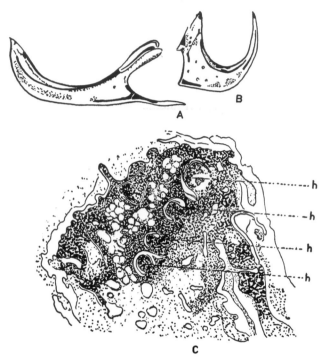

Fig. 23·3 *Pentastoma denticulatum,* larva of *Linguatula serrata,* in human lung: *A,* Claw.—*B,* Sheath of claw, isolated and cleared, × 300. —*C,* Histological section showing cross sections through the four claws (*h*), × 90. (After Straub, 1936. Courtesy, *Nederlandsch Tijdschrift voor Geneeskunde.*)

occur in various organs in the thorax or the abdomen. It is generally supposed that they cannot leave this site unless the intermediate host is devoured by a dog or another carnivorous definitive host. In that case the pentastomes are said to escape from the capsule when they are still in the dog's mouth and to proceed directly to the nasal cavity. There they shed their skin, becoming young adults that grow to sexual maturity and, six months after infection, initiate the production of eggs. However, the pentastomes may also escape from the living intermediate host; man is not a dead-end host, for he has been observed to discharge numbers of pentastomes by coughing or sneezing and to continue to do so for some weeks.[4]

The fibrous capsules containing pentastomes are often found in the human body during autopsies.[5] They do not cause any apparent damage, but they are important as a cause of error if they are diagnosed as tuberculous lesions.[6] In Amsterdam, Straub[5] found the lung infected in 56 out of 211 autopsies. The percentage of infection increased with the age of the subjects; from 4 percent in persons under 20 years of age to 44 percent in persons aged 60 and over. The majority harbored no more than one or two encapsulated parasites, three subjects only carried seven or eight parasites.

If the investigator does not succeed in extracting the pentastome from its capsule, it may be identified in fixed and stained histological sections by the spines on the rings and particularly by the claws on the cephalothorax, which remain unchanged even if the pentastome has been mutilated beyond recognition by the process of calcification (Fig. 23·3).

In other countries encapsulated pentastomes have often been encountered in the human body, although not so frequently as in Amsterdam. Moreover, the capsules were found in different sites, in the liver, the intestinal wall, the prostatic gland,[7] and in the anterior chamber of the eye.[15]

ARMILLIFER

Two species of this genus parasitize man. Unlike *Linguatula,* man never serves as definitive host, only as intermediate host of the larval stage, known as *porocephalus.* Armillifer, moreover, is not cosmopolitan, but limited to the tropics, of Asia in one species, of Africa in the other.

ARMILLIFER MONILIFORMIS

The adults of *Armillifer moniliformis* Diesing, 1835, inhabit the lungs of large snakes of the genus *Python* in southeastern Asia, from India to China south of the river Yangtze. As porocephalus they live in monkeys and various carnivores of the same area. In man they have rarely been reported.[8]

The female measures 70–91 × 4–7 mm, the male 25 × 2–5 mm as a maximum. The body is cylindrical, tapering posteriorly. Except for the cephalothorax, the segments are almost spherical; thus the animal looks like a string of beads. They vary in number from 28 to 30 in the female; in the male there are about 26 of them.[1] The unsegmented cephalothorax is wedge-shaped, the dorsal side convex, the ventral side flat. On that side lies the oral aperture, marked by a chitinous ring and flanked by two pairs of amber-colored claws 1 mm in length. The anus is situated at the posterior extremity of the terminal, obtusely conical segment, the vulva on the ventral side of that segment, and the male aperture on the ventral side of the first segment behind the cephalothorax. The eggs measure 108 × 80 μ, not including the outer shell that has a diameter of 144 μ. The intraovular larva measures 92 × 72 μ; its tail, 50 μ long, terminates in two spines; each of the four legs bears two claws of 10 μ length.

The eggs are probably passed in the snake's sputum. If monkeys are made to ingest them, larvas are found two months later on the omentum and in the mesenteric glands. They are bean-shaped, measure 300–400 by 220 μ, and are enveloped within a fibrous capsule. Eight months after the infecting meal they have reached the porocephalus stage on the omentum, the outer surface of the stomach, the intestines, the spleen, the kidneys, and within the lungs and the testes. Within the fibrous capsule the porocephalus lies coiled; it has a length of 4.5–5 mm; it possesses the beadlike segment of the adult and by its spiral curve resembles an Ammon's horn.[9]

If a snake ingests organs containing porocephali, the latter are liberated in the stomach. They pierce the stomach wall within the next 24 hours; after 4 to 23 days they reach the connective tissue in the vicinity of the lung, and after a month they are scttled inside the lung.[9]

ARMILLIFER ARMILLATUS

The adults of *Armillifer armillatus* Wyman, 1847, inhabit the lungs of snakes of the genera *Python* and *Bitis* in tropical Africa; the porocephalus stage lives in monkeys, carnivores, rodents, antelopes, and giraffes of the same region and frequently in man.

The adult differs from *A. moniliformis* by the fact that only the distal portion of each segment is swollen; thus the animal looks like a rod, carrying about 23 thick rings at some distance one from another (Fig. 23·4). In all other aspects the two species greatly resemble each other.

If an intermediate host ingests the eggs passed in the sputum of the snake, the larvas hatch in the small intestine. They penetrate the tissue of the intestinal wall and enter the blood vessels, or they pierce the wall and reach the peritoneal cavity. In this way they reach various viscera, in or on which they develop to the porocephalus stage, which resembles the same stage in *A. moniliformis*.

Fig. 23·4 *Armillifer armillatus,* natural size. (After Sambon, 1922. Courtesy, *Journal of Tropical Medicine and Hygiene.*)

If a python ingests organs containing porocephalus, the latter is liberated in the intestine of the snake. It pierces the intestinal wall and all other organs it meets on the way leading to its destination, the lungs, which it reaches within three days, and where it attains sexual maturity after a little over ten weeks.[10]

Human infection with the African porocephalus is much more common than with its Asiatic counterpart. Autopsies in west and central Africa revealed its presence in 8 to 22 percent of the subjects. Armillate porocephalus has been detected in the lung, the liver, the peritoneal cavity and the wall of the bowel.[11] Findings in the conjunctiva of the eye,[12] and roentgenological detection of calcified porocephali[13] have enabled investigators to observe porocephali in living subjects. Apparently, the parasite is not in the habit of causing much damage; occasionally, however, it is made responsible for serious morbid conditions affecting the intestinal tract and the biliary ducts.[14]

REFERENCES FOR CHAPTER XXIII

1. L. W. SAMBON. *J. Trop. Med. Hyg.,* 1922, 25: 188–206.
2. A. and M. HOBMAIER. *Am. J. Trop. Med.,* 1940, 20: 199–210.
3. E. C. FAUST. *Am. J. Trop. Med.,* 1927, 7: 314–317.

4. A. M. PAPADAKIS and A. N. HOURMOUZIADIS. *Trans. Roy. Soc. Trop. Med. Hyg.*, 1958, 52: 454–455.

5. M. STRAUB. *Ned. Tijdschr. Geneesk.*, 1936, 80: 1468–1471, English summary, 1471.

6. H. LAENGNER. *Centr. Bakteriol.*, Abt. I, Or., 1906, 40: 368–371.

7. W. ST. C. SYMMERS. *J. Pathol. Bacteriol.*, 1957, 73: 549–555.

8. A. SALM. *Geneesk. Tijdschr. Ned.-Indië*, 1907, 47: 11–13, English summary, 13.

9. F. FÜLLEBORN. *Beih. Arch. Schiffs- u. Tropenhyg.*, 1919, 23: 5–36.

10. A. BRODEN and J. RODHAIN. *Ann. Trop. Med. Parasitol.*, 1908, 1: 493–504; 1909, 2: 303–313; 1910, 4: 167–176.

11. J. RODHAIN and P. DECOSTER. *Ann. soc. belge méd. trop.*, 1951, 31: 331–335.

12. S. GRATAMA and P. H. VAN THIEL. *Documenta Med. Geograph. et Trop. Amsterdam*, 1957, 9: 374–376.

13. G. M. ARDRAN. *Brit. J. Radiol.*, 1948, 21: 342–345.

14. L. BOUCKAERT and A. FAIN. *Ann. soc. belge méd. trop.*, 1959, 39: 793–797.

15. W. HUNTER and R. P. HIGGINS *J. Parasitol.*, 1960, 46: 68.

CHAPTER XXIV

ACARINA: TICKS AND MITES

The Acarina form a subgroup of the spiderlike arthropods or arachnids, characterized (1) by the body being divided in two regions, the anterior *cephalothorax* and the posterior *abdomen,* which may fuse into one; (2) by the six pairs of appendages to the cephalothorax, viz. two pairs of mouth parts, the *cheliceras* and the *pedipalps,* and four pairs of legs. The arachnids take in the atmospheric air through (*a*) the so-called lungs, (*b*) air tubes closely resembling the *tracheas* of insects, and (*c*) the skin.

The acarids are small animals; as a rule their cephalothorax and abdomen are not, or are hardly, separate. Their mouth parts serve the purpose of piercing and sucking, their legs of locomotion and the grasping of objects. The skin has a chitinous cuticle; separate segments are rarely visible. From the mouth the intestinal tract takes a straight course to the anus, situated terminally or sub-terminally. Respiratory organs are either absent or they consist of two bundles of tracheas which take in the air through two air holes or *spiracles.* The eyes, if present, are simple. The sexes are separate, the males often smaller than the females. The male organs consist of one or more pairs of testes, whose vasa deferentia join into a single common duct. The female organs consist of two ovaries, whose oviducts open into the uterus. The female aperture usually lies in front of and at some distance from the anus. Sometimes the aperture for copulation is separate from that serving oviposition. As a rule acarids lay eggs. The emerging larva possesses only three pairs of legs. The stage emerging from the first molt has four pairs, but several molts have to be passed to attain sexual maturity.

The acarids to be mentioned here belong to a number of super-families, which, according to Matheson,[1] can be listed as follows.

(1) Posterior to the legs the body is much elongated; parasites inhabiting the hair follicles or the sebaceous glands ........DEMODICOIDEA
The body is oval or elliptical in shape, parasites inhabiting other parts of the host's body ....(2)

(2) Tracheas are present ....(3)

Tracheas are absent ....(6)

(3) A pair of spiracles, surrounded by a conspicuous spiracular plate or *peritreme,* are situated near the third or fourth pair of coxas ....(4)

Spiracles are located elsewhere, not surrounded by a conspicuous peritreme ....(5)

(4) Large hypostome, carrying numerous hooklets; peritremes adjoin the fourth pair of coxas ....IXODOIDEA

Small, unarmed hypostome; peritremes adjoin the third pair of coxas ....PARASITOIDEA

(5) Spiracles adjoin the base of the cheliceras .........TROMBIDOIDEA

Spiracles adjoin the base of the pedipalps .........TARSONEMOIDEA

(6) The surface of the body is marked by a fine striation of parallel lines; tarsi are provided with pedunculate ambulacra; parasites
SARCOPTOIDEA

No such markings are present on the surface of the body; tarsi are devoid of pedunculate ambulacra; not parasites ..TYROGLYPHOIDEA

The predaceous members of the Tyroglyphoidea and Tarsonem-oidea must be excluded from further consideration, as none of them depend on man's body for a dwelling place, nutrition, and multi-plication. Nevertheless, they may cause serious discomfort in the form of itching dermal eruptions and gastrointestinal or broncho-

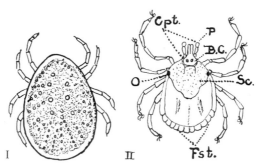

FIG. 24·1   I. An argasid tick (*Argas,* female).—II. An ixodid tick (*Amblyomma,* female): *Cpt,* Capitulum.—*P,* Palp.—*BC,* Base of capitulum. —*Sc,* Scutum.—*O,* Eye.—*Fst,* Festoons. (After Nuttall and Warburton. Courtesy, Cambridge University Press.)

pulmonary symptoms if man gets into close touch with them. That may easily happen, for stores of vegetable or animal foodstuffs are often infested by members of the Tyroglyphoidea, such as flour by *Aleurobius,* dried fruit by *Carpoglyphus,* sugar by *Glyciphagus,* and old cheese by *Tyroglyphus* (*Tyrophagus*); and workers in grain warehouses, and broom factories have been attacked by *Pediculoides, Tarsonemus,* and *Cheyletus,* members of the Tarsonemoidea. Actual epidemics of dermatitis, bronchitis, and gastroenteritis may result from a massive contact with these acarids; but these happenings fall outside the domain of parasitology.

To relieve cutaneous symptoms Faust et al.[2] mention Rogers' antipruritic lotion, containing 1 ml of phenol, zinc oxide 30 gm, glycerin 4 ml, lime water 15 ml, and rose water 100 ml. To relieve bronchopulmonary symptoms they mention Mapharsen or other modern arsenical therapy.

As to the other superfamilies listed above, the Ixodoidea or ticks, the Trombidoidea or harvest mites (together with the Parasitoidea), and the Sarcoptoidea or mange mites (together with the Demodicoidea) will be discussed below.

REFERENCES FOR CHAPTER XXIV

1. R. MATHESON. *Medical Entomology,* Ithaca, N. Y., 1950, Comstock Publishing Co.
2. E. C. FAUST, P. F. RUSSELL, and R. D. LINCICOME. *Clinical Parasitology,* Philadelphia, 1957, pp. 743, 746.

CHAPTER XXV

IXODOIDEA: THE TICKS

The ticks suck the blood or tissue fluid of their host. They can do so by the possession of a motile organ located at or near the anterior extremity of their ovoid body. This organ, the *capitulum,* is composed of a basal part, or *basis capituli* (Fig. 24·1:*BC*), which carries the sensory and the piercing and sucking mouth parts. The former, *the palps,* are situated laterally and are composed of four joints (Fig. 24·1:*P*; Fig. 25·1:*P*); the latter are situated in the middle

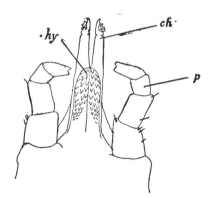

Fig. 25·1   *Ornithodoros moubata* capitulum, ventral view: *ch,* Chelicera.—*hy,* Hypostome.—*p,* Palp. (After Daniels. Courtesy, Baillière, Tindall & Cox.)

(Fig. 25·1:*Ch, hy*). Dorsally the piercing and sucking organ consists of two retractile sheathed rods, the *cheliceras,* carrying a barbed motile joint, or *digit,* at their apex (Fig. 25·1:*Ch*); ventrally they consist of a club-shaped organ, the *hypostome,* composed of two longitudinal halves, the greater part of whose surface is provided with hooks directed backwards (Fig. 25·1:*hy*). Cheliceras and hypostome pierce the skin of the host and attach themselves to the walls of the wound they have inflicted with the help of the barbed surface of the hypostome and of the digits of the cheliceras, which for that purpose are rotated outwards. The ingested blood flows through a tube, the walls of which are formed by the sheaths of the cheliceras and the hypostome.

The eight legs are composed of six joints; from base to apex the joints bear the name of coxa, trochanter, femur, tibia, first tarsal, and second tarsal. The latter carries two claws and a sucking pad, or *pulvillus,* at its apex.

The respiratory organs consist of two bundles of air tubes, or *tracheas,* that open into two air holes, or *spiracles,* situated near the left and right coxa of the fourth pair of legs. Each spiracle lies in the center of a conspicuous chitinous plate, the *peritreme.*

The sexual aperture of the males and the females is situated ventrally in the midline in the anterior part of the body; the anus, on the same line, in the posterior part.

All female ticks lay eggs.

The ticks are divided into the families of the Argasidae and the Ixodidae, distinguished by the position of the capitulum. In the argasids it is situated on the ventral side; thus it is invisible from the dorsal side (Fig. 24·1:*I*; Fig. 25·2); in the ixodids it is situated at the margin of the anterior extremity (Fig. 24·1:*II*), and so it is visible from both sides. Ecologically they differ by the relationship to their host. The argasids depend on man (or other warm-blooded hosts) for their nutrition; on man's house for a space to dwell and to multiply in; so they belong to the ecological group of "house vermin." The ixodids are wholly dependent on the "anatomical body" of their host; thus they belong to the "body vermin."

ARGASIDAE OR SOFT TICKS

Besides the characteristics mentioned above, the argasids can be identified by the absence of the hard chitinous shield, or *scutum* (Fig. 24·1:*Sc*), which covers the whole dorsal surface in the male ixodids and part of it in the females. Its presence has earned the ixodids the name of "hard ticks," just as the argasids are called "soft ticks" because of the lack of it. It is as good a name as any other, provided one remembers that soft ticks are as tough as leather. Among the genera of soft ticks, the genus *Argas* (Fig. 24·1:*I*) is characterized by a flat dorsal surface devoid of grooves and a sharp edge, the genus *Ornithodoros* (Fig. 25·2) by a convex, grooved dorsal surface and a rounded edge. Human parasites are known in the latter genus.

The species of the genus *Ornithodoros* are house vermin. During prolonged sittings they imbibe relatively large quantities of the blood of their several hosts, which they procure from a hemorrhage in the skin caused by the continual tearing movement of the cheliceras.[1] During the meal the *coxal glands* that open on the coxas of the anterior pair of legs produce a profuse secretion that floods

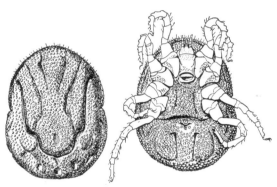

Fig. 25·2   *Ornithodoros moubata,* dorsal side (*left*) and ventral side of female, × 3½. (After Nuttall and Warburton. Courtesy, Cambridge University Press.)

the adjoining part of the host's skin. Other glands, the *salivary glands,* pour their secretion into the wound inflicted by the tick's mouth parts.

The species of *Ornithodoros* have a long span of life; moreover, they survive for a long time without food. *O. tholozani (papillipes)* is reported to have lived for twenty-five years, and seven of these were passed without food.[2]

Various species of *Ornithodoros* serve as intermediate hosts to certain blood parasites in rodents and man. They are spirochetes of the genus *Borrelia,* spiral-shaped, flexible microbes of a length of 10–20 μ and a width of 0.2–0.3 μ. Ornithodoros ingests the borrelias with the blood of its host. The microbes pierce the intestinal wall, thus reaching the hemocele, where they multiply by transverse fission. From the seventh day onward borrelias appear in the secretion of the coxal and salivary glands.[3] The tick returns the borrelias to the mammalian host by depositing them on the skin mixed with the coxal fluid, or within the skin mixed with the saliva. Once the tick has become infected with borrelias, it remains infected during the rest of its life. In central Asia *O. tholozani* was able to infect rodents by its bite thirteen years after it had acquired the infection.[2] Moreover, it is able to pass the borrelias to its offspring by means of *transovular* or *transovarial infection* (*v. Babesia*). In the United States, *O. turricata* has been found infected for five successive generations.[4] Finally, the male tick has been reported to infect its female partner by means of its male sexual products.[5]

Tropical Africa is the habitat of a borrelia, *B. duttoni,* that causes a human disease, *tick fever,* known for many years to be caused by the bite of *O. moubata* (Fig. 25·2). One of the biological varieties of this species, the "man-eating form," [6] belongs to the house vermin. The ticks inhabit the crevices in the mud walls of human habitations, and there the females lay their eggs. They take the blood of the human inhabitants; if one of them is sick with tick fever, *O. moubata* becomes infected with *B. duttoni.* Seven days later the tick is able to pass the borrelias to other human inhabitants.

Tick fever is also known in other countries; but the borrelias that cause them, and the species of *Ornithodoros* that transmit them, are not the same as in Central Africa. Ornithodoros in these countries does not represent house vermin in human habitations, but in animal habitations such as the burrows of wild rodents infected with rodent borrelias. Some of the latter can also live and multiply in the human body. In Morocco, for instance, wild rodents, such as *Meriones shawi* and *Oryctolagus cuniculus,* are infected with *Borrelia hispanica,* the causative agent of human tick fever in Spain and North Africa. This microbe is transmitted from rodent to rodent by the burrow-haunting tick *Ornithodoros erraticus*. It is not a house-haunting tick; nevertheless, it bites man if it gets the chance, thus passing the infection to him.[7] Thus tick fever becomes a sylvatic disease which man no longer acquires from the human inmates in his house, but from wild life in the fields. Similar conditions have been reported in West Africa,[8] the United States,[9] and central Asia.[2]

IXODIDAE OR HARD TICKS

The special features of the ixodids have been mentioned already: the terminal position of the capitulum, the hard dorsal scutum, and the fact that they are body vermin, dependent on the anatomical body of their host not only for nutrition but also for a space to dwell in—but not to multiply, for the one thing they do in free nature is to lay their eggs.

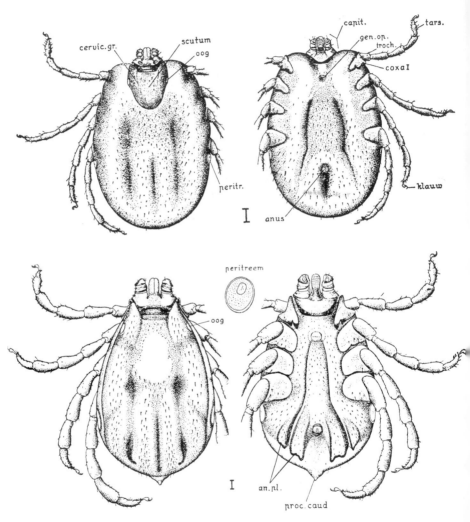

FIG. 25·3 *Boophilus annulatus:* UPPER FIGURE, female, × 13.—LOWER FIGURE, male, × 27. LEFT, dorsal view; RIGHT, ventral view:—*cervic.gr*, Cervical groove.—*peritr*, Peritreme.—*oog*, Eye.—*capit*, Capitulum.—*gen. op*, Genital aperture.—*troch*, Trochanter.—*klauw*, Claw.—*an.pl*, Anal plates.—*proc.caud*, Caudal process. (After Krijgsman and Ponto, 1932. Courtesy, Government Printing Office, Batavia.)

Uninterruptedly attached to the host, the proboscis buried in its skin, the female imbibes large quantities of blood. The attachment to the skin is rendered firmer by a plug, composed of the so-called "cement substance," that fixes the mouth parts in the skin. The tips

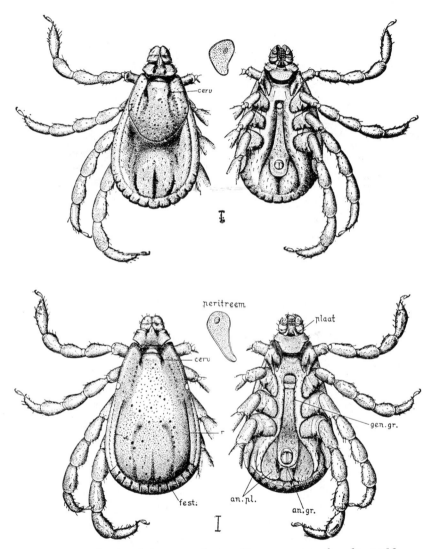

FIG. 25·4 *Rhipicephalus sanguineus:* UPPER FIGURE, female, × 16.— LOWER FIGURE, male, × 12. LEFT, dorsal view; RIGHT, ventral view.— *cerv*, Cervical groove.—*r*, Marginal groove.—*fest*, Festoons.—*gen.gr*, Genital groove.—*an.gr*, Anal groove.—*an.pl*, Anal plates. (After Krijgsman and Ponto, 1932. Courtesy, Government Printing Office, Batavia.)

of the mouth parts project beyond this plug, but they are kept
motionless and thus do not cause the hemorrhage argasid ticks
produce. Hard ticks obtain their food by their saliva liquefying

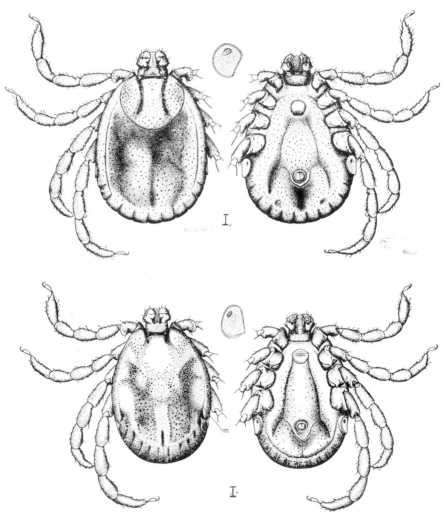

FIG. 25·5   *Haemaphysalis papuana*, × 16: UPPER FIGURE, female.—LOWER
FIGURE, male.—Showing peritremes. (After Krijgsman and Ponto, 1932.
Courtesy, Government Printing Office, Batavia.)

the tissue beyond the apex of the mouth parts. As liquefaction
proceeds, capillary walls become damaged and blood cells as well as
tissue cells are taken in by the tick. However, the presence of red

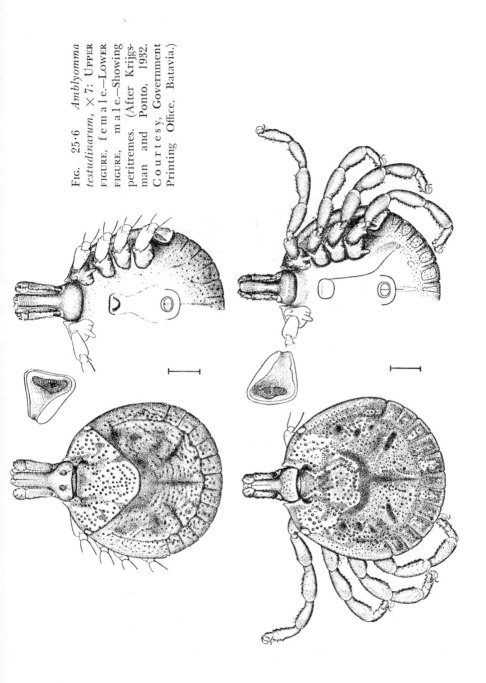

FIG. 25·6 *Amblyomma testudinarum*, ×7: UPPER FIGURE, f e m a l e.—LOWER FIGURE, m a l e.—Showing peritremes. (After Krijgsman and Ponto, 1932. C o u r t e s y, Government Printing Office, Batavia.)

blood cells in the meal does not appear to be essential for the growth and development of the tick; it matures as well if fed on tissue fluid only.[1]

Feeding in this way, the female produces huge numbers of eggs, which make its body swell to a perfect rotundity. When its eggs are ready to be laid, it retracts its proboscis from the host's skin and

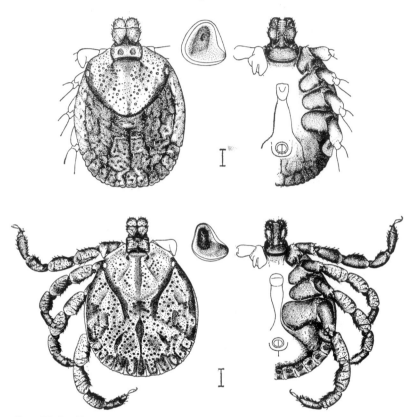

FIG. 25·7 *Dermacentor auratus,* × 10: UPPER FIGURE, female.—LOWER FIGURE, male.—Showing peritremes. (After Krijgsman and Ponto, 1932. Courtesy, Government Printing Office, Batavia.)

drops to the ground. There it oviposits, often on blades of grass, an activity which lasts for two to three weeks. By that time the female has returned to its normal flattened shape, which it never loses again, because it soon dies. The larvas hatch, often in free nature, and await the next host to pass by.

If that host is a human being, he thus becomes infected in free nature and not, as is the case with most vermin, in houses or other places where people crowd together. Other vermin are associated with overcrowding in narrow spaces and uncleanliness; hard ticks

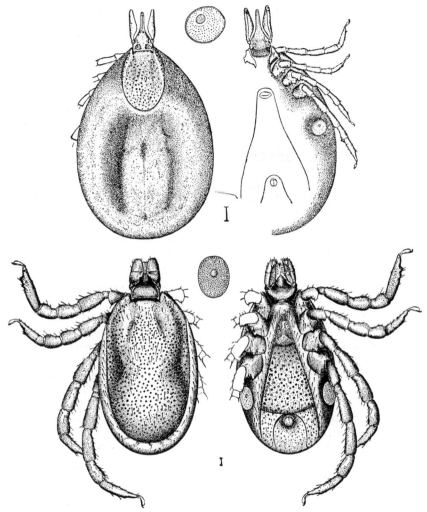

FIG. 25·8 *Ixodes granulatus:* UPPER FIGURE, female, × 15.—LOWER FIGURE, male, × 25.—Showing peritremes. (After Krijgsman and Ponto, 1932. Courtesy, Government Printing Office, Batavia.)

with green pastures, sunshine, and a fresh breeze. This, however, is not a rule without exceptions. The brown dog tick (*Rhipicephalus sanguineus*), for one, may invade human habitations and there lay its eggs, in the intervals between its being firmly attached to its natural host.

The six-legged larvas, known as "seed ticks," once they have attached themselves to a host, feed like the adults. After one molt they change to nymphs, with eight legs but sexually immature. The nymphs continue to feed and after a second molt become mature males or females. Some species of ixodids change from larva to nymph and from nymph to adult on a single individual host; they are "one-host ticks." Others require a different individual for larvas, nymphs, and adults; they are "three-host ticks." Still others pass their larval and nymphal stage on one individual and the adult stage on the next; they are "two-host ticks."

The genera of ixodids that are important to man can be listed as follows.[10]

(1) A semicircular groove, the *anal groove,* lies in front of the anus; the palps of the female are five times as long as wide; eyes are absent from the lateral margins of the scutum; the posterior margin of the tick shows no festoons (Fig. 25·8) . . . . *Ixodes*

The anal groove lies behind the anus or is absent . . . . (2)

(2) The anal groove is absent or inconspicuous; festoons are absent; the palps are very short (Fig. 25·3) . . . . *Boophilus*

The anal groove lies behind the anus, festoons (Fig. 25·6) are present . . . . (3)

(3) The palps are at least four times as long as wide; their second joint is longer than wide . . . . (4)

The palps are at most twice as long as wide; their second joint is hardly longer than wide . . . . (5)

(4) The second palpal joint is much longer than the apical joint (Fig. 25·6) . . . . *Amblyomma*

The second palpal joint is hardly longer than the apical joint
Hyalomma

(5) The coxas of the first pair of legs are not bifurcate; the base of the palps extends beyond the basis capituli; eyes are absent (Fig. 25·5)
Haemaphysalis

The coxas of the first pair of legs are bifurcate; the base of the palps does not extend beyond the basis capituli; eyes are present . . . . . . (6)

(6) The inner tooth of the fork formed by the first pair of coxas is more than twice as thick as the outer tooth; in the male, the fourth pair of coxas is much bigger than the third pair, and the peritremes are triangular, with rounded corners (Fig. 25·7) . . . . *Dermacentor*

The inner tooth of the fork formed by the first pair of coxas is no more than 1½ times as thick as the outer tooth; in the male the fourth pair of coxas is of the same size as the third pair, and the peritremes are comma-shaped (Fig. 25·4) . . . . *Rhipicephalus*

Hard ticks are of little importance as causative agents of diseases. The disease named after them, tick bite fever, has been proved to be a rickettsiosis caused by minute microorganisms, rickettsias, smaller than the smallest bacillus but larger than the largest virus.[11] There is (or there still is) one exception, *tick paralysis,* which is supposed to be due to a poison secreted by the tick because the patients recover when the ticks are removed, provided paralysis has not yet reached the bulbar stage. Tick paralysis in man has been ascribed to the bite of *Dermacentor andersoni* and *D. variabilis* in the northwestern United States and western Canada, to *Ixodes holocyclus* in eastern and western Australia, to *I. ricinus* in Europe, and to *I. pilosus* in South Africa.

A *specific therapy* does not exist against tick paralysis except, perhaps, the early removal of the tick. As a rule, it is better to allow the tick to drop off of its own accord than to pull it out of the skin, because this attempt may cause more or less serious damage. However, if the tick has to be removed this should be done by a few drops of chloroform or ether placed on the capitulum of the tick, which will cause it to relax its hold and allow it to be removed by easy traction.[11]

Ticks are of much greater importance as vectors of causative agents of a number of human and animal diseases. One example of this kind has already been given (*v. Babesia*). Others may be listed according to the nature of the causative agents; they may be rickettsias, viruses, or bacteria.

RICKETTSIAL DISEASES TRANSMITTED BY HARD TICKS

Among the rickettsial diseases transmitted by hard ticks the following may be mentioned.

(1) "Fièvre boutonneuse" in the Mediterranean Basin, perhaps also in the Sudan, Eritrea, and Ethiopia,[13, 46] caused by *Rickettsia conorii,* with the dog as reservoir host, and *Rhipicephalus sanguineus* as vector. Transovular (-ovarial) transmission has been reported in the latter.[14]

(2) "Kenya fever" in East Africa, caused by *Rickettsia pijperi,* transmitted by *Rhipicephalus simus, Haemaphysalis leachi,* and *Amblyomma variegatum,* with dogs and wild rodents, such as *Arvicanthis, Otomys, Tatera,* and *Xerus,* as reservoir hosts.[16]

(3) "Tick bite fever"[12] in South Africa, caused by the same rickettsia, transmitted by *Amblyomma hebraeum* in rural areas and *Haemaphysalis leachi* in the mining centers. Transovular (-ovarial) transmission, over four generations of ticks, has been reported in the latter species.[17]

Recently it has been suggested that all tick-borne rickettsioses found throughout Africa should be grouped together under the general terminology of "tick-borne typhus," with *R. conorii* as the causative agent.[17, 48]

(4) "Rocky Mountain spotted fever" in the United States and Canada, caused by *Rickettsia (Dermacentroxenus) rickettsii*, with wild rodents such as *Sylvilagus nuttalli*,[18] as reservoir hosts and *Dermacentor andersoni* as vector. Transovular (-ovarial) transmission has been observed, and also transmission from the male tick to the female through the medium of the sperm.[19] In the Atlantic States *Dermacentor variabilis* is the vector,[20] dogs and field mice the reservoir hosts.[21]

A related disease in Texas, Oklahoma, and Mexico is transmitted by *Amblyomma americanum, A. cayennense, Rhipicephalus sanguineus,* and two species of *Ornithodoros.* Wild rodents, perhaps dogs and cats, are reservoir hosts.[22]

North American "Bullis fever," transmitted by *Amblyomma americanum,*[23] may perhaps be mentioned in this conjunction, as well as "Colorado tick fever," in the western United States and Canada, with wild rodents such as *Citellus* as reservoir hosts [24] and *Dermacentor andersoni* as vector, a tick which is reported to pass on its infection by transovular (-ovarial) transmission.[25]

Typhus of São Paulo and Colombia is placed by some authors in this group; others consider its causative agent to be a separate species, *Rickettsia braziliensis.* The vector is *Amblyomma cayennense;* reservoir hosts are wild rodents.[26]

(5) "Spring typhus" in the steppes of Siberia, caused by *Rickettsia sibirica* and transmitted by *Dermacentor nuttalli, D. sylvarum, D. marginatus, D. pictus, Haemaphysalis concinna, H. punctata,* and *Ixodes persulcatus,* in the first of which transovular (-ovarial) transmission has been noted.[27] Wild rodents are reservoir hosts.[28] "Hemorrhagic fever" in the Crimea, transmitted by *Hyalomma marginatum,* may belong to this group.[29]

(6) "North Queensland tick typhus," a mild tick-borne spotted fever caused by *Rickettsia australis* and probably transmitted by *Ixodes holocyclus*.[11]

(7) In Ethiopia [15] ticks (*Amblyomma variegatum, Hyalomma rufipes*), collected on cattle, sheep, and goats, have been found infected with the causative agent of epidemic typhus, *Rickettsia prowazeki*, whose usual vectors are body lice. In Kenya this rickettsia has been found in wild rodents.[16]

(8) The preceding examples refer to the transmission of rickettsial diseases of the typhus group. The present one occupies a separate position; firstly, because the disease concerned, "Q fever," differs from the other rickettsial diseases by the absence of any skin rash; secondly, because the causative agent concerned, *Coxiella burnetii*, stands apart from the other rickettsias; thirdly, because the ticks concerned, although they constitute a formidable reservoir by their transovular (-ovarial) infection, are not usually held directly responsible for human infection.[30] The disease affects man's livestock and man himself in Australia, North America, West and Central Africa, the Mediterranean Basin, and various European countries. Fifteen species of hard ticks and two of soft ticks have been found infected in nature.

TREATMENT OF RICKETTSIOSES. The broad-spectrum antibiotics, such as chlortetracycline (Aureomycin), chloramphenicol, and oxytetracycline (Terramycin), have been found effective in the treatment of the typhus group as well as of Q fever. However, it should be borne in mind that these antibiotics are ricksettsiostatic rather than rickettsiocidal. For this reason the treatment should be continued for several days after the temperature reaches normal, so as to prevent relapses. The recommended dose for these antibiotics is 2 to 3 gm daily divided equally and given every six hours.

VIRUS DISEASES TRANSMITTED BY HARD TICKS

Among the virus diseases transmitted by hard ticks the following may be mentioned.

(1) Encephalitis attacking lumbermen and settlers in the forested and settled areas of the forest regions of eastern Siberia, particularly the regions of Khabarovsk and the Ussuri. The disease is prevalent from April until June, before the advent of the mosquito season.[31]

In the forested areas lumbermen acquire the infection from wild rodents, carnivores, ungulates, and birds through the medium of the ticks *Dermacentor sylvarum* and *Ixodes persulcatus,* which also pass the virus to their progeny by transovular (-ovarial) infection.[32] In the second half of July the virus in the ticks loses its activity, hibernates in the body of the ticks, and becomes reactivated the next spring.[33] In the settled areas agricultural laborers acquire their infection from domestic animals through the medium of the same ticks, to which *Haemaphysalis concinna* must be added.[34] In the Ural Mountains the same disease occurs. Wild rodents are reservoir hosts during the epidemic season; during the off season they are free from infection; the virus hibernates in the vector, *Ixodes persulcatus.*[35]

According to Smorodintsev and Ilienko [36] the infection with this virus extends from Korea in the east, to Germany in the west, and India in the south. In India it manifests itself in the form of the Kyasanur forest disease, which has monkeys, wild rats, and birds as reservoir hosts, and *Haemaphysalis spinigera* as vector.[37]

Related to this disease are (1) central European encephalomyelitis, with *Ixodes hexagonus* as vector,[38] and (2) "louping ill" of sheep in the Anglo-Scottish frontier area, which may attack man, and has *I. ricinus* as vector.[39]

(2) The virus of western equine encephalitis of the United States, transmitted by mosquitoes, may also be harbored by the tick *Dermacentor andersoni,* which can pass the virus on by transovular (-ovarial) infection. However, this has been observed only under experimental conditions and not in nature.[40] This also applies to mosquito-borne encephalitis in Japan and eastern Siberia. Ticks of the genera *Dermacentor, Ixodes,* and *Hyalomma* could be infected with the virus; the ticks remained infected through four successive generations, and by the end of this period they were able to pass the virus by their bite to experimental animals.[41] In the Trans-Ural area a similar disease is said to be transmitted by *Dermacentor marginatus.*[42]

BACTERIAL DISEASES TRANSMITTED BY TICKS

Among bacterial diseases transmitted by ticks, tularemia may be mentioned, whose causative agent is *Pasteurella tularensis.* In the United States *Dermacentor andersoni, D. variabilis, D. occidentalis, Haemaphysalis leporis-palustris,* and *Amblyomma americanum* are serving as vectors [43]; in Anatolia *Hyalomma aegyptium* and the soft tick *Ornithodoros lahorensis* [44]; in France *Dermacentor marginatus.*[45] It is to be noted, however, that ticks are only one of the means for *P. tularensis* to pass from its reservoir hosts (wild and domestic rodents, small carnivores, and cattle) to man.

REFERENCES FOR CHAPTER XXV

1. A. FOGGIE. *Ann. Trop. Med. Parasitol.*, 1959, 53: 27–34.
2. E. N. PAVLOVSKY and A. N. SKRUINNIK. *Trop. Diseases Bull.*, 1954, 51: 389–390.
3. M. G. R. VARMA. *Ann. Trop. Med. Parasitol.*, 1956, 50: 18–31.
4. G. E. DAVIS. *Public Health Repts. (U. S.)*, 1943, 58: 839–842.
5. O. WAGNER-JEVSEENKO. *Acta Trop., Basel*, 1958, 15: 118–168.
6. G. A. WALTON. *E. African Med. J.*, 1958, 35: 57–84.
7. G. BLANC and J. BRUNEAU. *Compt. rend. acad. sci. Paris*, 1955, 240: 129–131.
8. H. BOIRON. *Presse méd.*, 1949, 57: 165.
9. C. M. WHEELER. *Am. J. Trop. Med.*, 1938, 18: 641–658.
10. B. J. KRIJGSMAN and S. A. PONTO. *The Ticks of the Malay Archipelago*, Batavia, 1932, Govt. Print. Off.
11. R. MATHESON. *Medical Entomology*, Ithaca, N. Y., 1950, Comstock Publishing Co.
12. A. PIJPER. *Arch. inst. Pasteur Tunis*, 1936, 25: 388–401.
13. A. D. CHARTERS. *Trans. Roy. Soc. Trop. Med. Hyg.*, 1946, 39: 335–342.
14. E. BRUMPT. *Compt. rend. soc. biol. Paris*, 1932, 110: 1199–1202.
15. R. J. REISS-GUTFREUND. *Bull. soc. pathol. exotique*, 1956, 49: 946–1021.
16. R. B. HEISCH and A. E. C. HARVEY. *E. African Med. J.*, 1959, 36: 116–118.
17. J. GEAR and B. DE MEILLON. *S. African Med. J.*, 1941, 15: 389–392.
18. W. L. JELLISON. *Public Health Repts. (U. S.)*, 1945, 60: 958–961.
19. W. B. DAVIDSON. *Trop. Diseases Bull.*, 1942, 39: 201–202.
20. J. G. HUTTON. *J. Am. Med. Ass.*, 1941, 117: 413–416.
21. W. H. PRICE. *Am. J. Hyg.*, 1954, 60: 292–319.
22. R. R. PARKER et al. *Public Health Repts.*, Washington, D. C., 1943, 58: 721–729.
23. H. R. LIVESAY and M. POLLARD. *Am. J. Trop. Med.*, 1944, 24: 281–284.
24. C. M. EKLUND et al. *Science*, 1958, 128: 43.
25. L. FLORIO, M. S. MILLER, and E. R. MUGRAGE. *J. Immunol.*, 1950, 64: 257–263.
26. O. DE MAGELHAES. *Mem. inst. Oswaldo Cruz*, 1949, 47: 249–259.
27. T. T. CROCKER et al. *Public Health Repts. (U. S.)*, 1950, 65: 383–394.
28. P. ZDRODOWSKI and H. GOLINEVITCH. *Sixth Intern. Congr. Trop. Med.*, Lisbon, 1958, Abstracts, 194–195.
29. A. G. GROBOV. *Rev. Appl. Entomol.*, B, 1948, 36: 80.
30. E. H. DERRICK. *Med. J. Australia*, 1953 (1st half): 245–257.
31. M. P. CHUMAKOV and N. A. SEITLENOK. *Science*, 1940, 92: 263–264.
32. N. V. RUISHOV and A. V. KORLOVA. *Rev. Appl. Entomol.*, B, 1946, 34: 68–69.
33. E. N. PAVLOVSKY. *Rev. Appl. Entomol.*, B, 1943, 31: 70.
34. A. P. KUZYAKIN. *Rev. Appl. Entomol.*, B, 1943, 31: 249.
35. M. P. CHUMAKOV. *Rev. Appl. Entomol.*, B, 1943, 31: 70–71.

36. A. Smorodintsev and V. Ilienko. *Sixth Intern. Congr. Trop. Med.*, Lisbon, 1958, Abstracts, 165–166.

37. T. H. Work. *Sixth Intern. Congr. Trop. Med.*, Lisbon, 1958, Abstracts, 167–168; *Am. J. Public Health*, 1959, 49: 869–874.

38. H. A. E. van Tongeren. *Sixth Intern. Congr. Trop. Med.*, Lisbon, 1958, Abstracts, 166–167.

39. E. G. Brewis. *Lancet*, 1949 (1st half): 689–691.

40. J. Sylverton and G. P. Berry. *J. Exptl. Med.*, 1941, 73: 507–530.

41. M. P. Chumakov et al. *Rev. Appl. Entomol.*, B, 1947, 34: 176.

42. A. V. Vasilev. *Rev. Appl. Entomol.*, B, 1948, 36: 171.

43. E. L. Calhoun. *Am. J. Trop. Med. Hyg.*, 1954, 3: 360–366.

44. E. Gotschlich. *Münch. med. Wochschr.*, 1942, 89: 509–512.

45. G. Girard. *Presse méd.*, 1949, 57: 968–970.

46. D. and J. Olmer. *Rev. pathol. gén. Paris*, 1956, 56: 80–82.

47. T. M. Rivers and F. L. Horsfall, Jr. *Viral and Rickettsial Infections of Man*, 3d Ed., Philadelphia, 1959, p. 848.

48. Joint OIHP/WHO. *World Health Organization, Tech. Rept. Ser.*, No. 23, Geneva, Dec. 1950.

CHAPTER XXVI

TROMBIDOID AND PARASITOID MITES

TROMBIDOIDEA: CHIGGERS OR REDBUGS

This superfamily comprises the family of Trombiculinae, whose larvas parasitize various vertebrates. The larvas, known as chiggers, are of great importance as vectors of certain rickettsias.[1] In Japan they have long been reputed dangerous animals, as is proved by the first of three names by which they are known in that country, viz. tsutsugamushi (disease bug). The other two, kedani (hairy mite), and akamushi (red bug), mention their most conspicuous characteristics—their hairiness and their bright color.

The larvas, whose structure is represented in Fig. 26·1, are parasites; they depend on their host for a dwelling place and for food—not for multiplication, because they do not multiply. For a short time, a few days, occasionally for no more than 6 to 18 hours,[2] they require vertebrate proteins as food, which they procure by attaching themselves firmly to the skin of rodents, birds, or man. They insert their cheliceras into the skin (Fig. 26·2:*ch*), and their saliva is injected into the wound. This secretion dissolves a strictly localized portion of the dermal tissue and converts its periphery into a hyalin substance. This substance assumes the form of a tube that bears the name of *histosiphon* or *stylostome* (Fig. 26·2:*Sty*), comparable to the plug of cement substance in hard ticks. It is situated in the dermal tissue, and through it the mite imbibes the suspension of elements of the cutaneous tissue its saliva has dissolved.[3] This highly nutritious food enables the larva to grow considerably within a few days. Thereafter it no longer stands in need of it; accordingly it drops to the ground, thus leaving its first host—which is also its last, for during its subsequent development into nymph (Fig. 26·3:*b*) and adult (Fig. 26·3:*a*) it will need no other host. During that development it lives in the soil as a nonparasitic, predaceous animal. The adult females lay their eggs (Fig. 26·3:*e*) in that environment; from them

463

a fresh generation of larvas hatch, which will return to a parasitic mode of life.

At first sight it would seem impossible for such mites to serve as vectors of the causative agent of a disease. Nevertheless they do so in south and east Asia and the adjacent parts of Australia, particularly the species *Trombicula deliensis* and *T. akamushi*. The organism they transmit, *Rickettsia tsutsugamushi* (*R. orientalis*), the

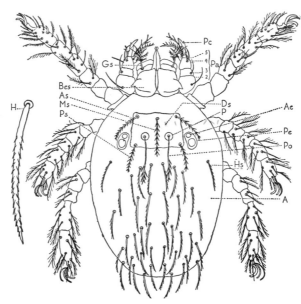

Fig. 26·1 *Trombicula akamushi,* larva: *A*, Abdomen.—*Ae*, Anterior eye. —*As*, Anterior lateral bristle of dorsal scutum.—*Bes*, Basal joint of chelicera.—*Ds*, Dorsal scutum.—*Gs*, Branched hair on second joint of chelicera (galea).—*H*, A dorsal hair at higher magnification.—*Hs*, Humeral bristle.—*Ms*, Median bristle of dorsal scutum.—*P*, Pseudostigma. —*Pa*, Pedipalp, composed of five joints marked 1–5.—*Pc*, Apical claw of pedipalp.—*Pe*, Posterior eye.—*Po*, Bristle on pseudostigma.—*Ps*, Posterior lateral bristle of dorsal scutum. (After Matheson, 1950. Courtesy, Comstock Publishing Co., Ithaca, N. Y.)

causative agent of "scrub typhus," is ingested by larvas that attack field-inhabiting rodents of the supergenus *Rattus* [4] or the genus *Microtus*,[5] which are infected with the rickettsias. The latter multiply in the body of the larva, which still harbors them when it becomes a nymph and ultimately an adult. If that adult is a female, it infects its progeny, the larvas of the next generation, through the medium of its eggs.[6] The second generation of larvas, turning parasites for a short time, infect other rodents by their bite or any other susceptible animal to which they may have attached themselves, including man. In this way man acquires a disease, originally known in Sumatra as "pseudo-typhus," [7] but better known as "scrub typhus" because it is acquired in free nature by passing through and camping in surroundings overgrown with grass or other low vegetation. The name "scrub typhus" might suggest that the infection is acquired in completely wild surroundings never touched by man, but this is not so, or at least it is not the rule. It is possible that wild rodents, in

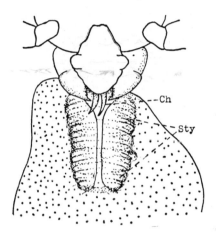

FIG. 26·2   Schematic representation of the production of a *histosiphon*, or *stylostome*, by a larval trombicula. The punctated area represents the cutaneous tissue of the host, into which the cheliceras (*ch*) are inserted: *sty*, longitudinal section through stylostome. (After Matheson, 1950. Courtesy, Comstock Publishing Co., Ithaca, N. Y.)

virgin jungle, constitute the original reservoir hosts; but the rodents from which man acquires his infection are semidomestic species that inhabit the fields first cultivated and subsequently neglected (or temporarily left fallow, like rice fields in Japan) by man.[4] If fields of that description are found in rural parts of a great eastern city, scrub typhus may even assume a semiurban character.[8]

   Faust et al.[9] recommend phenolated camphor solutions in pure mineral oil as a palliative against the intense pruritus on ankles, legs, external genitalia, groin, and waistline, where the larvas most commonly attach themselves.

PARASITOIDEA: BLOODSUCKING MITES

The members of this family suck blood and may be classified as "house vermin," since they depend on the anatomical body of the host for their food and on his habitation for a space to dwell and multiply in.

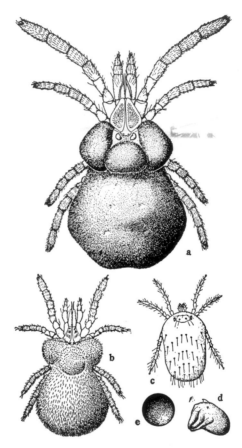

FIG. 26·3 Developmental stages of a trombiculid mite (*Eutrombicula batatas*): *a*, Adult.—*b*, Nymph.—*c*, Larva.—*d*, Deutovum, i.e. larva in embryonated egg.—*e*, Egg. (After Matheson, 1950. Courtesy, Comstock Publishing Co., Ithaca, N. Y.)

One of them is *Dermanyssus gallinae* (*D. avium*) that lives in chicken coops, dovecots, and birds' nests and feeds on the avian inhabitants' blood. The females are ¾ mm long, the males ⅗ mm. They greatly resemble *D. hirundinis* (Fig. 26·4) of swallows' nests.

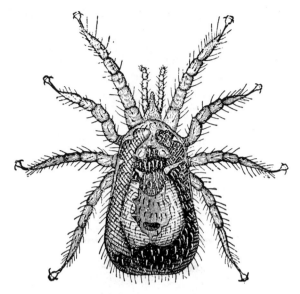

FIG. 26·4 *Dermanyssus hirundinis*, adult female, dorsal view, × 70. (After Delafond.)

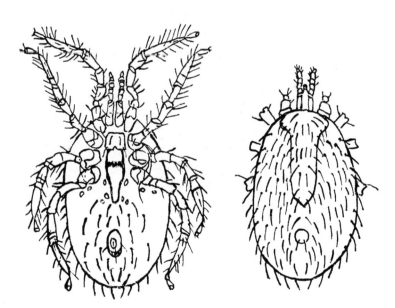

FIG. 26·5 *Allodermanyssus sanguinis*, adult female, × 40: *Left*, ventral view.—*Right*, dorsal view. (After Brumpt, 1949. Courtesy, Masson & Cie, Paris.)

They can survive for a long time without food; accordingly empty chicken coops or dovecots may remain infested with them for a long time. They may attack man, causing severe itching. Since they also settle in man's habitation, as has been observed, by Williams [21] and others, they may be regarded as parasites.

In the United States *D. gallinae* is of interest because it has been found naturally infected with the virus of western equine encephalitis and St. Louis encephalitis. These viruses may infect domestic fowl, which in their turn infect dermanyssus. Apparently the mite

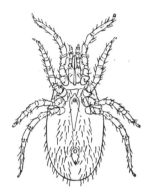

FIG. 26·6   *Ornithonyssus bacoti,* adult female, ventral view, × 40. (After Brumpt, 1922. Courtesy, Masson & Cie, Paris.)

is an excellent host, as it passes the virus to its progeny by transovular (-ovarial) infection. However, the part it plays in the ecology of the virus is still somewhat obscure, since it has not been demonstrated that dermanyssus infects other animals by its bite.[10]

There is no doubt to this effect in the case of *Allodermanyssus sanguineus* (Fig. 26·5), a species feeding on and living and multiplying in the nests of rats and mice (*Mus musculus*) infesting human habitations. In this site it may attack man and serve as the vector of *Rickettsia akari*,[18] which it transmits from rodent to man. In the latter, *R. akari* proves to be the causative agent of a fever, combined with cutaneous eruption, and known as "rickettsial pox." Initially it was reported only in New York [11, 19, 20]; since then it has also been encountered in Boston and Philadelphia, and more recently in Korea, as an infection of voles (*Microtus fortis*) far from human society.[12] The voles do not appear to suffer from the presence of the rickettsia. Similar conditions occur in the Rift Valley (Kenya), where gerbils (*Tatera nigricauda*) appear to be a reservoir of rickettsial pox.[17]

Ornithonyssus (Bdellonyssus, Liponyssus) bacoti is another member of this group (Fig. 26·6). It differs from dermanyssus by its cheliceras; their apical extremity is bifid, whereas it is single in dermanyssus. The females have a length of about 1 mm; the males are half that size. They parasitize house-infesting rodents and may attack man. The species has been reported to serve as an occasional intermediate host of various pathogenic microbes, such as the causative agent of tularemia,[13] endemic typhus,[14] rickettsial pox,[15] and western equine encephalomyelitis,[16] although it is of less importance than other vectors of these agents.

According to Faust et al.[9] local pruritus may be relieved by the application of phenolated camphor in a petrolatum base.

REFERENCES FOR CHAPTER XXVI

1. C. E. M. GUNTHER. *Proc. Linnean Soc. N. S. Wales,* 1952, 77: 1–60.
2. C. B. PHILIP, R. TRAUB, and J. E. SMADEL. *Am. J. Hyg.,* 1949, 50: 63–74.
3. B. M. JONES. *Parasitology,* 1950, 40: 247–260.
4. J. L. HARRISON and J. R. AUDY. *Ann. Trop. Med. Parasitol.,* 1951, 45: 186–194.
5. T. SUZUKI. *Trop. Diseases Bull.,* 1955, 52: 621–622.
6. T. T. MACKIE. *Trans. Roy. Soc. Trop. Med. Hyg.,* 1946, 40: 15–46.
7. W. A. P. SCHÜFFNER. *Philippine J. Sci.,* B, 1915, 10: 845–851.
8. R. GISPEN. *Documenta Med. Geograph. et Trop. Amsterdam,* 1950, 2: 23–35; 1951, 3: 155–162.
9. E. C. FAUST, P. F. RUSSELL, and R. D. LINCICOME. *Clinical Parasitology,* Philadelphia, 1957, pp. 752, 745.
10. W. McD. HAMMON and W. C. REEVES. *Brit. Med. J.,* 1946 (1st half): 613–614.
11. E. NICHOLLS, M. E. RINDGE, and G. G. RUSSELL. *Ann. Internal Med.,* 1953, 39: 92–103.
12. E. B. JACKSON, J. X. DANAUSKAS, M. C. COALE, and J. E. SMADEL. *Am. J. Hyg.,* 1957, 66: 301–308.
13. C. E. HOPLA. *Am. J. Trop. Med.,* 1951, 31: 768–783.
14. WEI TUNG LIU. *Am. J. Hyg.,* 1947, 45: 58–66.
15. C. B. PHILIP and L. E. HUGHES. *Am. J. Trop. Med.,* 1948, 28: 697–705.
16. W. McD. HAMMON. *Am. J. Trop. Med.,* 1948, 28: 515–525.
17. R. B. HEISCH and A. E. C. HARVEY. *E. African Med. J.,* 1959, 36: 116–118.
18. R. J. HUEBNER et al. *Public Health Repts. (U. S. A.),* 1946, 61: 1605–1614, 1677–1682; 62: 777–780.
19. B. SHANKMAN. *N. Y. Med. J.,* 1946, 44: 2156–2159.
20. M. GREENBERG, O. PELLITERI, I. F. KLEIN, and R. J. HUEBNER. *J. Am. Med. Assoc.,* 1947, 133: 901–906.
21. R. W. WILLIAMS. *Am. J. Trop. Med. Hyg.,* 1958, 7: 627–629.

CHAPTER XXVII

SARCOPTOID AND DEMODICOID MITES

Although the hard ticks are fully qualified parasites, and the soft ticks, the trombiculoids, and the parasitoids can be admitted as such, once the compromise implied in the term "house vermin" has been accepted, they cannot command any real interest as parasites because too little is known of the relationship with their host. They are important because they are vectors of pathogenic microbes, and this claim to human interest does not depend on their being parasites.

The animals to be discussed in this chapter are not only true parasites, because they belong to the category of "body vermin" wholly dependent on their host, but they can also claim parasitological interest because sufficient is known about the relationship they entertain with their host.

There are various genera and species of itch or mange mites. To man the most important is the one to be dealt with in the following section.

SARCOPTES SCABIEI: ITCH MITES

Sarcoptes scabiei (Linnaeus, 1758) Latreille, 1802, belongs to the category of body vermin; all stages of development are passed on or in the human body. The parasites can all survive for some time outside the human host, but there they never show any progress in their development.

MORPHOLOGY AND BIOLOGY

The Adults. The pearly gray "ovigerous" female measures $\frac{1}{3}$ to nearly $\frac{1}{2}$ mm in length, and $\frac{1}{4}$ to $\frac{1}{3}$ mm in width [1] (Fig. 27·1, 27·2). On the anterior margin the capitulum is situated, flanked by the first pair of anterior legs; the second pair is adjacent to the first pair; the two posterior pairs are situated ventrally, posterior to the equator. Two pairs of conspicuous hairs mark the line dividing the anterior part of the dorsal surface, *notothorax,* from the posterior part, *notogaster.* The dorsal and ventral surfaces are marked by a system of parallel, fine transverse striations; on the notothorax this system is interrupted by a median nonstriated area, the *plastron,* on the notogaster by two similar areas, situated laterally. The surface of these areas is thicker, more pigmented, and less smooth in appearance than the rest of the integument. The plastron is flanked by two groups of three conical spines, placed at the corners of a

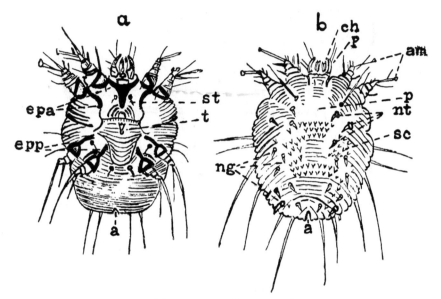

Fig. 27·1   *Sarcoptes scabiei,* ovigerous female, × 100: *Left,* ventral view. —*Right,* dorsal view: *a,* anus; *am,* ambulacra; *ch,* chelicera; *epa, epp,* epimeres; *ng,* seven notogastric spines; *nt,* three notothoracic spines; *P,* pedipalp; *p,* plastron; *sc,* scales; *st,* sternum; *t,* tocostome. (After Gudden.)

triangle with the apex facing backwards. On the notogaster two lateral groups of seven somewhat longer spines are implanted, each group arranged in a longitudinal outer row of four spines and an inner row of three spines. Moreover, the notogaster bears numerous transverse rows of minute triangular scales, pointing backwards, on the anterior two-thirds of its surface; they are interrupted by a median area without scales posterior to the plastron (Fig. 27·2:C).

The anus appears as a median longitudinal fissure at the posterior extremity, extending slightly farther cephalad on the dorsal side than on the ventral side. Dorsally, in front of this fissure, a papilla is situated with an aperture at its apex, the *copulatory papilla*, through the aperture of which the male products are introduced into the female body.[2] Ventrally and medially, slightly anterior to the equator, a minute transverse fissure is situated, the *tocostome;* it is

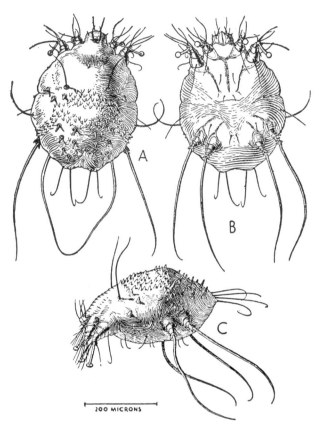

FIG. 27·2   *Sarcoptes scabiei*, ovigerous females, drawn after life, × 100: *A*, Dorsal aspect.—*B*, Ventral aspect.—*C*, From the side. (After Mellanby, 1944. Courtesy, Oxford University Press, London.)

bordered by two lips and can be closed by a transverse crease of the integument, the *operculum;* the eggs leave the female body through the tocostome.

The legs are inserted on the ventral side. From the base of each leg starts a narrow, brown, chitinous ridge in the direction of the center of the ventral side, the *epimere*. The epimeres of the first pair of legs join in the median line to form a single ridge, the *sternum;* it is directed caudad and terminates halfway between the junction of the epimeres and the tocostome. The epimeres of the three other pairs of legs terminate without having joined their opposite number. The two anterior pairs of legs are composed of five joints. They bear a number of hairs; the terminal joint also bears a pair of claws and a pedunculate sucking pad, or *ambulacrum.* The two posterior pairs are composed of four joints; they possess no ambulacrum; in its stead each apical joint carries a long hair.

The *capitulum,* the "head," fits into an anterior marginal notch, the *camerostome,* whose dorsal wall is called the *epistome.* The capitulum is composed of a basal part, supporting the other pieces: they are (1) a medioventral continuation of the basal part, the "lower lip," flanked by (2) two triangular thin lateral excrescences of the basal part, the "cheeks"; dorsally from the cheeks are situated (3) two triangular three-jointed pedipalps; mediodorsally lie (4) two cheliceras that articulate with the basal part. Each chelicera is composed of a spindle-shaped main stem, the "body," whose pointed extremity carries denticles on its inner surface; it carries a separate inner joint, the "digit," articulating with the main stem and forming a pair of pincers with the denticulated extremity of the body.[2]

The male (Fig. 27·3:*A*) is smaller than the ovigerous female, $\frac{1}{5}$ to $\frac{1}{3}$ mm in length, $\frac{1}{7}$ to $\frac{1}{6}$ mm in width. Some more differences are noticeable on the ventral side: (1) the epimeres of the two pairs of posterior legs are joined together; (2) the fourth pair of legs carries an ambulacrum; (3) between the posterior pairs of legs is situated a chitinous rod, the *epiandrium,* that terminates in a fork with two prongs which embrace a cavity that holds the external male genitals, closed by a thin cover, or "apron."

Development of the Young Stages. Notwithstanding the shortness of its legs, the ovigerous female moves fairly easily over the surface of the human skin, six times its own length in one minute.[3] The cheliceras, the pedipalps, and the sharp-edged outer surface of the apical joints of the anterior pair of legs serve as the tools that the female sets in motion to dig a burrow in the skin. As the ambulacra of the legs firmly adhere to the surface of the skin, the female is, in a manner of speech, "elbowing" its way into the skin. After an hour or so the female has dug itself in. As a rule, it digs its burrow in the horny layer of the skin, leaving the granular layer intact. The burrow takes a C- or S-shaped course, parallel to the surface of the skin. It is as wide as the female (Fig. 27·4), and a few millimeters long; 2–3 cm is its maximal length. The oldest portion of the

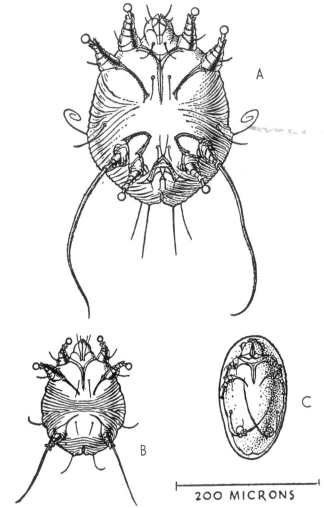

FIG. 27·3 *Sarcoptes scabiei,* × 190.—*A,* Male.—*B,* Larva.—*C,* Egg containing larva. (After Mellanby, 1944. Courtesy, Oxford University Press, London.)

burrow gradually disappears as a consequence of desquamation. Initially, the burrow appears as a fine, grayish white line; a raised whitish oval, with dark pigmentation at its front, marks the place occupied by the mite at its anterior end (Fig. 27·4:*A*); daily the mite extends its burrow over a distance of ½ to 5 mm. Later on, the burrow turns black from the accumulation of eggs and feces deposited by the females and the dirt rubbed into it. In the burrow the female may survive for nearly two months, ovipositing two or three times daily.[3] Within the eggs a larva develops (Fig. 27·3:*C*)

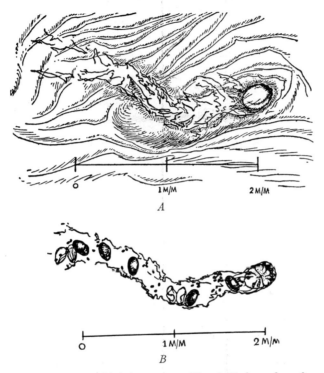

A

B

FIG. 27·4   *Sarcoptes scabiei*, burrow, × 24. *A*, Enlarged surface drawing.—*B*, Whole mount of biopsy of same burrow. (After Mellanby, 1944. Courtesy, Oxford University Press, London.)

and hatches after three to four days. The larvas (Fig. 27·3:*B*) possess three pairs of legs; their size is 140–160 × 100 μ. Shortly after hatching, they leave the burrow in which they were born; they move over the surface of the skin, but soon they hide in the hair follicles. Here they molt, thus becoming nymphs with four pairs of legs and a size of 175 × 135 μ. The nymphs likewise hide in the follicles of the hairs. From four to six days after the hatching of the larva, the nymph molts, thus turning into an adult male and a "young" female. The latter differs from an ovigerous female by its lesser size, ¼ × ⅕ mm or so, and by the absence of a tocostome (egg-laying aperture). The males and the young females dig burrows of less than 1 mm in which they stay for a short time only, for they copulate at the surface of the skin. After copulation, the young female molts once more and thus becomes an ovigerous, burrowing female a fortnight or so after it emerged from the eggshell in the form of a larva. Less than 10 percent of the deposited eggs yield this result because of the great mortality among the immature stages.[3]

Under normal conditions, burrows of a length of 1 mm or over contain only ovigerous females. In the so-called *Norwegian scabies,* or *scabies crustosa,* a single burrow harbors ovigerous females, larvas, nymphs, males, and young females.[4] Buxton[2] regarded the causative agent of Norwegian scabies as a separate variety, but Hermans[5] proved that subjects infected by a case of Norwegian scabies developed perfectly normal scabies. It seems therefore probable that the appearance of Norwegian scabies does not depend upon the parasite, but upon an underdeveloped defense mechanism of the host, due perhaps to impaired tactile irritability.[6]

HOST—PARASITE RELATIONSHIP

The Site of the Burrows. This differs with age and sex. In adult males Mellanby[3] found over three-fifths of the ovigerous females on the wrists and the hands; one-tenth or so were on the elbows, feet, and genitals; 4 percent were on the buttocks; 2 percent were on the skin of the arm pits; and the rest were in various other sites. In infants burrows occur indiscriminately, even on the head, a site which appears to be sedulously avoided in older subjects (except for Peters'[7] patient, aged 73, with burrows on her ears); in young children they are common on the feet. With advancing age burrows on the hands and the wrists become increasingly numerous, but in adult females they are often detected around the nipples.[8]

Except in cases of Norwegian scabies, the number of ovigerous females in untreated patients is restricted, eleven on an average. In more than half of them it is less than six; in 4 percent of them it exceeds fifty. The number of immature mites and males is perhaps twenty times as great.[3]

The Pruritus. This, the main symptom of the disease, cannot be laid at the door of the parasite; the host has himself to thank for it, as it is caused by his intolerance.

Initially he is not intolerant. If ovigerous females are placed on the skin of a subject who has had no previous experience of scabies, they start burrowing immediately; his skin does not respond to it, and he is in no way incommoded by it. After a month or longer, the skin begins to show signs of irritation in the form of edema, and the host begins to experience pruritus, to which he responds by scratching. The edema is harmful to the mites, because their burrows are flooded; the scratching is more harmful, because it drags the mites out of their burrows; the secondary pyodermia engendered by scratching is most harmful of all—it is fatal to the mites.[3] The number of ovigerous females, which may have risen to 50 on the twenty-fifth day after the infection, and to 500 on the one hundredth day, begins to decrease considerably under these adverse conditions.[9]

The response of a subject who has suffered from scabies at an earlier date is quite different. If he is infected by placing ovigerous females on his skin, he reacts, not after one month, but within 24 hours. The edema affecting the dermal tissue and the scratching stimulated by the pruritus afford the mites hardly any opportunity to multiply. On an average the hypersensitive subject harbors no more than three ovigerous females, compared with eleven in a nonsensitized subject. Accordingly, the sensitized subject offers less risk of infection to his fellow men than the subject who is still tolerant of the mites that infest his skin. The subject who for some reason or other never becomes sensitized, thus allowing the mites unlimited opportunities for multiplication, obviously offers the greater risk, as is the case in Norwegian scabies.

Prakken and Van Vloten [6] confirmed the existence of hypersensitivity to the presence of mites burrowing in the skin by an intradermal test with an antigen prepared from the scales of the skin of a case of Norwegian scabies. It was positive in subjects who were suffering or had suffered from scabies and negative in the absence of a history of scabies, unless the subjects had been artificially sensitized by the injection of blood serum of a scabies patient.

Infection with Scabies. This occurs through the medium of ovigerous females. The immature mites can pass from an infected subject to an uninfected one. If the latter is sensitized by a previous infection, an invasion of immature mites is sure to provoke a distressing papular reaction, but the mortality among the immature mites is so high that Mellanby [3] found it impossible to cause a permanent establishment of the parasite in the skin of the subject exposed to this mode of infection.

Similar invasions of immature mites are probably responsible for the exanthem experienced by subjects whose occupation brings them into contact with animals suffering from scabies caused by mites that are more or less closely related to the human mange mite, but belong to different species, such as *Notoedres cati* and *Otodectes* of cats,

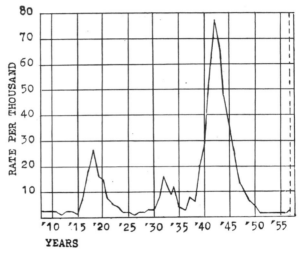

FIG. 27·5 Annual incidence of sarcoptic mange per 1000 Edinburgh schoolchildren, 1908–1957. (Graph drawn after figures published by Boog Watson.[12])

Chorioptes bovis of cattle, and *Psoroptes* of sheep, or at least to different races of *S. scabiei*. Nevertheless, the existence of true infections of man with animal mange mites cannot be denied, although it is probably incorrect to assume that such infections are an important cause of human scabies.

Successful transmission of scabies from man to man apparently requires a close contact, such as sharing a bed.[10] Inanimate objects may be of importance, but only under special circumstances; the inanimate object must pass quickly from one person to another, such as underwear, a towel, or bedding used by the person who is the source of infection [11]; that person, moreover, must be heavily infected, if he is to be an efficient source; an infection with 200 ovigerous females is regarded necessary for that purpose.[3] Thus, transmission by inanimate objects seems to be unlikely. Nevertheless, it would be wrong to ignore it completely, as ovigerous females, separated from the human body, may survive for two weeks as a maximum at a temperature of 13° C and a high humidity.

Social disturbances, such as war and economic crisis, have long since been recognized as creating an environment that scabies thrives on. The Edinburgh statistic over fifty years (Fig. 27·5), showing the apparent influence of two world wars and the economic crisis in the early thirties, is an excellent example to this effect.[12] It is not so evident what the nature of this influence is. Overcrowding and lack of soap are held responsible for the epidemic peaks, but it is not explained why the rise associated with World War II should start as early as 1939. The U. S. Army shows similar ups and downs, but not during the Korean War.[13] On the other hand, the decrease following the epidemics may well be the consequence of a reduction in the chance of infection following the establishment of hypersensitivity in a considerable portion of the population [3] and the development of an active antiscabies policy in the human community, stimulated by the very presence of the disease.[14]

TREATMENT OF SCABIES

A 10 percent sulfur ointment either alone or combined with 5 percent *Balsam of Peru*, U.S.P. are some of the older ointments that have proven satisfactory. In recent years the chlorinated hydrocarbons and benzyl benzoate have been found more effective, nonirritating and nonsensitizing. One percent of gamma benzene hexachloride (Kwell) in a lotion or cream has proven useful as a scabicide. The infested parts are first thoroughly cleansed with soap and water. The lotion or cream is then applied extensively on and around the affected parts. One application usually suffices, as BHC is ovicidal as well as larvicidal. However, it is desirable to repeat the treatment within a few days.

Benzyl benzoate lotions and DDT powder in inert ingredients, such as talcum or pyrophyllite, have also been used extensively either individually or combined in an emulsion. Some prefer to add 1 or 2 percent of benzocaine (Topocide) as an antipruritic.

DEMODEX FOLLICULORUM

Demodex folliculorum Simon, 1842, is a member, not of the super-family of the Sarcoptoidea, but of the Demodicoidea. However, its way of life sufficiently resembles that of *Sarcoptes scabiei* to justify its being discussed in this chapter.

Demodex is five to seven times as long as broad; the posterior two-thirds, the "abdomen," bears transverse striations; the anterior third, the "cephalothorax," carries a capitulum and four pairs of legs (Fig. 27·6). The capitulum carries two stylet-shaped cheliceras and two pedipalps composed of three (perhaps two) joints. Each leg has three joints; the apical joint bears two claws; the basal joint is connected with the medioventral sternum by means of an epimere. The female orifice is situated at the caudal extremity of the sternum,

Fig. 27·6 *Demodex folliculorum,* female, ventral aspect. (After Mégnin.)

the male orifice on the dorsal side, the anus near the posterior extremity on the ventral side. The superfamily comprises only one genus, composed of a number of species which are mainly character-ized by the hosts whose hair follicles they infest.[15]

The female measures 270–440 × 50–60 μ; the cephalothorax is from ¼ to ⅓ as long. The male measures 300 × 40–50 μ as a max-imum. The spindle-shaped eggs have a size of 60–80 × 40–50 μ. The larvas emerging from them have no legs to start with; later on they grow three pairs, which are increased to four in the nymphal stage. The nymph becomes an adult after two molts.

The parasites inhabit the hair follicles and the adjoining sebaceous glands of the face; they also penetrate the surrounding tissue (Fig. 27·7). They often evade detection and may be much more common than is generally supposed, particularly in old people. *D. follicu-lorum* is supposed to cause little damage, an opinion which is not shared by all observers [16] and which seems to be contradicted by the behavior of a related canine demodex. This is reported occasionally to cause a protracted skin disease in dogs, often ending fatally by the concomitant activity of pyogenic microbes. Nevertheless, asymptomatic carriers form the majority even in dogs,[17] notwithstanding the fact that the parasites may penetrate the regional lymph glands.[18]

The hypothesis has been brought forward [19] that *D. folliculorum* stimulates the dermal tissue to the formation of malignant growths and that it can serve as the vector of the causative agent of leprosy.

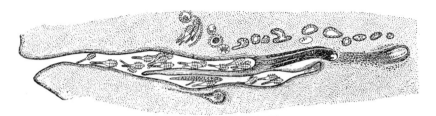

Fig. 27·7 *Demodex folliculorum* in hair follicle and associated sebaceous gland of a dog, × 32. (After Brumpt, 1922. Courtesy, Masson & Cie, Paris.)

This statement has been repeated on more than one occasion; at present it appears to be forgotten without being actually refuted.

According to Manson-Bahr [20] an ointment containing beta-naphthol and sublimated sulfur is said to be specific. One percent of gamma benzene hexachloride in a vanishing cream has also been reported to be effective.

REFERENCES FOR CHAPTER XXVII

1. C. Warburton. *Parasitology,* 1920, 12: 265–300.
2. P. A. Buxton. *Parasitology,* 1921, 13: 114–151.
3. K. Mellanby. *Scabies,* London, 1944, Oxford University Press.
4. S. L. Brug and J. Haga. *Mededeel. Dienst Volksgezandheid Ned. Indië,* Eng. Ed., 1930, 19: 250–253.
5. E. H. Hermans. *Ned. Tijdschr. Geneesk.,* 1948, 92: (English summary) 2980.
6. J. R. Prakken and Th. J. van Vloten. *Ned. Tijdschr. Geneesk.,* 1949, 93: 2592–2600, English summary, 2600.
7. F. Peters. *Ned. Tijdschr. Geneesk.,* 1946, 90: (English summary) 222.
8. E. H. Hermans. *Ned. Tijdcshr. Geneesk.,* 1942, 86: 626–632, English summary, 632.
9. K. Mellanby. *Parasitology,* 1944, 35: 197–206.
10. K. Mellanby. *Brit. Med. J.,* 1941 (1st half): 405–406.
11. K. Mellanby. *Bull. Entomol. Research,* 1942, 33: 267–271.
12. W. N. Boog Watson. *Medical Officer,* 1958: 293–294.
13. E. Epstein. *Arch. Dermatol. u. Syphilis,* 1955, 71: 192.

14. F. E. HELLIER. *Brit. Med. J.*, 1956 (2nd half): 1117.
15. S. HIRST. *The Genus Demodex Owen,* London, 1919, British Museum of Natural History.
16. S. AYRES and N. P. ANDERSON. *J. Am. Med. Assoc.*, 1932, 98: 1029.
17. W. UNSWORTH. *J. Comp. Pathol.*, 1946, 56: 114–127.
18. K. ENIGK. *Zentr. Bakteriol.*, Abt. I, Or., 1949, 153: 76–90.
19. A. BORREL. *Ann. inst. Pasteur, Paris,* 1909, 23: 97–128.
20. PH. H. MANSON-BAHR. *Tropical Diseases,* London, 1957, p. 1008.

CHAPTER XXVIII

INSECTA

Insects parasitizing man share two characteristics with all other insects; the adult body is composed of three distinct parts, *head, thorax,* and *abdomen,* and the head carries a single pair of *antennas* besides the mouth parts.

A complete set of mouth parts consists of (1) the unpaired upper lip, or *labrum,* welded to the continuation of the roof of the buccal cavity, or *epipharynx;* (2) the continuation of the bottom of the buccal cavity, or *hypopharynx;* (3) a pair of *mandibles;* (4) a pair of primary *maxillas,* with a pair of *maxillary palps* inserted at their base; (5) a pair of secondary maxillas, often joined together into a single organ, the lower lip, or *labium,* with a pair of *labial palps,* either inserted at their base or situated at their apex; in the latter case they are reduced in size and known as *labella.* Some of the insects to be described here do not possess a complete set of mouth parts.

The function of the mouth parts is either to bite off and masticate solid food or to imbibe liquid food. The latter activity is carried out in collaboration with an organ serving as a sucking pump and pressure pump, the *pharynx,* situated immediately behind the buccal cavity. If the fluid food is blood, the sucking mouth parts have the further function of piercing the skin of the animal whose blood the insect is going to imbibe.

The thorax is composed of three segments. In the insects described here the segments are fused, except for the fleas, but their presence is proved by the single pair of legs each segment carries on its ventral side and by the single pair of wings (fully developed or modified) borne by the second and third segments of some insects. From their base to their tip, the legs are composed of *coxa, trochanter, femur, tibia,* and one to five *tarsal joints* or *tarsals.*

The abdomen is usually composed of nine segments, of which eight can be identified as such, whereas the ninth may be modified beyond recognition.

Oxygen is introduced into the body through *spiracles* situated on the thorax and abdomen in a varying number of pairs. Into the spiracles open the air tubes or *tracheas* that distribute the atmospheric air throughout the body of the insect.

In a typical case, the young insect emerging from the egg is as unlike its mother as the caterpillar is to the butterfly. It is a vermiform *larva,* which after three molts becomes an often immobile *pupa,* out of which the adult insect emerges. However, this *complete metamorphosis* is not found in all insects. In some the newly hatched larva has the form of a miniature adult. After the first molt it retains the same general form, but it has grown in size and is now called a *nymph.* It has to molt once or several times before it reaches the adult stage. This development is known as *incomplete metamorphosis.*

The insects to be discussed in this and the next chapters can be listed as follows.

(1) Insects developing by incomplete metamorphosis ....(2)
    Insects developing by complete metamorphosis ....(3)

(2) Wingless, dorsoventrally flattened insects, with legs primarily adapted to grasping and mouth parts often hidden within a pouch underneath the buccal cavity, from which they are protruded when they are to be used ....*Anoplura,* or lice
    Wingless or winged, dorsoventrally flattened insects, with legs adapted to quick motion and mouth parts that are always visible, pressed against the ventral side of the head and the thorax
                                           Hemiptera, or true bugs

(3) Wingless, laterally flattened insects, with the third pair of legs adapted to jumping. The adults have piercing and sucking mouth parts, the larvas biting mouth parts ....*Siphonaptera,* or fleas
    Insects with one pair of wings on the second thoracic segments, and one pair of "halteres" on the third (*Diptera*) ....(4)

(4) Parasitic *Diptera* ....Parasitic larvas of certain flies
    Nonparasitic *Diptera* ....Gnats, mosquitoes, and flies that serve as vectors of various pathogenic agents

Lice, fleas, true bugs, and parasitic diptera will be discussed in Chapters XXIX–XXXI and XXXIII. Nonparasitic diptera, which form no proper part of the subject matter of this book, will nevertheless receive cursory attention in Chapter XXXII because some of them have been mentioned already as vectors of protozoan or helmintic parasites, while others are vectors of parasites not belonging to the animal kingdom that have been or will be mentioned in relation to certain parasitic arthropods.

CHAPTER XXIX

PEDICULIDAE: LICE

Insects known as lice belong to the order of Anoplura. They are small, a few millimeters in length, and live as "body vermin" on the skin of mammals and birds. Their food consists of blood of the host or parts of the skin and its hairs or feathers; in accordance with this, their mouth parts are adapted to piercing and sucking or to biting. They multiply on the skin of their host and attach their eggs to the hairs and feathers. In the human host, some attach their eggs to the fibers of the clothes. Lice that dispose of their eggs in this way must be classified as "house vermin."

FIG. 29·1 *Trichodectes pilosus,* female, × 20; a parasite of equines. (After Railliet.)

The antennas are composed of three to five joints; the eyes, if at all present, are simple; the thoracic segments are fused; the abdomen is composed of nine segments, but the two proximal ones may be absent. One pair of spiracles is located on the thorax, and six pairs on the abdomen.[1]

The Anoplura comprise two suborders—Mallophaga, with biting mouth parts, and Siphunculata, with piercing and sucking mouth parts. Although the Mallophaga rarely attack man, they are mentioned here because a canine parasite of the genus *Trichodectes*

(Fig. 29·1) serves as vector of the canine tapeworm *Dipylidium caninum*.

The Siphunculata comprise four families. One of them, the Haematopinidae, includes the rat louse, *Polyplax spinulosus* (Fig. 29·2), that transmits *Rickettsia typhi,* the causative agent of endemic typhus, from one rat to another, but not from rat to man.

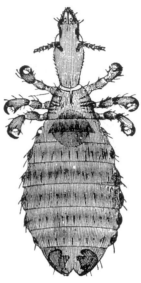

FIG. 29·2   *Haematopinus asini,* female, × 20. (After Railliet.)

Another family of the Siphunculata, that of the Pediculidae, is the one with which this chapter is concerned. Their members have antennas with either three joints or five joints. To the latter belong those that parasitize man—viz. *Pediculus humanus,* with an abdomen which is twice as long as wide and legs about equal in size, and *Phthirus pubis,* with an abdomen which is wider than long and front legs much more slender than the midlegs and hind legs.

PEDICULUS HUMANUS

The general features of *Pediculus humanus* Linnaeus, 1758, may be gathered from Fig. 29·3 and 29·4. The thoracic spiracles do not show in the picture—they are located near the mid coxas; the six pairs of abdominal spiracles are arranged in two marginal rows, one behind the other. The tibia, the fourth joint of the leg, carries an excrescence at its inner apical extremity, the "thumb" (Fig. 29·4:*th*), which can be reached by a claw located on the apex of the fifth, or tarsal, joint (Figs. 29·3 and 29·4:*cl*). Thumb and claw, touching each other, can grasp slender objects, such as hairs or fibers of some tissue.

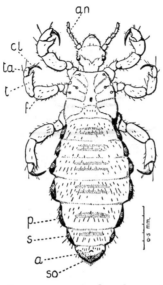

Fig. 29·3   *Pediculus humanus,* male dorsal aspect, × 24: *a,* Anus.—*an,* Antenna.—*cl,* Claw.—*f,* Femur.—*p,* Pleural plates.—*s,* Spiracle.—*so,* Sexual orifice.—*t,* Tibia.—*ta,* Tarsal joint. (After Buxton, 1947. Courtesy, Edward Arnold & Co., London.)

In the female the anus is situated at the posterior extremity of the abdomen. The vulva lies on the ventral side, anterior to the anus; it is flanked by two flat, hook-shaped chitinous plates, the *gonopods,* with which the female seizes the hair or the fiber to which it is going to attach the eggs it is depositing.

In the male the anus and the sexual orifice (Fig. 29·3:*a, so*) are shifted to the dorsal side; as a consequence the anus is situated cephalad from the sexual orifice. During the process of copulation, the male inserts a strongly chitinized pair of tongs (*edeagus*) into the vulva which, by opening, expand the vagina, thus allowing the introduction of the male copulatory organ.[2]

The relative position of sexual orifice and anus was once of considerable importance for the preparation of Weigl's vaccine [3] against typhus, by growing the causative agent, *Rickettsia prowazeki,* in the epithelial lining of the gut of the louse. For that purpose infectious material had to be introduced into the anal aperture and not into the sexual orifice.[4]

Fig. 29·5 shows the location of the mouth parts. Anteriorly the buccal cavity terminates in a short tube, the *haustellum.* It carries minute spines on its inner surface; it can be everted, and then the spines lie on its outer surface; thus they can be hooked into the wall of the wound caused by the louse piercing the skin of its host.

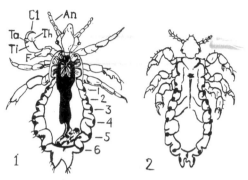

FIG. 29·4   *Pediculus humanus,* dorsal aspect, × 11: 1. *P. h. corporis,* female.—2. *P. h. capitis,* female.—*An,* Antenna.—*Cl,* Claw.—*Ta,* Tarsal joint.—*Ti,* Tibia.—*Th,* "Thumb" of tibia.—*F,* Femur.—1–6. Spiracles on 1st to 6th abdominal segment. (After Van Lith, 1922.)

The piercing organs, the *stylets,* are located within a pouch (*ss*) situated underneath the pharynx (*ap, pp*) and opening into the buccal cavity. The pouch can be everted, thereby extruding the stylets. The latter consist of (1) a pair of dorsal stylets, each one carrying a pair of armed hooks at its distal extremity and placed one on top of the other; (2) an unpaired tubular organ, the *hypopharynx,* through which passes the saliva that is injected into the wound; (3) an unpaired ventral stylet that supports the other piercing organs and has the form of a tube cut lengthwise.

When the louse is about to suck blood, the stylets are extruded through the oral aperture and the blood is sucked in by means of the activity of the anterior and posterior parts of the pharynx that expand and contract in turn. The saliva is produced by two pairs of glands, situated one behind the other in the thorax, the anterior pair kidney-shaped, the posterior pair U-shaped; it is conveyed to the hypopharynx through the salivary duct (sd). The saliva produced by the kidney-shaped glands is highly irritating to the skin.[5]

By the expansion and contraction of the pharynx the blood is passed on, by way of the esophagus, to the stomach. The undigested remnant enters the narrow portion of the midgut; it is inspissated in the hindgut and is evacuated in the form of minute black granules that turn into dust when dried.

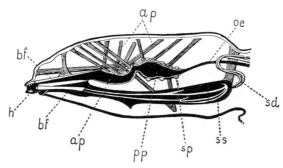

FIG. 29·5 *Pediculus humanus,* median longitudinal section through the head: *ap,* Anterior cavity of pharynx.—*bf,* Buccal cavity.—*dp,* Muscles expanding the pharyngeal cavity.—*h,* Haustellum.—*oe,* Esophagus.—*pp,* Posterior cavity of pharynx.—*sd,* Salivary ducts.—*sp,* Sphincter.—*ss,* Pouch containing stylets. (After Buxton, 1947. Courtesy, Edward Arnold & Co., London.)

Although the female louse may imbibe 1 mg of blood at a time, i.e. one-third of its body weight, this is not sufficient for an adequate nutrition. Apparently the food is lacking certain indispensable nutrients, a lack which is supposed to be provided for by microorganisms that are cultured inside a specialized organ, the *mycetoma,* situated ventrally in the wall of the midgut.[6]

In front of the first pair of salivary glands a number of large binucleate cells are situated, conspicuous by the greenish granules they harbor. They are called *nephrocytes*[6] and probably are of importance in the life cycle of human blood parasites of the genus *Borrelia* which are transmitted by lice.[7]

Female lice lay eggs, and the larvas emerge within three weeks or in less than one week, according to the temperature. The larva has the appearance of a miniature adult with a very short abdomen and antennas with only three joints. After one molt it becomes a nymph, and the nymph becomes an adult after a second molt, 13 to 16 days after the hatching of the larva. From a day to a day and a half after the last molt the female begins to lay eggs. It continues to do so except for the last day or two of its life, which lasts an average of 18 days, with a maximum of 46 days.[8]

Neither eggs nor lice survive an exposure to high temperatures. Eggs die within half an hour at 49° C; lice do not survive for more than 24 hours at a temperature of 39° C. Low temperatures are not nearly as lethal; at a temperature of −7° C lice survive more than 36 hours.

Lice separated from the human body die after five to six days at a temperature of 23° to 24° C; at 15° C their life is prolonged to ten days, but it becomes shorter if the temperature drops below that level.[9] Thus a house inhabited by a lice-infested family will become louse-free ten days after the inhabitants leave the premises. If the former inhabitants leave behind them garments infested with "nits" (i.e. louse eggs), the nits may hatch after 17 to 21 days at a temperature of 24° C and the emerging larvas may survive for another week. This postpones the date of riddance from lice from the 10th day to the 24th–28th day. If the temperature drops below 24° C, the larvas do not hatch; but the eggs remain viable and may hatch if the temperature rises. Taking all this into account, Buxton [10] considers a house to be louse-free if it has been left uninhabited for one month.

HEAD LICE AND BODY LICE

The above refers to *Pediculus humanus* as a whole. But this species is not a whole. It is composed of two groups of insects, known as head lice and body lice or *Pediculus humanus capitis* de Geer, 1778, and *P. h. corporis* de Geer, 1778 (*P. vestimenti* Nitzsch, 1818). Whether they are to be regarded as subspecies, varieties, or modifications induced by environmental conditions may be left undecided. The broad fact remains that they exist.

Head lice inhabit the hair-covered scalp; there they feed, multiply, and attach their eggs to the hairs of the scalp; from the eggs a second generation emerges, which continues its existence on the same host; thus head lice are true parasites or body vermin. They are of only secondary importance as vectors of diseases,[11] and as a general rule they are less unacceptable socially than body lice. A progressive population first lose their body lice; the disappearance of head lice follows at a later date.

The body lice inhabit man's underclothing; there they multiply and attach their eggs on the cloth fibers; they seek man's body only for the purpose of feeding. If the host is in the habit of wearing different clothing at night, body lice and their eggs are separated from the body for a time equal to one-quarter to one-third of their life span, though occasionally they remain attached to the body hairs. Thus they are not true parasites, but house vermin. Moreover, they are of primary importance as vectors of diseases, and socially they are decidedly more unacceptable than head lice.

Differences Between the Two Races. There are a number of characteristics to appease those who object to the taxonomic rank conferred on the two groups by the Linnean names cited above. These characteristics are the following.

(*a*) Head lice have shorter antennas than body lice, owing to the shortness of the third joint.

(*b*) The length of male lice is about 2.8 mm, as against 3.4 mm in body lice; that of the female is about 3.2 mm, as against 3.5–4 mm in body lice.

(*c*) Under natural conditions head lice are more pigmented than body lice. However, kept in complete darkness or exposed to light on a purely white substratum, head lice lose their pigment after molting; conversely body lice exposed to light on a black substratum become pigmented after molting.[12] Nevertheless, Van Lith [13] claims that head lice grown under these experimental conditions still show a narrow anterior margin of pigment on the head which is absent in body lice.

(*d*) In head lice the ventral abdominal muscles are limited to the fifth segment; in body lice they occur in the fourth segment as well, although not invariably so.

(*e*) A breeding experiment continued through 42 generations [14] proved that at least one characteristic breeds true to type, viz. the body weight of living unfed males; it was 0.84–0.96 mg in head lice and 1.38–1.49 mg in body lice. Head lice, in these experiments, proved the weaker of the two, with a lower percentage of eggs hatching, a higher mortality of larvas and nymphs, and a lesser resistance to lack of food.

(*f*) The "nits," the eggs of head and body lice, are slightly different (Fig. 29·6). Their size is about the same, 0.8 × 0.3 mm or so. Both have a lid surmounted by a single layer of air chambers; but the air chambers cover a smaller area in the nit of the body louse (Fig. 29·6:1, *b*) than in that of the head louse (Fig. 29·6:2, *b*). The nits are cemented to hairs or fibers with a substance secreted as a fluid that hardens when exposed to the air. In this hardened state it covers the lower part of the egg and the adjoining parts of the hair or fiber. The outline of the cement covering the egg of head lice passes smoothly into the outline of the cement covering the hair or fiber (Fig. 29·6:2, *a*); in the egg of the body louse there is an indentation interrupting the smooth course of the outline (Fig. 29·6:1, *a*).

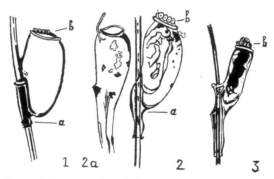

FIG. 29·6   Eggs of three species of lice, × 29: 1. *Pediculus humanus corporis.*—2. *P. h. capitis.*—2a. The same, empty shell.—3. *Phthirus pubis.*—1a, Deep indentation, 2a, shallow indentation at posterior extremity of egg.—b, Air chambers on operculum. (After Van Lith, 1922.)

There would be no need to point out this difference if head lice always oviposited on hairs of the scalp and body lice on fibers of clothing. They do, as a rule, but there are exceptions which render their behavior unfit to serve as a racial characteristic.

(g) Finally, there is a genetic argument in favor of regarding head lice and body lice as separate units, viz. the effect of interbreeding. The two races are perfectly fertile together, and the hybrid progeny is perfectly fertile too; but the numerous hermaphrodites produced indicate that a certain degree of genetic incompatibility exists between the gametes of the two races.[15]

Habitat of the Body Louse. The eggs are found in underwear, particularly in the seams, and on all objects in touch with the bare skin, even metallic objects. If the underclothing is scanty or badly torn, eggs also occur in the outer clothing and in footwear that is not taken off at night. Van Lith [13] also found the eggs attached to axillary, pubic, and perianal hairs, but not on hairs covering the scalp. Eggs were never found separate from man and the clothes he is wearing. They are, for instance, absent from bedding.

The lice are found in underwear, particularly in the parts covering the neck and the armpits. In heavily infested subjects, fever patients, and after death, lice are found in the outer clothes. High boots, worn night and day, may prove to be infested when all other garments are free from lice. Outside the human body, bedding and towels often harbor lice.[16]

Habitat of the Head Louse. *The eggs* are attached to the hairs at a distance of ½ to ¾ of a cm from the skin. They are also found nearer the apex of the hair, but these are either empty shells or dead eggs. In subjects wearing the hair long, eggs are found on hairs covering the nape and the temples; in those wearing it short the frontal hairs are preferred and also the whiskers, but not the moustache. The hairy parts of wigs, in the old days, were often infested with nits.[17] Eggs are not found outside the human body; they are absent from hats,[13] notwithstanding the presence of lice in that site.

The lice themselves are common enough in all kinds of headwear, the outer clothing, bedding, the upholstery of railway carriages, combs, hairbrushes, and towels. On the whole, head lice show a greater tendency to wander than body lice; as an instance, they may move from one hat to another hanging on the next peg. Accordingly, head lice spread more easily than body lice; conversely, adverse social conditions favoring the spread of head lice must get worse before they favor the spread of body lice.

RELATIONSHIP BETWEEN LICE AND THEIR HOSTS

Pediculid parasitism, characterized by *tolerance* and *numerical restraint,* can claim a place among the most successful and instructive examples of parasitism. Lice, like protozoa and unlike helminths, multiply indefinitely on the host's body; thus numerical restraint imposed by the host has the same effect as in protozoan infection.

There can be no doubt that lice are subjected to numerical restraint by their host, at least head lice are. In urban areas in England, children up to eight years of age are infected for over 40 percent, adults for 5 percent. In rural areas, where lousy heads are socially less acceptable, the rate of infection in children is 20 percent and in adults a little over 2 percent.[18] The size of the "louse load" may be gathered from the fact that three-fifths of the infected children harbored less than ten head lice.[19]

As to the counterpart of numerical restraint, the tolerance of the host, no exact observations are available. One has to rely on the numerous personal accounts of those who have come in close touch with lice, all agreeing that they became less and less sensitive to the bite of the insects and ended with being no longer aware of their presence.[6]

If experiments with rats may be applied to human conditions, the state of nutrition in which the host finds himself greatly influences his ability to impose numerical restraint. Fed on a normal diet, rats can keep their louse population at a low level, but they lose this ability if fed on a diet deficient in vitamins A and B_1. On the other hand, deficiency in piridoxine, folic acid, or choline did not impair this restraining ability; if anything, it had the opposite effect.[20]

Humoral and cellular reactions of the host may contribute to his ability to impose numerical restraint. But the defense mechanism he sets in action against lice is of an entirely different nature, viz. the conscious activity of catching and destroying the ectoparasites, as also practiced by animals, and the subconscious activity implied in submitting to the social rules of bodily cleanliness. According to Mellanby [19] the regular use of comb and hairbrush causes a considerable reduction in the population of head lice. A daily repeated complete change of the clothes worn during waking and sleeping hours, and an ample supply of underwear, have a similar restraining effect.[16]

Under these normal circumstances, the average number of body lice harbored by one individual may vary from ten to twenty.[6]

However, the well-balanced relationship between man and lice may be upset in times of economic and social distress, as occasioned by war and other catastrophes. If there is no soap and no fuel to light a fire for heating water, no washing can be effectively performed. If spare underwear is lacking and no combs or hairbrushes are available, people begin to lose interest in the appearance they present to their neighbors. If to these evils is added evacuation of large parts of the population, family ties are broken which still upheld a code of social conduct, and certain feelings of decency are lost, among them the shame engendered by being found lousy.

Under these abnormal conditions the "louse load" of a population may run into hundreds.

War experience offers this picture of a deteriorating host-parasite relationship in pediculid parasitism, which is no more than a caricature of a normally well-balanced coexistence. There would be no valid reason for upsetting this balance, if no complication existed, outside the normal relationship of host and parasite, that forced man ruthlessly to destroy body lice with all the modern insecticides at his disposal. That complication is the fact that body lice serve as vectors to causative agents of infectious diseases, namely (1) *Rickettsia prowazeki,* causing "epidemic typhus"; (2) *Rickettsia quintana,* causing the "Wolhynian" or "trench fever," and (3) the causative agents of louse-borne relapsing fever—*Borrelia recurrentis* and *B. obermeieri* in Europe, *B. berbera* in Africa, and *B. carteri* in India.[24]

Moreover, *Rickettsia typhi,* the cause of "endemic typhus," transmitted by fleas from its murine reservoir hosts to man, is said to be occasionally transmitted from man to man by body lice. Finally, body lice have been found naturally infected with *Pasteurella pestis,* the causative agent of plague.

PHTHIRUS PUBIS: THE CRAB LOUSE

Phthirus pubis Linnaeus, 1758, is distinguished from *Pediculus humanus* by its thickset, stumpy form, its small size (males 1.3×0.8 mm, females 1.5×1.0 mm), the slender pair of front legs, markedly distinct from the mid and hind legs with their huge claws, the big "snout" (i.e. the part of the head in front of the antennas), the fusion of the first to third abdominal segments, resulting in the first to third spiracles being placed side by side and not behind each other, and the four lateral appendages on the abdominal segments, which gradually increase in length while passing from the first pair, on the fused first-to-third segment, to the fourth pair on the sixth segment (Fig. 29·7). The eggs, attached to the pubic hairs like those of head lice to the hairs of the scalp, differ from the latter by the form of the air chambers on the lid of the egg. In head lice the air chambers are uniform in size (Fig. 29·6:2); in crab lice the central chambers are twice as high as the peripheral ones; as a result the lid has the appearance of a dish with apples piled on it (Fig. 29·6:3).

The eggs hatch in 7 to 9 days; the larvas molt to nymphs and the nymphs to adults in 13 to 17 days at the temperature of the pubic region (about 30° C).[21] The female crab louse is far less fertile than the body louse or even the head louse; no more than 20 to 26 eggs are deposited. With its mid and hind legs it grasps two hairs, and between the two it remains attached during its whole life, which hardly lasts a month,[21] rarely moving farther than a few centimeters from the spot it occupies. It is only when laying eggs that it looses its hold of one of the hairs. Thus the female is seen occupying the center of an area with a diameter of 6 cm or less, marked by less than 30 eggs attached to some of the hairs.

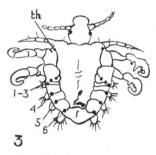

Fig. 29·7 *Phthirus pubis*, male, dorsal aspect, × 15: *th*, Thoracic spiracle.—1–3. The three anterior abdominal spiracles placed side by side.—4, 5, 6. The three posterior spiracles placed one behind the other. (After Van Lith, 1922.)

The crab louse is found on the pubic hairs; if they are shaved, the perineal hairs or the hairs on the thighs are chosen as the next best site. Crab lice are also reported on hairs growing on the trunk and the armpits, rarely on the scalp, and occasionally on the ciliary hairs and the eyebrows.[22]

Separated from the human body, crab lice die within 24 hours. Thus infection is successful only from intimate contact. As a consequence, infection with crab lice often implies exposure similar to that in venereal infection. Nevertheless, crab lice have been found in considerable numbers on straw covering the floor of sheds serving as temporary barracks. Moreover, it is often difficult even approximately to fix the place and time of infection, because months may elapse before the parasite carrier is incommoded by pruritus.

The so-called *maculae caeruleae* appear to be a reaction of the host specific to crab lice. They are painless, nonpruritic blueish spots about 1 cm in diameter which do not disappear on pressure. They may be found in the skin of the thighs and the lower abdomen 12 to 21 days after infection and are considered to be the effect of the secretion of the kidney-shaped salivary glands.[5]

Although Weyer [23] succeeded in infecting crab lice with *Rickettsia prowazeki* by rectal injection, this louse must be ranked third in importance as a natural vector of this microbe, notably because of its lack of activity.

TREATMENT OF PEDICULOSIS. One percent lotion or cream of benzene hexachloride (lindane, Kwell) has proven effective in infestations of the scalp or pubic region. The lotion or cream is rubbed into the scalp or pubic area and left on for 12 hours. In the latter it is advisable to shave the hair before the medication is applied. The parts are then cleansed with soap and water. A pyrophyllite powder of one percent BHC (gammexane) is also very effective. The powder is left on for several days, and is then removed with soap and water. One application is often effective, but the treatment should, nevertheless, be repeated after a few days.

In infestation with body lice an 8–10 percent DDT dusting powder may be freely dusted on the body or on the undergarments, especially in the seams and folds. Benzyl benzoate lotions are also extensively used as a pediculocide (see page 479). Bedding and clothing may be sprayed with DDT or fumigated with methyl bromide for half an hour in gasproof clothing bags. Dry heat or laundering of bedding with soap and a 5 percent DDT suspension have also proven satisfactory.

REFERENCES FOR CHAPTER XXIX

1. G. H. F. NUTTALL. *Parasitology,* 1919, 11: 329–346.
2. G. H. F. NUTTALL. *Parasitology,* 1917, 9: 293–324.
3. R. WEIGL. *Arch. inst. Pasteur Tunis,* 1933, 22: 315–320.
4. H. EYER et al. *Z. Hyg. Infektionskrankh.,* 1940, 122: 702–719.
5. E. N. PAVLOWSKY and A. K. STEIN. *Z. exptl. Med.,* 1924, 42: 15–24.
6. P. A. BUXTON. *The Louse,* London, 1947, Edw. Arnold & Co.
7. R. B. HEISCH. *Bull. soc. pathol. exotique,* 1955, 48: 322–325.
8. F. W. EVANS and F. F. SMITH. *Trop. Diseases Bull.,* 1953, 50: 398.
9. H. S. LEESON. *Bull. Entomol. Research,* 1941, 32: 49–51.
10. P. A. BUXTON. *Brit. Med. J.,* 1940 (2nd half): 603–604.
11. J. R. BUSVINE. *Brit. Med. Bull.,* 1943, 3: 215–240.
12. G. H. F. NUTTALL. *Parasitology,* 1919, 11: 201–220.
13. A. J. J. VAN LITH. *The Practice of Louse Control.* Thesis, Amsterdam, 1922.
14. J. R. BUSVINE. *Parasitology,* 1948, 39: 1–16.

15. D. KEILIN and G. H. F. NUTTALL. *Parasitology,* 1919, 11: 279–328.
16. J. MACLEOD and H. J. CRAUFURD-BENSON. *Parasitology,* 1941, 33: 211–218, 278–299.
17. H. ZINSSER. *Rats, Lice and History,* London, 1935, G. Routledge & Sons.
18. E. C. G. MADDOCK. *Monthly Bull. Ministry Health,* London, 1949, 8: 26–30.
19. K. MELLANBY. *Parasitology,* 1942, 34: 180–184.
20. L. KARTMAN. *J. Parasitol.,* 1949, 35: 367–374.
21. G. H. F. NUTTALL. *Parasitology,* 1918, 10: 383–405.
22. P. A. BUXTON. *Parasitology,* 1941, 33: 117–118.
23. F. WEYER. *Z. Tropenmed. Parasitol.,* 1952, 3: 302–309.
24. R. J. DUBOS. *Bacterial and Mycotic Infections of Man,* 3d ed., Philadelphia, 1959, J. B. Lippincott, p. 540.

CHAPTER XXX

SIPHONAPTERA: FLEAS

FLEAS AS HOUSE VERMIN

The Siphonaptera or Aphaniptera are wingless bloodsucking ecto-parasites. They belong mostly to the category of "house vermin," feeding on their host and inhabiting and multiplying in the host's house or nest. They differ from other ectoparasites because the adults are flattened laterally; for that reason their side aspect is pictured, never their dorsal or ventral aspect (Fig. 30·2). Develop-ing fleas undergo a complete metamorphosis, with larvas possessing biting mouth parts (Fig. 30·1), as distinct from the adults that possess piercing and bloodsucking mouth parts.

Adult fleas have a brown color, and measure a few millimeters in length. The head is more or less quadrangular, but the forehead is rounded. The antennas are situated in a hollow behind the eyes; they are short and three-jointed—the apical joint is the largest and club-shaped, with transverse striations. Sometimes a pair of simple eyes is present. The mouth parts consist of (1) a short lower lip flanked by two, long, jointed, labial palps (Fig. 30·3:C, LbP); (2) a pair of flat, triangular maxillas (Fig. 30·3:C, Mx), each provided with a jointed maxillary palp inserted at its base (Fig. 30·3:C, MxP); (3) a pair of long, slender limbs, the *lacinias*,[1] which jointly form a tube through which the blood is sucked up [2] (Fig. 32·3:2, Mx); in the ventral part of the wall of the tube lies the salivary duct (Fig. 32·3:2, Sga); the dorsal part is strengthened by an unpaired limb, the epipharynx (Fig. 32·3:2, Ep). When not in use, the lacinias repose within a trough formed by the labial palps (Fig. 32·3:2, LbPlp).

The thorax of the adult flea is composed of three distinct segments (Fig. 30·3:A, Pt, Mst, Mtt), each carrying a pair of legs on its ventral side. The first segment embraces the ventral side of the head, and thus the pair of legs belonging to that segment are attached underneath the head (Fig. 30·2). The legs have relatively large coxas (Fig. 30·3:*A, CxII*), small trochanters (Fig. 30·3:*A, TrII*), femurs and tibias, no larger than the coxas, and five tarsal joints each, with a pair of claws at the apex of the fifth segment. The joints of the hind legs are longer than those of the others, thus enabling fleas

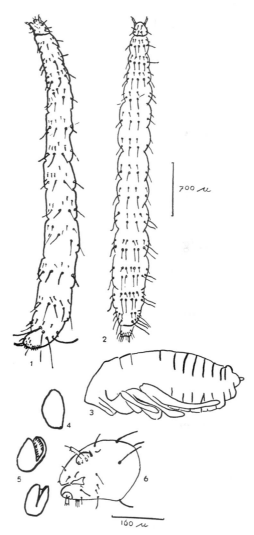

FIG. 30·1 *Ctenocephalides felis:* 1. Mature larva, side aspect.—2. The same, dorsal aspect.—3. Pupa, far advanced in development.—4. Egg.— 5. The same, after hatching.—6. Head of larva, side aspect. 1–5, × 30. 6, × 130. (After Elbel, 1950. Courtesy, *Journal of Parasitology.*)

to move by jumping. However, they can quickly move without jumping, supported by the hairs of the host's fur.

The abdomen consists of ten segments. The ninth carries on its dorsal surface a disk-shaped structure, the *pygidium* (Fig. 30·3:*A*, *Py*), covering the anus and bearing a large number of short hairs and a smaller number of long hairs. The males can be identified by the long, coiled, chitinous *edeagus,* or cirrus organ, situated in

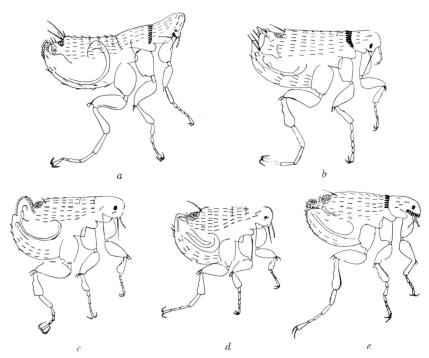

FIG. 30·2   Some fleas of human importance, males, × 20: *a, Ctenopsyllus segnis.—b, Nosospyllus fasciatus.—c, Pulex irritans.—d, Xenopsylla cheopis.—e, Ctenocephalides felis.* (After Turkhude. Courtesy, *Journal of Hygiene,* Cambridge.)

the distal half of the abdomen (Fig. 30·2:*c, d*), the females by the seminal receptacle (Fig. 30·3:*A, Rs*).

On the head, the thorax, or the abdomen one or more "combs" may be present—rows of flat, black, slender appendages (Fig. 30·2:in *a, b, e*; absent in *c, d*; Fig. 30·3:*D, E*).

Adult fleas feed exclusively on blood; it is sucked up through a tube (Fig. 32·3:2, *Fc*), by the activity of the pharyngeal pump; by the same activity it is pressed into the esophagus and ultimately into the midgut. Between the esophagus and the midgut the *proventriculus* is situated. It is a spherical structure, internally lined with seven rows of bristles that are directed backwards. They do not impede the flow of blood running from esophagus to midgut, but they prevent *regurgitation,* i.e. the return to the esophagus of the

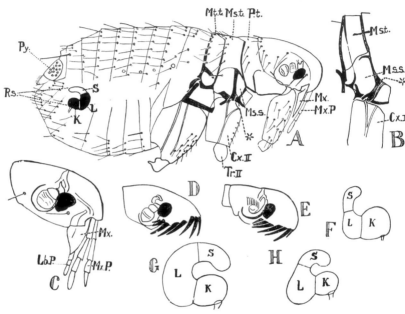

FIG. 30·3 *A. X. cheopis,* female: *Mx,* maxilla; *MxP,* maxillary palp; *Pt, Mst, Mtt,* pro-, meso-, metatergite; *Mss,* mesosternite; * vertical chitinous bar characteristic of this species, absent in *P. irritans* (see *B*); *CxII,* mid coxa; *TrII,* mid trochanter; *Py,* pygidium; *Rs,* seminal receptacle (*S,* "tail"; *L,* "body"; *K,* "head").—*B. P. irritans,* mesothoracic segment: *Mst,* mesotergite; *Mss,* mesosternite; * nonvertical chitinous bar (see *A*).—*C. P. irritans,* head: *Mx,* maxilla; *Mxp,* maxillary palp; *Lbp,* labial palp; compare the single hair on the occiput with the numerous hairs on the occiput of *A.*—*D. Ct. felis,* head.—*E. Ct. canis,* head.—*F.* Seminal receptacle of *X. braziliensis* (after Rothschild).—*G.* The same, of *X. cheopis.*—*H.* The same, of *X. astia.*

fluid contained in the midgut. The blood is digested in the extended posterior portion of the midgut, the stomach. The indigested remnant is inspissated in the rectum and evacuated in the form of minute, black, sticky globules that soon dry to dust.

The eggs of the fleas are pearly gray, about 0.7 × 0.4 mm in size.

They hatch after two to ten days.[3] The emerging larvas are vermiform, colorless, without limbs, 3–4 mm long; they are composed of twelve segments covered with scanty hairs; the first segment is provided with biting mouth parts (Fig. 30·1). The larvas feed on organic detritus they find in their surroundings. The larvas of some species of fleas (e.g. the rat flea *Nosopsyllus fasciatus*, Fig. 30·2:*b*) eat the feces of adult fleas. They can do so because the adults pass more of their time in the nests of their host than on its body and because the larvas also live in these nests. Species whose larvas do not feed on the feces of the adult fleas, such as the human flea *Pulex irritans* (Fig. 30·2:*c*), and the tropical rat flea *Xenopsylla cheopis* (Fig. 30·2:*d*), spend a considerable part of their adult life on the body of their host [4] or elsewhere.

Under favorable conditions as to temperature, humidity, and food, larval life is completed within two weeks. Then the larva spins a cocoon inside which it becomes a pupa. Under the same favorable climatic conditions the adult flea emerges one week after pupation. However, under adverse conditions the larval stage may be continued for 80 to 200 days and the pupal stage may last for one year and over. As adult fleas freshly emerged from the pupa can survive for a long time without food, it may happen that living adult fleas are found in a house which has been empty of human and murine occupants for over 13 months in the case of *X. cheopis* and for three years in the case of *P. irritans*.[3]

Fleas may be classified as animals parasitizing man if they take up their permanent abode in human habitations, where they attack man or animals that share man's house, such as cats and dogs, or domestic mice and rats. Fleas of wild animals not sharing man's house must be excluded, even if they bite man under particular circumstances.

The following is an enumeration of some of the fleas which fulfil the above condition, and which, moreover, are found in many parts of the world.

(1) There is a comb on the head, on the thorax, or on both ....(2)
  No comb is present ....(5)
(2) There is one comb only, on the thorax (Fig. 30·2:*b*) ...*Nosopsyllus fasciatus* (Bosc, 1801) Jordan, 1933; the rat flea of temperate areas
  There is a comb on the head and the thorax ....(3)
(3) The head is bluntly shaped, the eyes are large, the cephalic comb is large ....(4)

The head is tapering, the eyes are very small, the cephalic comb consists of a few teeth only (Fig. 30·2:a) ....*Ctenopsyllus segnis*
(Schönherr, 1816) Stewart, 1933; the mouse flea

(4) The head is short, its contour rounded; the frontal tooth of the
cephalic comb is much shorter than the second (Fig. 30·3:E)
Ctenocephalides canis (Curtis, 1826)
Stiles and Collins, 1930; the dog flea

The head is long and narrow, the frontal tooth of the cephalic comb
is not markedly shorter than the second (Fig. 30·3:D)
Ctenocephalides felis (Bouché, 1835) Stiles
and Collins, 1930; the cat flea

(5) Behind the antenna stands one hair (Fig. 30·3:C)
Pulex irritans Linnaeus, 1758; the human flea *

Behind the antenna stand a number of hairs, arranged in the form
of a V ....(6)

(6) The seminal receptacle has the form of Fig. 30·3:G ....*Xenopsylla
cheopis* Rothschild, 1909; the so-called "tropical" rat flea

The seminal receptacle has the form of Fig. 30·3:H
Xenopsylla astia Rothschild, 1911; a rat flea of Southeast Asia

The seminal receptacle has the form of Fig. 30·3:F .....*Xenopsylla
braziliensis* Baker, 1904; a rat flea of tropical South America

FLEAS AS VECTORS OF PARASITES

Except for the mouse flea, the species parasitizing animals are all
more or less ready to attack man, and the human flea may be found
on animals.[5] It is perhaps X. *cheopis* that bites man more readily
than any of the others, even when its natural host (the rat) is near at
hand. Still, even that species does not become permanently settled in
human habitations, unless man shares his house with rats or mice.

Apart from the tapeworms *Hymenolepis* and *Dipylidium,* with
dog fleas as intermediate hosts, the habitat of the fleas, their poorly
developed discrimination in the choice of their food, and other
conditions still to be mentioned, render them, and particularly X.
cheopis, efficient vectors of blood-inhabiting parasites man shares
with mammals. There are three of these parasites. One, a member
of the bacterial genus *Salmonella,* is of minor importance in this
respect. The others, *Rickettsia typhi* and *Pasteurella pestis,* merit
more attention.

* In the Western Hemisphere there exists a flea, *Pulex simulans* Baker, 1895, the
females of which are difficult to distinguish from *P. irritans.* It occurs from the northwestern United States through Mexico and Central America to the northern half of
South America. Primarily it is a parasite of prairie dogs, but it is also commonly found
on certain rodents, marsupials, carnivores, and deer.

Rickettsia typhi, the causative agent of *endemic* or *murine typhus* in man, has already been mentioned in Chapter XXIX dealing with lice, because the rat louse is the vector spreading the infection among the reservoir hosts, the rats. Here it is mentioned again because *X. cheopis* is the flea mainly responsible for the transmission of *R. typhi* from the reservoir host to man in the eastern United States, tropical South America, and numerous areas in the tropical and subtropical Old World.[6]

Pasteurella pestis is the causative agent of *bubonic plague* in wild and domestic rodents and in man.

In its sylvatic state [7] it is an infection and sometimes a fatal disease among wild rodents in various parts of the world, transmitted from rodent to rodent (and on occasions to man) by fleas unknown in human society, but thoroughly investigated in countries where sylvatic plague occurs, as in the western United States,[8] Central and South America,[9] Kenya,[10] South Africa,[11] and central Asia.[12]

In its domestic state it is a fatal disease of man and of rats inhabiting human habitations and other fixed or movable structures built by man, such as warehouses, ships, and railway cars. In this state it is transmitted from rat to rat and from rat to man by the well-known domestic fleas mentioned in the preceding section, principally by the "tropical" and "temperate" rat fleas *X. cheopis* and *N. fasciatus.* A comparison of the plague history in the Atlantic ports of the United States proved the former to be the more efficient; for it was in the ports where *X. cheopis* formed the majority of the rat-flea population that plague succeeded in gaining a temporary foothold, and not in those where *N. fasciatus* prevailed.[13]

In its exclusively human state, and apart from infection by contact, as occurring in pneumonic plague, it is transmitted from man to man by human ectoparasites, particularly by *Pulex irritans.*[14] This flea appears to be peculiarly suited to this function, because conditions prevailing in its dried feces are such as to allow a survival of *P. pestis* without loss of virulence for as long as 16 months.[15]

Of the three states described above, the sylvatic state is the most permanent, because it depends on reservoir hosts that are not destroyed by the infection. The domestic state, depending on rats that are killed by plague, is less stable. The exclusively human state is like a straw fire, flaring up suddenly and dying down just as suddenly, unless supported by the more solid foundation of murine infection.

Among the characteristics which render fleas efficient vectors of *P. pestis,* one, peculiar to *P. irritans,* has been mentioned already; viz. the dried feces of the flea constitute a favorable medium for pasteurella to survive and to maintain its virulence.

A characteristic peculiar to *X. cheopis* is the tendency of the proventriculus to become "blocked" by a thick growth of pasteurellas which prevents the blood imbibed by the flea from reaching the stomach, in the same manner as the proventriculus of the sandfly is blocked by proliferating leptomonads of *Leishmania donovani* (Chapter IV). As a consequence, the ingested blood gets no farther than the esophagus. It is regurgitated into the wound the mouth parts of the flea have inflicted in the skin of the host, mixed with clumps of pasteurellas torn away from the bacterial mass blocking the proventriculus.[16] Other fleas, such as *N. fasciatus,* are less likely to have their proventriculus blocked, or they do not survive the inanition which is the inevitable consequence of the blocking, as happens to *X. astia.*[17] Both conditions, obviously, detract from the efficiency of these fleas as vectors.

A third characteristic influencing this efficiency has been mentioned already. It is the dependence of the larvas of the fleas on the feces of the adult fleas. In the presence of this dependence, larvas and adults keep together in the nest of the host, as in *N. fasciatus;* in its absence, the adults often leave the nest and allow themselves to be transported in all kinds of cargo such as grain [4] and jute,[18] as happens to *X. cheopis*—a fact which obviously enhances the already considerable ability of this species to serve as a vector by favoring its long-distance transport.

Finally there is the greater or lesser inclination to take human blood which influences the flea's ability to transmit plague to man, rather than its general efficiency as a vector. Here again the "tropical" rat flea is superior to the "temperate" rat flea. The latter bites man readily under experimental conditions, but a boy may lie in a bed full of *N. fasciatus* without being incommoded except by the sensation of crawling vermin.[19] In view of experiences such as this one wonders how plague was transmitted in Amsterdam in 1666 and in London in 1665, unless Hirst [17] is correct in supposing that northwestern European rats in those days harbored *X. cheopis,* as they still do in secluded and warm spots in London and Liverpool,[20] Paris,[21] and the mines of St. Etienne,[22] or unless *N. fasciatus,* after all, can keep rat plague going without the help of *X. cheopis,* as it is reported to have done in Tacoma, Washington.[23]

FLEAS AS BODY VERMIN

TUNGA PENETRANS: THE CHIGOE OR SAND FLEA

Tunga (or *Sarcopsylla*) *penetrans* (Linnaeus, 1758) Jarocki, 1838, does not even belong to those doubtful parasites that are classified as "house vermin," because it does not need the protection of human

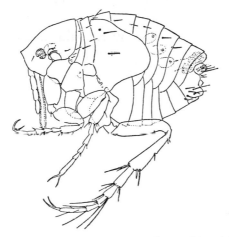

Fig. 30·4 *Tunga penetrans,* young female, × 50. (After F. Weyer, 1942. Courtesy, *Merkblätter, Institut für Schiffs- und Tropenkrankheiten,* Hamburg.)

or animal habitations. Nevertheless, it may be ranked as a true parasite, because one stage of its developmental cycle behaves as a representative of the group of "body vermin." That stage is the female after it has copulated, the so-called "impregnated female," which burrows into the skin of the host, where it feeds copiously, multiplies by producing eggs, and stays on till the end of its life.

In America (as far south as Uruguay and as far north as San Diego, California),[6] tropical Africa,[24] and the west coast of India (Karachi)[27] this species occupies a separate place among the fleas, not only for the true parasitism of the impregnated female but also on the basis of certain morphological characteristics of the adults (Fig. 30·4).

They are identified by their small size, hardly 1 mm in length, the proportionately large head, the angular forehead, the narrow thoracic segments, the apparently jointless labial palps, and the edeagus of the male, which is not coiled but straight except for one abrupt bend.

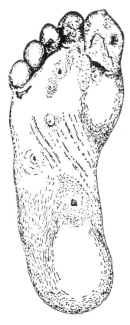

FIG. 30·5 Human foot with tumors containing ovigerous females of *T. penetrans*. (After F. Weyer, 1942. Courtesy, *Merkblätter, Institut für Schiffs- und Tropenkrankheiten,* Hamburg.)

The eggs, deposited by the parasitic female, drop to the ground, and larvas hatch in three to four days. They are free-living animals, in dry sandy soil in the neighborhood of (also inside) cow sheds, pig sties, poultry pens or human habitations. The larvas molt twice, the second molt producing a pupa situated within a cocoon. The adults emerge after about 17 days.[24] The males and young females attack all warm-blooded animals they can reach, and after copulation the female enters upon the parasitic stage of its life cycle.

It attaches itself to the skin of its host and within 5 to 10 minutes burrows into the epidermis, far into the corium, pushing before it the stratum lucidum and the underlying epithelium, which becomes much attenuated. After a few days a mass of horny matter develops, with an opening at its apex (Fig. 30·5), in the depths of which the posterior extremity of the female is discernible. It continuously passes feces; thus it is probable that the female is ingesting blood uninterruptedly.

When it has remained in this position for about a week, its eggs have matured. The female now offers the appearance of a yellowish sphere almost 5 mm in diameter (Fig. 30·6), with the head, thorax and legs protruding anteriorly. Posteriorly are discernible the terminal abdominal segments, through which feces and eggs are being passed. The yellowish sphere is the abdomen, expanded by the eggs it contains to such an extent that the lines demarcating the segments

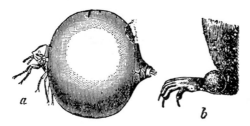

Fig. 30 6   *Tunga penetrans: a,* Ovigerous female, × 7.—*b,* Leg of field rat with tumor containing ovigerous female. (After Brumpt, 1922. Courtesy, Masson & Cie, Paris.)

are completely obliterated. According to Geigy and Herbig,[25] rupturing of the abdominal wall is prevented by the development of a specialized set of supporting muscles. The eggs produced by the female are discharged through the opening of the horny mass formed around and over the parasite. Finally the latter dies in its hiding place where its remnant remains in a mummified state, unless necrosis supervenes, in which case it is expelled together with necrotic tissue.[26]

In man, the lesions caused by the parasitic females mostly develop on the soles of the feet (Fig. 30·5), the skin between the toes, and at the root of the nails. They may also be found on the external male genitalia, the perianal region, the thighs, the hands, and the face, if these parts of the bare skin are exposed to the contaminated soil.

Many of the sores induced by the chigoes are secondarily infected and result in abscess formation, ulceration, and even gangrene of the affected parts.

According to Manson-Bahr,[27] the best *treatment* is removal of the parasitic female from its intercutaneous hiding place, under aseptic precautions and without rupturing it, followed by the application of a sterile dressing. In case the expert hand required for this purpose is not available, it is recommended to treat the affected part with chloroform, turpentine, or a mercurial ointment. It is furthermore recommended to rub parts of the skin particularly exposed to infection with a mixture of five drops of lysol in 30 gm of petrolatum.

REFERENCES FOR CHAPTER XXX

1. R. E. SNODGRASS. Nature, 1946, 158: 488.
2. V. NITZULESCU. *Bull. soc. pathol. exotique*, 1927, 20: 467–473.
3. A. W. BACOT. *J. Hyg., Cambridge (Engl.)*, Plague Suppl., No. 3, 1914, pp. 447–654.
4. M. SHARIF. *Parasitology*, 1948, 38: 253–263.
5. W. P. MACARTHUR. *Trans. Roy. Soc. Trop. Med. Hyg.*, 1946, 39: 343–344.
6. E. C. FAUST, P. F. RUSSELL, and D. R. LINCICOME. *Clinical Parasitology*, Philadelphia, 1957, pp. 887, 898–900.
7. R. JORGE. *Les Faunes régionales des rongeurs et des puces*, etc., Paris, 1928, Masson & Cie, pp. 36–54.
8. L. KARTMAN, F. M. PRINCE, S. F. QUAN, and H. E. STARK. *Ann. N. Y. Acad. Sci.*, 1958, 70: 668–711.
9. A. MACCHIAVELLO. *Bolet. ofic. sanit. panamer.*, 1957, 43: 225–250.
10. R. B. HEISCH. *Brit. Med. J.*, 1956 (2nd half): 669–673.
11. D. H. S. DAVIS. *J. Hyg., Cambridge (Engl.)*, 1953, 51: 427–449.
12. L. F. HIRST. *The Conquest of Plague*, Oxford, 1953, Clarendon Press.
13. C. FOX and E. C. SULLIVAN. *Public Health Repts. (U. S. A.)*, 1925, 40: 1909–1934.
14. G. BLANC and M. BALTAZARD. *Arch. inst. Pasteur, Maroc*, 1945, 3: 173–348.
15. G. BLANC and M. BALTAZARD. *Ann. inst. Pasteur, Paris*, 1946, 72: 486–489.
16. A. W. BACOT and C. J. MARTIN. *J. Hyg., Cambridge (Engl.)*, Plague Suppl., No. 3, 1914, pp. 423–439.
17. L. F. HIRST. *J. Hyg., Cambridge (Engl.)*, 1925, 24: 1–16.
18. E. W. NORRIS. *Public Health Repts. (U. S. A.)*, 1953, 68: 802–804.
19. G. KAPSENBERG. *Ned. Tijdschr. Geneesk.*, 1926, 70 (1st half): 1189–1190, English summary, 1190.
20. R. NEWSTEAD and A. M. EVANS. *Ann. Trop. Med. Parasitol.*, 1921, 15: 287–300.
21. G. GIRARD. *Presse méd.*, 1946, 54: 379.
22. E. ROMAN. *Bull. soc. zool. France*, 1938, 63: 302.
23. C. O. MOHR. *Am. J. Trop. Med.*, 1951, 31: 355–372.
24. E. P. HICKS. *Ann. Trop. Med. Parasitol.*, 1931, 24: 575–586.
25. R. GEIGY and A. HERBIG. *Acta tropica, Basel*, 1949, 6: 246–262.
26. W. F. ESSED. *Geneesk. Tijdschr. Ned. Indië*, 1926, 66: 424–429, English summary, 429.
27. PH. H. MANSON-BAHR. *Tropical Diseases*, London, 1957, pp. 688, 690.

CHAPTER XXXI

HETEROPTERA OR TRUE BUGS

Insects belonging to the group of the Heteroptera (or Hemiptera) that parasitize man develop by incomplete metamorphosis. Their mouth parts in all stages are adapted to piercing the skin and sucking blood. They are attached to the anterior extremity of the head and comprise the following elements: (1) The three-jointed labium, or lower lip, on which repose the piercing and sucking organs when they are not functioning. (2) A pair of bladelike mandibles, armed with minute teeth at their distal extremity. (3) A pair of maxillas, each shaped like one half of a tube, which, when fitted together lengthwise, form a complete tube. The ventral part of each half tube shows a groove; when the two halves are fitted together so as to form a tube, the grooves also form a tube, situated underneath the other one, which is much wider. The wide tube serves to suck up the blood, the narrow one to inject the saliva into the wound (Fig. 32·3:1, *Fc, Sc*).

The species to be described here belong to two families. One, the Cimicidae, have vestigial wings; the other, the Triatomidae, have four wings when they reach the adult stage.

CIMICIDAE

CIMEX LECTULARIUS: THE BEDBUG

The male *Cimex lectularius* Linnaeus, 1758, measures 4.9–6.5 × 2.5–3.2 mm, the female 4.8–8.4 × 2.9–3.9 mm.[1] They are dorsoventrally flattened and have a mahogany-brown color; the larvas are yellowish. The cuticle bears fine hairs (Fig. 31·1). The head is pentagonal; it carries two bulging eyes, two antennas in front of the eyes, and medially a square expansion, to the ventral side of which the mouth parts are attached. The antennas are four-jointed; the basal joint is short, the second joint is the longest, the length of the the apical joint is two-thirds of that of the third joint. When not functioning, the mouth parts lie pressed against the ventral side of the head and the thorax; when functioning, they are directed perpendicularly to the surface of the skin they are piercing.

The thorax shows two of the three segments of which it is composed. The anterior one, the prothorax, has a frontal indentation, in which the basal part of the head is fitted; it carries on its dorsal side (pronotum) two anterolateral, flat, crescent-shaped expansions that reach as far as the level of the eyes. The second thoracic segment, the mesothorax, carries a pair of vestigial wings. The third

FIG. 31·1   *Cimex lectularius,* male, × 9. (After Brumpt, 1913. Courtesy, Masson & Cie, Paris.)

thoracic segment, the metathorax, cannot be identified from the outside. It possesses two glands which produce a secretion emanating the peculiar smell characteristic of bedbugs and other heteropterous insects; the glands open at the base of that segment where it joins the abdomen.

The slender legs are composed of coxa, trochanter, femur, tibia, and two tarsal joints, with two claws to the apical one.

The almost circular abdomen has eight visible segments. The female shows a fissure on the right ventral side of the fifth segment, which functions as vulva during copulation. It leads into the so-called *organ of Berlese* into which the spermatozoa are introduced. The eggs are discharged from another orifice, situated medioventrally not far from the posterior extremity. The male often shows a curved chitinous organ protruding at its posterior extremity, the *edeagus,* which directs the movement of the male copulatory organ.[2]

The eggs, at first milky white, later on yellowish in color, measure

0.8–1.31 × 0.44–0.62 mm. Apically they are slightly curved; as a consequence, the operculum they carry is placed obliquely relative to the longitudinal axis of the egg (Fig. 31·2:3). If the ovipositing female and the male that fertilized it are both well fed, the egg production varies from 133 to 173 per female. Female lice, producing the same quantity or more, do so after a single copulation; female bedbugs have to copulate repeatedly to obtain the same effect.[3] No hatching occurs at a temperature below 13° C. At that temperature the larva emerges in seven weeks, at 18° C in three weeks, and at 28° C in four days.[4] In the nymphal stage (Fig. 31·2:1, 2) five molts take place; previous to each molt the nymph has to take at least one

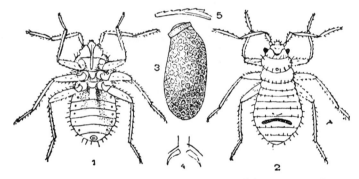

FIG. 31·2 *Cimex lectularius:* 1. Newly hatched larva, ventral aspect.— 2. The same, dorsal aspect.—3. Egg × 26.—4. Tarsal claws.—5. Single hair of larva. (After Brumpt, 1922. Courtesy, Masson & Cie, Paris.)

meal of blood. Feeding and molting do not occur at a temperature below 13° C. Development from egg until adult is completed in eight months at a temperature of 15° C, and in five weeks at 28° C. All stages of development feed on blood exclusively, and all of them are able to survive long periods of fasting.

The span of life of sexually active adult bedbugs varies from 23 to 167 days in females, and from 94 to 189 days in males.[5] Fasting females, which show no sexual activity, may survive to a maximum of 565 days at a temperature of 13° C.[4] The quantity of blood a female ingests at one meal may equal twice its body weight; females weighing not quite 5 mg were observed to take from 8 to a little over 10 mg of blood, followed by a daily production of 6 to 9 eggs.[6]

Bedbugs belong to the category of house vermin. Except for their food, they are independent of the human body, but they are dependent upon the human habitation and the temperature that prevails there. In unheated bedrooms development comes to a standstill in the period from November until May of an English winter, and four-fifths of the population of bedbugs succumb during that time. If the bedrooms are heated, development continues, although at a slower rate than in summer, and mortality does not rise so high. The degree of infestation varies considerably. Figures, collected before World War II in large English cities, record an infestation of about 1 per-cent of the human habitations.[7] In Amsterdam a higher rate, of 9 percent, was recorded in the same period,[8] but even that probably

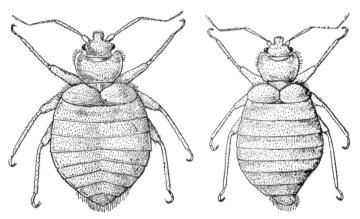

Fig. 31·3 *Cimex rotundatus,* × 12. *Left,* female; *right,* male. (After Brumpt, 1922. Courtesy, Masson & Cie, Paris.)

remains far below the maximum. As a rule bedbugs attack man taking his night's rest, but in public conveyances such as street cars they have been known to attack the passengers.[9]

In accordance with their status as house vermin, bedbugs lay their eggs in the house. To find the places they select for this purpose requires the knowledge of a specialist of wide experience. This knowledge is indispensable for the correct application of modern residual insecticides, as a substitute for the effective, but very dan-gerous, cyanide gas, which often proved as destructive to human as to bedbug life. Unlike pediculid infestation of houses, which dis-appears spontaneously from ten days to one month after the de-parture of the human inhabitants, bedbug infestation lasts for many months, even in the absence of nonhuman mammalian settlers. For practical purposes it may be asserted that louse-infested empty houses do not exist, but bug-infested empty houses are common.

Bedbugs have often been signalized as vectors of diseases, for which their close association with man appears to render them particularly well adapted. Some of these accusations could not be substantiated; they do not transmit leishmanias, and the borrelias that were thought to be found in their body turned out to be the particularly long spermatozoa characteristic of *C. lectularius*. They cannot be wholly acquitted of the charge that they transmit *Pasteurella pestis* directly from man to man [10]; if they do, they rank third, after fleas and lice.

In tropical regions *Cimex rotundatus* Signoret, 1852 (*C. hemipterus* Fabricius) takes the place of *C. lectularius* as house vermin, although in some of them, such as the Sudan,[12] *C. lectularius* appears to infiltrate along the main trade routes, *C. rotundatus* being relegated to the more secluded rural areas. The latter can be distinguished by the anterolateral expansions of the pronotum, which are much narrower than in *C. lectularius* (Fig. 31·3).

Various species of the genus *Cimex*, such as *C. columbarius* in dovecots and poultry pens, *C. hirundinis* in swallows' nests, and *C. vespertilionis* of bats, are nest vermin to warm-blooded animals. If they live in close contact with houses, their parasites may attack man; they may even temporarily settle in the human habitation and thus become house vermin.

TRIATOMIDAE

The members of this group known as "cone-nose" or "assassin" bugs are winged insects when they are adults, but in the preadult stages some of them live like the cimicids, as wingless insects, dependent upon the human habitation for protection from light, drought, and heat and on its inhabitants for food.[11]

The adults have a length of 2 to 3 cm, with a head characterized by its cone-shaped anterior extremity. They have long, four-jointed antennas and bulging eyes, with an ocellus behind each eye. The mouth parts occupy the same position as in the cimicids, but they are less closely pressed against the ventral side of the head and the thorax. The thorax has a conical shape, its surface is marked by narrow longitudinal ridges, separated by wide, shallow grooves. There are two pairs of wings; the anterior pair has a horny basal part, the *elytrum;* the distal portion is thin; the posterior pair is thin throughout.

The life cycle comprises five wingless preadult stages and requires several months for its completion. All stages feed on human or animal blood, but they have been observed sucking the body fluid of other insects and the liquid feces of triatomids of their own species.

The triatomids or cone-nose bugs are of particular importance to man as vectors of *Trypanosoma cruzi* in Mexico and Central and South America (Chapter IV). They comprise numerous species,

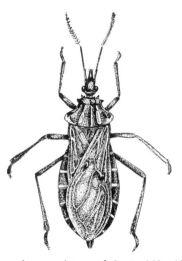

FIG. 31·4   *Panstrongylus megistus,* adult, × 1½. (After Chagas, 1909. Courtesy, *Memórias do instituto Oswaldo Cruz,* Rio de Janeiro.)

such as *Triatoma infestans* with the basal joint of the labium almost as long as the second joint, and *Rhodnius prolixus,* with a very short basal joint. The first is one of the most important vectors throughout extensive parts of the South American continent; the second takes the place of *T. infestans* in Venezuela, where it also serves as vector of *Trypanosoma rangeli* (Chapter IV). A third species, *Panstrongylus megistus* (Fig. 31·4), with antennas implanted just in front of the eyes, is one of the first triatomids Chagas [13] identified as vectors of *T. cruzi.*

REFERENCES FOR CHAPTER XXXI

1. A. HASE. *Die Bettwanze,* Berlin, 1917, Paul Parey.
2. S. R. CHRISTOPHERS and F. W. CRAGG. *Indian J. Med. Research,* 1922, 9: 445–463.

3. F. W. CRAGG. *Indian J. Med. Research,* 1923, 11: 449–473.
4. P. A. BUXTON and C. G. JOHNSON. *Med. Research Council (Brit.) Spec. Rep. Ser.,* No. 245, 1942, 6–17.
5. L. H. DUNN. *Am. J. Trop. Med.,* 1924, 4: 77–83.
6. C. G. JOHNSON. *J. Hyg., Cambridge (Engl.),* 1942, 41: 345–361.
7. C. MATHESON. *Bull. Entomol. Research,* 1941, 32: 165–171.
8. N. L. WIBAUT and M. N. STORK. *Domestic Insects,* Rotterdam, 1935, Nijgh & Van Ditmar.
9. D. J. H. VERMEER and C. VROEGE. *Ned. Tijdschr. Geneesk.,* 1949, 93: 4161–4167, English summary, 4167.
10. G. BLANC and M. BALTAZARD. *Arch. inst. Pasteur, Maroc,* 1945, 3: 173–348.
11. J. W. A. ABALOS and P. WYGODZYNSKI. *Las Triatominas Argentinas,* Inst. de Medicina regional, Monogr. No. 2, 1951, Tucuman, R. A.
12. E. C. FAUST, P. F. RUSSELL, and D. R. LINCICOME. *Clinical Parasitology,* Philadelphia, 1957, p. 784.
13. C. CHAGAS. *Mem. Inst. Oswaldo Cruz,* Rio de Janeiro, 1909, 2: 159–218.

CHAPTER XXXII

NONPARASITIC DIPTERA

The dipterous or two-winged insects include numerous bloodsucking (and also some nonbloodsucking) species of great importance as vectors of the causative agents of various infectious diseases. They take the blood of man and of other animals, but these "hosts" do not provide them with a shelter wherein to live and to multiply. Thus they cannot be classified as parasites, not even as "house vermin." On the other hand, certain diptera are true parasites in their larval stage. These will be discussed in Chapter XXXIII. In this chapter a short account will be given of the diptera in general, followed by a cursory survey of the nonparasitic vectors.

A GENERAL SURVEY

Diptera are insects with a complete metamorphosis. The adults are characterized by a thorax with fused segments, the presence of the joints being still marked by a pair of legs on their ventral side, a single pair of wings on the midjoint, and a single pair of highly modified wings, or *halteres,* on the posterior joint (Fig. 32·1).

The mouth parts are adapted to piercing and sucking, or to sucking alone. The following description (Fig. 32·2 and 32·3:3) refers to the former class. They lie bundled together, enveloped by a sheath, the lower lip or *labium* (Fig. 32·2:*hg*; Fig. 32·3:3, *g*). Mouth parts and sheath together are called *proboscis.* The labium carries two small appendages at its distal extremity, the two *labella,* also called *oliva* (Fig. 32·1:*o*). A *labrum,* welded to an *epipharynx* (Fig. 32·2:*c*; Fig. 32·3:3, *c*), and a *hypopharynx* (Fig. 32·2:*e*; 32·3:3, *e*) are always present; but the *mandibles* (Fig. 32·2:*dd*; Fig. 32·3:3, *d*) may be absent, and the *maxillas* (Fig. 32·2:*ff*; Fig. 32·3:3, *f*) may be represented only by their *maxillary palps* (Fig. 32·2:*bb*). The tube through which liquid food is sucked up has a dorsal wall formed by labrum and epipharynx; its ventral wall consists of the hypopharynx, sometimes flanked by the mandibles and the maxillas (Fig. 32·3:3). The hypopharynx is itself a tube, through which saliva is injected into the wound inflicted by the piercing organs (Fig. 32·3:3, *i*). The *antennas* are composed of eight or more joints (Fig. 32·1:*a*; Fig. 32·2:*aa*) or of three (Fig. 32·12:*a*), four, or five.

The wings are thin films, supported by veins or rays whose number and course are characteristic for each family. The following veins

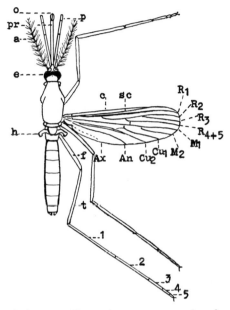

Fig. 32·1 *Anopheles maculipennis* as an example of a dipterous insect: *a*, Antennas.—*e*, eyes.—*o*, Labella.—*pr*, Proboscis.—*p*, Palp.—*h*, Halteres.—*f*, Femur.—*t*, Tibia.—1–5. 1st–5th tarsal.—*c*, Costa.—*sc*, Subcosta.—R_1, R_2, R_3, First, second and third radial veins.—R_{4+5}, Fused fourth and fifth radial veins.—M_1 and M_2, first and second median veins. —Cu_1 and Cu_2, First and second cubital veins.—*An*, Anal vein.—*Ax*, Vestigial axillary vein. (After J. Smart, 1948. Courtesy, Trustees of the British Museum.)

may be distinguished. (1) The *costa* runs along the upper margin, or along the whole margin. (2) The *subcosta* runs underneath the basal third or half of the costa (Fig. 32·1:*Sc*). (3) The five *radial veins* (R_1 to R_5) are partly fused in Fig. 32·1. R_1 is separate, R_2 and R_3 form a single bifurcate vein, R_4 and R_5 are completely fused. (4) The two *median veins* (M_1 and M_2) are fused to a bifurcate vein in Fig. 32·1; so are (5) the two cubital veins (Cu_1 and Cu_2). Finally there is (6) the *anal vein* (Fig. 32·1:*An*) and (7) the *axillary vein;* the last one is vestigial in Fig. 32·1.*

The legs are slender (Fig. 32·1) or stout (Fig. 32·11). They are composed of coxa, trochanter, femur, and tibia (Fig. 32·1:*f, t*); there are five tarsal joints (Fig. 32·1:1–5). The shape of the whole body and the wings can likewise be described as slender (Fig. 32·1) or stout (Fig. 32·11). The larvas usually possess no legs and are provided with biting mouth parts. They are often aquatic (Figs. 32·4 and 32·5), whereas the adults are always airborne. The pupa is sometimes motile (Fig. 32·6) but it never takes food.

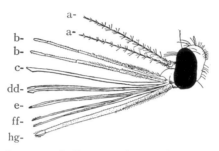

FIG. 32·2   Mouth parts of dipterous insect (head of *Anopheles*): *aa*, Antennas.—*bb*, Maxillary palps.—*c*, Labrum.—*dd*, Mandibles.—*e*, Hypopharynx.—*ff*, Maxillas.—*hg*, Labium with labella. (After Manson's *Tropical Diseases,* French translation. Courtesy, Masson & Cie, Paris.)

The bloodsucking diptera obtain their food by piercing the skin with the mouth parts, with or without the participation of the labium. Some of them, such as the mosquitoes, insert their mouth parts into a cutaneous capillary; others, such as tabanids, have coarse mouth parts that rupture the capillaries and suck the extravasated blood. Gordon and Crewe [1] have described the latter method as "pool feeding."

The diptera which are important to man, either as vectors of infectious diseases, or as parasites, can be classified as follows.

---

* Another way to indicate the veins of the wings also uses the names of costa and subcosta, but the first radial is called first longitudinal; the partly fused second and third radial, second longitudinal; the completely fused fourth and fifth radial, third longitudinal; the partly fused first and second median, fourth longitudinal; the partly fused first and second cubital, fifth longitudinal; and the anal vein, sixth longitudinal. This nomenclature is particularly used in the description of mosquitoes.

(1) The antennas have 8 joints, or more ....(2)

The antennas have 3 to 5 joints ....(6)

(2) The antennas, with 9 to 11 joints, are about as long as the head, and carry no hairs arranged in circles around the stem. The body is stocky and hunchbacked, the legs stout. On the wings, the costa, subcosta, first radial, and the fused radials 4 and 5, are the only well-developed veins (family of Simulidae, Fig. 21·23) ....*Simulium*

The antennas, with 14 to 16 joints, are longer than the head and carry hairs arranged in circles around the stem ....(3)

(3) The antennas, with 15 joints, are about twice as long as the head; the proboscis is short. The wings are dark, with bright circular patches, and pilose, but the hairs are not inserted on the veins.

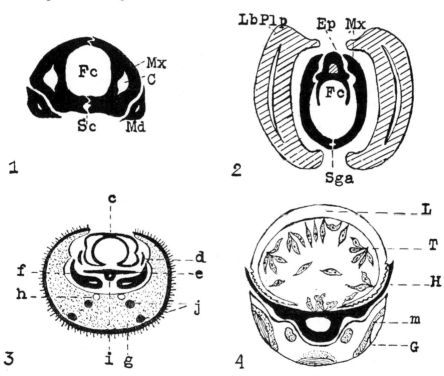

FIG. 32·3   Cross section through the mouth parts of 1. *Cimex lectularis,* 2. *Pulex irritans,* 3. *Anopheles,* 4. *Glossina.*—(1) *Fc,* food channel; *Mx,* maxilla; *C,* hollow in maxilla; *Md,* mandible; *Sc,* salivary canal.—(2) *Fc,* food channel; *LbPlp,* labial palp; *Ep,* epipharynx; *Mx,* lacinia (of maxilla); *Sga,* salivary canal.—(3) *C,* labrum-epipharynx; *d,* mandible; *e,* hypopharynx; *f,* maxilla; *i,* salivary canal; *g,* labium; *h,* trachea; *j,* muscles.—(4) *L,* labrum; *H,* hypopharynx with salivary canal; *G,* labium; *m,* muscles; *T,* trypanosomes in food channel. (1, 2 after Matheson, 1950. Courtesy, Comstock Publishing Co., Ithaca, N. Y. 3, 4 after Brumpt, 1922. Courtesy, Masson & Cie, Paris.)

They carry two bifurcate veins. The upper branch of the first represents the fused radial veins, the lower branch is the single median vein. The second bifurcate vein is formed by the partly fused cubital veins (family of Ceratopogonidae, Fig. 21·19) ....*Culicoides*
The antennas are at least three times as long as the head. The wings are without color, but there are hairs or scales inserted on the veins of the wings, and these are sometimes colored ....(4)

Fig. 32·4 Aquatic larva of dipterous insect (*Anopheles* sp.). (After Nuttal and Shipley. Courtesy, *Journal of Hygiene,* Cambridge.)

(4) The veins of the wings and the whole body are densely pilose (Figs. 32·7, 32·8). The antennas are 14 to 16-jointed. The wings have a pointed extremity and possess two bifurcate veins. The fork of the first carries three prongs; they represent the second, the third, and the fused fourth and fifth radial veins. The second bifurcate vein is formed by the partly fused cubital veins. Between the forks lies the single median vein. Above the first fork lie the short subcosta

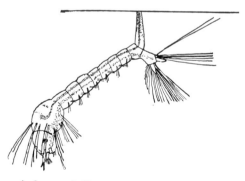

Fig. 32·5 Aquatic larva of dipterous insect (*Culex* sp.). (After Nuttall and Shipley. Courtesy, *Journal of Hygiene,* Cambridge.)

and the first radial vein; below the second fork the anal and axillary veins (family of Psychodidae) ....*Phlebotomus*
The veins of the wings carry scales; the body is scantily or densely covered with scales and hairs. The wings have a rounded extremity and carry three bifurcate veins, of two prongs each (Fig. 32·1). They are formed by the partly fused second and third radial vein, first and second median vein, first and second cubital vein. Between the first and second fork lie the completely fused fourth and fifth radial veins; above the first fork lie the subcosta and the first radial vein; below the third lies the anal vein. The axillary vein is vestigial (subfamily of Culicinae) ....(5)

FIG. 32·6 Aquatic pupa of dipterous insect (*Anopheles* sp.). (After Grünberg. Courtesy, Gustav Fischer, Jena.)

FIG. 32·7 *Phlebotomus papatasii*, × 11. (After Stephens and Christophers; from Grünberg. Courtesy, Gustav Fischer, Jena.)

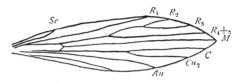

FIG. 32·8 *Phlebotomus papatasii*, wing: *sc*, Subcosta.—R_1, First radial.—R_2, Second radial.—R_3, Third radial.—R_{4+5}, Fused fourth and fifth radials.—*M*, Fused medians.—*C*, First cubital.—Cu_2, Second cubital.—*An*, Anal.—*Last vein*, Axillary. (After Grünberg. Courtesy, Gustav Fischer, Jena.)

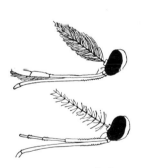

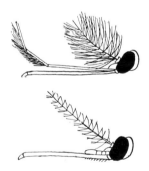

FIG. 32·9 *Anopheles* sp., head: *top:* male; *bottom:* female. (After Manson. Courtesy, Masson & Cie, Paris.)

FIG. 32·10 *Culex* sp., head: *top:* male; *bottom:* female. (After Manson. Courtesy, Masson & Cie, Paris.)

(5) The palps of the female are as long as the proboscis (Fig. 32·9). The males, to be identified by their plumose antennas (Fig. 32·9), have also long palps, but they have a club-shaped apical extremity. The larvas have no siphon (Fig. 32·4), and the position of the adult female on a vertical wall usually is like that pictured in Fig. 32·13:*A*

Anophelini

The palps of the female are much shorter than the proboscis (Fig. 32·10); those of the males are long, but they have a tapering extremity (Fig. 32·10). The larvas possess a siphon (Fig. 32·5), and the position of the adult female on a vertical wall is like that pictured in Fig. 32·13:*B* ....*Culicini*

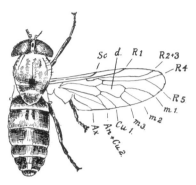

FIG. 32·11 *Tabanus bovinus*, × 2. *Sc*, Subcosta.—R_1, First radial.—R_{2+3}, Fused second and third radials.—R_4 and R_5, Fourth and fifth radials.—M_1, M_2 and M_3, Partly fused first to third medians, encircling the discal cell, *d.*—Cu_1, First cubital.—$An + Cu_2$, Partly fused anal and second cubital.—*Ax*, Axillary. (After Ed. Sergent. Courtesy, Masson & Cie, Paris.)

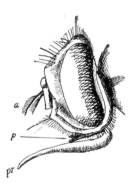

FIG. 32·12 *Stomoxys calcitrans*, head, × 7½: *a*, Arista on third joint of antenna.—*p*, Palps.—*pr*, Proboscis. (After Grünberg. Courtesy, Gustav Fischer, Jena.)

(6) The antennas have three joints; the apical one is composed of a number of fused ones; they are longer than the head and are directed forward. The body is stocky, the head flat, the legs stout. On the wings lie two bifurcate veins, formed by the partly fused fourth and fifth radial veins, and the first and second cubital veins. Between the two lie the completely fused median veins; lower down they form two branches, which reunite still farther down; the ring

thus formed completely surrounds a part of the wing, called the *discal cell* (Fig. 32·11:*d*); from the distal portion of the ring depart the now separate first to third median veins. The base of the anal vein is connected with the cubital veins, at that point still fused; its apex joins the second cubital vein, which has become separated from the first, thus forming the second bifurcate vein (Fig. 32·11:*An +* *Cu₂*). The wing is marked by brown patches (family of Tabanidae)

Chrysops

The antennas have three joints. They are shorter than the head and lie compressed against it. A branched hair, inserted on the basis of the third joint, the *arista,* is directed forward (Fig. 32·12:*a*). The veins of the wings do not show any bifurcation. The subcosta, the first radial, the fused third and fourth, and the fourth and fifth radial veins lie close together and run parallel to the upper margin of the wing. The single median, cubital, anal, and axillary veins are directed obliquely downwards. The median vein (Fig. 32·18:*M*) is joined to the cubital vein by a cross vein ....*Muscoidea*

DIPTERA AS VECTORS OF CAUSATIVE AGENTS OF INFECTIOUS DISEASES

Various species of the genus *Simulium* (Fig. 21·23), or black flies, have been mentioned as vectors of African and American *Onchocerca volvulus;* the same applies to *Culicoides* (Fig. 21·19) in relation to *Acanthocheilonema perstans, A. streptocerca,* and *Mansonella ozzardi.*

Species of *Culicoides* are also vectors of eastern equine encephalo-myelitis in Georgia [20] and of Venezuelan equine encephalitis.[21]

Representatives of the genus *Phlebotomus* (Figs. 32·7 and 32·8), or sand flies, serve as vectors of the causative agent of kala-azar (*Leishmania donovani*) such as *P. argentipes* (India), *P. chinensis* (China), *P. perniciosus* (Mediterranean Basin), *P. longipalpis* (South America); of oriental sore (*L. tropica*) such as *P. papatasii* and *P. caucasicus* in central Asia; and of neotropical cutaneous leishmaniasis (*L. braziliensis*) such as *P. intermedius* in the São Paulo area of Brazil. Moreover, *P. papatasii* and others are the vectors of the virus of "pappataci" (papatasi) or "sand fly fever" in southeastern Europe, Egypt,[1a] south and east Asia [2]; *P. verrucarum* and others, of *Bartonella bacilliformis,*[2a] the causative agent of Oroya fever and its cutaneous manifestation, verruga peruviana, in Peru and Colombia.[3]

Various species of the Anophelini are the exclusive vectors of the causative agents of malarial fevers, the four species of the genus

Plasmodium, and they share this function with certain Culicini in respect of *Wuchereria malayi* and rural *W. bancrofti.*

As regards the transmission of malaria parasites, most species of Anophelini are able to perform this function under experimental conditions, but this does not imply that they actually do so in nature. In the days of malaria control by antilarval measures, the insight (1) that a comparatively small number of Anophelini are to be ranked as first-class vectors, (2) that many of them have more or less specialized breeding places, and (3) that the removal of the latter,

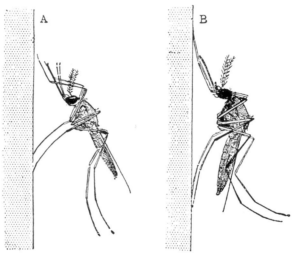

Fig. 32·13 Position of female *Anopheles* (*A*) and female *Culex* (*B*) seated on vertical wall. (After Winckel. Courtesy, Kina Bureau, Amsterdam.)

leaving those of less dangerous species of Anophelini untouched, materially reduces malaria in the area, led Sir Malcolm Watson to the concept, and the practical application, of "species sanitation," i.e. control measures directed against one or a few species only, neglecting all others.

Experience in northeastern Brazil from 1930 to 1942 has shown that malaria and Anophelini may be present in a tropical country without giving rise to alarming conditions, but that the introduction of a single exotic species, *Anopheles gambiae,* of African origin, may lead to a complete deterioration of health conditions, calling for nothing less than "species eradication," the unconditional destruction of the intruder.[4]

The introduction of residual insecticides in the practice of malaria control has not rendered a differentiation of the various species of Anophelini superfluous, but it has posed different problems. It is no longer the larvas and their breeding places, but the adults, their resting places, and their span of life, that will decide on how and when to carry out campaigns of house spraying.

Culicini have been mentioned as vectors of urban and rural Malayan, Bancroftian, and Pacific filariasis (Chapter XXI).

Members of this group are of great importance as vectors of the viruses of western and eastern equine encephalomyelitis in horses and man in North, Central, and South America, and of St. Louis encephalitis in man in North America. Many species of wild birds constitute the sylvatic reservoir of the virus.

The virus of the *western equine encephalitis* is transmitted by *Culex tarsalis* from wild birds to wild birds and also to horses and man. The virus of *eastern equine encephalitis* is transmitted within the avian population by *Culiseta melanura,* a swamp-breeding culicine that rarely bites man. The virus of *St. Louis encephalitis* in rural areas has the same cycle as western equine encephalitis, except that horses do not respond to the infection by falling ill; in urban surroundings culicines of the "pipicns complex" (*C. pipiens, C. molestus, C. fatigans-quinquefasciatus*) transmit the virus from birds to man.[5]

A human virus disease in Japan and other countries, known as "B encephalitis," is transmitted to man by *Culex tritaeniorhynchus.*[6] The reservoir hosts are herons and pigs, whose infection spills over to man at the time it reaches its highest annual level.[7] In eastern Siberia the same or a closely related virus attacks man in autumn; it is transmitted by *Aëdes togoi* and *A. japonicus.*[8]

In central, south and east Africa and in the Western Hemisphere, mosquitoes have been encountered infected with viruses that experimentally cause encephalitis in mice. Some of these viruses must have entered human inhabitants of those parts, because serological proof has been collected of their past or actual presence. Others are known to cause diseases in man such as Semliki Forest and West Nile encephalitis, Rift Valley and Bwamba fever in Central Africa, and Ilhéus encephalitis in Brazil.

The culicine *Aëdes aegypti (Stegomyia fasciata* or *calopus),* a vector of the virus of yellow fever, is of world-wide importance (Fig.

32·14) as it is found in both palaeo- and neotropical (and subtropical) regions. In the Western Hemisphere its life is so closely linked with man that the species might perhaps be classified as house vermin and thus as a parasite dependent on the human body for its food and on his house for shelter and the rearing of its larvas.

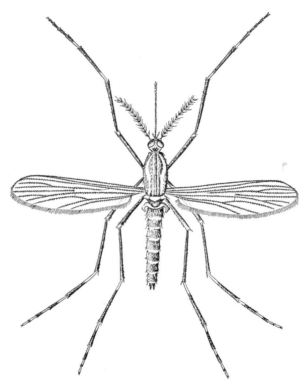

Fig. 32·14   *Aëdes aegypti.* (After Matheson, 1950. Courtesy, Comstock Publishing Co., Ithaca, N. Y.)

In yellow fever transmitted by *A. aegypti,* the sick man is the source of infection for his fellow men. The mosquitoes become infected by sucking his blood during the first to third day of his illness. Twelve days after the infecting meal the mosquito has become able to return the infection to man.

However, in South America and Africa, yellow fever virus can exist without man. In this sylvatic state it lives in monkeys, and its vectors are mosquitoes whose life cycles are not closely associated with man's anatomical and social body. This sylvatic yellow fever, or "jungle yellow fever," [9] attacks laborers working in the forest, while it spares their wives and children, whose occupation does not take them to that dangerous area. But jungle yellow fever may be converted to "urban yellow fever" if it reaches a human settlement where *Aëdes aegypti* are numerous.

In South and Central America jungle yellow fever is transmitted by the "little blue mosquitoes," members of the genus *Haemagogus,* which transmit the virus to the simian genera *Ateles, Alouatta,* and *Cebus.* The monkeys live in the forest canopy [10] together with mos-

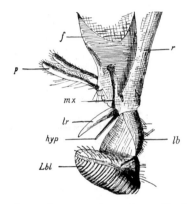

Fig. 32 15 *Musca domestica,* mouth parts: *r,* Rostrum.—*f,* Fulcrum.— *p,* Palps.—*mx,* Vestigial maxillas.—*lr,* Labrum.—*hyp,* Hypopharynx.— *lb,* Labium.—*Lbl,* Labella, showing transversal grooves or pseudo-tracheas. (After Grünberg. Courtesy, Gustav Fischer, Jena.)

quitoes such as *Haemogogus spegazzinii* (and its subspecies *H. s. falco*), *H. equinus,* and *H. iridicolor.* Man entering the forest does not necessarily become infected by the arboreal mosquitoes. Infection occurs (1) if the mosquitoes descend to ground level because the canopy is broken by trees shedding their leaves, either as a consequence of their being naturally deciduous or under the influence of a sharp drought,[11] or (2) if man forces the mosquitoes to come down by felling the trees.[12]

In Honduras and Guatemala *H. mesodentatus* serves as vector. This strictly arboreal mosquito does not bite man; thus jungle yellow fever does not attack man in those parts.[13] Somewhat similar conditions are encountered in central Africa, where the vector of simian yellow fever, *Aëdes africanus,* does not bite man.[14] Nevertheless, man is exposed to infection, because he is bitten at ground level by a mosquito, *Aëdes simpsoni,* which itself becomes infected by biting forest monkeys that are in the habit of descending to ground level to raid the plantations around human settlements in the neighborhood of the forest.

In New Guinea dengue fever is known as a rural disease; its virus is transmitted by *Aëdes scutellaris.*[15] In Malaya both the urban and rural forms are known, the former transmitted by *A. aegypti,* the latter by *A. albopictus.*[16] Philippine hemorrhagic fever, clinically different from but virologically closely related to dengue, is also transmitted by *A. aegypti.*[17]

The genus *Chrysops,* family of Tabanidae or horseflies, has been mentioned (Figs. 21·13, 21·15) as including species that serve as vectors of the filarial parasite *Loa loa* (Chapter XXI).

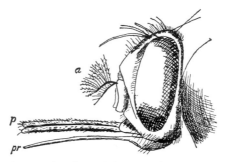

FIG. 32·16 *Glossina* sp., head: *a,* Arista on third antennal joint, carrying hairs each of which carries secondary hairs.—*p,* Palps.—*pr,* Proboscis. (After Grünberg. Courtesy, Gustav Fischer, Jena.)

The Muscoidea or true flies comprise species that pierce the skin and suck blood, whose mouth parts are depicted in Figs. 32·12 and 32·16, or that cannot pierce the skin but can take only liquid food, whose mouth parts are shown in Fig. 32·15.

The most important vectors of diseases among the bloodsucking flies are the members of the genus *Glossina.* They are limited to tropical Africa, where they are the vectors of various species of trypanosomes that cause diseases in domestic animals, and of the two human species discussed in Chapter IV. As in all bloodsucking flies, the head carries a long, slender proboscis directed forward (Fig. 32·3:4). They are characterized by palps that are as long as the proboscis (Fig. 32·16:*p*), secondary hairs on the hairs of the arista (Fig. 32·16:*a*), and the course taken by the median vein of the wing

(Fig. 32·18:*M*), which changes its downward course into an upward course at the point where it is joined by the cross vein, which connects it with the cubital vein. Biologically, *Glossina* is distinguished by its singular mode of perpetuation; one egg at a time hatches inside the uterus, and one larva is born at a time, which immediately pupates after birth (Fig. 32·17).

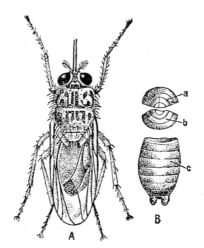

FIG. 32·17   *Glossina palpalis*, × 4: *A*, Adult.—*B*, Empty puparium with *a*, *b*, lid and *c*, body. (After Brumpt, 1922. Courtesy, Masson & Cie, Paris.)

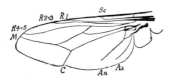

FIG. 32·18   *Glossina* sp., wing: *Sc*, Subcosta.—*R₁*, First radial.—*R₂₊₃*, Fused second and third radials.—*R₄₊₅*, Fused fourth and fifth radials.—*M*, Fused medians.—*C*, Fused cubitals.—*An*, Anal.—*Ax*, Axillary. (After Grünberg. Courtesy, Gustav Fischer, Jena.)

Another bloodsucking fly, *Stomoxys calcitrans*, the biting stable fly, a cosmopolitan (Figs. 32·12 and 33·12:5), has been held responsible for the transmission of toxoplasma (Chapter VII) and the virus of poliomyelitis.

Nonbloodsucking flies can take only liquid food which passes through grooves, *pseudotracheas,* at the surface of the labella of the labium (Fig. 32·15:*Lbl*) and then enters the sucking tube formed by the labrum and the hypopharynx (Fig. 32·15:*lr, hyp*) when they are pressed close together. Nevertheless, the flies feed on solid food, which they have to convert into a solution or a suspension prior to sucking it up. This they achieve by vomiting intestinal fluid over the solid food they are to ingest. Flies that live in man's surroundings feed on man's food and on fecal matter. These feces may contain pathogenic intestinal bacteria and viruses that can survive in the flies' intestine for some days. If they do, the behavior of the flies renders them particularly fit to contaminate human food. As a matter of fact, nonbloodsucking flies have been found infected in nature with bacteria of the genus *Shigella* [18] and the virus of poliomyelitis.[19] There are still other pathogenic organisms, such as pyogenic cocci, the causative agent of yaws, helminth ova, and protozoal cysts, for the transmission of which nonbloodsucking flies have been held responsible.

REFERENCES FOR CHAPTER XXXII

1. R. M. GORDON and W. CREWE. *Ann. Trop. Med. Parasitol.*, 1948, 42: 334–356.
1a. R. M. TAYLOR. *Sixth Intern. Congr. Trop. Med.*, Lisbon, 1958, Abstracts, 165.
2. A. B. SABIN, C. B. PHILIP, and J. R. PAUL. *J. Am. Med. Assoc.*, 1944, 125: 603–606.
2a. E. G. NAUCK. *Forsch. u. Fortschr.*, 1958, 32: 129–131.
3. M. HERTIG. *Fourth Intern. Congr. Trop. Med.*, Washington, D. C., 1948, 2: 1609–1618.
4. F. L. SOPER and D. B. WILSON. *Anopheles gambiae in Brazil*, New York, 1943, The Rockefeller Foundation.
5. A. D. HESS and P. HOLDEN. *Ann. N. Y. Acad. Sci.*, 1958, 70: 294–311.
6. W. McD. HAMMON and W. D. TIGERTT. *Am. J. Hyg.*, 1949, 50: 51–56.
7. E. L. BUESCHER. *Sixth Intern. Congr. Trop. Med.*, Lisbon, 1958, Abstracts, 164.
8. J. WARREN. *Am. J. Trop. Med.*, 1946, 26: 417–436.
9. F. L. SOPER. *Am. J. Public Health*, 1937, 27: 1–14.
10. G. K. STRODE. *Yellow Fever*, New York, 1951, McGraw-Hill Book Co., Inc.
11. P. GALINDO and H. TRAPIDO. *Am. J. Trop. Med. Hyg.*, 1957, 6: 145–152.
12. R. M. TAYLOR and H. W. LAEMMERT. *Am. J. Trop. Med.*, 1946, 26 (Suppl. to No. 6): 1–69.
13. M. J. BOSHELL and G. A. BEVIER. *Am. J. Trop. Med. Hyg.*, 1958, 7: 25–35.
14. K. C. SMITHBURN, A. J. HADDOW, and W. H. R. LUMSDEN. *Ann. Trop. Med. Parasitol.*, 1949, 43: 74–89.
15. M. J. MACKERRAS. *Trans. Roy. Soc. Trop. Med. Hyg.*, 1946, 40: 295–312.
16. C. E. G. SMITH. *J. Trop. Med. Hyg.*, 1956, 59: 243–251.

17. W. McD. Hammon et al. *Sixth Intern. Congr. Trop. Med.*, Lisbon, 1958, Abstracts, 163–164.
18. P. C. Flu. *Geneesk. Tijdschr. Ned. Indië*, 1915, 55: 902–906, English summary, 906.
19. J. L. Melnick. *Am. J. Hyg.*, 1949, 49: 8–16.
20. L. H. Karstad, O. K. Fletcher, J. Spalatin, R. Roberts, and R. P. Hanson. *Science*, 1957, 125: 395–396.
21. F. F. Ferguson. *Public Health Monogr.* No. 23, Washington, D. C., 1954, Govt. Printing Office.

CHAPTER XXXIII

PARASITIC DIPTERA

All parasitic diptera belong to the superfamily of the Muscoidea; they are recognized as parasites because their larvas are said to lead a parasitic existence.

The form of the larvas differs greatly from one species to another, as may be gathered from a comparison of Figs. 33·2:4, 33·8, 33·15, 33·18, and 33·19. They have biting mouth parts not adapted to sucking blood, but by their bite they may inflict wounds from which blood exudes that they ingest. The mature larva pupates, i.e. its skin becomes hard, brown, and barrel-shaped, known as a *puparium*. Inside the puparium, metamorphosis is achieved in free nature, because the parasitic larva leaves its host before pupation commences.

The larvas have an anterior and a posterior pair of spiracles. The posterior pair of the mature larva show certain characteristics by which it may be identified, as shown in Fig. 33·12. This is of importance, since it is the larva, and not the adult fly, that is encountered as a parasite in man. However, the usefulness of this mode of identification is limited to the finding of the full-grown larva, and this stage is not reached in man's body if man is not the natural host of the parasite conccrned, as is the case in most of the warble flies.

The larvas to be discussed in this chapter are *obligatory parasites,* living in the intestinal tract, the urinary bladder, the cutaneous and subcutaneous tissue, the nasal, auricular, and ocular cavities of living animals, including man. The larvas of other species of flies may lead the same parasitic existence, although they need not do so; they are *facultative parasites.* Finally, there are flies whose larvas lead a free-living existence, but which are able to survive in cavities of the animal body, connected with the outer world, in which they happen to find themselves.

The morbid conditions resulting from the presence of these larvas are known under the general name of *myiasis.* According to the organs affected, a distinction is made between *cutaneous, nasal, ocular* (ophthalmomyiasis), *auricular, vesical,* and *intestinal myiasis*.

The flies whose larvas are obligatory parasites may be arranged into three groups.

(1) The adult flies have a short life; they limit their activity to copulation and oviposition; they take no food, and their mouth parts are vestigial (Fig. 33·7:*P,M*) ....Warble flies or botflies

The adult flies have a longer span of life, during which they take food, with normally developed mouth parts ....(2)

(2) The dorsal side of the abdomen is gray, marked with black squares or dots. The arista is hairless, either over its whole length or at its distal extremity. The adults are viviparous ......Sarcophagid flies

Usually bluish, greenish, or violet flies, sometimes with a coppery sheen. The arista is pilose over its whole length. The adults are oviparous ....Calliphorid flies

THE WARBLE FLIES

The species of the four families of warble flies are almost wholly parasitic. Only the pupal stage and the short-lived adult stage are free-living. They can be arranged in the following manner, in which the habitat of the third-stage larva refers to the normal host, and not to man (except in dermatobia).

(1) The median vein runs straight to the margin of the wing, without changing its course at the junction with the cross vein (as it does in Fig. 32·18:*M*). The mature larvas live in the intestine of horses (family of Gasterophilidae) ....*Gasterophilus*

The median vein shows the deviation from its course at the junction with the cross vein as depicted in Fig. 32·18:*M* ....(2)

(2) The course of the median vein differs from that depicted in Fig. 32·18:*M*; it fails to reach the margin of the wing by joining the distal extremity of the fused fourth and fifth radial vein ....(3)

The course of the median vein is in conformity with that depicted in Fig. 32·18:*M* ....(4)

(3) The vestigial proboscis is very short (Fig. 33·7). The larvas live in the nasal cavity and its sinuses of sheep in several parts of the world (family of Oestridae) ....*Oestrus*

The vestigial proboscis has the form of a tape. The larvas live in the nasal cavity and its sinuses of horses and donkeys, in Europe, North Africa, north and west Asia (family of Oestridae)
Rhinoestrus

(4) The mature larvas carry no rings of spines. They live in the subcutaneous tissue, particularly of cattle, in Europe, Asia, North Africa, and North America (family of Hypodermatidae) ..*Hypoderma*

The mature larvas carry rings of spines. They live in the subcutaneous tissue of cattle, dogs, and various other mammals, including
man, in the neotropical region (family of Cuterebridae)

Dermatobia

HYPODERMA

This genus contains two closely related species, *Hypoderma bovis*
de Geer, 1776, and *H. lineatum* de Villers, 1789. Both are indigenous in Europe, the latter also in the Western Hemisphere.

The adults are 12 to 16 mm long. Except for three or four
longitudinal black, bald stripes on the dorsal side of the thorax,
they are densely pilose; the hairs are brightly colored on the anterior
half of thorax and abdomen; they are black on the posterior half
of those parts; a black transverse band divides the bright anterior

Fig. 33·1 *Hypoderma bovis,* female, × 4. (After Matheson, 1950.
Courtesy, Comstock Publishing Co., Ithaca, N. Y.)

half of the abdomen in a narrow anterior part and a wider posterior
part. At its posterior extremity the female carries an ovipository
tube (Fig. 33·1).

During dry warm weather, in June or July,[1] the adult females
commence oviposition. They attach their eggs to the hairs of the legs
or the flanks of cattle. The minute larvas, of less than 1 mm, emerge
in four to seven days; it takes them a few hours to penetrate the skin
of the host.[2] The larvas that emerged in the middle of July are met
with again in September, in the tissue of the esophageal wall.

These larvas have increased in size, to a length of 6 to 14 mm
(Fig. 33·2:1), and are smooth in appearance, although they are

sparsely covered with minute spines, which are more numerous at the
cephalic and caudal extremities (Fig. 33·3); and they are completely
diaphanous. They are usually called second-stage larvas, although

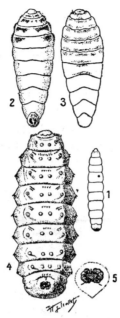

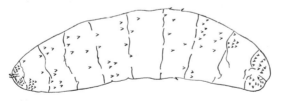

FIG. 33·2   *Hypoderma* sp. Development of larva, × 2: 1. Second stage.
—2. Third stage, dorsal aspect.—3. Third stage, ventral aspect.—4. Mature larva.—5. Posterior spiracles of the same. (After Brumpt, 1922.
Courtesy, Masson & Cie, Paris.)

FIG. 33·3   *Hypoderma bovis,* second-stage larva, × 7, removed from
anterior chamber of human eye by Professor A. Hagedoorn, Amsterdam.

they have developed without molting from the minute larvas born
in July.[3] A further characteristic is the form of the oral hooklets at
the extremity of a pair of chitinous rods. In *H. bovis* each hooklet
is a semicircular structure with a bifid anterior limb and a blunt

posterior limb; in *H. lineatum* each hooklet is more crescentic, with both limbs sharply pointed.[2]

From September onward the esophageal larvas migrate from the pharyngeal to the cardiac region of the wall of the esophagus. By way of the diaphragm and the inner side of one of the ribs, they migrate to the corresponding intervertebral foramen and thus they reach the subdural adipose tissue surrounding the spinal cord.[4] They have now an average length of 14 mm. From this temporary site they reach the subcutaneous tissue of the back of the host in January or later.

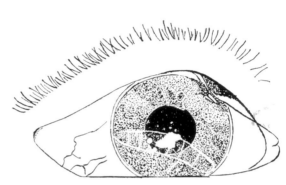

FIG. 33·4   *Hypoderma bovis.* The larva pictured in Fig. 32·3 in its original position in human eye. (After photograph by Professor A. Hagedoorn, Amsterdam.)

In this new site the parasite provokes cellular reactions of the host, which up to that time had apparently been kept in abeyance. A granulomatous wall is formed around the larva, which it pierces, however, with its tapering posterior extremity (Fig. 33·2:2, 3). Thus a granulomatous tumor is formed, with an ulcer in its center, at the bottom of which lies the tapering caudal part of the larva with its two posterior spiracles (Fig. 33·12:11, 12).

The larva in this site has changed its form and appearance. It has become white and opaque, with numerous spines on its ventral side. It has increased in size, and its form is conical, with a blunt anterior extremity and a tapering caudal extremity (Fig. 33·2:2, 3). Formerly it was supposed to have originated from the spinal larva by molting, but according to Knipling[3] no molting marks the transition from the spinal larva to the cutaneous larva.

However, there can be no doubt that the transition of that stage to the mature larva (Fig. 33·2:4) is marked by molting. The mature larva has a uniform width; its size is 22–28 × 11–15 mm; the ventral side is convex, the dorsal side flat, the lateral sides carry three rows of small knobs. About the month of May the larva leaves the host by way of the ulcer in the center of the cutaneous tumor. It drops to the ground; its skin becomes a hard and dark-colored puparium. From this puparium the adult fly emerges some five weeks later, approximately one year after the eggs were laid which produced the esophageal larvas that lived from July until September, the spinal larvas from September until January, and the subcutaneous larvas from January until May.

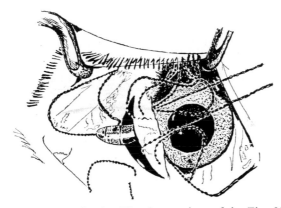

FIG. 33·5 *Hypoderma bovis.* The larva pictured in Fig. 33·3 in the act of being removed from the human eye. (After photograph by Professor A. Hagedoorn, Amsterdam.)

Occasionally larvas of hypoderma penetrate the human skin. They move aimlessly through the subcutaneous tissue, provoking more or less marked cellular and humoral reactions of the host, which become apparent by furunculous swellings on the scalp, the eyelids, the neck, the trunk, the genitals, and the legs. Swellings that continuously change their sites may succeed one another for months, but finally, often in February, seven months after the infection, which probably occurred in July,[5] a larva emerges from one or more of these swellings which, in all these months, has developed no farther than to the second stage. Similar results have been obtained by experimental infection of a human being [6]; after five months a larva of 7½ mm was detected in the subject's buccal mucosa. According to Sigalas and Pautrizel,[7] mature larvas never develop in the human body; the penultimate stage may be reached in children; in adults it is extremely rare.[8] Thus larvas wandering in the human body never pupate. To hypoderma man is a dead-end host.

The larva fares no better *if it invades the human eye,* as it occasionally does. Suurküla [9] mentions 23 cases of that kind. They are serious, as they often require enucleation. If the larva can be extirpated whole, correct identification is possible (Figs. 33·3, 33·4, 33·5). Histological sections through the enucleated eye allow only a tentative diagnosis.[10] Most cases were identified as due to *H. bovis,* but Anderson [11] reports a case due to *H. lineatum.*

Various observations [12, 13] point to the fact that hypodermas oviposit as freely on older animals as on young ones, but that older animals are much less afflicted by boils than young ones. This is regarded as an indication that repeated infections stimulate the bovine host to resistance, which enables it to reduce the number of larvas that complete their development in its body.

OTHER WARBLE FLIES

The larvas of members of the genus *Gasterophilus,* or horse bots, parasitize the intestinal tract of horses. Some of them, such as *G. haemorrhoidalis* Linnaeus, 1758, *G. intestinalis* de Geer, 1776, and *G. nasalis* Linnaeus, 1758, are cosmopolitans. The large, brown, hairy flies, with attenuated posterior abdominal segments, emerge from the puparia in July. They live for no longer than three days. During this time they deposit large numbers of eggs, which they attach to the hairs of horses near the mouth. The eggs hatch within a week, and the emerging minute larvas, of 1 mm, manage to reach the horse's mouth by some means or other. Arrived in the mouth, they burrow in the buccal mucosa, and there they feed on blood. After a month they emerge from their burrows and molt. The resulting larvas of the second stage have a length of 3–5 mm. Initially their heads are buried in the mucosa of the pharynx, but soon they migrate to either the stomach, the duodenum, or the rectum, the site selected depending on the species concerned. In these new surroundings they behave as in the preceding one. After a month and a half they molt to larvas of the third stage, which have a length of 20 mm, but otherwise occupy the site and continue the life of their predecessors for the next eight months (Fig. 33·12:10). In the period between June and September of the next year the larvas are passed with the feces and pupate on the ground. After two to four weeks the adult flies emerge from the puparium, an event that terminates the developmental cycle, which takes about one year for its completion.[14]

Intestinal infection with third-stage larvas has been observed in man. As a rule, however, the development of the larvas of G. *haemorrhoidalis* and G. *intestinalis* within the human body does not

FIG. 33·6 *Gasterophilus* sp., larva removed from human skin, × 65. (After Brumpt, 1922. Courtesy, Masson & Cie, Paris.)

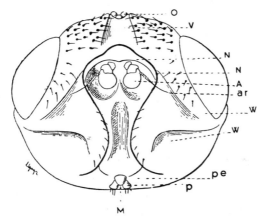

FIG. 33·7 *Oestrus ovis*, female head, × 11: *A*, Antenna.—*ar*, Arista.— *o*, Ocelli.—*V*, Frons.—*N*, Frontal sutures.—*W*, Cheek.—*pe*, Peristome.— *p*, Vestigial palps.—*M*, Vestigial proboscis. (After Brumpt, 1922. Courtesy, Masson & Cie, Paris.)

proceed beyond the first stage (Fig. 33·6). The larvas wander in the superficial layers of the skin above the stratum germinativum or the corium. According to Faust et al.[15] they can be identified in that site by massaging a small amount of clear mineral oil over the infested skin, through which the black transverse bands of spines of the larvas can then be seen. Their behavior gives rise to an eruption that continuously changes its place, and is known as "creeping eruption" or "cutaneous larva migrans."

In Russia gasterophilus larvas parasitizing man are far from rare,[16] and they have also been reported in Corsica.[17] In the Western Hemisphere, according to Faust et al.[15] creeping eruption due to *Ancylostoma braziliense* is practically coextensive with that of gasterophilus.

Oestrus ovis Linnaeus, 1758, or gadfly, is a representative of the third family of warble flies, the Oestridae. They are large, dark-gray flies covered with light-brown hairs, with black spots on the dorsal side of the thorax and the abdomen. The viviparous female bears its

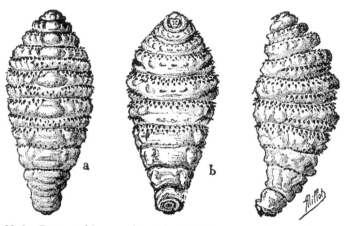

FIG. 33·8   *Dermatobia cyaniventris,* × 2½, mature larva, known as "torcel" or "berne" in the French West Indies: *a,* Dorsal aspect.—*b,* Ventral aspect.—*c,* Side aspect. (After Brumpt, 1922. Courtesy, Masson & Cie, Paris.)

larvas in or near the nasal orifice of sheep, goats, and camels. The larvas migrate to the sinuses of the nasal cavity, and in that site they reach maturity within a few months. The mature larvas (Fig. 33·12:13) are evacuated through the nasal orifice by sneezing; they drop to the ground, and there they pupate. The adult fly emerges from the puparium at the end of a few weeks.

In man the larvas do not develop beyond their first stage. They occupy, not man's nasal cavity, but his conjunctiva. Human infections have been reported in Switzerland, southern Europe, Algeria, Russia, and the Cape Verde Islands; they are rarely seen in the United States.[15]

The Russian gadfly, a nasal warble fly of horses and other equines, *Rhinoestrus purpureus* Braun, 1858, often attacks the eyes of members of the Kirghiz tribes.[18]

The fourth family of warble flies, the Cuterebridae, is known by its neotropical representative, *Dermatobia hominis* (Modeer 1786) Say, 1882 (Fig. 33·10), the tropical warble fly. It has a length of 12 to 18 mm, with a yellowish face, a black frons, a bluish-black thorax, and an abdomen of metallic blue. The third antennal joint is bright orange, the legs are orange, and the wings are dark brown.

FIG. 33·9 *Dermatobia cyaniventris*, young larva, known in French West Indies as "ver macaque": *a*, Natural size.—*b*, × 4½. (After Brumpt, 1922. Courtesy, Masson & Cie, Paris.)

The larvas parasitize the cutaneous tissue of various carnivores, rodents, deer, monkeys, and domestic animals, such as cattle, pigs, goats, mules, and dogs. Unlike other warble flies, the larva completes its development in the human host.

The fly attaches its eggs to the abdomen of mosquitoes and other bloodsucking winged insects (Fig. 33·11). After five to six days the larvas within the eggs are ready to emerge. If at that moment the insect alights on the human or animal skin with the object of taking blood, the warmth radiating from the skin stimulates the larvas to leave the eggshell and to drop on the skin.[19] They then penetrate the skin within an hour or so. As a rule they remain in the part of the skin they thus penetrate; rarely they migrate to other parts, as happened in the case of an infant whose brain was invaded by a larva wandering through the skin to the large fontanella, through which it entered the cerebral cavity.[20]

The larva is characterized by several rings of comparatively large spines. It is located head downwards within the tissue of the skin. The narrower caudal part is turned upwards. The posterior

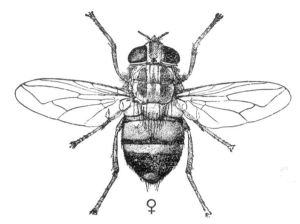

FIG. 33·10 *Dermatobia cyaniventris,* female, × 2. (After Brumpt, 1922. Courtesy, Masson & Cie, Paris.)

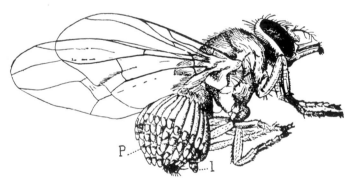

FIG. 33·11 *Dermatobia cyaniventris,* eggs attached to abdomen of bloodsucking fly, × 6: *P,* Eggs.—*I,* Larva emerging from egg. (After Brumpt, 1936. Courtesy, Masson & Cie, Paris.)

spiracles, at the posterior extremity of that part, are thus placed at the bottom of an ulcer that pierces the superficial layers of the skin. The immature larva has the shape of a ball with a taillike appendage (Fig. 33·9). The mature larva is spindle-shaped, with a tapering posterior extremity (Fig. 33·8). At that stage, which is reached after

46 to 55 days, the larva has grown to a size of 20–25 × 9–11 mm. The pupal stage, which is passed outside the body of the host, lasts from over three weeks to one month, and even to two months and a half.

SARCOPHAGID FLIES

The adult flies of this family are characterized by the hairless tip of the arista (Fig. 33·13:*ar*), by the silvery gray dorsal side, marked with black dots, and by bearing young larvas instead of laying eggs. The larvas are obligatory or facultative parasites.

The obligatory parasites belong to the Old World species *Wohlfahrtia magnifica* Schiner, 1862 (Fig. 33·14), and the American *W. vigil* Walker, 1849. The adults are 7 to 14 mm long; the dorsum of the silvery-gray abdomen is marked by three median black patches; the basal half of the arista is almost bald; the third joint of the antenna is one and a half times as long as broad or less. The female fly bears 124 to 168 larvas; they are all born at the same time on the skin of the host—rodents, small carnivores, or man. Larviposition always takes place on a living subject, never on carrion. The fly never enters human habitations, but attacks man sleeping in the open.

The larvas (Fig. 33·15; Fig. 33·12:8) penetrate the unbroken skin of the host and stay inside for the next seven to nine days. At the end of that time they have reached maturity; they extricate themselves from the cutaneous tissue, drop to the ground, and pupate. The adult fly emerges from the puparium after 10 to 17 days, the female soon becomes fertilized and proceeds to larviposition shortly afterwards.

In Canada [21] and the United States [22] *W. vigil* is a frequent cause of cutaneous myiasis, particularly in children passing the night in the open. In Russia [23] *W. magnifica* is not limited to the skin, but causes auricular, nasal, and ocular myiasis during the summer months.

Another member of the same genus, *Wohlfahrtia opaca* (or *meigeni*), can likewise cause myiasis. Nevertheless, it is not an obligatory parasite; it is known to deposit its larvas on carrion as well as on living beings.

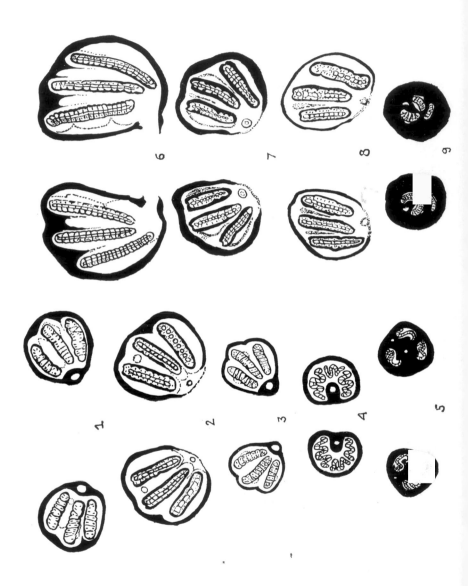

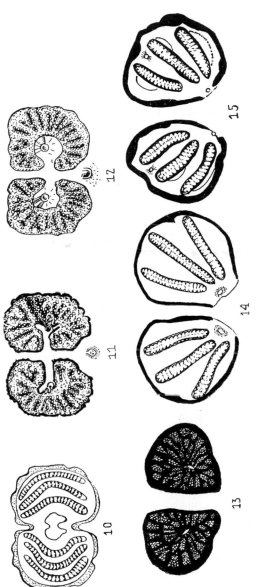

FIG. 33·12 Pairs of posterior spiracles of third-stage larvas of various Muscids, drawn to the same scale. In each can be distinguished (1) three "slits," straight or convoluted. absent in 11–13; (2) a chitinous rim surrounding, sometimes (5, 9) enveloping, the slits; (3) a "button" at the base of the slits, either separate, or included in the rim. 1, *Calliphora vomitoria*; 2, *Phormia regina*; 3, *Lucilia sericata*; 4, *Musca domestica*; 5, *Stomoxys calcitrans*; 6, *Sarcophaga bullata*; 7, *Callitroga macellaria*; 8, *Wohlfahrtia vigil*; 9, *Muscina stabulans*; 10, *Gasterophilus intestinalis*; 11, *Hypoderma bovis*; 12, *Hypoderma lineatum*; 13, *Oestrus ovis*; 14, *Chrysomyia megcephala*; 15, *Chrysomyia bezziana*. (1–9, after L. S. West, 1951; 10–13, after R. Matheson, 1950. Courtesy, Comstock Publishing Co., Ithaca, N. Y. 14, 15, after J. Smart, 1948. Courtesy, Trustees of the British Museum, London.)

The adult flies of the genus *Sarcophaga* are of the same size as those of *Wohlfahrtia*, but the dorsal side of the abdomen shows a checkered pattern in silvery gray and black. The basal half of the arista carries long hairs, and the third joint of the antenna (Fig. 33·13:*A*) is three times as long as broad.

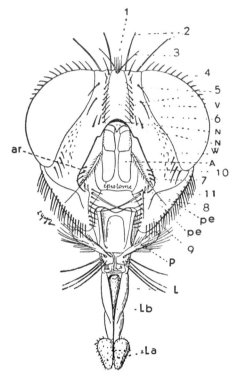

FIG. 33·14 *Wohlfahrtia magnifica*, female, × 1½. (After Brumpt, 1922. Courtesy, Masson & Cie, Paris.)

FIG. 33·13 *Sarcophaga carnaria*, head, × 11. 1–11, various groups of bristles: *A*, Antenna.—*ar*, Arista.—*W*, Forehead.—*N*, Frontal sutures.—*pe*, Peristome.—*p*, Palp.—*L*, Labrum.—*Lb*, Labium.—*La*, Labella. (After Brumpt, 1922. Courtesy, Masson & Cie, Paris.)

The females of *Sarcophaga carnaria* Linnaeus, 1758, *S. haemorrhoidalis* Fallen, 1816, and others deposit their larvas on human food, particularly meat; if the larvas are ingested, they are able to complete their development within the human intestine, thus becoming the cause of intestinal myiasis. The mature larvas (Fig. 33·12:6) are passed in the feces and pupate outside the host's body

Sarcophaga haemorrhoidalis and *S. fuscicauda* Böttcher, 1912, are known to larviposit in open wounds, thus causing cutaneous myiasis. However, their parasitic habits form no essential part of their life cycle; thus they are no more than facultative parasites.

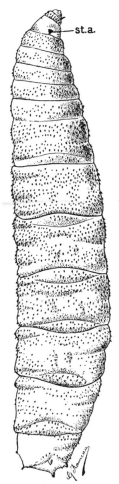

FIG. 33·15 *Wohlfahrtia magnifica,* mature larva, side aspect, × 7. *St.a,* Anterior spiracle. (After Brumpt, 1922. Courtesy, Masson & Cie, Paris.)

CALLIPHORID FLIES

As in sarcophagid flies, and unlike warble flies, obligatory and facultative parasitic larvas are found in more or less closely related genera—sometimes within one genus—of the calliphorid flies.

Callitroga hominivorax (or *americana*) is known as the causative agent of a form of cutaneous myiasis associated with severe disfigurement. The fly whose larvas are responsible for this disease is 10–13 mm long; its head has a yellow color; its eyes are orange; its thorax is marked by three dark longitudinal stripes; its abdomen has a blue-green color with a silvery sheen (Fig. 33·16).

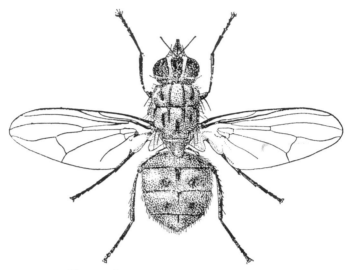

Fig. 33·16 *Callitroga hominivorax,* female, × 6¼. (After Brumpt, 1922. Courtesy, Masson & Cie, Paris.)

The larvas, known as *screwworms,* are obligatory parasites. They are hatched from eggs that the fly deposits in wounds in the skin of living animals. Screwworms occur in the Western Hemisphere, from the southern part of the United States to southern Brazil. They attack cattle, sheep, and goats. In man they are found in the skin, the nasal passages, the eye and the vagina. In the United States 86 percent of the cases of cutaneous myiasis are due to this parasite.[24]

Callitroga macellaria Fabricius, 1775, is indigenous in an area reaching from Canada to Patagonia. As an adult fly it resembles the preceding species. Its larvas (Fig. 33·12:7) are said to cause cutaneous myiasis in pre-existing wounds, but there exists some doubt as to their identity; most such larvas probably belong to the preceding species.[15]

Chrysomyia bezziana, a bluish-green species with dark thoracic stripes and dark transverse abdominal bands, replaces *Callitroga* in the Old World. Its larvas (Fig. 33·12:15, 14) are among the most important causative agents of myiasis of the skin, the ear, the eye, and the gums in Asia and Africa.[25] They have also been observed invading the bones of the skull.[26] As they are dependent on the living body of the host, they must rank as obligatory parasites.

Cordylobia anthropophaga (Fig. 33·17), the *tumbu fly,* is a calliphorid which by its yellowish-gray color differs greatly from the other and more brightly colored members of this family. This exclusively African fly oviposits on the ground. Thus it is left for the young larvas to find their host, in whose skin they bury them-

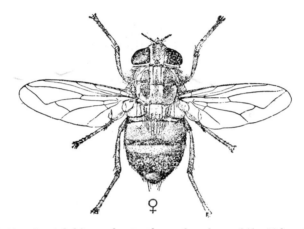

FIG. 33·17 *Cordylobia anthropophaga,* female, × 3½. (After Brumpt, 1922. Courtesy, Masson & Cie, Paris.)

selves and thereby cause a cutaneous myiasis which takes the form of suppurative swellings.[27] The larvas are dependent on a living host; thus they are obligatory parasites (Fig. 33·18).

Man, rats, and dogs often serve the parasite as hosts, but numerous other animals can do so. In some of them the larvas reach maturity, emerge from the furunculous swelling, drop to the ground, and pupate; in others they die without having achieved complete development; the animals that harbor them are dead-end hosts. The guinea pig is one of them. After repeated infections, this rodent is known to develop resistance against further infections, which becomes apparent by the death of the larva shortly after its penetrating the skin of its host and by immunological reactions between the body fluids of the host and the parasite. These are manifested by the formation of precipitates within the intestinal tract and around the oral and anal orifices of the larva, reminiscent of the immunological response of the host to the larvas of certain nematodes. However, such reactions are found only in dead-end hosts and never in those which permit a complete development of the parasite.[28]

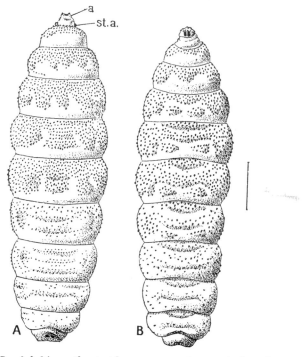

Fig. 33·18 *Cordylobia anthropophaga,* mature larva, *A,* dorsal, *B,* ventral aspect, × 6½: *a,* Antenna.—*st.a,* Anterior spiracle. To the right of the letter A the posterior spiracles can be seen. (After Brumpt, 1922. Courtesy, Masson & Cie, Paris.)

The larvas of other calliphorid flies, such as the well-known "bluebottle flies," *Calliphora vomitoria* (Fig. 33·12:1) and *C. vicina* (or *erythrocephala*), and the "black blowfly," *Phormia regina* (Fig. 33·12:2), oviposit on meat and occasionally on open wounds; thus they may become the cause of cutaneous, perhaps also of intestinal, myiasis.

The "green-bottle flies," of the genus *Lucilia* (or *Phaenicia*), such as *Lucilia sericata,* a green fly with a coppery sheen, often lay their eggs in open wounds. The emerging larvas (Fig. 33·12:3) when left undisturbed cause extensive damage, particularly in ovine hosts, by destroying large areas of cutaneous tissue and neatly laying bare the underlying muscular tissue, like a dissection in an anatomical theater. Thus they devour their victim alive, protecting it from bacterial invasion by their bactericidal secretions. Such a thing sometimes happened to the wounded lying helplessly on a field of battle, but protected from the suppurative and gangrenous processes that inevitably awaited them in the hospital. This experience gave rise to the notion that a wounded soldier might be better off uncared for on a battlefield than in a hospital. In modern times before the advent of antibiotics, larvas of lucilia were actually employed with the object of destroying pyogenic cocci, particularly in certain cases of osteomyelitis.

However, it will be clear from the foregoing that the term "parasite" is hardly applicable to the lucilias, whether in sheep, where they can exercise their skill in dissection undisturbed, or in man in whose body they produce myiasis of the skin, the eye, the urinary bladder,[29] and the inner ear.[30] They behave as predators; their victim is a prey, not a host, because they can destroy it without destroying themselves.

There remains for discussion one calliphorid fly, the "Congo floor maggot," *Auchmeromyia luteola.* It is described as the only ectoparasitic fly specific to man and the only bloodsucking fly larva that parasitizes man.[31] Like the tumbu fly, it lays its eggs on the floor of native huts or on dry sand. The larvas attack man asleep on the bare infested floor; they inflict a wound on the skin with their biting mouth parts and imbibe the exuding blood. Thus they are blood-lappers rather than bloodsuckers. According to the definition adhered to in this book, they are not parasites, for they are dependent upon the human body only for procuring their food. They may, however, be classified as "house vermin" if the larvas prove to be dependent upon the human habitation and if oviposition takes place only within the shelter afforded by that habitation. For in that case, the fly would be dependent on man's body (*sensu lato*) for its food and a space to live and to multiply in.

Other Flies. The common house fly, *Musca domestica,* and stable fly, *Muscina stabulans,* often imbibe the secretion of wounds and may lay their eggs in that situation. The emerging larvas (Fig. 33·12:5, 4, 9) are thus in a position to cause cutaneous myiasis and have been known to do so.[32] They have also been reported as occurring in large numbers in the urethra of children. A facultative parasitism of this description has also been observed in the larvas of various other muscid flies, such as the lesser housefly, *Fannia* (*Homalomyia* or *Anthomyia*) *canicularis,* recognizable by the long and slender pilose appendages spread over the whole body (Fig. 33·19), whose larvas often cause intestinal and vesical myiasis in man. The same has been observed in its close relative, *F. scalaris.*

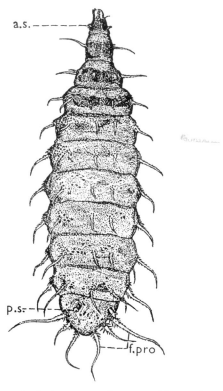

FIG. 33·19   *Fannia canicularis,* mature larva, × 10: *as,* Anterior spiracles.—*f.pro,* Appendages over all parts of the body.—*ps,* Posterior spiracles. (After Patton and Evans, 1929, *Insects, Ticks, Mites and Venomous Animals.*)

Other families, such as that of the *Syrphidae,* may take part in this facultative parasitism. *Eristalis* (or *Tubifera*) *tenax* and other species of this genus, whose larvas are characterized by a long caudal appendage, have been reported as the causative agents of intestinal [33] and genitourinary [34] myiasis.

With the exception of the larvas of the warble flies, whose status as true parasites is beyond doubt, the relationship between the parasitic muscoid larvas and their hosts is ill-defined. In view of the conditions known in lucilia, it appears for the moment doubtful whether the muscoid larvas can at all be regarded as parasites. Even the dependence on living beings of larvas that have been termed "obligatory parasites," may perhaps be compared with the dependence of some carnivores on their living prey rather than being regarded as a true host-parasite relationship; just as the larvas termed "facultative parasites," like *Wohlfahrtia opaca,* may preferably be compared with carrion-feeding carnivores. Thus in the future a discussion of the "parasitic" muscoid larvas may have to be dismissed altogether from the subject matter of parasitology. For the moment, however, knowledge is insufficient to justify such a drastic purge.

REFERENCES FOR CHAPTER XXXIII

1. P. KOOREVAAR. *Centr. Bakteriol.,* Abt. I, 1898, 23: 888–892.
2. C. WARBURTON. *Parasitology,* 1922, 14: 322.
3. E. F. KNIPLING. *J. Parasitol.,* 1935, 21: 70.
4. S. HADWEN. *Parasitology,* 1915, 7: 331–338.
5. H. SCHMID. *Schweiz. med. Wochschr.,* 1958, 88: 601–602.
6. A. SMITH and D. P. GREAVES. *Brit. Med. J.,* 1946 (2nd half): 120–121.
7. R. SIGALAS and R. PAUTRIZEL. *Bull. soc. pathol. exotique,* 1948, 41: 380–384.
8. J. LAPIERRE. *Bull. soc. pathol. exotique,* 1958, 51: 232–238.
9. J. SUURKÜLA. *Klin. Monatsbl. Augenheilk.,* Beiheft 13, Stuttgart, 1942, F. Enke.
10. M. C. ENNEMA. *Arch. Ophthalmol.,* 1934, 12: 180–187.
11. W. B. ANDERSON. *J. Ophthalmol.,* 1935, 18: 699–705.
12. S. HADWEN and J. S. FULTON. *Parasitology,* 1924, 16: 98–106.
13. W. J. BEVAN and E. E. EDWARDS. *Bull. Entomol. Research,* 1951, 41: 639–662.
14. F. ZUMPT. *Deut. Tropenmed. Z.,* 1941, 45: 569–576.
15. E. C. FAUST, P. F. RUSSELL, and D. R. LINCICOME. *Clinical Parasitology,* Philadelphia, 1957, pp. 874, 875, 876.
16. E. N. PAVLOVSKY and A. K. STEIN. *Parasitology,* 1924, 16: 32–43.
17. CH. JOYEUX. *Bull. soc. pathol. exotique,* 1938, 31: 922–924.
18. I. A. PORTCHINSKY. *Rev. Appl. Entomol.,* B, 1915, 3: 217–218.
19. F. KNAB. *Proc. Entomol. Soc. Washington D. C.,* 1916, 18: 179–183.
20. L. H. DUNN. *J. Parasitol.,* 1934, 20: 219–226.
21. E. M. WALKER. *Can. Public Health J.,* 1931, 22: 504–508.
22. F. GASSNER and M. T. JAMES. *J. Parasitol.,* 1948, 43: 44–50.
23. I. A. PORTCHINSKY. *Rev. Appl. Entomol.,* B, 1916, 4: 88–89.
24. J. M. BRENNAN. *J. Econ. Entomol.,* 1938, 31: 646–649.
25. W. S. PATTON. *Indian J. Med. Research,* 1922, 9: 635–655.
26. H. GALLIARD. *Bull. soc. pathol. exotique,* 1948, 41: 230–233.
27. E. ROUBAUD. *Les producteurs de myiasis,* Paris, 1914, Masson & Cie.

28. D. B. Blacklock and R. M. Gordon. *Ann. Trop. Med. Parasitol.,* 1927, 21: 181–224.
29. A. C. Chandler. *J. Parasitol.,* 1941, 27: 465.
30. H. W. F. Brauneck. *Brit. Med. J.,* 1949 (2nd half): 1335.
31. C. Garrett-Jones. *Bull. Entomol. Research,* 1951, 41: 679–708.
32. W. S. Patton and N. A. Cookson. *Lancet,* 1925 (1st half): 1291.
33. L. van den Berghe and G. Bonné. *Ann. soc. belge méd. trop.,* 1944, 24: 67–70.
34. C. J. Supple. *J. Am. Med. Assoc.,* 1958, 167: 1838–1839.

CHAPTER XXXIV

INSECTICIDES AND REPELLENTS

Insecticides are natural or synthetic toxicants that are lethal to all kinds of arthropods, not only insects; moreover, they kill arthropod vectors of parasites, such as mosquitoes or tsetse flies, as well as arthropod parasites, such as lice.

Insecticides make part of a larger group of toxicants, named *pesticides,* which include *rodenticides* and *molluscocides.* The first destroy the rodent reservoir hosts of various animal, vegetable, and viral parasites; the latter destroy the molluscan intermediate hosts of the trematodes.[1]

Repellents are natural or synthetic substances that influence arthropods in such a way that they are deterred from settling on man's skin or on his clothes, if the repellents are rubbed on the skin or impregnated in the clothes.

INSECTICIDES

Insecticides fall into two groups, (1) *residual* insecticides and (2) *space-sprayed* insecticides.[2] Both are applied to sites where man and arthropods are wont to meet. Often this site is the human habitation, and in that case the inside of the walls is coated with a minute layer of the insecticide (*residual spraying* or *spray painting* [2]), or the interior of the house is filled for a short time with a mist composed of minute droplets of the insecticide (*space spraying*).

The residual insecticide, either powdered or dissolved, suspended, or emulsified in some liquid, is deposited on the walls of the house or on another solid substratum, such as blades of grass or leaves of trees. If an arthropod alights on that substratum and touches the layer of insecticide, it picks up a quantity of toxicant sufficient to kill it. The substratum thus treated remains poisonous for a period which may vary in length from a few days to several months. Hence the name *remanent* insecticides.

Insecticides distributed by space spraying are not intended to settle down on the walls of the house. A solution of such an insecticide must be converted into an *aerosol,* a mist of droplets of a size of 50 μ or less, produced within an area closed in on all sides. These droplets keep floating in the air for about one hour. They are intended to hit, and thereby to kill, any insect flying about within that space and within that hour. It is essential that the insects should be kept on the wing, either of their own free will or stimulated by substances added to the solution of the insecticide. Space spraying kills all insects flying within the closed area, but insects entering it when the droplets have ceased floating are no longer injured; space spraying has no residual effect.

SOME IMPORTANT INSECTICIDES

The most important *nonresidual insecticide* is a natural product, *pyrethrum,* an extract from the dried and powdered flower heads of *Chrysanthemum cinerariaefolium,* as grown in Dalmatia, Japan, Kenya, and elsewhere. The powder is known from of old as Persian insect powder, but the standardized insecticide is an extract which should contain at least 19 percent of equal parts of the active principles pyrethrin I and II.[1] Combined with small quantities of DDT and other chlorinated hydrocarbons, this insecticide is space-sprayed as an aerosol with the object of killing mosquitoes inadvertently carried in aircraft.[2] The addition of piperonyl butoxide increases the toxicity of the pyrethrins.

The residual insecticides can be divided into (*a*) *chlorinated hydrocarbons* and (*b*) *organophosphorus compounds.* The latter are extensively used in agriculture. Up till recently, owing to their high toxicity, their use in human dwellings was not encouraged. However, development of resistance of flies and mosquitoes to the former group appears to diminish the reluctance to use the latter group. This, at least, applies to houseflies, in the control of which two organophosphorus compounds, viz. *malathion* (diethoxy-carbonylethyl-dimethyl-dithiophosphate) and *diazinon* (isopropyl-methylpyrimidinyl-diethyl-thiophosphate), have been used extensively.[3] Selection pressure (*v. infra*) from organophosphorus compounds induces resistance to themselves and also to chlorinated hydrocarbon insecticides.[5]

The chlorinated hydrocarbons fall into two groups.

The first group comprises *DDT* (dichloro-diphenyl-trichloro-ethane or chlorophenothane U.S.P.), *TDE* (DDD, dichloro-diphenyl-dichloroethane, or Rothane D_1) and *methoxychlor* (dimethoxy-diphenyl-trichloroethane).

The second group comprises *aldrin* (hexachloro-hexahydro-dimethanonaphthalene or Octalene), *dieldrin* (hexachloro-octahydro-dimethanonaphthalene or Octalox), *chlordane* (octachloro-methano-tetrahydroindane, Okta-Klor or Velsicol 1068), *heptachlor* (heptachloro-methano-tetrahydroindane, Velsicol 104 or Velsicol heptachlor), *toxaphene* (chlorinated camphene), and *benzene hexachloride* (hexachloro-cyclohexane, BHC) in its three varieties of *technical BHC* with 12 to 16 percent of the gamma isomer (gammexane or gamma benzene hexachloride), *refined BHC* with 17 to 98 percent of that isomer, and *lindane* with 99 percent and over of the gamma isomer.

Mosquito resistance to DDT extends to its analogues TDE and methoxychlor, but not to the members of the second group. Conversely, mosquito resistance to dieldrin and BHC extends to all members of the second group, but not to DDT and its analogues.[4] However, resistance to both groups of chlorinated hydrocarbons may develop eventually.

Resistance to insecticides has developed in respect of chlorinated hydrocarbons, organophosphorus compounds, and pyrethrins, but resistance to the first group of insecticides has been studied most thoroughly.[8] A great variety of insects may exhibit resistance, but it has been investigated most comprehensively in houseflies and various mosquitoes, notably in members of the genus *Anopheles*.

A marked degree of resistance may be detected in certain insects, even if they have never been in touch with the insecticide to which they are resistant. Usually, however, resistance develops after the insect population has been exposed to the insecticide for a varying length of time. This does not imply that resistance to a certain insecticide is an acquired characteristic induced by environmental conditions, viz. by exposure to the insecticide. On the contrary, numerous observations support the hypothesis that resistance is based on one or more genetic factors, present in a small number of individuals of a population never exposed to the insecticide. Eventually, every individual will possess these factors, as a consequence of *selective pressure,* i.e. the selective destruction of all individuals not possessing them.[5]

REACTION TO INSECTICIDES OF ARTHROPODS PARASITIZING MAN

Hard Ticks. Hard ticks, separated from their hosts, can be killed in free nature (so called *area control*) by the application of any of the chlorinated hydrocarbons at a rate of 450 to 900 gm of toxicant per acre, equivalent to 190 liters of a solution or suspension, or 18 kg of a powder mixture. Of the gamma isomer of BHC, 225 gm per acre is sufficient.

Occasionally the free-living stages of hard ticks invade human habitations. The brown dog tick, *Rhipicephalus sanguineus,* is especially inclined to do so. Spraying baseboards, floor, and wall cracks with solutions or suspensions of 5 percent DDT or chlordane should prove effective. If not, 0.5 percent lindane has yielded satisfactory results; if that fails, spraying with 0.5 percent of the organophosphorus compound diazinon may achieve results.[3]

Soft Ticks. Ornithodoros moubata, infesting human habitations in various parts of Africa, has been successfully controlled by the application of the gamma isomer of BHC on the floor and the lower (30 cm) wall surface, in the form of a suspension. The quantity of the toxicant required varies, according to the individual reports, from 0.5 to 12.5 gm per square meter, in each of two successive applications at intervals of 4 to 6 weeks.[3]

Trombiculid Larvas. For their destruction in free nature (area control) solutions or suspensions are recommended containing 900 gm of toxaphene or chlordane, 110 to 225 gm of lindane, or 225 to 450 gm of dieldrin per acre.[3]

Body Lice. Lice not resistant to DDT can be successfully controlled by treating the human carrier with talcum powder containing 10 percent of DDT. Although it does not kill the nits, a single application of 50 gm of the powder per person suffices to eradicate the infestation because the effectiveness of the powder outlasts the life of the nits before hatching.

Lice resistant to DDT are controlled with an ointment, lotion, or shampoo, available commercially as Kwell, and containing 1 percent of lindane. In this case, however, the time the insecticide stays effective is less than the life of the nits before hatching. Thus two applications are required, with an interval of one week.[3]

Resistance to all chlorinated hydrocarbons is countered by a weekly application of a formulation containing 0.2 percent of pyrethrins, 2 percent of sulfoxide (dioxymethylene-octyl-sulfinyl-propyl-benzene) as a "synergist" to increase the effect of the pyrethrins, 2 percent of dinitro-anisol to kill the nits, and 0.1 percent of isopropyl cresol to retard the oxidation of the pyrethrins.[6]

Head and Crab Lice. The following emulsion, known as NBIN, has been recommended. It contains 68 percent of benzyl benzoate, 6 percent of DDT, 12 percent of benzocaine, and 14 percent of an emulsifier known as Tween 80, a poly-alkylene derivative of sorbitan mono-oleate. This emulsion is diluted 1 to 5 with water, and with it the hair on the scalp or in the pubic region is thoroughly sponged or sprayed. The hair is left unwashed for the next 24 hours, the time required to kill both lice and nits.[3]

Fleas. In India the density of the tropical rat flea, *Xenopsylla cheopis,* is reported to have become markedly reduced by indoor residual spraying of 2 gm of DDT per square meter, applied for the sake of malaria control. The application of a powder containing 5 or 10 percent of DDT to rat runs and areas likely to harbor rats is known readily to control *X. cheopis.* The higher concentration is preferable, because the lower is less active against dog fleas and cat fleas.

The latter fleas, and also human fleas, have even been reported resistant to DDT and chlordane, and there appears to be a growing tendency for the organophosphorus compounds to take the place of the chlorinated hydrocarbons.[3]

Bedbugs. House infestations with DDT-sensitive bedbugs are reported to be readily eliminated by the application of a 5 percent solution or suspension of DDT to the baseboards, wall crevices, bedsteads, and mattresses of infested rooms (2 gm per square meter). Bedbugs resistant to DDT can be destroyed by 0.1 to 0.9 gm of the gamma isomer of BHC per square meter. Bedbugs resistant to the last-named insecticide can be killed by malathion or diazinon in 0.5 to 1.0 percent solution.[3]

Triatomid Bugs. Satisfactory results have been reported after residual spraying of infected premises with 0.5 gm of the gamma isomer of BHC, or 1.25 gm of dieldrin, per square meter.[3]

Warble Flies. Faust et al.[7] advocate the spraying of a 5 percent DDT suspension to parts of the horses most commonly harboring the eggs of *Gasterophilus,* in order to kill them before they hatch. According to these authors efficient control may also be obtained in cattle exposed to the egg-laying attacks of *Hypoderma* or of blood-sucking insects carrying the ova of *Dermatobia.*

House Vermin Among Mosquitoes. As has been stated elsewhere, the only mosquito which might perhaps be classified as a parasite is *Aedes aegypti* in the Americas, because it is wholly dependent on man, his house, and his backyard. This dependence, usually described as "domestic habits," implies a dispersal capacity of less than 270 meters of the adults and the larvas. It renders the species particularly vulnerable to a combined antiadult and antilarval spraying with a 5 percent suspension of DDT, known as *perifocal* spraying. This method includes the interior and exterior of all possible breeding places and adjacent wall surfaces.

Strains of *A. aegypti* resistant to DDT have been observed in the Caribbean area and in South America. Substitution of dieldrin, or the gamma isomer of BHC, for DDT has yielded satisfactory results.[3]

REPELLENTS

Ticks. Repellents are most effective when applied to clothing. Greatly recommended is a clothing impregnant designated M–1960, which contains 30 percent of butylethylpropanediol, the same amounts of butylacetanilide and benzyl benzoate, and 10 percent of an emulsifier, such as Tween 80 or Triton X–100. This formulation has been adopted as the standard all-purpose clothing repellent by the United States Army, but it has not been registered for general use.[3] Other effective repellents are indalone, dimethyl carbate, and dimethyl phthalate.

Trombiculid Larvas. The above clothing impregnant is also used in repelling these larvas. All outer clothing are impregnated with 2 gm of the repellent per 0.1 square meter of cloth, or a total of 75 gm to a jacket, trousers, and socks. Underwear should not be treated.[3]

Fleas. Diethyltoluamid is reported to be a superior flea repellent, when used in impregnating socks and outer garments. Seventy-five gm of the repellent are added to 1½ liters of water containing 5 parts per thousand of an emulsifier such as Tween 80 or Triton X–100 or 2 percent of soap. The clothes are saturated with the emulsion, wrung lightly, and dried thoroughly before wearing.[3] This mixture is available commercially as a 15 percent pressurized spray known as "Off."

Aedes aegypti. Unlike the preceding arthropods, mosquitoes, to be successfully repelled, require more than a clothing impregnant. In addition they require a substance which protects the skin without injuring it. M–1960 is useful as a clothes impregnant, but it cannot be used for the protection of the skin because it contains butylethylpropanediol which is injurious to the skin. Diethyltoluamid (available as "Off") is not; it is less injurious than other repellents to plastic objects, rayon cloth, and fingernail polish; it feels less oily on the skin; and it can be diluted with some alcohol without detriment to the repellent effect—conditions which combine to increase its cosmetic acceptability.[3]

REFERENCES FOR CHAPTER XXXIV

1. WORLD HEALTH ORGANIZATION. *Normes pour les pesticides,* 438 pp., Geneva, 1957, Palais des Nations, pp. 3, 4, 66, 353–367.
2. P. F. RUSSELL. *Malaria,* 210 pp., Oxford, 1952, Blackwell, pp. 129, 135–137.
3. WORLD HEALTH ORGANIZATION. *Tech. Rep. Series,* No. 153: 68 pp., Geneva, 1958, Palais des Nations, pp. 11, 21, 29–39, 41, 43–46; also No. 191, 1960.
4. A. W. A. BROWN. *Seminar on Insecticides,* 1958, World Health Organization, pp. 12–24.
5. A. W. A. BROWN. *Bull. World Health Organization,* 1958, 18: 309–391.
6. A. N. SMITH. *Insecticides—62,* 11 pp., Geneva, 1957, World Health Organization.
7. E. C. FAUST, P. F. RUSSELL, and D. R. LINCICOME. *Clinical Parasitology,* 1078 pp., Philadelphia, 1957, Lea & Febiger, p. 880.
8. A. W. A. BROWN. *Insecticide Resistance in Arthropods,* 240 pp., Geneva, 1958, World Health Organization.

PART SIX

Technical Methods and Diagnostic Procedures

CHAPTER XXXV

LABORATORY EQUIPMENT FOR PARASITOLOGICAL STUDY

THE MICROSCOPE

The microscope used in the study of animals parasitizing man has nothing special about it. It consists of a V-shaped foot, surmounted near the narrow end by a short vertical piece on which hinges the body of the microscope equipped with the optical, illuminating, and object-carrying apparatus (Fig. 35·1).

The optical apparatus consists of the tube and the inner tube. The first is provided with milled heads for coarse and fine adjustment, and a triple nosepiece at its lower end in which are screwed the low-power, high-power, and oil-immersion objectives, so that they swing into position in order of increasing magnification when they are rotated clockwise. Into the upper end of the inner tube an eyepiece can be fitted, of which there are at least two, of 5 × and 10 ×.

The illuminating apparatus acts in conjunction with some source of light, natural (a bright cloud) or artificial (ranging from a kerosene lamp to an electrical apparatus fitted into the microscope). It consists of a mirror, a substage condenser, and an iris diaphragm. The mirror has a plane and a concave side, the first to be used with the condenser, the second without it.

The object-carrying apparatus consists of a fixed stage and a mechanical stage. The first is fixed rigidly to the body of the microscope; it has a central aperture to admit the light reflected by the mirror, and concentrated by the condenser onto the object to be examined. The mechanical stage surmounts the fixed stage and serves to move the object to be examined.

CARE OF THE MICROSCOPE

In order to prevent dust passing into the tube, an eyepiece should always be kept in it. When not in use, the microscope should always

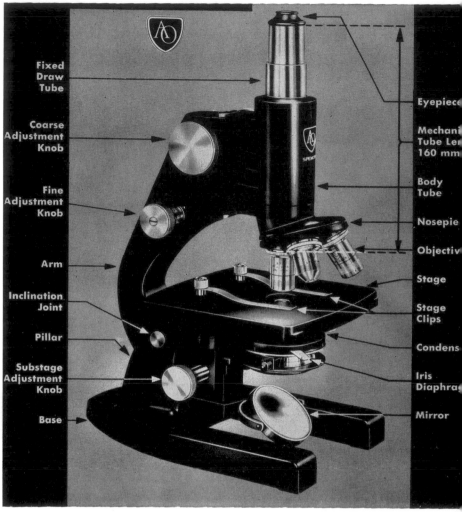

Fixed
Draw
Tube

Coarse
Adjustment
Knob

Fine
Adjustment
Knob

Arm

Inclination
Joint

Pillar

Substage
Adjustment
Knob

Base

Eyepiece

Mechani
Tube Ler
160 mm

Body
Tube

Nosepie

Objectiv

Stage

Stage
Clips

Condens

Iris
Diaphra

Mirror

FIG. 35·1   A laboratory microscope, showing the major parts.

be kept in its box, under a glass or plastic hood, or wrapped in a clean duster.

After use, the cedar oil, or nonresinous immersion oil, should be wiped off the immersion lens, which is cleaned with as little xylol as possible and dried with a soft (i.e. repeatedly washed) handkerchief which is set apart for the purpose, protected from dust and grit. Lenses in general are to be cleaned by wiping across them, and not by a circular movement. Alcohol is to be avoided.

USE OF THE MICROSCOPE

Stained objects, such as blood slides, can be examined with an open iris diaphragm. Unstained objects, such as a suspension of fecal matter in water, require the diaphragm to be partly closed, the degree of closure depending on the magnification employed. Gross objects, such as proglottids or medium-sized nematodes, cleared in glycerol or pure carbolic acid, are examined with low power, concave mirror, and the condenser racked down and swung out of action. It is frequently more convenient to examine gross specimens with a hand lens or a dissecting microscope.

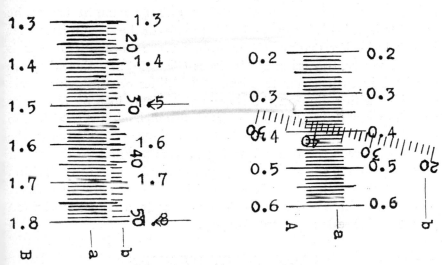

FIG. 35·2 *A*, ocular micrometer, *b* (marked 20–50 along one side), not yet in correct position with regard to stage micrometer, *a* (marked 0.2–0.6 along both sides).—*B*, ocular micrometer, *b* (marked as above), in correct position with regard to stage micrometer, *a* (marked 1.3–1.8 along both sides). Arrows, pointing to numbers 1.5 and 1.8, indicate place where mark on the ocular micrometer coincides with that on stage micrometer.

Microscopic objects are first examined with the low power (numerical aperture 16 mm or ⅔ inch), if necessary with the high power (numerical aperture 4 mm or ⅙ inch) or the oil immersion (numerical aperture 2 mm or ¹⁄₁₂ inch).

The use of the oil immersion is indicated in preparations examined without a coverslip. In mounted slides both high power and oil immersion can be used if there is solid Canada balsam between slide and coverslip. If there is water between, oil immersion can be used only if the aqueous film is kept very thin.

MEASUREMENT OF MICROSCOPIC OBJECTS

Measurement is carried out with the aid of an ocular micrometer and a stage micrometer. The first is a glass disk with a diameter slightly smaller than that of the eyepiece and a scale engraved on it; it is placed on a rim fitted within the eyepiece. The stage micrometer, mounted on a microscope slide, has a scale engraved on it which consists of a millimeter divided into a hundred parts, each division equaling 10 μ. It is with the ocular micrometer that the measurement has to be performed; for that reason it has to be calibrated, and this is achieved with the aid of the stage micrometer in the following manner. The scale on the stage micrometer is focused so that two scales are in focus (Fig. 35·2:A); then they are arranged in such a way that one of the lines on the ocular scale coincides with a line on the stage scale. Next, looking along the superimposed scales, another pair of lines is selected which also exactly coincide (Fig. 35·2:B), and the number of divisions in the interval between the two coinciding pairs is counted on the ocular scale (say, a) and the stage scale (say, b) separately. As one division on the stage scale measures 10 μ, b divisions measure $b \times 10$ μ. They correspond with a divisions on the ocular scale, and so one division on the ocular scale represents $10b/a$ μ.

LABORATORY UTENSILS

The following is a list of apparatus, glassware, chemicals, reagents, staining material, and culture media ingredients that are more or less representative of supplies and equipment of a parasitology laboratory. The list is not intended to be comprehensive, especially, as far as chemicals, staining material and culture media ingredients are concerned. These vary in each laboratory, depending upon the methods employed. Laboratory animals for inoculation are not included.

APPARATUS

Autoclave
Balances
Bacterial filters, complete
Binocular dissecting microscope

Centrifuges
Filing cabinets for records, slides, and other specimens
Hemacytometer, complete
Hydrometers (Baumé)

Icebox
Incubators (25° C and 37° C)
Lenses, hand, × 6 and × 10
Micrometer
Microscopes, binocular, fully
    equipped
Microtome and accessories
Oven
Photoelectric light meter
Refrigerator
Trichinoscope
Westergren apparatus

GLASSWARE

Beakers, Pyrex glass, with lips
Bottles, brown and colorless
Centrifuge tubes, plain and gradu-
    ated, of 15 and 50 ml
Coplin jars
Coverslips of 22 × 22, 22 × 35, 22 ×
    40 mm
Flasks, Erlenmeyer and other, as-
    sorted sizes
Funnels, ordinary and separatory
Glass vessels, graduated and plain,
    cylindrical and conical
Medicine droppers
Petri dishes
Pipettes, ordinary and graduated
    capillary
Slides (microscope), of 75 × 26 and
    75 × 37 mm
Staining dishes and jars
Stoll apparatus for egg count
Syringes, assorted sizes
Thermometers 100° C.
Test tubes, assorted sizes
Tubes for needle storage, and with
    plastic screw top covers
Watch glasses

ENAMELWARE

Asparagus boilers
Pails
Pans
Trays, black and white

OTHER SUPPLIES

Absorbent cotton
Alcohol lamps

Applicators, wooden
Blotting paper
Bunsen burners
Clamps
Filters, Seitz and others
Forceps, various sizes
Gauze, surgical, or cheesecloth
Glass beads
Grinder and chopper
Lens paper
Needles, fixed in handles, pointed
    and ground flat at the tip with a
    cutting edge
Paper carton containers, waxed, with
    tight-fitting lid
Paper cups
Pencils, diamond, and for writing on
    glass
Pipette holders
Pipette shakers
Platinum loops
Rubber gloves
Rubber tubes
Scissors
Scotch tape
Sieves
Stands for filters, burettes, pipettes,
    etc.
Stoppers, cork and rubber, assorted
    sizes
Teats, rubber
Test tube brushes
Test-tube holders
Test-tube racks
Timing clocks
Tongs
Tongue blades
Tripods
Tubing, glass
Waring Blendor
Wires
Wire baskets
Wire mesh

CHEMICALS   (CHEMICALLY
    PURE)

Acetone
Alcohol, absolute, 95, 70, 40 percent
Anticoagulants (potassium oxalate,
    sodium citrate, heparin)

Calcium carbonate
Calcium chloride
Cedar oil 100/1.30 for oil immersion or nonresinous immersion oil, refraction index nD 1.515 (Shell, Ltd., The Hague, Netherlands)
Chloroform
Cleaning fluid
Detergents
Disodium phosphate
Distilled water
Ether
Formaldehyde 40 percent (formalin)
Glycerol (glycerin)
Hydrochloric acid
Iodine (crystals)
Lysol
Liquid petrolatum
Mercuric chloride, powder
Merthiolate, tincture
Methanol (methyl alcohol)
Pepsin
Phenol (carbol)
Physiologic saline (Coca's or McCoy's solution)
Picric acid (crystals)
Polyvinyl alcohol
Potassium acid phosphate
Potassium bichromate
Potassium chloride
Potassium iodide
Saponin
Sodium bicarbonate
Sodium borate (borax)
Sodium chloride
Sodium citrate
Sodium hydroxide
Sodium hyposulfite
Sodium lauryl sulfate
Sodium phosphate
Sulfuric acid
Talcum (Venetian)
Toluol
Vaseline (petrolatum)
Xylol (xylene)
Zinc sulfate

REAGENTS

Fixatives—Bouin's, Schaudinn's, Zenker's

Indicators—paper (litmus, pH), phenolphthalein, phenol red
Mounting media—Berlese's fluid, Canada balsam, cedar oil, permount, resin of dammar
Solutions—Ehrlich's, Fehling's, Locke's, Ringer's, Tyrode's

CULTURE MEDIA AND INGREDIENTS

Agar
Bacto-agar
Bacto-beef (dehydrated)
Bacto-peptone (Neopeptone)
Balamuth's egg-yolk infusion
Cleveland and Collier's bacto *Endamoeba* medium
Dextrose
Liver extract powder
Maltose
Nelson's alcoholic extract medium
Sterile horse serum and rice powder
For details see Chapter XXXVIII. *See also* CHEMICALS, *above.*

STAINS

Hematoxylin stains (Delafield, Heidenhain)
Romanovsky's stains (Field, Giemsa, Kiewiet de Jonge, Leishman, Wright)

STAINING MATERIALS

Absolute alcohol
Azure I and II
Basic fuchsin
Carmine
Chromic acid
D'Antoni's iodine solution
Eosin
Ferric ammonium sulfate
Hematoxylin
Lugol's solution
Methylene blue
Violet (crystal and gentian)
For details see Chapter XXXIX. See also list of CHEMICALS, *above.*

CHAPTER XXXVI

EXAMINATION FOR PROTOZOA AND HELMINTHS: FECES, URINE, AND SPUTUM

DIRECT EXAMINATION OF FECES

The material for direct examination is collected in waxed paper containers with tight-fitting lids. For shipment of specimens fixed in bulk, glass bottles are used with plastic screw-top covers.

The following reagents are required: (1) a 2 percent aqueous solution of eosin [1]; (2) Lugol's solution (2 gm iodine, 3 gm KI, in 100 ml distilled water) or preferably D'Antoni's solution [2] (1 percent of KI in a saturated solution of iodine crystals), in addition to the routine use of physiological saline.

The two solutions serve the following purpose.

(1) *Eosin* stains everything pink except living protoplasm.[3] Therefore, with a low-power objective, the eosin preparation reveals the presence of living protozoal trophozoites, protozoal cysts, thin-shelled helminth ova, and helminth larvas, as pearly-white objects against a pink background, which then can be further examined with a high-power objective. If these objects are dead they stain pink. For this reason, the eosin solution also serves as a test for viability of cysts.[1] Chromatoid bodies in histolytica cysts are conspicuous in eosin preparations; so are the nuclei in eight-nucleate coli cysts; the "trough" near the anterior end of a chilomastix trophozoite shows as an elongated pink area on a colorless background, provided the eosin preparations are very thin; otherwise they do not reveal much structure. The main object of the eosin solution is to show the presence of protozoa, and it is particularly useful for the detection of cysts of amoebas.[4]

(2) The *iodine preparation* is helpful, provided the cysts are fairly numerous, for they cannot readily be located with the low-power objective. The iodine preparation shows (*a*) the reddish-brown glycogen vacuole, surrounded by yellow peripheral protoplasm and a

single nucleus, characteristic of many cysts of *E. histolytica;* (*b*) the equally conspicuous glycogen vacuole accompanied by two large nuclei, characteristic of many cysts of *E. coli;* (*c*) the comparatively small, but deeply staining and sharply outlined glycogen vacuole, accompanied by a single nucleus with a well-marked large karyosome characteristic of the cysts of *I. bütschlii;* (*d*) the nuclei in advanced stages of development of histolytica and coli cysts; (*e*) the "glycogen vacuole" of *Blastocystis hominis,* which reveals its true nature by staining a pale yellow. Chromatoid bodies do not show so well as in living cysts.

Purged specimens, obtained after the administration of saline purgative, are used by some authors on all occasions. However, Faust et al.[5] and Hoare[4] resort to this method only in cases presenting strong clinical suspicion of intestinal amebiasis, usually in the cecal area, but proving consistently negative on routine examination of the stools. Phospho-soda, and sodium sulfate are recommended as purgatives, rather than Epsom salts, because they are probably better for delivering the trophozoites in an undamaged motile condition.[5] The mucous particles in the liquid portion of the evacuation offer the best chance for the recovery of *E. histolytica.* The same applies to *enema specimens,* which should be obtained by high instillation of tepid physiological saline to irrigate the cecal area.

Specimens fixed in bulk, in 5 percent formaldehyde, are useful for shipment by mail. But they do not equal fresh specimens because (1) eosin preparations cannot be made, (2) tissue-invading (histolytic) trophozoites of *E. histolytica* do not show erythrocytes, (3) the glycogen vacuole in the cysts does not stain with iodine. The MIF stain-preservation technique[6] is reported to yield better results than simple formalin fixation. It is performed by introducing 0.15 ml of Lugol's solution into a glass container, followed by 2.35 ml of a solution prepared by mixing in 250 ml of distilled water 200 ml of tincture of merthiolate No. 99 "Lilly," 25 ml of formaldehyde U.S.P., and 5 ml of glycerol, to which 10 to 15 parts of freshly prepared Lugol's solution are added. In this mixture 0.25 gm of feces is thoroughly comminuted.

Eggs of helminths can be found in the same preparations. The eosin preparation, originally devised for facilitating the detection of cysts, lends the same service in the search for helminth eggs with a thin, colorless shell. For those with a thick brownish-yellow shell it has no advantage over saline. However, the thick-shelled eggs can be conveniently demonstrated in fecal smears dried on a slide and covered with cedar oil or non-resinous Shell Oil, nD 1.515 (with or without a coverslip). Most fecal matter becomes transparent, and almost invisible when opening the diaphragm wide, but the eggs show all the more clearly on the transparent background. Thin-shelled colorless eggs, on the contrary, cannot be distinguished from the elements forming the background.[6a]

Various elements occasionally found in feces may be mistaken for animals parasitizing man, such as: (*a*) living epithelial cells and white blood cells; (*b*) vegetable food particles; (*c*) air bubbles; (*d*) oil drops; (*e*) *Meloidogne javanica* (*Heterodera radicicola*), a nematode parasitizing plants, whose eggs, of 82 –120 × 24–43 μ, may be mistaken for trichostrongylus eggs because of their numerous blastomeres; (*f*) *Blastocystis hominis,* a unicellular fungus, with a spherical body of 8–14 μ and a peripheral layer of cytoplasm with one or more nuclei surrounding a large central vacuole that does not stain brown with iodine.

For *cultivation of intestinal protozoa,* see Chapter XXXVIII; for *fixing and staining,* Chapter XXXIX.

CONCENTRATION OF PROTOZOA, EGGS, AND LARVAS IN FECES

SEDIMENTATION AND CENTRIFUGATION

Simple Water Sedimentation. Ten grams of feces or more are thoroughly mixed with ten times their volume of water until there results a homogeneous suspension. It is poured into a conic glass, in which the sediment is allowed to settle. After an hour, two-thirds of the supernatant fluid is decanted, fresh water is added, to fill the glass to the brim, and the sediment is resuspended by a thorough stirring. This procedure is repeated two or three times, until the supernatant fluid is fairly clear. After the final removal of the supernatant water, a drop of the sediment is examined on a slide under a coverglass. The method is particularly recommended for trematode eggs that are passed in a state of embryonation and for unfertilized ascaris eggs.

Glycerol Sedimentation (after Faust and Ingalls).[7] Ten grams of feces are thoroughly comminuted in 10 to 20 times their volume of

0.5 percent of glycerol. The suspension is strained through 2 to 4 layers of moist cheesecloth, into a 250 to 500 ml conical glass, where it is left to settle for one hour. Two-thirds of the supernatant fluid is decanted and replaced by fresh glycerol solution, filling the container to the brim. Settling, decanting the supernatant fluid, and filling up with fresh solution, are repeated twice, the second settling being reduced to ¾ hour, and the third to ½ hour. When the supernatant fluid becomes fairly clear, it is decanted, a drop of the sediment is placed on a slide of 75 × 37 mm under a coverglass for microscopic examination at low power.

Telemann's Method of Acid-Ether Centrifugation.[22] Mix in a mortar a fecal specimen the size of a bean with 5 ml of water, comminute thoroughly, add 5 ml of a 25 percent solution of hydrochloric acid, and repeat the process of comminution. The mixture is strained through moist cheesecloth into a centrifuge tube. To the strained suspension is added an equal volume of ether. The two are thoroughly mixed and then centrifuged for 10 minutes at 2500 r.p.m. Four layers appear: from top to bottom, ether, fecal detritus, hydrochloric acid, sediment. All but the bottom layer are decanted; the sediment is collected on a glass slide, covered with a coverslip, and examined under the microscope. Telemann's technique is appropriate for the concentration of the eggs of all helminths, but not for protozoa.

The acid-ether technique has been modified by Weller and Dammin[23] by the addition of a few drops of a 10 percent solution of Triton NE (Triton X 30) as a detergent. It is said to yield a greater concentration of schistosome eggs. Another modification is the one devised by Loughlin and Stoll[24] who added equal parts of xylene and ether instead of pure ether. It is claimed to be superior to the original Telemann method as it is more apt to concentrate trichocephalus, hookworm, and unfertilized ascaris eggs.

Merthiolate-Iodine-Formaldehyde Concentration (MIFC) after Blagg et al.[8] Starting with Sapero and Lawless's MIF mixture described above (p. 574), in which fecal material has been comminuted, the suspension is shaken vigorously for five seconds, and strained through two layers of wet cheesecloth into a 15 ml centrifuge tube. Four ml of ether is added and the tube is closed with a rubber stopper and shaken vigorously. One should not omit removing the stopper from time to time during the process of shaking. The stopper is then removed and the tube is left standing for two minutes and then centrifuged for one minute at 1600 r.p.m. Four layers now appear in the tube: from the bottom upwards, sediment containing the ova, the MIF-fluid, a plug of fecal detritus, and a layer of ether. The ether is decanted, the plug is removed, the MIF-fluid is pipetted off, and the sediment examined.

Bayer's Concentration Method.[9] To a suspension of 1–2 gm of feces in 10 ml of water is added 10 ml of the following solution: 2 gm of $CuCl_2$, 2 gm of $Cu(C_2H_4O_2)_2$, 100 ml of a 40 percent formaldehyde solution, 500 ml of camphorated water (10 ml camphorated alcohol with 190 ml of hot water), 400 ml of distilled water, 12 gm of glacial acetic acid. The mixture is stirred and allowed to sediment for a short time. The supernatant fluid is decanted into a globe-shaped separatory funnel, 10 to 15 ml of ether is added to the mixture, and it is then thoroughly shaken for three minutes; take care to remove the stopper now and then. Next the underlying fluid is drained off and centrifuged for two minutes at 2500 r.p.m. The supernatant fluid is decanted, and the sediment is examined. Bayer's technique is recommended only for protozoal cysts.

FLOTATION AND CENTRIFUGAL FLOTATION

Bass's Brine Flotation[10] *with Willis's Modification.*[11] A quantity of feces the size of a pea is well comminuted in a concentrated solution of sodium chloride with a specific gravity of 1.200. A glass cylinder is filled to the brim with this suspension, and a microscope slide is placed on top of the surface film. The eggs rising in the fluid adhere to the glass slide. The slide is removed after half an hour, inverted, and examined microscopically.

The method is suitable for fertilized ascaris, and trichocephalus. Hookworm eggs, strongyloides larvas, and protozoal cysts are shrunken badly, the latter two sometimes beyond recognition. Embryonated trematode eggs, unfertilized ascaris eggs, and taenia eggs do not float in brine.

Faust's Zinc Sulfate Centrifugal Flotation.[5] Ten milliliters of a suspension of 1 part of feces in 10 parts of lukewarm water are strained into a centrifuge tube through one layer of wet cheesecloth and centrifuged for 60 seconds at 2300 r.p.m. The supernatant fluid is poured off, the sediment is resuspended, and more water is added to fill the tube. This process is repeated until the supernatant fluid is clear. The latter is replaced by a solution of zinc sulfate of a specific gravity of 1.180 (a 33 percent aqueous solution of $ZnSO_4 \cdot 7H_2O$, crystalline), filling the tube to the brim, in which the sediment is resuspended and centrifuged as above. Finally, several loopfuls are removed from the surface onto a glass slide, one drop of d'Antoni's iodine [2] is gently mixed with it, mounted with a coverslip, and examined.

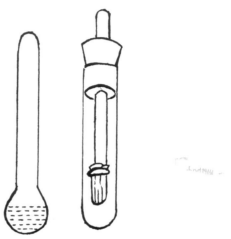

FIG. 36·1   *Right,* N.I.H. swab.—*Left,* glass pestle, × ½. (After Swellengrebel and Schüffner, 1943. Courtesy, *Nederlands Tijdschrift voor Geneeskunde.*)

The method is suitable for the eggs of various helminths and protozoan cysts, but not for the eggs of trematodes, cestodes, and unfertilized ascaris.

SPECIAL EXAMINATIONS FOR PROTOZOA AND HELMINTHS IN FECES, URINE, AND SPUTUM

EXAMINATION FOR PIN WORMS

Scotch Tape, after Graham.[12] From a roll of 2.5-cm wide adhesive cellulose tape a 5-cm length of tape is torn off. With the forefinger the sticky side of the tape is applied to the perianal area; after removal the tape is placed sticky side down on a labeled glass slide and pressed down with the finger to exclude air bubbles. It is examined under the microscope for ova, with a low-power, and confirmed with a high-power objective (Fig. 36·2).

N.I.H. Swab, after Hall.[13] A glass rod tipped with cellophane, held in its place with a rubber band, is employed to swab the perianal area of the patient. The cellophane with adhering material is removed from the rod, flattened on a glass slide, and examined for eggs with a low-power objective, under a coverslip (Fig. 36·1:right).

Glass Pestle.[14] The pestle is a 10-cm long, thick-walled tube, blown out at one end into a globe 1.75 cm in diameter, which is ground rough on a carborundum stone (Fig. 36·1:left). The moistened globe is rubbed on the perianal skin for ten seconds, applying a rotatory motion. The resulting suspension is transferred onto a labeled glass slide and allowed to dry. The dried drop is examined with a low-power objective, after being covered with nonresinous Shell Oil, nD 1.515 or cedar oil; for examination with a high-power objective it is mounted with a coverslip (Fig. 36·3).

MacKeith and Watson [15] consider the pestle to be cleanly and to give an easily examined specimen; but the tape is simpler.

The same methods may be employed for the detection of taenia eggs.

EXAMINATION FOR OTHER ADULT OR LARVAL WORMS IN FECES

Adult worms spontaneously appearing in feces are ascaris, pinworms, and very rarely males of trichinella. As a rule they can be easily identified after the feces have been washed through a sieve with tap water.

Proglottids of Taenias. These are easily detected by their size and pale color. To differentiate *fresh* specimens of *T. saginata* and *T. solium* by the number of lateral branches on the longitudinal uterine stem, it suffices to press a specimen between two slides and examine it with a hand lens. If not clearly visible the specimen may be first cleared by immersion in a phenol-xylol mixture (carbolic acid 75 percent, xylene 25 percent) for a short period. Fixed material is more difficult to handle; therefore sending in fresh specimens is to be insisted on. If only fixed material is available, it may still be used by clearing the specimen by leaving it for 24 hours in glycerol, or in pure carbolic acid for a much shorter period.

For the purpose of staining, fresh proglottids are left in distilled water for half an hour. Then they are passed through 40 percent alcohol for 3 minutes, and transferred to 70 percent alcohol. They are stained in a mixture consisting of 200 ml of a 30 percent solution of lactic acid, in which 0.6 gm of carmine is dissolved by boiling; after cooling, the mixture is filtered. In this mixture the objects are left for 30 minutes, after which they are washed in tap water that has to be changed several times. Finally, they are passed through 40, 70, 90, 100 percent alcohol, and salicylate of methyl, and mounted with resin of dammar.

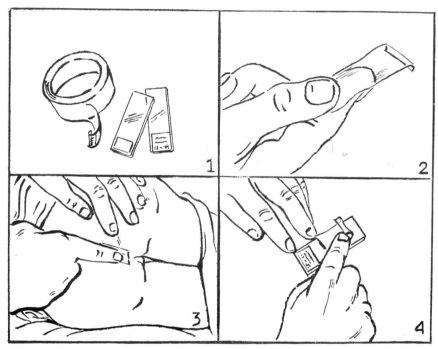

Fig. 36·2   Graham's adhesive cellulose-tape technique: 1. Role of tape and labeled slides.—2. Two-inch length of tape held over forefinger.—3. Sticky side of tape applied by forefinger to perianal skin.—4. Tape stuck down to labeled slide. (After MacKeith and Watson, 1948. Courtesy, *The Practitioner,* London.)

Worms Passed in the Stools after Anthelmintic Treatment. These are isolated by washing the fecal matter through the meshes of a wire-gauze sieve with an abundance of water. Helminths of the size of hookworms and over are retained on the sieve; they are transferred to physiological saline before they are identified and counted. Helminths that pass through the meshes are isolated by mixing the feces with water in a glass cylinder. The sediment is repeatedly washed and resedimented after adding fresh water. Finally, the sediment is poured into a Petri dish and examined with a hand lens over a dark background.

Worms Spontaneously Passed in the Feces as Larvas (Strongyloides). These may be recovered with *Baermann's technique,* originally devised for recovering hookworm larvas from the soil.[16] The tube of a funnel is fitted with a rubber tube 5 cm long and closed

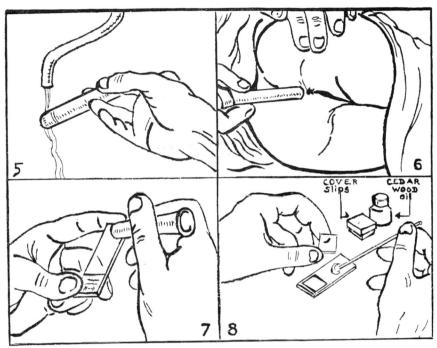

Fig. 36·3 Schüffner and Swellengrebel's glass-pestle technique: 5. Tip of pestle (for correct shape see Fig. 36·1 left) wetted.—6. Rubbed on perianal skin.—7. Suspension transferred onto labeled slide.—8. Drop of nonresinous immersion oil, nD 1.515 added on dried suspension and mounted with coverslip, if necessary. (After MacKeith and Watson, 1948. Courtesy, *The Practitioner,* London.)

with a burette clamp. A piece of fine wire gauze molded into the shape of a deep dish with a concave bottom and lined with surgical gauze is fitted inside the funnel. Several grams of feces are placed on the gauze, and the funnel is filled with water of 40–42° C, until it touches the convex bottom of the wire-gauze dish. Within one to two hours the larvas emerging from the feces slip through the wire-gauze meshes, and collect into the rubber tube. They are drained off into a Petri dish by opening the clamp. The same purpose is served by Fülleborn's technique of culturing free-living strongyloides (see Chapter XXXVIII).

Miracidia Hatching Technique, after Faust and Meleney.[17] Whole specimens of feces are worked through a wire-mesh screen, placed in a 1 or 2-liter container, stirred vigorously, and left undisturbed for half an hour. The supernatant fluid is decanted down to the lighter portion of the sediment; the container is refilled and the decanting repeated until the supernatant fluid remains fairly clear. Then the sediment is transferred to an Erlenmeyer flask filled with clean tap water and is left overnight at 20° to 30° C. The following morning the supernatant fluid is carefully searched against a dark background with a hand lens. Miracidia appear as minute, white, boat-shaped organisms, swimming rapidly in a straight course. In perfectly clear water they usually are most numerous in the small surface area of the Erlenmeyer flask.

Water Centrifugal Concentration Combined with Hatching, after Most et al.[18] Ten to fifteen grams of feces and 100 ml of lukewarm tap water are placed in a 125-ml Erlenmeyer flask. The flask is closed with a stopper and the contents are shaken for one to two minutes and strained through two layers of wet gauze into a centrifuge tube 12×2.5 cm, with a conical bottom. The contents are centrifuged three times for 30 seconds at 1500 r.p.m. After each centrifugation the supernatant fluid is decanted, tap water at 40° C is added up to the 40-ml mark, and the tube is closed with a stopper and shaken. After the third centrifugation the supernatant fluid is again poured off; four drops of the sediment are placed on a glass slide under a coverslip of 22×40 mm. If the examination is negative, ten drops of water are added to the remaining sediment, which is then left overnight in a warm place. Next morning the whole sediment is poured into the lid of a Petri dish and examined for hatched miracidia under a dissecting microscope.

QUANTITATIVE METHODS WITH EGGS

Beaver's Direct Egg-Count.[18a] The eggs are counted in a fixed amount of a fecal suspension, whose density has been evaluated by its turbidity, i.e. its power to reduce the light emitted by a lamp whose rays are directed towards the window of a photoelectric foot-candle meter and are made to pass through the fecal emulsion. The result of Stoll's egg count (see below) can be correlated with that obtained in fecal smears of a fixed size and turbidity. The photo-electric light meter is calibrated by standard precipitates of barium sulfate, made on the spot and kept in suspension by the addition of glycerol.

Stoll and Hausheer's Dilution Egg-Count.[19] An Erlenmeyer flask with a long neck marked at the 56-ml and 60-ml levels is filled up to the 56-ml mark with decinormal (0.405 percent) sodium hydrox-ide. Then feces are added until the fluid reaches the 60-ml level. After adding ten glass beads, the flask is closed with a rubber stopper and thoroughly shaken until the contents have been converted into a homogeneous suspension. After repeated shaking, 0.15 ml is drawn up into a graduated capillary pipette, transferred to a slide of 75 $\times$ 37 mm, and mounted with a coverslip of 40 $\times$ 22 mm. The total number of eggs under the coverslip is counted. This is repeated three times, and the average from the three counts, multiplied by 100, yields the number of eggs in 1 ml of well-formed stools. Cor-rections are made according to the consistency of stool as follows. For mushy stools the count is multiplied by two, for mushy-diarrheic stools by three, and for liquid stools by four.

EGGS, LARVAS, AND PROTOZOA IN URINE

Trichomonas vaginalis[25] and very rarely *E. histolytica* may be found in urine.

In urine specimens collected at the end of micturition, preferably from the morning, and kept in a conic sedimentation glass, the eggs of *Schistosoma haematobium* are usually recovered, and occasionally those of *S. mansoni.* According to Newsome and Halawani,[20] miracidia may be recovered from eggs in urine if it is left to sediment in a conic glass for two hours or more. The supernatant urine is removed, leaving 5 ml of sediment. This is centrifuged at less than 1000 r.p.m. for one minute, the supernatant urine is again siphoned off, and 5 ml or more of water added. The centrifuging is repeated, and the water is replaced by 4 ml of fresh water. The glass is left for an hour, and the specimen is then examined for the presence of hatched miracidia.

In cases of chyluria microfilarias of *W. bancrofti* may be found in the sediment after centrifugation of the urine.

Faust et al.[5] mention rare findings of *Strongyloides stercoralis* in urine. Spurious parasitism of *Anguillula aceti* in urine is occasionally encountered.[21]

EGGS, LARVAS, AND PROTOZOA IN SPUTUM

Eggs of *Paragonimus westermani* are often found in the sputum of subjects infected with this parasite. Fragments of the laminated wall of the *hydatid,* together with or without scolices and separate hooklets, may be coughed up when a pulmonary hydatid ruptures and its component parts are discharged into a bronchus. Tissue-invading (histoloytic) trophozoites of *E. histolytica* may be found in the sputum if a pulmonary amebic abscess is ruptured.

P. westermani ova may be found by direct examination of a preparation of the brownish or blood-flecked mucoid sputum. If unsuccessful, a small amount of the sputum is mixed with an equal amount of a 3 percent solution of sodium hydroxide and centrifuged. The supernate is poured off and a drop of the sediment is examined. Incidentally, it should be mentioned that *P. westermani* ova are usually also found concurrently in the sedimented stool specimen.

REFERENCES FOR CHAPTER XXXVI

1. W. A. KUENEN and N. H. SWELLENGREBEL. *Centr. Bakteriol.,* Abt. I, Or., 1913, 71: 378–410; S. L. BRUG. *Arch. Schiffs- u. Tropenhyg.,* 1936, 40: 521–522.
2. J. S. D'ANTONI. *Am. J. Trop. Med.,* 1937, 17: 79–84.
3. E. STRASSBURGER. *Das botanische Practicum,* Jena, 1902, Gustav Fischer, 357.
4. C. A. HOARE. *Handbook of Medical Protozoölogy,* London, 1949, Baillière, Tindall & Cox, pp. 278, 279.
5. E. C. FAUST, P. F. RUSSELL, and D. R. LINCICOME. *Clinical Parasitology,* Philadelphia, 1957, Lea & Febiger, pp. 952, 960.
6. J. J. SAPERO and D. K. LAWLESS. *Am. J. Trop. Med. Hyg.,* 1953, 2: 613–619.
6a. G. HEIN. *J. Lab. Clin. Med.,* 1927, 12: 1117–1118.
7. E. C. FAUST and J. W. INGALLS. *Am. J. Trop. Med.,* 1946, 26: 559–584.
8. W. BLAGG, E. L. SCHLOEGEL, N. S. MANSOUR, and G. I. KHALAF. *Am. J. Trop. Med. Hyg.,* 1955, 4: 23–28.
9. Y. RODENHUIS. *On the Existence of Different Races of E. histolytica,* The Hague, 1924, L. J. C. Boucher, p. 10.
10. C. C. BASS. *J. Am. Med. Assoc.,* 1906, 47: 185–189; F. FÜLLEBORN. *Deut. med. Wochschr.,* 1920, 46: 714.
11. H. H. WILLIS. *Med. J. Australia,* 1921, 8: 375–376.
12. C. F. GRAHAM. *Am. J. Trop. Med.,* 1941, 21: 157–161.
13. M. C. HALL. *Am. J. Trop. Med.,* 1937, 17: 445–453.
14. W. A. P. SCHÜFFNER and N. H. SWELLENGREBEL. *Zentr. Bakteriol.,* Abt. I, Or., 1943, 151: 71–80.
15. R. MACKEITH and J. R. WATSON. *Practitioner,* 1948, 160: 264–270.

16. G. BAERMANN. *Geneesk. Tijdschr. Ned. Indië,* 1917, 57: 579–669, English summary, 669.
17. E. C. FAUST and H. E. MELENEY. *Am. J. Hyg.,* Monogr. Ser. No. 3, Baltimore, 1924.
18. H. MOST, C. A. KANE, P. H. LAVIETES, E. F. SCHROEDER, A. BEHM, L. BLUM, B. KATZIN, and J. M. HAYMAN, JR. *Am. J. Trop. Med.,* 1950, 30: 239–299.
18a. P. C. BEAVER. *J. Parasitol.,* 1949, 35: 125–135; 1950, 36: 451–456.
19. N. R. STOLL and W. C. HAUSHEER. *Am. J. Hyg.,* 1926, 6 (March Suppl.): 134–145.
20. J. NEWSOME and A. HALAWANI. *Trans. Roy. Soc. Trop. Med. Hyg.,* 1950, 44: 67–76.
21. P. KOURÍ and J. G. BASNUEVO. *Helmintologia humana,* Havana, 1949, Muñiz Hnos.
22. W. TELEMANN. *Deut. med. Wochschr.,* 1908, 34: 1510–1511.
23. T. H. WELLER and G. J. DAMMIN. *Am. J. Clin. Pathol.,* 1945, 15: 496–500.
24. E. H. LOUGHLIN and N. R. STOLL. *Am. J. Trop. Med.,* 1946, 26: 517–527.
25. R. E. TRUSSEL. *Trichomonas Vaginalis and Trichomoniasis,* Springfield, Ill., 1947, Charles C Thomas, pp. 118, 121.

CHAPTER XXXVII

EXAMINATION FOR PROTOZOA AND HELMINTHS: BLOOD AND BODY FLUIDS

EXAMINATION OF BLOOD

Blood is examined in the form of a single drop from a prick in the distal phalanx of a finger or, preferably, from a minute cut made in the ear lobe with the sharp edge of a dissecting needle ground flat at the tip (Fig. 37·1). For special purposes larger quantities are taken from the median basilic vein.

The drop of blood is examined fresh by putting a coverslip on it (*fresh wet film*) or as a dry film. There are two kinds of dry films, the *thin dry film* and the *thick dry film*.

A *thin film* ought to show one layer of red cells, all lying flat. It is prepared by collecting with the flat side of a glass slide (without touching the skin) a drop of blood oozing from a minute puncture in the ear lobe (Fig. 37·2). Thus a drop of blood is placed near the end of the thoroughly cleaned slide. Another slide, the "spreader," with ground edges, has one of the corners of a short side broken off. This "spreading edge" is placed on the slide so as to touch the drop of blood. The spreader, held in a slanting position and touching the slide with its spreading edge only (Fig. 37·3), is pushed forward gently but firmly over the surface of the slide. The drop of blood filling the angle between spreader and slide is drawn behind the spreader. Thus it is spread evenly over the slide. The thin film thus prepared dries almost immediately. Its width is less than the slide to which it adheres, and so its long edges are open for examination.

To prepare a *thick film* (after Ronald Ross, modified by Dempwolff) the preliminaries are the same as for the thin film. The slide with the collected drop is stood on edge, allowing the drop to run downward over a distance of 2 cm, helped along, if need be, with a needle; then the slide is turned for the drop to run backward.

Thus it spreads fairly evenly and does not take an unduly long time to dry. If there is no particular hurry, the slide is left to dry more thoroughly overnight, to diminish the risk of being washed off. Houseflies are to be kept away; they manage to lap up a whole slideful of thick films within an astonishingly short time.

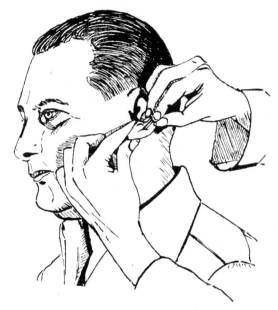

Fig. 37·1   Ear lobe, lifted by left hand, is scratched longitudinally with a needle, ground flat and sharp-edged at the tip.

In one field of the microscope the thick film shows 40 times more blood than a thin blood film, but if it is too thick, it is useless. It is also useless if it cannot be dehemoglobinized with water. This is impossible after fixation by chemicals, by exposure to the air for longer than a few weeks (in the tropics), by exposure to direct sunlight, or by heating. A thick film is not firmly fixed to the glass slide; so rinsing should be done cautiously, and drying by standing it on edge; no filter paper is to be used.

For *fixing* and *staining* of blood slides see Chapter XXXIX.

MICROFILARIAS

When looking for microfilarias in blood, it is important to take account of the hour of examination (see Chapter XXI). Because of their large size microfilarias may be examined in a fresh wet film with a low-power objective. As to dry films, a thin film is preferable to ascertain the location of the principal anatomical features and the presence or absence of a sheath, but in mass examination the thick film has decided advantages.

To ascertain the number of microfilarias, for the purpose of establishing the presence or absence of periodicity, a large thick film must be examined in its totality with a low-power objective.

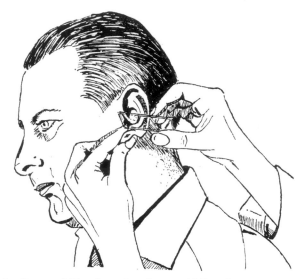

FIG. 37·2   Drop of blood, oozing from middle of scratch, about to be taken up by slide that is not to touch the skin of the lobe.

If the parasites are scanty, *Knott's* [1] *technique for concentration of microfilarias* may be applied. It consists of adding 1 ml of venous blood to 9 ml of a 2 percent formalin solution in a 15-ml tube. The mixture is centrifuged, the supernatant fluid is decanted, and the sediment is spread on a slide and examined either fresh or after staining with Giemsa's fluid (see Chapter XXXIX). Of course, the blood must be taken in accordance with the periodicity of the microfilarias whose presence is suspected.

This also applies to the older *saponine method of concentration,* which has the advantage of showing living and motile microfilarias. It is performed by adding 1 ml of venous blood to 9 ml of a solution of 0.1 gm saponine and 0.3 gm citrate of sodium in 100 ml physiologic saline; the mixture is centrifuged for 10 minutes at 1500 r.p.m. and the sediment is examined.

The same methods may be applied in the search for the much smaller larvas of *Trichinella spiralis* during the second week of the infection.

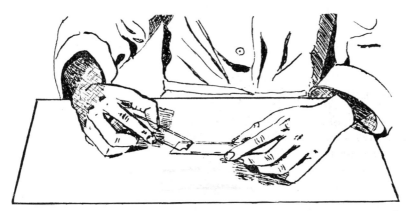

FIG. 37·3 "Spreader" (one corner broken off), poised on horizontal slide (kept in position by left hand) at an angle of 45°, touches drop of blood, and is about to be moved in the direction of left hand, in order to make a thin film.

HEMOFLAGELLATES

Hemoflagellates may be found in the blood or tissue fluids (see below, p. 590) of patients by direct examination, in cultures (see Chapter XXXVIII, p. 598), or after inoculation of laboratory animals. Their presence may also be diagnosed by specific serological or chemical tests (see Chapter XL, p. 616).

Fresh wet blood films are used in the detection of trypanosomes, because the disturbance their locomotion causes among the red blood cells can be observed with a low-power objective. In mass examinations one relies mainly on dry thick films.

T. cruzi can be detected in the peripheral circulation only during the febrile stages of Chagas' disease, and even then it is rarely recovered. Cultivation of the parasite in triatomid bugs, known as Brumpt's *xenodiagnosis*,[2] is regarded by many investigators as the most satisfactory method for the detection of the flagellate in the blood. It requires a stock of laboratory-bred, uninfected (beware of *Trypanosome rangeli!*) triatomids. Their fourth-stage larvas are made to ingest the patient's blood. Twenty days after the infecting meal metacyclic trypanosomes may be found in the rectal ampulla of the bug. In field work the procedure is also employed for examination of dogs and other reservoir hosts suspected of harboring *T. cruzi.*

In *Rhodesian trypanosomiasis* the parasite, according to Kleine,[3] can be found as readily in the thick blood film as in the enlarged cervical glands. In *Gambian trypanosomiasis,* on the contrary, the flagellates are rarely detected in the thick blood film. The number of positive findings may be raised by applying the method of *triple centrifugation.*[4] This method is based on the observation that in centrifuged citrated blood the trypanosomes, together with the leucocytes, collect in the upper layer of the centrifugate, on top of the erythrocytes. This upper layer, together with the supernatant fluid, is pipetted off and centrifuged twice. Occasionally, *T. gambiense* is found in the blood, while the puncture of the cervical glands yields negative results.

In *visceral leishmaniasis* direct investigation of the blood yields results only in cases of Indian kala-azar. Only thin dry films are examined, concentrating on areas where leucocytes are most numerous, viz. the longitudinal edges of the film and the long drawnout strands of cells at the end of the film (for dermal leishmanias see below, p. 594).

Animal inoculation is widely used for the detection of hemoflagellates in the peripheral circulation or in other body fluids (see below, p. 592). In the diagnosis of Chagas' disease (*T. cruzi*) the animals inoculated are guinea pigs and young mice; in Gambian trypanosomiasis monkeys are used, and their inoculation may take as long as ten weeks to yield results. In visceral leishmaniasis, animal inoculation has become a reliable means for establishing the presence of leishmanias, since hamsters have been discovered as animals suitable for this purpose. It takes several months to ascertain their presence in this way.

BLOOD SPOROZOA

The examination of the peripheral blood for the presence of *malaria parasites* can provide the answer to the following questions.

(1) *The individual or clinical question:* "Is this particular patient

suffering from malaria?, i.e. Can he be cured by a specific anti-malarial drug; and how badly does he need it?

Although the answer can be given by administering the drug and awaiting the result, the detection of the parasite is usually regarded as an indispensable support of the clinical diagnosis. This is not a too onerous requirement, for plasmodia can usually be found within a reasonable time in the blood of a patient ill with malarial fever, provided he has not yet ingested a specific drug. In the absence of falciparum malaria, specific treatment may be withheld until plasmodia have been found. If *P. falciparum* is indigenous in the patient's country, specific treatment is to be initiated without delay.

In malarious areas it is recommended to search for malaria parasites in the blood of every patient. This is good practice, provided it is borne in mind that a "symptomless" carrier may be ill with a disease which bears no relationship to the plasmodia he is harboring.

(2) *The collective or epidemiological question:* How many people, in this particular area, are carriers of plasmodia?

To answer this question the people examined are selected at random, and separated into age groups, with a reasonable number to each group; moreover, the species of parasites encountered, falciparum gametocytes separately, are noted for each positive slide, and their number counted with reference to 300 leucocytes.

In examining patients' blood there is no fixed limit to the time to be spent on one slide. However, a limit is generally set in epidemiological surveys, viz. three minutes to a thick film showing an average of 40 leucocytes per microscopic field, exclusive of the time required for collecting the data mentioned above.

The examination of a thin film requires too much time to be practicable in epidemiological surveys. In clinical practice it still has its use, e.g. in falciparum infection. According to Covell et al.,[5] the microscope sometimes gives a more reliable indication of the gravity of the case than the clinical examination. The danger point of 10 percent of red cells infected, to which this warning refers, can be more conveniently established by counting ten infected red cells in a hundred than 1500 parasites to 30 leucocytes.

In the early days plasmodia were searched for in *fresh blood between slide and coverslip.* There, one could actually see the vivacity of *P. vivax,* and witness exflagellation once in a while. But the examination was a bedside procedure, and the microscope had to be carried on the physician's bicycle as he made his daily rounds. Modern developments, mass survey among them, inevitably caused the investigator to abandon this method and to lose touch with the living parasite.

For *fixing and staining* malaria parasites, see Chapter XXXIX.

Babesia bovis in the single human case quoted in Chapter VII was readily detected in the thin film. In veterinary practice *B. bovis* and its close relatives are detected in the same way; thick films do not appear to be appropriate. Babesias are known to be often rare in the peripheral circulation and to retire into internal organs, such as the kidney, myocardium, and brain. Sergent's [6] method of *isodiagnosis,* i.e. injection of 100–150 ml of blood into a susceptible bovine, might prove helpful in a human case in which babesias cannot be found. The same applies to xenodiagnosis, i.e. allowing appropriate species of ticks to ingest the blood of the patient and to search for developmental stages in the organs of the tick after its metamorphosis.

EXAMINATION OF BODY FLUIDS AND TISSUES

RECOVERY OF PARASITES FROM ASPIRATES

Duodenal Intubation. Direct examination of aspirates from the duodenum may reveal the presence of trophozoites of giardia, larvas of strongyloides, and ova of clonorchis, opistorchis, dicrocoelium, fasciolopsis, and fasciola. Kourí and Basnuevo [7] recommend the examination of the yellow mucous floccules ("oviferous floccules") floating in the bilious aspirate.

Proctoscopic Aspiration. This may reveal the presence of *Entamoeba histolytica.* Rectal snips removed by biopsy, treated with potassium hydroxide (5 percent solution), and pressed between two slides may show eggs of *Schistosoma mansoni.*

Aspirates from Lesions in Liver, Spleen, and Lungs. These may yield material of diagnostic value if it contains *Entamoeba histolytica.* Ishak et al.[13] recommend the use of the Vim-Silverman needle for biopsy of liver and spleen in the search for schistosomes. This method is not to be applied in cases suspected of hydatidosis, with the object of demonstrating the presence of scolices or hydatid sand (i.e. separate hooklets), because of the risk of scolices escaping and producing daughter cysts by vesiculation. As to visceral leishmaniasis, spleen puncture may reveal the presence of *L. donovani* when blood examination fails to do so. However, some [8] prefer not to use this method because of the risk to the patient. Liver puncture is regarded as less dangerous, but it is of little value.

Aspirates from Lymph Nodes, Bone Marrow, and the Cerebrospinal Cavity. Puncture of the enlarged posterior cervical gland and demonstration of trypanosomes in the aspirated juice is one of the most important methods for the diagnosis of African trypanosomiasis. It is positive in over 80 percent of the early cases. Trypanosomes are not easily detectable in a medium of white blood cells. Unlike red blood cells white cells are not readily agitated by the lashing flagella of the motile parasites.

For the diagnosis of visceral leishmaniasis, parasites may be detected in the juice aspirated from an enlarged inguinal gland; for the examination of an oriental sore the nonulcerating cutaneous lesion is punctured, or if it is ulcerated, the base of the ulcer is reached by a deep puncture through the indurated skin surrounding the ulcer.

Sternal puncture, reaching the bone marrow within the sternum, is regarded as one of the most reliable methods for the detection of *L. donovani.* In children tibial puncture may be preferable. Sternal puncture is also reported to yield satisfactory results in the detection of *Trypanosoma gambiense.*

Lumbar puncture is used in the advanced stages of African trypanosomiasis, when the parasites have invaded the central nervous system. At that stage the trypanosomes may be found in the aspirated cerebrospinal fluid. However, the chances of finding them there are limited. A. Broden, in the Congo,[8] found them there in less than 5 percent of the cases examined. At that stage one relies mainly on cytological (cell count) and biochemical (total protein contents and albumin-globulin ratio) changes in the cerebrospinal fluid as an index of the progress of the parasitic invasion of the central nervous system.

EXAMINATION OF SKIN SCRAPINGS

A method to demonstrate the presence of larvas of *Onchocerca volvulus* or *Acanthocheilonema streptocerca* in the skin consists of removing a small portion of the skin, or *snip,* with a sharp razor blade, preferably of the middorsal region, to one side of the midline.

The snip is placed in a drop of tepid normal saline; in positive cases the larvas can be seen to emerge from it, under a low-power objective.

In *scabies* the skin snip serves to remove the whole burrow, with the gravid female inside it. The snip is mounted in *Berlese's fluid,* consisting of water 20 ml, chloral hydrate 160 gm, well-powdered gum arabic 15 gm, glucose syrup 10 ml, glacial acetic acid 5 gm [9] (Fig. 27·4).

Fixed and stained *impression smears* of a superficial nonbleeding abrasion of the skin of young children infected with *Plasmodium falciparum* in the Congo have been reported as showing the dividing stages of the parasite, otherwise to be found only in the internal organs. In the same kind of smears *L. donovani* may be detected in cases of post-kala-azar dermal leishmanoid. Impression smears of mucocutaneous lesions in American dermal leishmaniasis may show *L. braziliensis.* The smear should be taken from the scraped edge of the ulcer.

SKELETAL MUSCLES

Immature *Trichinella spiralis* in human muscle tissue may be detected by examining small pieces of the deltoid, biceps, gastrocnemius or pectoralis major muscles. A portion of the tissue, obtained by biopsy, is compressed with a trichinoscope and examined directly with a low-power objective. Another portion is digested with artificial gastric juice (0.6 percent pepsin and 0.3 percent hydrochloric acid) for several hours at 37° C and examined directly in the Petri dish under the dissecting microscope; or the digest is centrifuged and the sediment examined after mounting with a coverslip.

The digestive method may be employed for the examination of human muscle tissue obtained by autopsy. In such cases it is usual to examine the diaphragmatic muscle. Pork and pork products are examined in a similar fashion. After thorough grinding in a meat grinder, the product should be incubated at 37° C for 24 to 36 hours, with an occasional agitation.

Another parasite encountered in human muscles, particularly in the myocardium, is *Sarcocystis lindemanni.* Ordinary histological examination of the tissue is the only method in use for its detection.

OTHER TISSUES

Toxoplasma. Smears of cerebrospinal fluid (or crushed tissues), dried, fixed with methyl alcohol, and stained with Giemsa solution (see Chapter XXXIX), are suitable for practical purposes. For histological examination sections of $4\,\mu$ are required. The tissues are fixed with neutral formol saline or Bouin and stained with Giemsa solution or hematoxylin-eosin.[10] The presence of toxoplasmas in human material may be demonstrated by intracerebral or intraperitoneal injection into rabbits, mice, guinea pigs, or hamsters. After four days smears are made of the peritoneal or cerebral fluid.

Pneumocystis. Van der Meer and Brug [12] fixed and stained impression smears of lung tissue with Giemsa solution in the customary way (see Chapter XXXIX). Histological sections were fixed in 10 percent formaldehyde and stained with a solution of 1.020 gm of azure and 0.025 gm of eosin in 25 ml of methyl alcohol, mixed with distilled water in a proportion of 1 in 2. The staining was continued for one hour and was followed by differentiation in alcohol.

Visceral Larva Migrans. According to Faust et al.[11] the larvas may be detected in material obtained by biopsy from the surface of the liver.

Entamoeba histolytica. In histological sections through amebic ulcers in the colon or the liver, removed by biopsy or autopsy, fixed in various ways, and stained with hematoxylin and eosin, the invading (histolytic) trophozoites may often be seen in large numbers. Care must be taken not to confuse them with certain ganglion cells in the intestinal wall which may resemble amoebas.

REFERENCES FOR CHAPTER XXXVII

1. J. KNOTT. *Trans. Roy. Soc. Trop. Med. Hyg.,* 1939, 33: 191–196.
2. E. BRUMPT. *Bull. soc. pathol. exotique,* 1914, 7: 702–710.
3. F. K. KLEINE. *Deut. med. Wochschr.,* 1909, 35: 469–470, 924–925.
4. C. JOYEUX and A. SICÉ. *Précis de médecine des pays chauds,* Paris, 1950, Masson & Cie., p. 862.
5. G. COVELL et al. *Chemotherapy of Malaria,* Geneva, 1955, World Health Organization.
6. ED. SERGENT et al. *Etudes sur les piroplasmoses bovines,* Alger, 1946.
7. P. KOURÍ and J. G. BASNUEVO. *Helmintologia humana,* Havana, 1949, Muñiz Hnos, pp. 677, 678.
8. PH. H. MANSON-BAHR. *Tropical Diseases,* London, 1957, Cassell & Co.
9. K. MELLANBY. *Scabies,* London, 1944, Oxford University Press, pp. 10, 11.
10. R. LAINSON. *Trans. Roy. Soc. Trop. Med. Hyg.,* 1958, 52: 396–407.
11. E. C. FAUST, P. F. RUSSELL, and D. R. LINCICOME. *Clinical Parasitology,* Philadelphia, 1957, Lea & Febiger, pp. 954, 955.
12. G. VAN DER MEER and S. L. BRUG. *Ann. soc. belge méd. trop.,* 1942, 22: 301–307.
13. K. G. ISHAK et al. *Am. J. Clin. Pathol.,* 1959, 31: 46–59.

CHAPTER XXXVIII

CULTURAL METHODS AND MEDIA FOR PROTOZOA

MEDIA FOR AMOEBAE AND OTHER INTESTINAL PROTOZOA

BALAMUTH'S EGG—YOLK INFUSION MEDIUM[1]

A quantity of 288 gm of dehydrated egg-yolk is emulsified in a mixture of 288 ml of distilled water and 1000 ml of 0.85 percent saline. Under constant stirring the emulsion is heated for 20 minutes or so until coagulation is completed. After adding 160 ml of distilled water the mixture is filtered through a muslin bag and its volume is brought up to 1000 ml with physiological saline. The filtrate is divided equally into two 1-liter Erlenmeyer flasks, autoclaved for 20 minutes at 121° C, and cooled overnight in a refrigerator. Next morning, the cool mixture is passed through a Büchner funnel, using two pieces of Whatman qualitative filter paper and applying negative pressure with an exhaust pump. The filtrate is measured, and to it is added an equal volume of Balamuth's M/15 buffer solution (see below), and 5 ml of crude liver extract (Lilly, No. 408) per liter of the filtrate. The medium is then dispensed in tubes, 6 ml per tube, and autoclaved for 20 minutes at 121° C. Sterility is tested by incubating for 24 hours at 37° C and sterile rice powder is added to each tube prior to its use.

The M/15 buffer solution is prepared by mixing the following solutions; (a) 1 M K_2HPO_4 174.180 gm and distilled water to make up 1000 ml; (b) 1 M KH_2PO_4 136.092 gm and distilled water to make up 1000 ml. The two are mixed in a proportion of 4.3 parts of (a) and 0.7 part of (b), and to 1 part of this mixture 14 parts of distilled water are added.

BOECK AND DRBOHLAV'S DIPHASIC MEDIUM[2]

The contents of four eggs and 50 ml of sterile Locke's solution (9 gm NaCl, 0.2 gm $CaCl_2$, 0.4 gm KCl, 0.2 gm $NaHCO_3$, 2.5 gm glucose and 1000 ml distilled water) are broken up in a sterile flask with glass beads. Slanted test tubes, filled with a quantity of the mixture sufficient to produce a slant of 3 cm, are heated at 70° C until their contents are solidified and then autoclaved for 20 minutes at 121° C. A mixture composed of equal parts of (a) sterile Locke's solution and (b) sterile, inactivated human serum (or 1 percent crystallized egg albumin in Locke's solution), passed through a Berkefeld filter and incubated to test sterility, is added to each tube to overlay the slant.

CLEVELAND AND COLLIERS' MEDIUM[3]

In the modification used by *Brug* in Amsterdam (unpublished), sterile test tubes of 10 × 1 cm, filled with 2 ml of horse serum passed through a Seitz filter, are slanted and the serum coagulated, the resulting slants being 4 cm long. The tubes are sterilized one hour at 80° C for three consecutive days. Immediately before use a mixture of 1 volume of Seitz-filtered horse serum and 6 volumes of sterile physiological saline is dispensed into the tubes to overlay the slants. Six tubes are inoculated with a particle of feces, taken up with a platinum loop and rubbed against the wall of the tube till it is well suspended in the liquid covering the slant. After inoculation, to each of the six tubes is added 30 mg of finely powdered rice starch, sterilized dry at 160° C for half an hour, and to three of them 25 mg of carbonate of lime sterilized in the same way. Usually, growth in the tubes with lime is better than in those without. For the first week, daily subinoculations are required; when the culture is well started, once in two or three days suffices.

For subinoculation most of the overlying liquid is decanted; the remainder is shaken repeatedly, the suspension is taken up with a sterile glass pipette, one drop is reserved for microscopic examination, and with the remainder fresh tubes are inoculated.

For cultivation of *Trichomonas* and *Chilomastix* the same medium is used, without the serum slant. In successful cultures, subinoculation twice weekly is sufficient.

Balantidium coli grows in the same medium as the flagellates, but slightly more rice starch (50 mg) and carbonate of lime (30 mg) are required. Moreover, to each tube should be added 4 drops of Sörensen's mixture, which contains 28 ml of a solution of 9.078 gm of KH$_2$PO$_4$ per liter of distilled water, and 72 ml of a solution of 11.876 gm of Na$_2$HPO$_4$ per liter of distilled water.

NELSON'S ALCOHOLIC EXTRACT MEDIUM[4]

Ten parts of egg-yolk and 90 parts of 95 percent alcohol are mixed in a flask and extracted for 48 hours with an occasional agitation. Ten milliliters of this "stock extract" are dealcoholized by heating in a water bath, and mixed with 20 ml of 2 percent agar in buffered 0.5 percent saline (melted by heating). The mixture is dispensed in tubes, 2 ml per tube, and allowed to solidify in a slanted position. The slants are overlaid with 0.5 percent buffered saline, and at the time of inoculation, sterilized rice flour is added to the medium.

Mention should be made that the addition of small amounts of streptomycin and penicillin to culture media suppresses bacterial overgrowth and favors the growth of *E. histolytica*. This has been shown by Spingarn and Edelman [9] and others.

HOARE'S MAINTENANCE OF OOCYSTS OF COCCIDIA IN VITRO[5]

Feces containing oocysts of *Isospora belli* are spread on the bottom of a Petri dish covered with a solution of 1 percent of chromic acid or 2 percent of potassium bichromate in order to impede the growth of fungi and bacteria without damaging the oocysts. The Petri dish is covered and kept at room temperature; the development of sporocysts and sporozoites is completed in 1 to 4 days.

MEDIA FOR LEISHMANIA AND OTHER HEMOFLAGELLATES

NOVY, MACNEAL, AND NICOLLE'S (NNN) MEDIUM

A sterile solution of agar 14 gm and NaCl 6 gm, in 900 ml of distilled water, dispensed in test tubes, is melted at 45° C. To the contents of each tube is added ⅓ of its volume of defibrinated rabbit's blood, collected under aseptic conditions. The contents are allowed to solidify in a slanted position, preferably on ice, so as to increase the quantity of fluid collecting at the bottom of the slant; for in this fluid the hemoflagellates develop. Then the tubes are incubated, to test their sterility, and afterwards kept cool, their cotton plug covered with a rubber cap or tin foil, to reduce evaporation.

Attempts at cultivating *L. tropica* or *L. braziliensis* are usually frustrated by bacterial contamination. It is therefore recommended to add 200–500 units of penicillin per ml of the fluid collecting at the bottom of the NNN slant.

The infective material is inoculated into and grown in the condensation fluid at 22–24° C. Subcultures are made once a week.

The NNN medium is employed for cultivation of *Leishmania*, *Trypanosoma cruzi*, and *T. lewisi*, but not for *T. gambiense* and *T. rhodesiense*.

SENEKJI'S BLOOD CULTURE MEDIUM[6]

Fifty parts of "bacto" beef extract dissolved in 1000 parts of distilled water are heated at 50° C for one hour and at 80° C for five minutes. After filtering through filter paper, 20 parts of "Nobel" agar, 20 parts of "neo" peptone, and 5 parts of chemically pure sodium chloride are added. Then the *p*H is adjusted to 7.2–7.4, and sterilization is performed at 121° C for 20 minutes. Finally, a volume of sterile defibrinated rabbit's blood is added equivalent to one-tenth the volume of the medium. It stimulates an uncommonly luxuriant growth of *Leishmania* and *Trypanosoma cruzi*.

BRUTSAERT AND HENRARD'S MEDIUM[7]

In each of a number of test tubes is dispensed (1) 2–2.5 ml of Ringer's solution containing 0.6 percent of sodium chloride, or the same volume of Tyrode's fluid, (2) 2 ml normal human or rabbit's blood containing 1 percent of sodium citrate. The tubes are incubated to test for sterility and stored in the refrigerator.

One milliliter of sterilized "Liquoïde Roche" (sodium polyanethyl sulfonate) is taken into a syringe; then 5 ml of the blood to be examined is drawn into it, and 0.5 ml of the mixture is put into the culture tubes. The latter are incubated at 28° C for ten days, and subcultured every ten days.

The medium is employed for the cultivation of *Trypanosoma gambiense*, which does not grow in the NNN medium.

CULTIVATION OF FREE–LIVING STAGES OF HELMINTHS

HOOKWORMS

Several grams of feces containing hookworm eggs, mixed with thirty times the volume of moist medicinal carbon, are put in a glass vessel and kept at a temperature of 25° C. After 3 to 5 days the filariform larvas develop and move to the surface of the mass of carbon. They climb along any vertical object emerging from the mass (e.g. hyphens of fungi which also develop in this medium) and along other larvas which preceded them, thus forming the "braids of larvas" whose tip shows a circular movement.

STRONGYLOIDES STERCORALIS[8]

Petri dishes filled with neutralized nutrient agar (1.5 gm of agar, 10 ml of nutrient broth, 90 ml of distilled water) are inoculated with several grams of feces, thoroughly mixed with medicinal carbon and some water. The resulting semifluid mixture is spread over the central portion of four dishes in a layer of 5-mm thickness, leaving a margin of 3 cm uncovered. Two dishes are kept at 37° C; they are examined after 24 hours for directly developed filariform larvas. The other two dishes are kept at 25° C; they are examined on the fifth or sixth day for indirectly developed filariform larvas, or at an earlier date for free-living males and females. If the larvas are numerous, their presence may be detected by the numerous convoluted traces they leave on the bacterial growth that covers the surface of the agar. If they are scarce, the outer margin of the nutrient medium is washed with a few milliliters of water, which is made to run in all directions by agitating the dish. Finally, the fluid is poured into a tube and subjected to a short centrifugation.

REFERENCES FOR CHAPTER XXXVIII

1. W. BALAMUTH. *Am. J. Clin. Pathol.,* 1946, 16: 380–384.
2. W. C. BOECK and J. DRBOHLAV. *Am. J. Hyg.,* 1925, 5: 371–407.
3. L. R. CLEVELAND and J. COLLIERS. *Am. J. Hyg.,* 1930, 12: 606–613.
4. E. C. NELSON. *Am. J. Trop. Med.,* 1947, 27: 545–552.
5. C. A. HOARE. *Handbook of Medical Protozoölogy,* London, 1949, p. 310.
6. H. A. SENEKJI. *Trans. Roy. Soc. Trop. Med. Hyg.,* 1939, 33: 267–269.
7. P. BRUTSAERT and C. HENRARD. *Compt. rend. soc. biol. Paris,* 1938, 127: 1469–1472.
8. F. FÜLLEBORN. *Arch. Schiffs- u. Tropenhyg.,* 1911, 15: 368.
9. C. L. SPINGARN and M. H. EDELMAN. *Am. J. Trop. Med. Hyg.,* 1952, 1: 412–416.

CHAPTER XXXIX

FIXATION AND STAINING METHODS

FIXATIVES

SCHAUDINN'S FLUID[1]

This fixative consists of 100 ml of a saturated aqueous solution of corrosive sublimate (mercuric chloride), 50 ml of 95 percent alcohol, and 7.5 ml of glacial acetic acid. It is used for fixing wet fecal smears. Mucosanguineous or fecal material is spread on a glass slide in a thin film, the former without any previous preparation, the latter after mixing with some egg white to promote adhesion to the glass. Without drying, the slide is immersed face downward into a glass vessel containing the fixative, but is not allowed to touch the bottom. Then the slide is turned face upward and lowered onto the bottom of the container. After 10 minutes, the slide is washed in 50 percent alcohol for 5 minutes and rinsed in water; the sublimate is removed by keeping the slide for 10 minutes in a 70 percent alcoholic solution of iodine the color of brown sherry. The iodine is then removed by 5 minutes' exposure to an 0.2 percent aqueous solution of sodium hyposulfite, rinsing being repeated between the manipulations and after.

BROOKE AND GOLDMAN'S POLYVINYL ALCOHOL FIXATIVE[2]

This solution is used for fixing fecal smears that are dried, thus avoiding the risk of their being washed off. It consists of 93.5 ml of Schaudinn's fluid, 1.5 ml of glycerol, and 5 ml of glacial acetic acid. The mixture is heated to 75° C and then 5 gm of powdered polyvinyl alcohol are added as it is stirred continuously. One drop of a homogeneous fecal suspension, mixed with three drops of the fixative, is spread on a glass slide and left to dry overnight at 37° C. Next morning the sublimate is removed with 70 percent iodinized alcohol.

For the fixation of tissues invaded by parasites, the following fixatives are recommended.[1]

ZENKER'S FLUID

Dissolve 1.5 gm of corrosive sublimate and 5 ml of glacial acetic acid in Müller's solution (2.5 gm of potassium bichromate, 1.0 gm of sodium sulfate, 100 ml of distilled water). Freshly collected specimens of tissue are kept in the fixative for 3 to 12 hours; they are then washed in running tap water overnight. Next morning the sublimate is removed from the specimens by immersion in a weak alcohol solution of iodine for one hour. The preparation for sectioning with the microtome is performed according to the well-known histological technique.

BOUIN'S PICRO—FORMOL

The fixative consists of 75 ml of a saturated aqueous solution of picric acid, 25 ml of 40 percent formaldehyde, 5 ml of glacial acetic acid. In Dobell's modification a saturated solution of picric acid in 90 percent ethanol takes the place of the aqueous solution. Tissues are kept in the fixative for no longer than 18 hours. The picric acid is removed by 70 percent alcohol, which must be repeatedly changed.

Bouin's fluid is also used for fixing smears. These should not be kept in the fixative for more than 30 minutes.

HEMATOXYLIN STAINS

DELAFIELD'S HEMATOXYLIN

This stain is available in a ready-made solution and keeps indefinitely. Intestinal protozoa stained with it do not show minute cytological details; thus it is useful only for routine examination. The fecal smear is stained for 10 minutes in a 1 to 10 dilution of the stain. Then it is rinsed in tap water until the color has changed from violet to blue, which takes about half an hour. Finally, the smear is dehydrated and mounted in Canada balsam.

Fixed thin blood films and dehemoglobinized thick films, to be examined for microfilarias, are stained in the same way. So are sections, but with the modification that they are counterstained for 1 minute in a 1 percent aqueous solution of eosin, after they have turned blue by rinsing in tap water.

HEIDENHAIN'S IRON HEMATOXYLIN

According to Hoare [1] iron hematoxylin is one of the best cytological stains for all kinds of intestinal protozoa, but it is also the most difficult to use; therefore it is not recommended for routine purposes. The difficulty lies in the fact that it overstains the parasites; thus the stained preparations must be differentiated to bring out the desired cytological details, and this differentiation can only be achieved satisfactorily by following its progress under the microscope. Moreover, one protozoon requires a longer continued differentiation than another; thus a quadrinucleate histolytica cyst may have become too pale while the eight-nucleate coli cyst next to it is still quite black. As a matter of fact, this is one of the means of differentiating between the (very rare) eight-nucleate histolytica cyst and the eight-nucleate coli cyst. A decided advantage of Heidenhain's stain is that the erythrocytes ingested by the invasive (histolytic) trophozoites of *E. histolytica* stain a deep black. Thus hematophagous trophozoites may be found in a fixed and stained smear, while they were apparently absent in the fresh eosin preparation. Of course, this is of importance only to those who regard hematophagy as essential for the identification of tissue-invading (histolytic) trophozoites.

The reagents required are (1) a 0.5 percent solution of hematoxylin, prepared by dissolving 1 gm of hematoxylin in 10 ml of heated absolute alcohol, adding 190 ml of distilled water, and leaving the solution to ripen in a warm place, exposed to light, for a fortnight; (2) a 4 percent aqueous solution of pale violet (not rusty yellow) iron-alum crystals.

The smears are first mordanted for six hours in the iron-alum solution. They are then washed and stained for six hours, preferably overnight, in the hematoxylin solution. After a washing in distilled water, the process of differentiation follows. A drop of the iron-alum solution is placed on the smear, mounted with a coverslip, and the progress of the differentiation is watched under the microscope. When it is completed, the preparation is washed for half an hour in tap water, after which it is dehydrated and mounted in Canada balsam.

FAUST'S RAPID IRON HEMATOXYLIN STAIN [3]

The smear is fixed in Schaudinn's fluid, heated at a temperature of 60° C for 2 minutes, and immersed successively in 70 percent alcohol, 70 percent alcohol to which enough iodine has been added to give it a port-wine color; then again in 70 and 50 percent alcohol for 2 minutes each, and washed in running water for 2 minutes. It is then mordanted in 2 percent aqueous iron-alum solution at 40° C for 2 minutes. After a washing in running water for 3 minutes, it is stained in a 0.5 percent aqueous hematoxylin for 10–15 minutes. It is then washed for 2 minutes and differentiated in a saturated picric acid solution for 5 minutes. It is then washed again in running water for 12 to 15 minutes, immersed successively for 2 minutes each in 70 percent, 95 percent (twice), and absolute alcohol, cleared with xylol, and mounted in Canada balsam or Permount.

ROMANOVSKY STAINS

GIEMSA'S STAIN

This stain is available in ready-made solution. However, each fresh bottle has to be tested for its staining properties, and period of staining; the dilution to be used is determined accordingly. The dilutions quoted here are those of a "good bottle."

The *thin film* is fixed with methanol for 2 minutes. After being dried between filter paper, it is stained with a mixture consisting of 1 drop of Giemsa solution to 1 ml of water with a pH of 7. The staining is continued for a time varying from 20 minutes to 1 hour, according to the degree of staining required. As regards malaria parasites, it is most satisfactory when Schüffner's stippling shows faintly and Maurer's [4] patches show not at all, if a fair number of parasites are present.

When the stain is washed off, the greenish metallic scum at the surface of the staining fluid should be removed without its touching the preparation. To achieve this, the glass slide is held horizontally, so as to prevent the stain from running off, and dipped into a bowl of water, stained side upward. The scum can then be seen floating off in the shape of a carmine colored film.

The *thick film* is not fixed in alcohol. It is immersed in water until dehemoglobinized. Then it is stained and washed as described for the thin film, and dried again; washing is to be performed with great care to prevent the film being washed off the slide. For the same reason it should not be dried with filter paper, but stood on edge to drain and dry in air.

In a successful thick film the thicker portions have a clear and homogcncous background, the parasites standing out clearly between the leucocytes and even small rings showing as a red nucleus to which a small dot of blue protoplasm is attached. Stippling or flecks, however, are absent. To see them one has to to turn to the thin edges, which have stained more deeply; the picture, however, has lost the clearness of the thicker portion of the preparation: the background is no longer homogeneous, because the stroma of the dehemoglobinized red cells, the fibrin strands, and the platelets are stained.

The *staining of motile hemoflagellates* has to be judged by the flagellum staining red. *Leishmanias* inside macrophages or other cells often have their protoplasm staining faintly or not at all. In the latter case nothing is to be seen but the nucleus and the kinetoplast. In histological sections they always appear like that.

The procedure of *staining dry fecal smears* is never used for *amoebas,* as they are damaged beyond recognition. Intestinal flagellates, particularly *Trichomonas* and *Giardia lamblia,* may be dried, fixed in 90 percent alcohol, and stained with Giemsa's solution. The flagella are well stained and show very clear pictures, although such preparations are worthless from a cytological point of view.

WRIGHT'S STAIN

The stain is available in thc form of powder, 50 mg of which is dissolved in 10 ml of chemically pure methanol. The undiluted stain is put on the *thin film* and left for 1 minute. Distilled water is then added, drop by drop, until a greenish metallic scum appears. Staining is continued for 2 to 3 minutes. The preparation is washed by adding distilled water. For the *thick film* the stain must be diluted with thirty times the volume of distilled water, or the preparation is first dehemoglobinized and then stained as above.

LEISHMAN'S STAIN

This is also available as a powder; 15 mg dissolved in 10 ml of chemically pure methanol, ready for use after 24 hours. Five to ten drops of the undiluted stain are left on the thin film for half a minute, then 10 to 20 drops of distilled water (pH 7 to 7.2) are added and mixed with the first. Staining is continued for 15 to 20 minutes. The *thick film* is first dehemoglobinized and then stained like a thin film.

G. W. KIEWIET DE JONGE'S STAIN

If neither Leishman's nor Wright's powder is available, Kiewiet de Jonge's stain yields as good results. It consists of a solution of 40 mg of azure II and 25 mg of eosin in 25 ml of methanol, which is applied in the same fashion as Leishman's stain.

FIELD'S STAIN

This stain, used for thick films, is performed with the aid of two separate solutions, A and B. Both contain "buffered water" which consists of 5.0 gm of anhydrous Na_2HPO_4 and 6.25 gm of anhydrous KH_2PO_4 dissolved in 500 ml of distilled water. Solution A contains 0.8 gm of medicinal methylene blue and 0.5 gm of azure I dissolved in 500 ml of "buffered water." Solution B contains 1.0 gm of eosin dissolved in 500 ml of "buffered water." The thick film slide is dipped in A for 1 to 3 seconds, rinsed in "buffered water" for 2 to 3 seconds, dipped in B for 1 to 3 seconds, rinsed in tap water for 2 to 3 seconds, and left to dry.

PATRICK MANSON'S BORAX METHYLENE BLUE

If none of the commercial Romanovsky products are available, and neither are their most important component parts, azure I and II, this old-fashioned stain may be usefully employed; it does almost as well and is practically foolproof. Unfortunately it is useless for thick films. It contains 3 gm of methylene blue and 5 gm of sodium borate in 100 ml of distilled water, and is diluted 1 to 6 before use. After ¼ to ¾ minute's staining, the red cells are faintly greenish-yellow, the parasites blue and sharply outlined. The nuclei do not show well or do not show at all except in gametocytes, in which they appear as vacuoles.

ELEMENTS OCCASIONALLY FOUND IN BLOOD SLIDES

The most serious cause of error is constituted by small, water-inhabiting flagellates that stain well with Giemsa. In case of doubt, it is recommended to look for them on the glass slide outside the film of blood. If they are found there as well as inside the precincts of the film they are contaminants and not parasites.

REFERENCES FOR CHAPTER XXXIX

1. C. A. HOARE. *Handbook of Medical Protozoology*, London, 1949, pp. 300, 288, 297.
2. M. M. BROOKE and M. GOLDMAN. *J. Lab. Clin. Med.*, 1949, 34: 1554–1560.
3. E. C. FAUST, P. F. RUSSELL, and D. R. LINCICOME. *Clinical Parasitology*, Philadelphia, 1957, Lea & Febiger, p. 947.
4. G. MAURER. *Centr. Bakteriol.*, Abt. I, Or., 1902, 32: 695–718.
5. J. W. FIELD. *Trans. Roy. Soc. Trop. Med. Hyg.*, 1941, 35: 35–42.

CHAPTER XL

IMMUNOSEROLOGICAL AND INTRADERMAL PROCEDURES FOR HELMINTHS AND PROTOZOA

TRICHINELLA SPIRALIS

BENTONITE FLOCCULATION TEST, AFTER BOZICEVICH ET AL.[1, 53] AND SADUN ET AL.[2]

The antigen employed consists of a saline extract of trichinella larvas mixed with twice its volume of a specially prepared suspension of standard volclay (Wyoming bentonite), designated as *stock bentonite*. The extract is allowed to be adsorbed for 15 to 18 hours at 4° C. The adsorbing stock bentonite has become a "sensitized stock bentonite mixture." This mixture is converted into "stock antigen" by the further adsorption of thionin blue O, or methylene blue, to the bentonite particles coated with trichinella extract. The "stock antigen" is changed into "test antigen" by the addition of "Tween 80" (the poly-oxy-ethylene derivative of sorbitan-mono-oleate), a detergent which prevents spontaneous flocculation without preventing specific flocculation, unless too much of the detergent is added. The flocculation test is performed with the test antigen and the patient's serum, which has been inactivated (30 minutes at 56° C) and diluted to 1:5, 1:10, and 1:20. Saline and a positive and negative serum serve as controls.

Recently Inella and Redner [3] have introduced the latex-agglutination test in which a stock suspension of latex (polystyrene) particles in distilled water, to which trichinella extract has been adsorbed, has taken the place of bentonite. This test has not yet been adequately evaluated.

COMPLEMENT–FIXATION TEST

The antigen is a saline extract of trichinella larvas prepared by a series of freezings and thawings. The test is performed according to the standardized Kolmer technique.[4]

608

Trichinas, isolated from the muscles of heavily infected rats, rabbits, or guinea pigs by digesting the meat with artificial gastric juice (0.6 percent of pepsin, 0.3 percent of HCl), serve as antigen and the serum of the person suspected of harboring *T. spiralis* serves as antibody. A hundred muscle-trichinellas, isolated under aseptic precautions, are placed in the hollow of a hollow-ground glass slide, together with a quantity of the serum to be tested sufficient to fill up the hollow and mounted with a coverslip. The slide is put in a moist chamber and kept at 37° C for 24 hours. In positive cases, a precipitate develops around the mouth of the larvas. The test becomes positive within three weeks after the onset of the disease.

The antibody reaction described above appears to be different from that which occurs when the patient's serum acts on adult trichinellas. In that case the precipitate develops around the vulva and the anus as well as around the mouth of the female. The anti-adult reaction reaches its maximum between the 25th and the 35th day after infection, whereas the antilarva reaction reaches its maximum between the 45th and 60th day.[6]

The antigen, according to the technique developed by W. G. Sawitz,[7] is prepared as follows. Eighty grams of muscle tissue of heavily infected rats is digested for 5 to 12 hours at 37° C in 1500 ml of artificial gastric juice (see above). The product of the digestion is diluted with an equal amount of water and filtered through six layers of cheesecloth. The filtrate is allowed to sediment for two hours in a glass cylinder; then the upper third of the supernatant fluid is pipetted off and is replaced by an equal amount of warm water. This process of washing is repeated until the supernatant fluid is clear. The purified fluid is left overnight in a 3-liter conic glass. The following morning the sediment is transferred to a Petri dish, in which it is allowed to dry. The dried sediment is extracted with ether for 24 hours, after which the supernatant ether is removed. The residue is dried for 48 hours *in vacuo* over sulfuric acid. The dry product is pulverized in a mortar and kept in sterile ampoules. It may also be dissolved in a suitable solvent (for which the solution described by McCoy and by Coca is recommended), 1 to 100 parts by weight. This solution constitutes the stock antigen.

The intradermal test is performed with the stock antigen diluted 1 to 50 or 1 to 80, in order to dilute the dried antigen 1 to 5000 or 1 to 8000, the dilution being kept in a refrigerator until used. It is injected intradermally on the volar surface of the forearm in a quantity of 0.1 ml; an equal amount of the solvent serves as a control. In positive cases, clinical or subclinical, there is an immediate reaction consisting of a blanched wheal, with or without pseudopods, surrounded by an erythematous area, 35 mm or more in diameter, which appears within 15 to 20 minutes. In early cases of trichinosis a delayed reaction occurs in the form of an erythematous reaction appearing 12 to 18 hours after the injection of the antigen.

ECHINOCOCCUS GRANULOSUS

COMPLEMENT FIXATION (WEINBERG'S TEST)

The antigen employed in this test is *Dennis's purified powdered antigen*,[8] which has the advantage over simple hydatid fluid of not being anticomplementary and possessing a higher degree of sensitivity and specificity. It is prepared from hydatid fluid of hepatic cysts of sheep or cattle, 1 liter of which is cooled, mixed with 50 ml of trichloracetic acid, and kept in a refrigerator. Overnight flocculation occurs, and next morning the precipitate of protein is separated by repeated centrifugation, and the acid is removed by washing with distilled water. Then the protein is redissolved in 50 ml of distilled water, rendered alkaline by adding a 10 percent solution of NaOH, drop by drop. After removal of the insoluble residue and cooling of the solution, the protein is reprecipitated with normal acetic acid and left overnight in the refrigerator. The following morning the precipitate is separated by centrifugation, freed from acid by washing, and dried, first at room temperature and then at $37°$ C over calcium chloride. The dried precipitate is stored in a desiccator over calcium chloride. The stock antigen is a solution of this product, 1 to 1000, in slightly alkalinized physiological saline, sterilized by passing through a Seitz filter or by adding 0.5 percent of chloroform.

For the complement-fixation test, Dennis's purified powdered antigen is diluted 1 to 5000 (the stock solution 1 to 5). The test is performed according to Kolmer's modification of the Wassermann test.[4]

INTRADERMAL TEST (CASONI'S TEST)

This test is performed with Dennis's purified powdered antigen diluted 1 to 5000 in physiological saline, of which 0.2 ml is injected intradermally. In positive cases the reaction is immediate and appears as a raised blanched wheal, with or without pseudopods, 7 mm or more in diameter, surrounded by an erythematous area of 25 mm or more in diameter. Frequently, itching is experienced at the site of the antigen, but not at the site of the saline control. Sterile human cyst fluid properly diluted, if available, is preferred.

PRECIPITIN TEST

Fresh hydatid fluid from sheep's cysts containing viable scolices,[9] preserved by adding 0.05 percent of phenol, serves as antigen in this test. It is performed in small agglutination tubes one-quarter filled with the serum to be tested. The serum is carefully overlaid with a drop of the antigen. After 36 hours, a positive case shows an opaque disk at the point where the two columns meet, the degree of opacity and the thickness of the disk being a gauge of the intensity of the reaction.

Other serological tests used in echinococcosis are Boyden's tannic acid hemagglutination test, and the bentonite flocculation test as used in trichiniasis.[10]

FILARIA

INTRADERMAL TEST

The antigen employed in this test is prepared by Bozicevich and Hutter,[11] using the following technique. Adult *Dirofilaria immitis* are aseptically removed from an infected dog's right ventricle and washed in sterile physiological saline. They are then placed in sterile test tubes, immersed in sterile distilled water, and frozen in dry ice. Next they are thawed, cut into small pieces, ground in a mortar while still moist, dried in a desiccator, and reground. The product is extracted with physiological saline, 1 to 100 by weight, and left for 24 hours in the refrigerator. The extract is twice frozen and thawed in succession, after which it is incubated at 56° C for four hours. The incubated extract is centrifuged for 15 minutes at 15,000 r.p.m. and fractionally sterilized at 56° C for one hour on three consecutive days, and 0.03 percent of phenol is added to insure bacterial sterility. The final product is the stock antigen.

To perform the intradermal test, the stock antigen is diluted 1 to 8000 in physiological saline. Injected intradermally in positive cases, there follows an immediate reaction; after 15 minutes a wheal appears whose size exceeds by 3 mm that of its control. The increased wheal may also show pseudopods, and it is surrounded by an erythematous area. No reaction is seen at the site of the saline control. The test is positive in infections with *W. bancrofti, L. loa,* and *O. volvulus.* In onchocerca infections an antigen prepared from *O. volvulus* gives slightly better results than the dirofilaria antigen. *Complement-fixation tests* in onchocerciasis patients give much better results with an antigen prepared from *O. volvulus* than with the dirofilaria antigen.[12]

SCHISTOSOMES

FAIRLEY'S COMPLEMENT–FIXATION TEST[13]

The positive test is a group reaction. It does not differentiate between the species of schistosomes. The antigen is prepared from snails heavily infected with cercarias of *S. mansoni* or (preferably) *S. spindale* (a bovine schistosome from southern Asia). The livers are separated, teased out with needles, and placed in a vessel to which absolute alcohol is added: 1 ml to each liver. After shaking for 20 minutes, the tissue is extracted for 24 hours at 37° C. It is thoroughly shaken again and filtered through paper. The clear yellow filtrate is concentrated in a water bath at 45° C by bubbling air through the solution with an exhaust pump until it becomes turbid. Enough alcohol is then added to clarify the solution, and the concentrated extract is dispensed in 1-ml ampoules and stored in the refrigerator. The test is carried out with a dilution of 1 to 39 saline.

Many authors agree that the test is useful to detect worms that have not yet started oviposition, but it may fail to disclose the presence of infections of more than three years' duration.[14] Most et al.[15] value the test as an aid in assessing the effect of the treatment, but this opinion has not remained unchallenged.[14]

FAIRLEY AND WILLIAM'S INTRADERMAL TEST[16]

The antigen consists of a saline extract of dried livers of snails infected with *S. spindale,* sterilized by filtration through a Seitz filter. The test is carried out by injecting 0.1 ml of the extract intradermally; it is regarded as positive only if the wheal doubles its diameter within 20 minutes and shows some pseudopods. A saline extract of normal livers is used as a control.

Oliver-González and Pratt's [17] antigen is prepared from mansoni cercarias discharged into distilled water by infected snails. The cercarias are concentrated by centrifugation, washed, dried, pulverized, weighed, and extracted with saline in a proportion of 1 to 5000 by weight. The test is carried out by intradermal injection of 0.05 ml of the dilution; sterile saline serves as a control. Ten minutes after the injection the size of the wheal exceeds that of its control by at least 4 mm.

It is generally agreed that schistosome skin-testing antigens, cercarial or adult, are group antigens and not specific. Moreover, they are not useful as a guide for therapy since positive skin tests are frequently elicited in individuals who have had a schistosome infection in the past and are not harboring living parasites when tested. From a practical point of view the skin test is a useful screening tool in epidemiologic surveys in endemic areas preliminary to the more laborious but more precise and reliable stool examination. Actually the only guide for therapy is the finding of viable eggs in the fecal specimen or in a rectal snip obtained on a sigmoidoscopic examination.

OLIVER–GONZÁLEZ' CIRCUMOVAL TEST[18]

This is carried out by mixing various dilutions of the serum to be tested with viable schistosome ova. In positive cases a precipitate is formed around the ova. The test is reported to be particularly useful in evaluating the effect of the treatment.[19]

VOGEL AND MINNING'S ZHR TEST ("ZERKARIEN HÜLLEN REAKTION")[20]

This test is considered positive when a drop of the serum to be tested, mixed with a drop of water containing 10–50 cercarias, provokes the formation of a transparent membrane around the latter. The motility of the cercarias is not impeded by this membrane.

SENTERFIT'S MIRACIDIA IMMOBILIZATION TEST[21]

In a positive test the serum of the infected individual immobilizes actively motile miracidia obtained from freshly hatched ova.

OTHER TREMATODES

FASCIOLA HEPATICA

For the detection of the parasite during its larval invasion, and in patients or asymptomatic carriers in whose feces no eggs can be found, Lavier and Stefanopoulo's method [22] of preparing an antigen for intradermal test and complement-fixation test may be useful.

Adult worms are washed in saline, dried in an exsiccator over concentrated sulfuric acid, and pulverized in a mortar. One gram of the powder, mixed with 100 ml of saline, is kept at 37° C for one day, the mixture being shaken now and then. Then it is centrifuged for 20 minutes at 3000 r.p.m.; the supernatant fluid is passed through a Seitz filter, dispensed in ampoules, and stored in the refrigerator. For the intradermal test the filtrate is diluted 1 to 4 or 5. In positive cases a wheal appears 3 to 5 minutes after the injection, develops pseudopods, quickly attains a size of 1 to 3 cm, and becomes surrounded by a much wider erythematous zone.

The antigen for complement fixation is prepared by extracting 1 gm of the dried and powdered worms with 100 ml of absolute alcohol for 24 hours at 37° C, agitating frequently. After filtering through paper, the extract is reduced to 30 ml, by evaporation on a water bath at 40° C. By adding 20 ml of absolute ethanol the extract, which has become cloudy during the process of evaporation, is cleared again. It is sealed in ampoules and stored in the refrigerator. It is used in a dilution of 1 to 20.

PARAGONIMUS WESTERMANI

Sadun et al.[23] prepared a purified acid-soluble protein fraction from adult *P. westermani*. This antigen provoked a specific *intradermal reaction*. Occasionally, subjects infected with schistosomes or clonorchis developed a wheal, but it was smaller and less distinct than in persons infected with paragonimus.

With a purified acid-insoluble protein fraction *complement fixation* was achieved. The test proved slightly less sensitive than the intradermal test, but it did not provoke false positive reactions.

PROTOZOA

ENTAMOEBA HISTOLYTICA

Complement-Fixation Test. Encouraging results have been recorded with alcoholic [24] and saline [25] extracts of *E. histolytica* obtained from dysenteric mucoid discharges or cultures.[25a] These extracts have been used as an antigen in testing sera for complement-fixing antibodies taken from cases of intestinal amebiasis, clinical amebic hepatitis, and proven cases of amebic abscess of the liver, as well as from healthy individuals. These studies show that the test is of some value in confirming a clinical diagnosis of hepatitis, and particularly of amebic abscess of the liver. Recently an antigen has been prepared from 3-days-old cultures of *E. histolytica,* grown on a particular bacterial species. The amoebas are disintegrated by autolysis, and the resulting product, cleared by high-speed centrifugation, constitutes the antigen. According to Bozicevich [26] it is of great value in the diagnosis, but he foresees the necessity of polyvalent antigens to obtain completely satisfactory results.

Hematologic and Biochemical Tests. Some observers, Powell [27] among others, believe that the hemogram, the serum protein pattern, and other liver function tests are of little value in the diagnosis of intestinal amebiasis or in differentiating amebic liver involvement from other conditions affecting that organ. On the other hand, Nelson and co-workers,[28] Kean,[28a] and others place great reliance on abnormal liver function tests, particularly the cephalin cholesterol flocculation test, as an ancillary tool in the diagnosis and therapeutic assessment of hepatitis associated with chronic intestinal amebiasis.

MALARIA PARASITES

Seroimmunologic Tests. The complement-fixation reaction was first applied clinically by Kligler and Yoheli [48] in 1941 to determine the incidence of malaria in latent drug-suppressed cases in endemic areas. They used the Coggeshall [51, 52] antigen obtained from infected monkey blood. Their results were quite satisfactory especially in persons who had had overt clinical symptoms prior to the use of antimalarial suppressives. Lippincott and associates [49] in 1945 in an exhaustive study found the test positive in less than 50 percent of their series of proven cases of malaria. They felt that the test was not of practical value in cases of latent malaria nor as a therapeutic guide. The test never received wide clinical application.

The precipitin test likewise was never adopted for clinical use. Taliaferro and Taliaferro [50] in an extensive trial with several antigens came to the conclusion that the test was not useful as a diagnostic tool.

LEISHMANIA

Complement-Fixation Tests. As an aid in the diagnosis of kala-azar, complement-fixation tests have been carried out with nonspecific antigens prepared from tubercle bacilli or Kedrowsky's acid-fast bacillus [29] and from *Mycobacterium butyricum.*[30] The first two are reported to equal sternal puncture in their diagnostic value.

Montenegro's Skin Test. In persons infected with *L. braziliensis* an allergic skin reaction, Montenegro's reaction, can be provoked by intracutaneous injection of parasites grown for 12 days in NNN medium and suspended in 0.1 ml of saline with 0.4 percent of phenol. An erythematous wheal appears in 48 hours, which may last for 4–5 days or longer.

Montenegro's skin test has been found useful in differentiating isolated mucocutaneous leishmanoids from similar fungal lesions such as those seen in sporotrichosis.

The test is negative in American visceral leishmaniasis, but it has been reported positive in East African kala-azar.[31]

In dermal leishmaniasis of the Old World a skin test has been devised with *Trypanosoma equiperdum* as an antigen.[32]

Agglutination Tests. In leishmanian infections the tests serve two different ends: (1) the identification of the isolated, cultivated, but as yet unidentified parasite; (2) the demonstration of specific agglutinins in the patient's serum, directed against *L. donovani* or, alternatively, against *Trypanosoma cruzi.*

The first is achieved by agglutinating the unidentified leishmania with the serum of rabbits hyperimmunized against one of the three species of leishmania.[33]

The second end is achieved by testing the agglutinatory power of the patient's serum to *L. donovani* and *T. cruzi,* as an adjuvant in establishing the differential diagnosis between American kala-azar and Chagas' disease.[34]

Biochemical Tests. (A) NAPIER'S FORMOL-GEL TEST,[35] as an aid in the diagnosis of kala-azar, is executed by putting 1 ml of clear patient's serum in a small test tube. To this is added 1 drop of commercial formaldehyde; the mixture is well shaken and then kept at room temperature. After 3 to 20 minutes the mixture has been converted into an opalescent whitish gel, if the disease has lasted for 3 to 4 months; in earlier stages the mixture becomes opaque but no jellification occurs. Fox and Mackic [36] put a single drop of the serum to be tested on a glass slide and place the slide, face downwards, on top of a watch glass containing some drops of 40 percent formaldehyde. The fumes of formaldehyde bring about the jellification within five minutes.

Napier's test, if it is positive, is regarded as diagnostic of kala-azar, but it is not specific. It is positive whenever there is an increase of euglobulin in the serum, as in leprosy, trypanosomiasis, schistosomiasis, and a number of nonparasitic diseases.

(B) CHOPRA'S ANTIMONY TEST,[37] likewise an aid in the diagnosis of kala-azar, is carried out by adding a drop of a 4 percent solution of stibosan, or urea stibamine, to 1 ml of the serum diluted 1 to 10 with distilled water. In positive cases a flocculent precipitate is produced.

(C) THE SERUM GLOBULIN TEST,[38] serving the same purpose, is carried out in two ways: (1) by adding 1 ml of serum of the patient to 2–3 ml of distilled water; (2) by adding 2 drops of the patient's blood to 1 ml of distilled water. In positive cases a heavy white precipitate is formed within half an hour.

TRYPANOSOMA CRUZI

A complement-fixation test, known as the *Machado test,*[39] improved by Kelser,[40] is carried out with an antigen that consists of an alcoholic extract of cultured *T. cruzi.* The test is an aid in the diagnosis of Chagas' disease or inapparent infection with *T. cruzi.*

In the *intradermal skin test* devised by Mayer and Pifano [41] the antigen consists of cultured *T. cruzi* killed in 0.5 percent phenol and suspended in physiological saline. The specific local reaction reaches its maximum in 48 hours.

For *agglutination tests* in *T. cruzi,* see above, p. 616.

TOXOPLASMA

Sabin and Feldman's Dye Test.[42, 43] The test is based on the fact that methylene blue stains living toxoplasmas not located intracellularly, especially when supported by an "activator." It does not stain the living parasites if they are treated with serum of a person who is (or was) infected with toxoplasmas. The test is considered negative if at least nine-tenths of the toxoplasmas are stained, and positive if less than half of them are.

The following substances are needed:

(*a*) The serum to be tested is diluted to 1/1–1/32 (six dilutions); if of animal origin it must be heated at 56° C for 20 minutes.

(*b*) The "activator," i.e. serum of persons known to show a negative test (no more than 10 percent of them possess a serum suitable for the purpose), is stored at −20° C immediately after collection, because the activating principle is very unstable.

(*c*) Toxoplasmas of a strain known to stain readily under normal conditions are collected from the peritoneal cavity of white mice (of a race known to be suitable) infected intraperitoneally 3–4 days before and are mixed with heparin (6 mg percent).

(*d*) The dye solution to be used in the test must be prepared immediately before use by mixing 3 parts of a saturated alcoholic solution of methylene blue with 10 parts of a soda-borax buffer at pH 11 (973 ml 0.53 percent Na_2CO_3 and 27 ml 1.91 percent $Na_2B_4O_7$, $10H_2O$).

The test is carried out in the following way.

To each one of six tubes is added: (*a*) 0.1 ml of one of the six serum dilutions, (*b*) 0.2 ml of activator, (*c*) 0.1 ml of toxoplasma suspension. The resulting serum dilutions now range from $\frac{1}{4}$ to $\frac{1}{128}$. The tubes are shaken and incubated for one hour at 37° C. Then 0.2 ml of the dye solution is added to each tube, and after repeated shaking they are kept overnight at 4° C. Next day the proportion of stained toxoplasmas is ascertained in each tube.

As controls a mixture is used containing (1) a serum of a known titer as a substitute for the serum to be tested, (2) saline as a substitute of the same, (3) 0.3 ml of saline, 0.05 ml of activator, and 0.05 ml of toxoplasma suspension.

Intradermal Protection Test.[44] The serum to be tested, mixed with a suspension of living toxoplasmas, is injected intradermally in the shaven abdominal skin of a rabbit, to the left of the midline. Symmetrically, on the right side, a second injection is made, this time omitting the serum. A positive test shows a clear-cut difference between the reactions to the two injections. Only positive tests are of any value.

Frenkel's Toxoplasmin Test.[45] This test is applied to the presumptive patient, on the assumption that he is hypersensitive to the metabolites of toxoplasmas destroyed by ultraviolet radiation and autolyzed by successive freezing and thawing, repeated 5–10 times. The final product (toxoplasmin) contains 8000 autolyzed parasites per 0.1 ml. It is injected intradermally, following the procedure employed with tuberculin. The test is considered positive if after 48 hours an induration of 5 to 10 mm persists, and an erythema of 10 to 30 mm.

Warren's and Russ' Complement Fixation Test.[46] The antibody employed in this test is the serum of the presumptive patient. The antigen consists of the chorioallantoic membrane of hens' or ducks' eggs (incubated for 10 days), on which toxoplasmas have been grown for 5 days. After trituration, the membranes are immersed in phosphate buffer at pH 7.4, 1.5 ml to every membrane. The mixture is repeatedly submitted to freezing ($-60°$ C) and thawing ($+37°$ C) and centrifuged for 15 minutes at 2000 r.p.m. The supernatant fluid is pipetted off and centrifuged for one hour at $5°$ C and 13,000 r.p.m. Then merthiolate is added to a final dilution of 1:10,000. The antigen is stored in a refrigerator. The test becomes positive later and reverts to negative earlier than in the Sabin-Feldman test.

Jacobs' and Lunde's Hemagglutination Test.[47] This test is based on the observation that erythrocytes sensitized by toxoplasma antigen are agglutinated by sera of persons infected with this parasite. Thus the latter can be identified in this manner. There are certain conditions to be observed: (1) the toxoplasma antigen being a protein, it cannot sensitize the erythrocytes unless they are previously treated with tannic acid; (2) from the serum of the presumptive parasite carrier any nonspecific antibodies must be removed through absorption by nonsensitized erythrocytes. The antigen is prepared by lysis of toxoplasmas in distilled water.

REFERENCES FOR CHAPTER XL

1. J. BOZICEVICH et al. *Public Health Repts. (U. S.)*, 1951, 66: 806–814.
2. E. H. SADUN and L. NORMAN. *Public Health Lab.*, 1955, 13: 147–152.
3. F. INELLA and W. J. REDNER. *J. Am. Med. Assoc.*, 1959, 171: 885–887.
4. A. J. KOLMER, E. H. SPAULDING, and W. H. ROBINSON. *Approved Laboratory Technic*, 5th ed., New York, 1951, pp. 815–825.
5. H. ROTH. *Nature*, 1945, 155: 758–759.
6. J. OLIVER-GONZÁLEZ. *J. Infectious Diseases*, 1941, 69: 254–270.
7. E. C. FAUST, P. F. RUSSELL, and D. R. LINCICOME. *Clinical Parasitology*, Philadelphia, 1957, pp. 984, 985.
8. E. W. DENNIS. *J. Parasitol.*, 1937, 23: 62–67.
9. N. HAMILTON FAIRLEY. *Med. J. Australia*, 1922 (1st half): 341–346.
10. I. G. KAGAN, D. S. ALLAIN, and L. NORMAN. *Am. J. Trop. Med. Hyg.*, 1959, 8: 51–55.
11. J. BOZICEVICH and A. M. HUTTER. *Am. J. Trop. Med.*, 1944, 24: 203–208.
12. J. BOZICEVICH, A. DONOVAN, L. MAZZOTTI, A. F. DÍAZ, and E. PADILLA. *Am. J. Trop. Med.*, 1947, 27: 51–62.
13. N. HAMILTON FAIRLEY. *Arch. Schiffs- u. Tropenhyg.*, 1926, 30: 372–383.
14. F. SCHOFIELD. *Trans. Roy. Soc. Trop. Med. Hyg.*, 1959, 53: 64–74.
15. H. MOST et al. *Am. J. Trop. Med.*, 1950, 30: 239–299.
16. N. HAMILTON FAIRLEY and F. E. WILLIAMS. *Med. J. Australia*, 1927 (2nd half): 811–818.
17. J. OLIVER-GONZÁLEZ and C. K. PRATT. *Puerto Rico J. Public Health Trop. Med.*, 1944, 20: 242–248.
18. J. OLIVER-GONZÁLEZ. *J. Infectious Diseases*, 1954, 95: 86–91.
19. R. RODRIGUEZ-MOLINA et al. *Am. J. Trop. Med. Hyg.*, 1959, 8: 565–569.
20. H. VOGEL and W. MINNING. *Zentr. Bakteriol.*, Abt. I, Or., 1949, 153: 91–105.
21. L. B. SENTERFIT. *Proc. Soc. Exptl. Biol. Med.*, 1953, 84: 5–7.
22. G. LAVIER and J. STEFANOPOULO. *Bull. soc. pathol. exotique*, 1944, 37: 302–307.
23. E. H. SADUN, A. A. BUCK, and B. C. WALTON. *J. Parasitol.*, 1958, 44 (suppl.): 17.
24. C. F. CRAIG. *Am. J. Trop. Med.*, 1929, 9: 277–296.
25. C. W. REES, J. BOZICEVICH, L. V. REARDON, and F. JONES. *Am. J. Trop. Med.*, 1942, 22: 581–586.
25a. K. L. HUSSEY and H. W. BROWN. *Am. J. Trop. Med.*, 1950, 30: 147–154.
26. J. BOZICEVICH. *Sixth Intern. Congr. Trop. Med.*, Lisbon, 1958, Abstracts, 79–80.
27. S. J. POWELL. *Am. J. Trop. Med. Hyg.*, 1959, 8: 331–335, 336–341.
28. T. L. NELSON, H. H. ANDERSON, and O. THOMAS. *Am. J. Trop. Med. Hyg.*, 1955, 4: 812–821.
28a. B. H. KEAN. *Am. J. Digest. Diseases*, 1957, 2: 342–347.
29. P. C. SEN GUPTA. *Indian Med. Gaz.*, 1943, 78: 336–339; 1944, 79: 465–469.
30. J. PELLEGRINO, Z. BRENER, and U. M. SANTOS. *J. Parasitol.*, 1958, 44: 645.
31. P. E. C. MANSON-BAHR, R. B. HEISCH, and P. C. C. GARNHAM. *Trans. Roy. Soc. Trop. Med. Hyg.*, 1959, 53: 380–383.
32. R. DESPIEDS, H. COLLOMB, J. MATHURIN, and J. RANQUE. *Bull. soc. pathol. exotique*, 1958, 51: 501–504.
33. H. NOGUCHI. *J. Exptl. Med.*, 1926, 44: 327–337.
34. H. SENEKJI and R. A. LEWIS. *Am. J. Trop. Med.*, 1945, 25: 185–188.

35. L. E. NAPIER. *Indian Med. Gaz.*, 1921, 56: 238–241.
36. E. C. R. Fox and F. P. MACKIE. *Indian Med. Gaz.*, 1921, 56: 374–376.
37. R. N. CHOPRA, J. C. DAS GUPTA, and J. C. DAVID. *Indian Med. Gaz.*, 1927, 62: 688–691.
38. U. N. BRAHMACHARI and P. B. SEN. *Indian Med. Gaz.*, 1923, 58: 295–298.
39. C. GUERREIRO and A. MACHADO. *Brasil-méd.*, 1913, 27: 318–325.
40. R. A. KELSER. *Am. J. Trop. Med.*, 1936, 16: 405–415.
41. M. MAYER and C. PIFANO. *Brasil-méd.*, 1941, 55: 317–319.
42. A. B. SABIN and H. A. FELDMAN. *Science,* 1948, 108: 660–663.
43. L. JACOBS and M. K. COOK. *Am. J. Trop. Med. Hyg.*, 1954, 3: 860–867.
44. A. B. SABIN. *Proc. Soc. Exptl. Biol. Med.*, 1942, 51: 6–12.
45. J. F. FRENKEL. *Proc. Soc. Exptl. Biol. Med.*, 1948, 68: 634–639.
46. J. WARREN and S. B. RUSS. *Proc. Soc. Exptl. Biol. Med.*, 1948, 67: 55–58.
47. L. JACOBS and M. N. LUNDE. *J. Parasitol.,* 1957, 43: 308–314.
48. I. J. KLIGLER and M. YOHELI. *Am. J. Trop. Med.*, 1941, 21: 531–543.
49. S. W. LIPPINCOTT, H. H. GORDON, W. B. HESSELBROCK, and A. MARBLE. *J. Clin. Invest.,* 1945, 24: 362–371.
50. W. H. and L. G. TALIAFERRO. *J. Prev. Med.*, 1928, 2: 147–167.
51. L. T. COGGESHALL and M. D. EATON. *J. Exptl. Med.*, 1938, 67: 871 ff.
52. M. D. EATON and L. T. COGGESHALL. *J. Exptl. Med.*, 1939, 69: 379 ff.
53. H. VOGEL, D. WIDELOCK, and H. T. FUERST. *J. Infectious Dis.*, 1957, 100: 40–47.

INDEX OF NAMES

INDEX OF SUBJECTS